DERRICK CARTLIDGE

WILD OATS AND THE WOODEN PILLOW

THE TWENTY-TWO PRESS

Cover Painting: 'S.E. Coast of England' by Katrin Cartlidge, 1998

First published in Great Britain in 2004
by The Twenty-Two Press
PO Box 47357
London NW3 2SQ

A catalogue record for this book is available from the British Library

Designed & Produced in Great Britain by: Clinton Smith Design Consultants, London

ISBN No. 0-9547200-0-8

This book is an account of my childhood and adolescence, from my birth in 1923 until the end of World War II. It deals pretty explicitly with poverty, ignorance, innocence, sex, violence and abuse. I wrote about my life as I remember it, recounting the events and my reactions the way I experienced them as a child and in my teens, not with hindsight and adult judgments. The names of some of the characters have been changed to protect their identity.

I would like to say a big thank you to my close family and many friends who have greatly encouraged and helped me over several years to complete this book. I will always be grateful for their patience and practical contributions, especially my wife Bobbi, our son Tony, our daughters Michelle and Katrin; and I am also greatly indebted to our friend Judith Elliott, who spent many hours of painstaking scrutiny editing my manuscript.

Derrick Cartlidge
London, February 2004

For my family: Bobbi, Tony, Michelle, Katrin and our grandsons Theo, Alexander and Stefan

CHAPTER ONE

Born: 9 March 1923 at Queen Charlotte's Hospital, Hammersmith
Names: Hayden Francis
Mother: Barbara Daisy Cartlidge, Caterer's Clerk, Paddington
Father: Unknown

So states my birth certificate. At a glance you'd know that I wasn't exactly born with a silver spoon in my mouth. If I had been, I think my poor young mother would soon have pawned it. Not to this day, except perhaps for a few brief seconds after my birth, have I ever seen or felt her.

It's not hard to imagine that in the early twenties the distraught and disgraced girl was subject to considerable pressure to part with her baby. That, I presume, was why, within a few days of being born, I was placed in a small private boarding school at Southend-on-Sea, Essex, run by a Miss Minter. Most of the boarders were put into the care of this elderly spinster because their parents were unable or unwilling to keep them. To comprehend the conditions that existed in this home for waifs and strays, you'd have to go back to the England of Dickens. I was brought up in a poverty of the worst kind – genteel poverty. Unlike the wretched children of the poor who could go out into the streets and beg or steal, I had to survive somehow on the meagre amount of food that was all Miss Minter could afford to buy.

With the pitiful income she received from the parents, she was always up to her neck in debt. Frequently the local tradespeople refused to deliver her order until they had been paid what was outstanding. When this happened, the children and staff had to make do with bread and marge for a few days. More than once during my childhood the poor well-meaning woman was carted off to debtor's prison, where she remained until the debt was cleared or until the merchants felt they'd had their pound of flesh. When she was in jail, we boarders were left in the care of untrained and unpaid staff who told us that Miss Minter was ill and had to go to hospital for a while. To avoid prison, she'd occasionally – with no questions asked – take in an unwanted orphan for a lump sum. The ridiculously small amount she got enabled her to settle her more pressing debts. I was one of three she took in on those terms. I've no idea who paid her to take me in; perhaps it was my unknown father who reluctantly coughed up and chipped in with my mother's parents. In any event it solved the immediate problem of what to do with the baby who had brought shame on them.

Not once throughout my entire childhood was any one person legally responsible for me, nor did any authority ever bother to check that I was being satisfactorily cared for or educated. As far as Miss Minter was concerned, I was just one more mouth to feed that no parent was paying her for. To compensate for this, from the age of about eight, I had to more or less work my way through childhood. Doing all the chores left me with very little time to spend in the classroom. At eleven I could barely read or write or recite my three times table. But what I could do well in advance of my years was scrub floors, fetch and carry coal, chop wood, clean out and light fires, and make up beds for the boarders whose parents were paying for them to be there. I was a dab hand at laying and clearing dining tables and at helping with the washing-up.

As a reward for all this work, I was given a penny a week pocket money. Every Saturday I had to make the difficult decision on how best to spend my hard-earned coin. I agonised on whether or not I'd buy a ha'penny sherbet and two farthing doodahs or four gobstoppers. For a penny I could have had a small packet of Jelly Babies. However, none of these had the ingredient I most craved for - the delicious taste you had when chocolate slowly dissolved in your mouth. I gave in to this craving every so often by blowing my whole weekly income on a Milky Way. The devil himself could have had my soul in exchange for a Mars Bar. But alas, I never did have one, because, you see, they were an unattainable tuppence.

Funds permitting, the weekly menu never varied. Monday was shepherd's pie, injected with tiny scraps of meat shaved off the bone from Sunday's joint. Tuesday was everyone's favourite - a single sausage with a large helping of greasy chips. On Wednesday mousetrap cheese was sparingly grated over soggy boiled potatoes. Absolutely nobody looked forward to Thursday's mashed parsnips covered in a thick, brown, gluey sauce that could well have doubled as a paperhanger's paste. Miss Minter, being a good Christian, made sure it was fish on Friday - a piece of boiled cod. I was nearly into my teens before I realised that cod wasn't the only fish to inhabit the sea. Saturday's fishcakes were fried mashed potatoes laced with a mixture of shredded-up fish skin and any bits we'd left on our plates the previous day. Vegetables were either swedes or cabbage. Fruit was non-existent except on Christmas Day, when we were each given a tangerine and an apple. I have no memory of ever having anything fresh like lettuce or tomatoes. Breakfast was the same year in and year out: lumpy porridge followed by fried bread steeped in lard that butchers sold in huge chunks cheaply to the poor. Twice a week at teatime as a treat, jam was spread on our bread, and then scraped off again. Still, it was better than just bread and marge.

Miss Minter believed that to waste God-given food was a mortal sin, and any child that did should be punished by having anything they left on their plate served up at the next meal and then again for as many times as it took, until out of sheer hunger the offender finally gave in and ate it. Despite this dreadful practice, I don't remember ever having meat put in front of me. It was totally accepted that I didn't eat it. I can only assume that when I was a very small child a battle of wills ensued that ended up with me as the victor. On the two meat days in the week, I had to make do with a little gravy poured over my potatoes on Sunday and just the chips on Tuesday.

Eggs were as rare as gold nuggets. We had two a year - one on Easter Sunday and the other on our birthday. The Easter egg was under constant threat of withdrawal if a member of staff thought we had collectively misbehaved. Although I looked forward months ahead to my birthday egg, a lot of the joy went out of it because I was aware that some twenty pairs of eyes were enviously watching my every mouthful. The only way to cut this uncomfortable feeling short was to bolt the precious egg down. This was a pity as I would have preferred to savour slowly what was, after all, the only birthday present I was going to get. Some of the others, when they got theirs, took a sadistic delight in dragging the whole thing out. Ceremoniously they'd crack open the shell, then peel it flick by flick with a thumbnail. When they'd made sure all eyes were on them, they dipped a finger of toast deep into the runny yolk and then, to tantalise, would slowly pull it out and lick it clean. With this method they made their egg last an agonisingly long time.

Out of approximately thirty boarders, only ten were boys. The only dumped babies - apart from myself - were Joan and Mary. Mary was three years older than me and Joan six. They didn't have to do anything like as many domestic chores as I had to, partly because they responded better to being taught than I did, and partly because in Miss Minter's opinion, boys - in common with all males - were more suited to doing the donkey work. Mary was unofficially adopted by one of the staff, a middle-aged woman called Miss Laver. She was so besotted with her little charge that she had her removed from the girls' dormitory and put in her room, despite it having only one bed. Unlike Joan and me, Mary at least had somebody who loved and cared about her.

As for the other children there, they very rarely saw their parents. A few of the luckier ones did go home for three days over Christmas, but most had to make do with a half-a-day's outing two or three times a year. Although all of them, by any normal standards, were dreadfully neglected, to me they were pampered pets. They could talk about their mummies and daddies, and some even got a birthday card with a sixpenny postal order enclosed in it. But the ones I most envied were those who went home for Christmas. In short, I was acutely jealous of them all, so to even the score a bit, I bullied them. I could do this because I was naturally a lot stronger than they were. At about six years old, I was the Lord of the Flies. If they didn't do my bidding, I threatened the boys with having their ears twisted and the girls with getting their pigtails pulled. The threats must have sufficed, because I don't remember doing any of this.

Being so resentful made me a very difficult and rebellious child. I had frequent outbursts of uncontrollable temper. They were so violent that I sometimes frightened not only myself but the all-female members of staff. I'd kick and scream and throw things at anyone who tried to approach me. If I'd had a particularly long screaming fit, my voice would give out and for the next couple of days my vocal cords were so strained that I could only manage to speak in a whisper. After some of my tantrums I'd go upstairs to the dormitory and lie on my bed with my face buried into the pillow and weep unseen. Through my tears,

I'd cry out: 'Mummy, Mummy, why did you ...? Please, oh please, do come and fetch me soon.' What made me call out to her I do not know, because deep down inside of me I knew she never would.

Having no one to cuddle and kiss me goodnight when I got into bed, I comforted myself by rocking from side to side. With a hand between my legs and both feet flipping in unison with my twisting body, I rocked myself to sleep. I'd fantasise that my mother came to collect me. My vision of her was that she was even more beautiful than a picture I'd once seen of the Blessed Virgin Mary. In my waking dream she picked me up and hugged me close to her. When she put me down, she held my hand and led me out of the place I was so unhappy in. As we walked along, she promised that never again would we be parted. Her house was one in a neat row of terraced dwellings. All the trees in it were in blossom. The inside of her home was cosy and warm. Laid out on the kitchen table were thin slices of bread thickly spread with real butter. She told me I could help myself to the strawberry jam. On a silver dish was the most delicious looking chocolate cake that I could imagine. My mother would talk to me as I ate it, smiling and laughing a lot. After tea, she bathed me. I didn't have to share with two other boys, which meant I could splash about in the deep water for as long as I liked before standing up to let her soap me in. I liked the feel of her slippery hands rubbing up and down my body. Playfully she'd rinse me by holding a large jug of water above my head and letting it cascade down all over me. She dabbed me dry with a big white towel. The bed I shared with her had clean and ironed sheets. I fell asleep, in my make-believe world and in the real one, with my imagined mother's arm wrapped around my waist holding me close to her soft warm body. This compulsive need to rock myself to sleep stayed with me right up into adulthood.

Throughout most of my childhood, whenever we went out, it was always in crocodile fashion, which we hated. Twice a day, once after breakfast and again at four, thirty of us, in pairs and holding hands, were paraded like infant convicts through the streets. Only in the summer holidays on fine days, when we were taken down to the beach, were we ever allowed to break ranks and run about freely like normal children.

One day, on the way back from a morning on the beach, we came to a halt outside a public house while we waited to be shepherded across a main road. A large blonde lady, a little unsteady on her legs, came out and saw us. She crossed the pub's forecourt and bent down right by me.

"Oh, what an adorable little boy," she said as she lifted me up.

My face became wedged between the bare parts of her breasts that bulged out above her low-cut blouse. I found it difficult to breathe in there, but I was content to stay snuggled up in the soft, warm and unfamiliar surroundings for a very long time. Alas, my few moments of bliss were soon shattered by the shrill voice of the teacher.

"Put that child down!"

"Please let me keep him. I lost my little boy, you see."

"Take me, lady, I'd really love for you to have me."

But I don't think she heard my muffled plea.

"If you do not release the boy at once, I'll go and fetch a policeman," said the teacher.

Reluctantly the woman put me down. She knelt on the pavement beside me, tears rolling down her cheeks as she held my face between her hands and kissed me. The image and feel of that unhappy, bereft mother stays with me.

With no parents to praise me, even for something as important as taking my first few steps, I masterminded a few stunts that would ensure some response from the adults around me. The first piece of mischief I got up to, when I was about nine, came to me in a flash of inspiration just after I'd lugged up a heavy bucket of coal from the cellar. I'd placed a lit candle in its holder on the floor near a long curtain that concealed some unsightly shelving. Whilst raking out the cinders from the grate, I noticed that every now and then the draught from an open window blew the flimsy material over the candle flame. It wasn't long before the curtain caught alight. I waited until the flames licked the ceiling before dashing into the kitchen shouting: "Cook - the curtains are on fire!"

I grabbed the bucket of water she was using to peel the potatoes, then, with a well-aimed throw, I doused the fire.

"You clever little boy," said the cook, who was obviously taken aback by my prompt action. "You've probably prevented the whole school from burning down. I think Miss Minter ought to give you an extra penny as a reward for showing such presence of mind."

I never did get the penny but to be praised - albeit undeservedly - was reward enough for me.

The next spectacular I contrived was shortly after we'd all been taken to the cinema for the very first time. The main film, a love story starring John Bowles and Bebe Daniels, didn't amuse me much. But the second feature had me on the edge of my seat. Charlie Chan, the detective, and his Number-One son were investigating the death of a man who was shot in the head. He was found slouched over his office desk with a pistol in his hand and the door bolted from the inside.

"He has committed suicide," said Number-One son.

"Excuse please, not necessarily so. The dead man had many enemies, perhaps he was murdered."

"But Honourable Father, the room was bolted."

The inscrutable Mr Chan thought for a moment, then demonstrated how it could be done. He stood outside the office with the door ajar, then looped an open-ended piece of string around the bolt's head and shut the door. A slight pull on the string made the shaft slide forward. Now the room was bolted from within. His Number-One son was impressed, and so was I.

A few weeks later I mimicked what I'd seen, embellishing it with an idea of my own. First making sure I wasn't followed, I went to the upstairs bathroom, put the plug in the bath and turned both taps full on. When the water started to overflow, using Mr Chan's technique, I bolted the door. Then I went up to the next landing and waited all agog for the drama to unfold. It wasn't long before water began to pour through the ceiling below. Miss Minter and Miss Laver came panting up the stairs. They tried in vain to push the door open, but it wouldn't budge.

"Oh dear, what can we do," said Miss Minter agitatedly, then, as an afterthought, added, "oh my goodness, a child might be in there."

By now water was seeping out from under the bathroom door and running down the stairs. This was the moment I'd been waiting for. I made a dash for the door and hit it hard with my shoulder. The bolt gave way and it burst open. I scurried across the flooded floor, pulled out the plug and turned off the taps. Once again I was praised to the hilt and declared to be the hero of the moment.

The father of one of the girl boarders heard about the nine-yearold orphan boy who had never been taken out and had no relatives he could go and visit. That was why I was invited, along with his daughter Stella, to spend three days over Easter at his home in Walthamstow. When Miss Minter told me, I was so excited that I ran up a temperature and had to be confined to bed for a day. One thing about going did worry me a bit; I'd have to forgo my much looked-forward-to Easter egg. When I told Stella about my worry, she just laughed.

"Hayden, you won't have only one measly egg, you'll get one every morning and have real butter on your toast. My daddy always buys me a big chocolate egg all wrapped up in shiny silver paper from Woolworth's. I'm sure he'll get you one as well."

At midday on Good Friday, Stella and I waited by the front door for her father to arrive.

"Will your mother come with him?" I said.

"I haven't got a mum, she bunked off when I was two, that's why Daddy had to send me to this place."

"What does your Daddy work at?"

"He's a commercial traveller."

"What's that?"

"He drives around England selling sewing machines."

"That sounds like a very important job."

"It is," said Stella proudly.

Stella had a small suitcase, I had the clothes I stood up in, and tucked under my arm in a brown paper bag was a recently washed pair of pyjamas. We'd waited by the front door for over an hour before Mr Starbuck pulled up in a little Austin Eight. He got out and hugged his daughter, then shook me by the hand. He was a slim man and not very tall, with a thin moustache that might well have been pencilled in, and wore his trilby at a rakish angle. He looked very neat in his single-breasted suit and shiny black patent-leather shoes.

Stella got in the front and I in the back. This was my first time in a vehicle. I'd never been in a bus, let alone a motor car before. To be driven through streets that I'd only ever walked, was to me like riding on a magic carpet.

Out on the open road I got my very first look at the world outside Southend. Part of our route took us through the Essex countryside. I literally screamed with delight when I saw cows and horses grazing in the fields. I'd only ever seen pictures of them before between the pages of children's books. An hour and a half later, we arrived in Walthamstow. Stella's home was tiny, two up and two down with a poky kitchen built onto the back wall. A shed at the end of the minute garden was the toilet. Not having a bathroom meant you had to wash over the kitchen sink.

To stretch our legs before dusk, we all went to Epping Forest. Unaccustomed to walking about freely, I had to keep reminding myself not to hold Stella by the hand as we strolled along. As we left the forest, a man on a tricycle rode by, pushing in front of him a blue container that said 'Stop me and buy one'.

"Would you like one, lad?" asked Mr Starbuck.

"Like one what ?"

"An ice cream."

Never having had one, I hesitated a moment before saying: "Yes, please."

I took a big bite into the slab, then spat it out because it was too cold to hold in my mouth.

"Don't bite into it, silly, lick it," said Stella.

On the way back we stopped off and got fish and chips for supper. In the space of a day, I'd notched up three firsts - a ride in a motor car, an ice cream, and my first plateful of fish and chips.

At bedtime, Stella went into what she called 'her' room, while I had to share a bed with her father. During the night I woke up and found that my pyjama trousers had been pulled down to my knees and Mr Starbuck's arm was around my waist, holding me in a tight grip. Something hard was rubbing up and down my bottom, gathering speed as it did so. Puzzled and worried about what he was doing, I thought it best if I pretended to be asleep. The rubbing intensified and he started to breathe heavily. Seconds later all went quiet and he released the grip he had on me and turned onto his side with his back towards me. It was only when he began to snore, that I felt confident enough to go back to sleep again.

At breakfast, Mr Starbuck behaved as if nothing had occurred during the night, and I began to wonder if I hadn't dreamt the whole thing. But then I remembered that when I took off my pyjama trousers I had to pull on them a bit because they were slightly stuck to my buttocks. While her father was shaving, I told Stella about what had happened.

"Daddy does that to me as well, but I put up with it, 'cos I love him. He didn't hurt you, did he ?"

"No,.not really."

"Are you sorry you came here?"

"Oh no, I'm having the very, very best time of my life."

"So it's all right then, isn't it?"

"I suppose so."

When her father came back into the room, he said that he'd planned a real treat for us both.

"I'm going to take you to visit the Crystal Palace. It's a big building made almost completely out of glass. When you've had a good look at it, we'll go down the hill and watch the dirt-track racing."

"What's that, Daddy?"

"It's men on motorcycles whizzing around an earth track at a tremendous speed. When that's over I'll take you to Lyons and you can have whatever you fancy. How does that sound to you?"

"It sounds wonderful, Daddy."

Our route to South London took us down Whitehall. By sheer luck, we passed by just when they were changing the Guard. I watched enthralled by the awe-inspiring pageantry of it all. When the show was over, we got back into the car and moved on to Westminster Bridge. Mr Starbuck pointed out to us the Houses of Parliament and the Abbey. They looked magnificent, illuminated from the side by the low rays of an early spring sun. I stood on my toes and peered over the bridge at the water below. Mr Starbuck threw an empty matchbox into the river. In the fast-flowing current it moved away at quite a pace.

"If that little box stays afloat, it could well be in Southend tomorrow," he said.

As I looked puzzled, he explained:

"This river is called the Thames. Its estuary is even further away from London than your boarding school."

"Estuary?"

"Where the river flows out into the sea. One day, Hayden, I promise to take you and Stella on the paddle steamer that leaves from Tower Bridge and goes all the way down river to Southend Pier."

Up to now, no promise ever made to me had been fulfilled, so I didn't really think he'd keep his, and as it turned out, he didn't.

Crystal Palace was like a cathedral built out of glass. Its wide frontage had long wings flanking it. Two tall towers at either end of the building supplied the water to the many magnificent fountains, situated in various parts of the huge garden. They cascaded high into the air in fan-shaped jets. I watched, fascinated, the descending water that mirrored the light of the sun. A section of the interior was made into a menagerie which contained a variety of wild animals. There were no elephants and rhinoceroses and Mr Starbuck told us it was because they might cut loose and run amok, bringing tons of glass crashing down on the spectators. As the smell of the menagerie was intense, we didn't stay too long but moved on to the sweeter air of the concert hall and the vast exhibition rooms. After that we strolled about in the grand garden. Acres of spring flowers were in bloom. I would have liked to have stayed on in this sea of many colours, but we had to make our way down the hill to where the motorcycle racing would soon begin.

By the time we arrived the riders were astride their bikes, revving up their engines and waiting for the starter's gun. In their leather helmets and fur-edged goggles, they were - except for the number pinned on their backs - indistinguishable. When the race began, an ear-piercing roar came from the exhausts of their bikes as they sped off down the track at an alarming pace. At hairpin bends the riders stuck out a leg and let the soles of their boots skim along the surface of the dry earth. As they whizzed past, clouds of dust sprayed the spectators nearest to the railing. It was thrilling to see these fearless men on their machines taking enormous risks to be out front.

After the race we went to Joe Lyons to eat. I'd never been inside a restaurant, so what everyone took for granted was new to me. Mr Starbuck picked up the menu and asked me what I'd like to have. Not ever having been offered a choice before, I just looked at him blankly.

"What about a Welsh rarebit?" he suggested.

"No thanks. I don't eat meat."

Stella laughed at my reply.

"It's not Hayden's fault if he doesn't know what it is."

He explained what it was, then, as I hesitated, he began to reel off a whole list of dishes I'd never heard of. Finally he mentioned eggs. Quick as a flash I said 'Yes' to them. When two poached eggs on buttered toast were put in front of me, I could barely believe what I was seeing. I was about to eat a year's ration in one meal.

By the time I was back in Walthamstow, more new experiences had been crammed into one day than all my previous nine years.

During the night, I was again woken up by Mr Starbuck molesting me. In fact, he bothered me for the three nights I shared his bed.

Just as Stella had predicted, on the table at breakfast on Easter Sunday was a box, containing a chocolate egg all beautifully wrapped in shiny silver paper. Stella opened hers and consumed it immediately whereas I sat admiring mine for a very long time before caving in, and letting it dissolve piece by piece in my mouth.

That day's excursion was to the Zoo. It was mid-morning when we arrived, only to find it closed. A notice by the entrance told the crowd of adults and children who were looking forward to going in, that on Sundays the Zoological Gardens was open to Society Members only until two p.m. I was so disappointed that it took all my self-control to stop myself from bursting into tears. Stella, on the other hand, wasn't upset at all. She knew how resourceful her daddy was.

"What we'll do," he said, rubbing his hands together, "is hop back into the car and drive round to the lake on the other side of the park. I'll hire a boat and take you for a row, then we'll come back here when it opens."

The expression on my face went from one of abject misery to a wide grin.

After lunch on the Bank Holiday Monday, Stella and I sat silent and glum in the car as we were driven back to school. Stella wept bitterly when her father gave her a goodbye hug. He tried to make her feel better by reminding her that he'd collect her again at Christmas. As it was now early April, that didn't console her a lot.

CHAPTER TWO

In July 1932 Miss Minter was unexpectedly left some money by her sister, who had been married to a solicitor and had no children. This windfall enabled her to settle all her debts and have enough left over to embark on her life's ambition to be the principal of a private day school. In August, we moved from the unfashionable suburb of Southend to more salubrious premises in Westcliff. Miss Minter named her new school St Margaret's and put up a sign announcing that it was a day school for girls between the ages of five and eleven. All the untrained staff apart from Miss Laver were dismissed and replaced by more qualified teachers.

To give the new school an identifiable image, the girl boarders were fitted out with uniforms. This was a new experience for them, as previously the only clothes they'd ever worn had, by necessity, been second-hand. On the twice-daily walk they were paraded through the town like a mobile advertisement in their school blazers, made from brown cloth edged with orange braid.

All the rooms were painted in the same colours, even the hall and stairway. The top half of the walls were bright orange, the lower half dark brown. A two-inch wide black line separated the two. Only in Miss Minter's room could you rest your eyes from the monotony of it all. To this day, orange and brown are my least favourite colours.

The new premises were much larger than the one we had vacated. There were four big rooms on each floor of the five-storey house. The most spacious room on the ground level was turned into a miniature assembly hall. It even had a small stage built at one end. The other three were the kitchen, the dining room and a common room for the staff. Half of the first floor Miss Minter had as her living quarters. The next two were classrooms or bedrooms for those of the staff who lived in.

At the very top of the building were three dormitories, two for the twenty girl boarders and one for us ten boys. We were sent up to bed at seven o'clock - summer or winter - long before we were tired. Being so far away from the staff below, we could lark about as much as we liked, provided that one boy kept cave. His job was to peer down the open stairwell and shout if anyone started to come up. We had ample time to scamper back into our rooms, so that if a member of staff appeared, we were under the blankets and looked as though we were peacefully asleep. But it was such a climb, they hardly ever did.

My friends - Tom, Eddy, Bunty and Ian - were within a month or so of my age. Tom's parents were stationed in India; his father was an infantryman and his mother an army nurse. He had not seen them for years and had forgotten what they looked like. He only knew they were still alive when he got a card on his birthday and at Christmas.

Eddy, Bunty and Ian were all in the same boat. None of them had identifiable fathers. Their mothers had to work long hours to earn enough to keep themselves and board their sons out. Ian, who was a bit on the simple side, was completely dominated by me. He was, in effect, my Man Friday. All he received by way of payment for being my obedient servant was a vague promise of protection should any of the other boys pick on him. It was he who had to stand in for me when it was my turn to be on lookout duty. Only once did he summon up enough courage to disobey me. His mother had, out of the blue, sent him a sixpenny postal order. I told him that as I'd not got a mother, he ought to share it with me.

"It's not my fault that you haven't got a mum," he said defiantly.

"If I'd been sent sixpence, I'd give you half," I said.

"You haven't got anybody who'd send you a postal order."

His reply hurt and annoyed me.

"If you don't give me half, you won't be getting any either," I said menacingly. I picked up a chair and placed it under the long flex that hung from the centre of the ceiling. By the look on Ian's face I think he feared I was going to hang him.

"What are you doing?" he said nervously.

"I'm going to blow both of us up."

I crossed the room and turned on the light switch. I picked up a new bulb I'd been given to replace the dud one. Then I went over to where he was sitting and held him by his hair.

"Now, Ian," I said, pressing the bulb against his lips, "when I put this light into the socket, with the switch on, there'll be a huge flash and then you, me, and the school will be blown to bits."

"Go on, do it, see if I care."

I released the hold I had on him and cupped his face between the palms of my hands. "Before we die, are you sure you won't change your mind?" I said solemnly.

He didn't answer, but just stared back at me. I let go of him and stood up on the chair, then, with all the sham pathos I could summon up, I cried out: "Goodbye Ian, goodbye school, and goodbye world!"

To my dismay, Ian remained silent, so I was left with no alternative but to carry out my threat. I thrust my arm upwards to within a hair's breadth of the live brass fitting, hesitating for a moment, when it dawned on me that I might well electrocute myself and leave Ian unscathed. Preferring the possibility of injury or even death to losing face, I moved my hand up an inch to reach the socket. To my relief, and in the nick of time, he called out: "Stop it, stop it, I'll give you half."

Although my behaviour was appalling, you have to bear in mind that the stakes were high. Threepence could buy not only a Mars Bar but a Milky Way as well.

The day for us boarders really only began when we were sent up to bed and the fun started. We must have been the only children for miles around who actually looked forward to bedtime. Our lookout system was nigh-on foolproof. But one night, dressed only in our pyjamas, four of us boys got out through a dormer window on the roof. Using the small flat surface above it as a platform, we climbed up to the top and sat astride the arched tiles waving and calling out to people waiting to go into the cinema opposite the school. Some right-minded citizens standing in the queue must have become alarmed when they spotted four boys playing about precariously on the roof, and reported us to one of the staff. We'd not been out there long when our lookout shouted up to us to come back in, someone was on the way up. In my haste, I slid down the slates and very nearly went over the edge. By the time the teacher arrived, breathless, all of us were under the blankets feigning sleep. Our little ruse didn't fool her for a moment, for she burst into the dormitory and screamed out loud enough to awaken the dead:

"Which four of you were out on the roof? Own up this very instant!"

None of us stirred.

"All right, in that case all of you will be punished. You'll go without your pocket money for the next four weeks."

With that threat hanging over them, those who were innocent jumped out of their beds and in unison said: "Please miss, it wasn't us."

The rest of us still had our heads under the blankets.

"Hayden, Tom, Eddy, Bunty - get out of your beds immediately."

We did, and stood sheepishly by them and gazing at the floor.

"Look at me when I'm speaking to you," bawled the teacher. "Because of your disgraceful behaviour, to say nothing of giving the school a bad name, plus the fact that you were quite prepared to let others be punished for your wrongdoings, I will now have your pocket money stopped, not for four weeks but eight. You will also lose your Easter egg."

With that off her chest, she stomped out of the room. With Easter being almost nine months away, the loss of the egg didn't upset us too much. Being deprived of our penny a week really did. But the worst punishment of all was that we were checked on a few times every evening which put a stop to our larking about. Luckily, the stairs were just too much for the teachers, middle-aged and unfit, to cope with. So, two weeks later, the checking ceased and things returned to normal.

Now, instead of just us boys mucking about, we persuaded a few of the more adventurous girls to join us in our room. In no time at all the games we used to play amongst ourselves - rough-housing, pillow-fighting and the like - changed irrevocably. The girls brought much more imagination into our play. It wasn't long before they had us playing 'Mummies and Daddies' and 'Doctors, Nurses and Patients'. In one game we were cast as naughty boys who had to be scolded, and if we continued to misbehave, got a spanking.

Although all this imaginative play was new to us, we very quickly got the hang of it and became willing partners in acting out the fantasies of the girls. Inexplicably and very gradually, a new dimension entered into our play. We began to view our newly found friends, not just as objects to be ridiculed or teased, but as individuals in their own right. It began to dawn on us that Joyce, Stella, Avril,

Daphne and Monica looked very pretty when they unplaited their long hair and let it hang down their nightdresses. The neatly cut fringes that covered half their foreheads like a pelmet, turned them unmistakably into girls. Their bodies didn't go straight down from the hips, but were curved, and their bottoms were more rounded than ours. Monica even had the beginning of breasts developing. We not only saw how unlike their shape was, but could feel it with our hands when, acting as 'doctor', we examined the parts that they said hurt them. Without realising it, our games became sexually orientated. We'd never heard of the word 'sex' taken in isolation. We knew that the `sexes' meant the difference between the genders and nothing more. How we'd arrived on earth was never explained. All we'd been told was that Jesus was the result of Mary's Immaculate Conception - whatever that meant - and that mortals were found as babies swathed in a sheet under a gooseberry bush.

Every night we knelt by our beds and prayed. Parrot-fashion we'd recite the Lord's Prayer. We didn't ask to be forgiven for the games we played because we didn't think them to be sinful. When we larked about we were always dressed in our nightclothes, and it would have remained that way if only Joyce hadn't dared me to drop my pyjama trousers. Being the leader of the pack, I had to accept. I untied the waist cord and let them drop. The five girls gathered around to have a look. To my relief they didn't start to giggle but just stared at my exposed part in silence.

"Have you had a good enough gander yet?" I asked after a second or two.

They nodded and averted their gaze.

"Now I dare you, Joyce," I said, with a smirk on my face.

"Go on, Joyce," called out Tom, "fair's fair, Hayden showed you what he'd got."

Coyly she lifted her nightdress and showed me what she hadn't. I was quite surprised that there was really nothing much to see. What I'd expected to be hidden away under her nightie I cannot now imagine, an oven door perhaps behind which babies were cooked.

However, any vague feeling of disappointment I had soon vanished when Joyce went beyond the dare by removing her garment. With a defiant gesture she twirled it around her head and threw it down to my feet. It wasn't long before all of us were running about naked. As we outnumbered the girls by two to one, they became, as it were, the fillings in a sandwich when we cuddled them. This close contact with their naked bodies caused something to happen that none of us had experienced before. What we'd nicknamed our 'winkles' began to grow: they grew and grew until they became almost unrecognisable. Like pegs they stood out rigid enough to hang our schoolcaps on, and only deflated gradually when the nymphettes returned to their room.

From that night on, all the noisy games we used to play ceased. Now we spent our long evenings like Babes in the Wood all huddled close together. Had any one of the staff listened outside our dormitory, they would hardly have heard a sound.

Had a teacher walked in without warning and chastised us, in our innocence, we wouldn't have understood why.

By touching, stroking and petting, we gave to one another the affection that was so blatantly missing in our formative years. Neither jealousy nor possessiveness had any part to play in our little community. As for me, I could, for the first time in my life, both give and receive affection, and because of this I changed quite a lot. I stopped bullying the others and became kinder to Ian. My uncontrollable temper only surfaced now when I was really provoked.

Perhaps the substitute that we neglected children had now found for ourselves in the absence of any parental love is what ultimately saved us from growing up to be anti-social adults who go through life with a huge chip on their shoulders.

CHAPTER THREE

Mid-September was when St Margaret's School officially opened. All expectant, on the big day, I hid behind a slightly opened door so that I could spy on the new pupils as they arrived. Miss Minter and her staff waited by the entrance to welcome the girls and their mothers. Just before nine, the first few turned up. On seeing them, my jaw dropped a little. They stood apprehensively in the hall, holding onto their mothers. They all looked very smart in their brand new uniforms and clean white knee-length socks. The shoes they had on were hardly worn. Their hair was well-groomed and the skin on their face was clear and rosy-cheeked. Compared to us boarders they were a picture of health and middle-class wealth. They seemed to me as if they had come from another planet. The youngest clung to their mothers for some time before they could be persuaded to let go. What all the fuss was about completely escaped me. After all, the little darlings would be collected again in a few hours and return home for lunch.

At breakfast, Miss Minter told us that we were to be especially friendly and helpful to the newcomers, and warned us that we would be severely punished if we were not. With that threat resounding in my ears, I trained myself to conjure up a wide false smile whenever I passed one of them in the corridors.

Now that classes were given by qualified teachers who kept to a properly laid-out school curriculum, and since all those who attended them were girls, there was nowhere for me to go. By the time the autumn term started, all the boy boarders had been found places in the local council school. I was the exception, I think because it suited Miss Minter to have me continue to be a drudge around the house. To have one boy tagged on to a line of girls, walking in pairs and holding hands, would have looked incongruous, so it was decided that at nine and a half I was old enough to be allowed out on my own. Freed at last from the hated crocodile, I felt like a bird let out of its cage.

My time, like Cinderella's, was spent on menial tasks and running errands. If it was raining I'd keep out of sight up in the dormitory, trying with considerable difficulty to read the communal Felix the Cat book or one of the comics I'd stolen out of the day pupils' jackets. But whenever possible I'd skive off down to the sea front, a few minutes' walk away, and sit for long periods staring out to sea. Sitting there alone I could think about the world around me. To some extent, my thoughts gave me a DIY education. And provided I'd done all my chores, no one seemed to notice when I disappeared for a couple of hours or so.

In the season, Mondays was a day full of hope for me. At weekends, hordes of day trippers from London descended on to the beaches of Southend and Westcliff, and if I was in luck I could, by scouring the sand where they'd been sitting, find a farthing or ha'penny that had dropped out of their pockets. On one very hot day in August, after an hour's beachcombing, I'd picked up three farthings. I desperately wanted a Rossi ice cream but unfortunately they cost a penny, so for a long time I continued my search, but to no avail. Armed with only three farthings I walked up the steep Pier Hill to Rossi's Ice-cream Parlour in the High Street. On the way I asked a well dressed man if he'd give a penny for my three farthings, but he ignored me and hurried on. When I arrived, I joined a queue that spilled out of the parlour down into the street. In the baking sun I stood there for some time before it was my turn.

"A penny or a tuppenny, sonny?" asked the lady behind the counter.

"A penny one please, miss," I replied timidly.

She picked up a cone and skilfully heaped onto it the generous twirl of icecream that made Rossi's so popular. Then, from her great height, she bent down and handed it to me. With my other arm I reached up to the counter that was above my head and laid out my three tiny coins.

"I need one more, boy," she said.

"Could you please let me off, miss? I never found another one, you see," I said. The cornet was tantalisingly close to my parched lips.

"Three farthings isn't a penny. Give it me back and be quick about it, you're holding up the queue."

I was tempted to make a run for it, but couldn't as the crowd behind me was too thick to make a quick getaway. I tried hard to hold back my tears as I handed it back.

"Now be off with you," she said sharply.

I looked up at her and through my tears shouted out: "I hate you, miss. And I hate you too!" I said to the people queuing, as I elbowed my way back into the street.

Although my total lack of education didn't seem to worry Miss Minter at all, she suddenly got a bee in her bonnet that something ought to be done about my religious tuition so as to prepare me for Confirmation the following year. Now on Saturday afternoons, instead of going down to the beach, I had to go to Father Sharp, who was the priest at the church we attended before we moved to Westcliff. Getting there wasn't easy as it meant a hike of almost two miles. When I asked Miss Minter why I couldn't go to the local church that we now went to on Sundays, her reply was that as Father Sharp was High Church, she preferred me to be taught by him. For weeks, every Saturday, I sat with a few other boys I'd never met before, trying to understand the priest as he laboriously took us through the catechism. Just before we all began to nod off, he took us into the church and walked us round the fourteen Stations of the Cross. On first sight the pictures depicting the Agony of Christ's Passion genuinely moved me, but after being dragged around them for umpteen times, I had a job to stop myself from yawning.

Father Sharp also felt it was his duty to warn us of the terrible things that would befall us if we succumbed to the sins of the flesh. He never precisely explained what they were, but reading between the lines, I think he was saying that the sort of lark I got up to with the girls in the dormitory was one of them.

Quite unwittingly, the priest had added a pinch of spice to my evenings. 'Sharpie', as we called him, lectured us all on how best we could dispel any wicked thoughts that crept into our minds. He said that when we felt that the devil was gaining the upper hand, we should go in haste to the bathroom and put the part that was leading us into temptation over the basin and flick cold water over it. Well, that was all right for him because he was over six feet tall, but we small boys would have had to stand on a high stool before we could even begin to splash away. He also said that in the struggle against evil it would help us if we slept with both our hands above the blankets.

"Not long from now," continued Father Sharp, "you boys will be able to emit a fluid that the Almighty only intended for the procreation of mankind. When this life-giving fluid leaves your body, you will experience a very pleasurable sensation. Human nature being what it is, you might be tempted to induce by self-manipulation this sensation again and again. If you do, it is incumbent on me to warn you that what you are emitting is the very marrow from your bones, and marrow, boys, is irreplaceable. So if you do not heed my words your hollow bones will soon start to crumble and you will end up a boneless and spineless creature, who has to spend the rest of his life in a wheelchair."

I was in my late teens before I realised that a man being pushed about in a wheelchair hadn't necessarily spent his youth wanking three times a day.

"My advice is to concentrate your minds on how best to play a first-class game of cricket."

That little talk was the sum total of my sex education.

Ignoring the priest's warning, the very next day I let Joyce coax me upstairs and take me into the bathroom, then bolt the door behind us.

"Why have you locked us in?" I asked.

"Because I want to say something secret."

"Secret?"

"It's about what we were told how babies are found under the gooseberry bushes. One of the day girls said it isn't true. She told me that babies come out of their mummy's tummy three months after the daddy has weed on the mummy's belly button."

"Is that why you brought me up here, just to tell me that?"

"No, it isn't, I want you to be a daddy to my baby."

"I think you'll have to wait until you are grown up."

"Grown-ups had dolls to play with when they were little, I didn't, you can give me a real live doll."

"I can't."

"Why can't you?"

"Because I don't need to do a wee at the moment."

"Then go into the kitchen and drink lots and lots of water, and come back up here when you want to go."

Never having been able to afford to give anything to anyone, I was only too pleased to do what she wanted. I went downstairs and downed three large glasses on the trot, then sat around on a dining-room chair and patiently waited for the call of nature. I thought it would be only a matter of minutes, but I sat there for what seemed like ages before going back up. When I got to the bathroom, Joyce wasn't there. Eventually I found her sitting on her bed all by herself in the girls' dormitory.

"Can you do a wee now, Hayden?" she asked.

"Yes, and we'd better hurry up before I wet myself," I replied.

We went into the bathroom and while she undressed, I hung on by hopping up and down with my hand held firmly between my legs. It seemed to take for ever before she lay down on the cold and dry white enamel of the waterless bath. I got in at the tap end.

"Hayden, you can't get into the bath with your shoes on," she said, sounding for all the world like one of the teachers. I jumped back out and quickly removed them. By now I was bursting to go.

"Is it all right if I start?" I said, with a sense of urgency in my voice.

"Yes, go on."

I took aim but missed.

"Not down there, silly, do it into my belly button!"

I guided the stream until it was bang on target.

"That's better," she said, protecting her face from the spray with her bare hands. When I'd done my bit, I suggested that she had a quick bath before a teacher came up and caught us.

"If I do that, the baby won't come," she said, as she dabbed herself dry with the communal towel. Well, I'd done what she asked me to do, but I had little faith that my contribution would give Joyce the baby doll she so desperately wanted.

I was hopeless at the Catechism, and as I'd had no training in memorising anything, it was almost impossible for me to respond to Father Sharp's tuition. He phoned Miss Minter and told her that I might do better if I was in the choir.

For my audition with the choir master, I had to sing the first verse of 'Onward Christian soldiers'. I'd only got as far as 'marching as to war' when he threw his hands up in the air and said: "Stop, please do stop."

After he'd regained his composure, he told me to follow him to the vestry whereupon he announced to Father Sharp that he'd found him another altar boy.

So now, instead of going to Confirmation classes on Saturdays, I got stuck with having to be the altar boy at early morning Sunday Mass, and then hang around to be a server in the mid-morning Service. This service felt like it went on for ever. I didn't like one bit trailing behind the priest and his entourage as they made their way slowly up the aisle to the high altar. The smoke from the censer, as I swung it to and fro, wafted up my nostrils and made me feel slightly sick. I never really got the hang of where I should be at any given time, particularly at early morning Mass when it was vital that I knew my moves, since I was the only one in attendance on the priest. If Father Sharp turned to his left or right to take the chalice or wafers from me, I'd invariably be on the wrong side of him.

"Other side, boy," he'd hiss at me, but without fail, the very next week I'd make the same mistake.

Fortunately my inability to perform properly worked to my advantage, because it persuaded Father Sharp for the second time to phone Miss Minter and suggest to her that perhaps it would be best if I attended our local church and let Father Gould take over my tuition.

The next Sunday, after morning service, I waited with Miss Minter by the church porch until Father Gould appeared.

"This is the boy that Father Sharp found to be such a problem," said Miss Minter with a sigh.

Father Gould was a tall man with thick black hair that was brushed straight back from his forehead. He had a face like an amiable ape. He looked down at me and smiled, and as he spoke to Miss Minter, he stroked my hair.

"I find it hard to believe that such an intelligent and nice- looking boy could be a problem. What's your name, my son?"

"Hayden Cartlidge, father."

"Well, Hayden, if you come to the vicarage after school on Friday, we'll make a start on preparing you for your Confirmation. I think you and I will get along splendidly. You can see the vicarage from here. It's the house with the green gate, on the other side of the road. I'll get my housekeeper to bring in a few little cakes. I presume you like cake, don't you?"

"Yes," I replied promptly.

"Good, so I'll see you on Friday then, at about four."

Cakes! For those I'd put up with the tedious catechism being rammed into my head every day of the week.

I'd hardly removed my finger from the front-door bell when Father Gould opened it.

"My goodness, you are punctual," he said as I entered.

He couldn't have known, of course, that for the last twenty minutes I'd been sitting on an old tombstone in the churchyard, waiting patiently for the clock to strike four.

"Come into my study, my housekeeper won't disturb us in there."

In the room was a leather-topped desk standing in front of a large bay window. On it was a gold-rimmed plate with four delicious-looking Lyons' Fairy Teacakes all nestled in coloured fluted paper. Some time passed before I could avert my gaze from them to the priest. He sat down on a high-backed mahogany chair and I on a smaller one on the other side of the room.

"Bring your chair and come and sit by me at the desk."

I placed myself at the other end of it.

"Now, Hayden, tell me about yourself."

"Not a lot I could tell you, father, because I'm an orphan. I've been looked after by Miss Minter since I was a baby."

"Are both your parents dead then?"

"No, they left me with her. They didn't want me."

"Oh dear, that's rather sad. I'm quite sure that if she saw you now your mother would be proud to have a fine-looking son like you. Come over to me and sit on my lap."

I did, because it got me two steps nearer to the cakes. No sooner was I seated on his well-creased black trousers than he placed his hands on my legs and up my shorts. His strange behaviour did not bother me, because all I was thinking about was how long I would have to wait before I was given a cake.

"You have the most beautiful legs I've ever seen on a young boy," he said, as he slid his hands up and down my thighs, letting them occasionally disappear up my short trousers. I'd heard the word 'beautiful' applied to the sky, scenery, a dress and many other things but never before to limbs. I'd only ever thought of them purely as a means to transport myself from one location to another.

When the priest took his hands away I assumed he was going to offer me a cake, but he didn't. Instead he held my face between his palms and started kissing it all over. He even nibbled my ear lobes. When he stuck his tongue into one of them, a thought flashed through my mind, that as I'd not washed them lately, he'd say 'you dirty boy, leave my house at once' but to my amazement, he just continued to lick away, first at one and then the other, like a busy bee collecting pollen. Eventually he released the grip on my face and pulled the plate of cakes towards me. As I tucked into them, he carried on running his hands up and down my legs. When it was time for me to leave, the only religious instruction I'd received was that some priests like stroking the legs of young boys.

This performance with the priest went on every Friday for nigh-on half a year. It never varied, he fumbled me about while I tucked into the cakes I got by way of payment for letting him do it. It only began not to be worth it when he started to poke his long tongue into my small mouth and twirl it around. This new practice of his made me feel so sick that it put me off eating my reward.

In the hope of getting him to stop; before getting into bed I prayed to God to ask his deputy to stop putting his tongue into my mouth. But he didn't, and so I came to the conclusion that the Almighty had more important things to do than attend to the plea of one small boy. In desperation, on a wet Saturday afternoon, I walked all the way to Southend to ask Father Sharp if he would intercede on my behalf. After I'd told him all about Father Gould's behaviour, all he said was (as he ran his hands up my short trousers):

"Hayden, my son, the Good Lord has blessed you with a wonderful body. You must expect that sometimes people will want to appreciate it by touching and stroking your lovely limbs. You should learn to share your God-given gift with others."

I didn't really understand what he was saying, though I had a vague notion that I was some sort of dish that priests could help themselves to whenever the urge came over them. Fed up that he'd do nothing to help me, I made my way back in the pouring rain. However, he'd done one thing for me; he had taught me never again to trust one of God's representatives on earth.

Finally, the only way I managed to stop Father Gould's nauseating practice was to gather up enough courage to tell him to his face that I didn't like what he was doing to me, and say that I'd no longer be coming on Fridays. I told Miss Minter I didn't need to go again as I had completed all the religious instruction I needed before my Confirmation. Although I missed not having the cakes, at least I no longer had to put up with the priest poking his long tongue into my mouth. The only lasting damage his disgusting habit did was that for the rest of my life I couldn't give or receive a French kiss, even when I loved someone very much.

CHAPTER FOUR

At Christmas boarders went home, leaving only a few of us behind. In the years before Miss Minter got her inheritance, with virtually no money to spare, she did her best to give those that remained some sort of a Christmas. Each of us was given sixpence to spend in Woolworth's on a packet of ten cards. A cardboard box, crudely covered with red crinkly paper, was put into the dining room for us to post them in. We all spent a long time agonising over who we would give our precious gift to, as the cards were the only present we were in a position to give or receive and were cherished for the whole year.

At no time during my childhood did I get a present that needed wrapping paper. The only toys I had were the empty matchboxes that the cook collected for me. With imagination, I could transform them into almost anything. They became forts, soldiers, houses, docks, and an endless variety of trains and trucks.

Just before Christmas, we spent our evenings pasting together bits of coloured paper that were collected throughout the year and then cut into strips for us to make into paper chains. In common with all small children, we could put a stocking at the end of our bed on Christmas Eve in the expectation of Santa Claus calling. I always got so excited about his visit that getting to sleep wasn't easy. Why I became so whooped up, I do not know, for I knew only too well what the stocking would contain, as it was always the same, namely one apple, one tangerine, two boiled sweets and three toffees. The Christmas dinner was a real feast: roast turkey, purchased at the eleventh hour on Christmas Eve, when they were all but given away. For afters, we had home-made Christmas pudding and mince pies. Although I couldn't eat the meat, it didn't lessen my enjoyment of the meal.

Before saying grace, Miss Minter addressed the gathering with the same little speech she gave every year.

"First of all, children, I want to thank each and every one of you for the splendid cards I've received. I do hope that you enjoy this day, because, bearing in mind my advanced years and failing health, the Good Lord may not spare me long enough to be with you all next year."

'Hope so,' we muttered unkindly under our breath.

One Christmas, when Stella returned, she brought with her a piano made out of sugar. Her father had given it to her as a present for me. The sugar must have been mixed with gypsum, for no matter how long I gnawed away at it, my teeth couldn't penetrate it. Finally, in desperation, I broke it up by whamming it hard with a hammer. Even then, the fragmented pieces took a lot of sucking before they would dissolve.

Shortly after I'd solved the piano problem, I came down with a high temperature. I was so feverish that in any normal household a doctor would have been summoned immediately, but as the fee for a home visit was astronomically high - five shillings to be precise - I'd have had to be at death's door before Dr Mallinson was called out. Whenever Miss Minter was worried about you, she put you into her room and laid you down on a camp bed next to hers. There was a bad and a good side to this arrangement. The former was that she snored, the latter was that when you woke up, a biscuit would be on the small table that separated your bed from hers.

I woke up before dawn on the third day feeling a lot better. Unhappily, no biscuit was there. However, I cheered up when I noticed that in a tumbler of water there were two sweets, all sugary pink and white, realistically made to look like teeth. I assumed they'd been submerged to soften them so that I didn't have the problem I'd had with the piano. I fished the smaller of the two out and started to suck it, but no matter how vigorously I sucked away, I got nowhere. So I tried the bigger one, and got no joy from that either. I popped them back into the water in the hope that if they soaked a little longer, they'd be more manageable. But alas, when I awoke again, they were not there.

At the end of the summer term in 1933, when I was ten and St Margaret's had existed for a year, the father of a day pupil offered a puppy to the school. He thought that we deprived boarders
should have a dog as company and an animal to play with. Miss Minter begrudgingly accepted it, but only because he was an influential local businessman. The puppy was a cross between an Alsatian and a Golden Retriever. As soon as it was handed over, it became crystal-clear that to care
 for it was going to be my responsibility. I didn't mind. When I held the small, fluffy golden ball in my hands, I immediately fell in love with it.

Without giving a thought as to the animal's gender, Miss Minter said: "Hayden, we will call your new little friend Peter."

In her eyes, dogs and horses were male, cats and cows female, and as for bulls - well, she preferred not to think about them.

By the time Peter was sixteen months old, she'd already produced the first of her many litters. From the day of her arrival, she was my constant companion. She was by my side when I was making beds, sweeping floors or going on errands. We enjoyed being together most of all when we ran along the beach, jumping or clambering over the breakwater barriers, placed along the shore at 100-yard intervals. At low tide we'd walk on the hard path that went a long way out on the mudflats. Peter was in her element, for here she was as free as the seagulls she loved to chase. When the gulls flew off, she'd amuse herself teasing the crabs that she flicked out from under the tarred and barnacled planks that edged the sides of the stony path, prancing around them in circles, barking away as she did her little dance. Very astutely she'd approach a crab from the rear of its snapping claws and pick it up with her teeth, then with a mighty swing of her head she'd send it hurtling through the air. The poor thing invariably ended up topsy-turvy some distance away, and I had to go squelching through the mud to right it.

The world out there, away from the town, was our private domain. The only other people visible, a long way off, were men in waders, turning over the mud with a fork, collecting the worms that they used as bait for fishing off the pier.

One day, on a cold and windy February morning, we'd not been out on the mud for very long when the ebb tide turned. The sea then starts to come in at a slow walking pace, and nearly reaches the beach before it submerges the large higher banks of mud. If you don't keep well ahead of the incoming tide, you can easily become stranded a long way from the shore. Knowing this, I turned to go back, but Peter went off to chase the gulls. I ran after her, but she assumed I was playing and though I kept calling her she never came. When I finally caught her, the surrounding sea was deepening by the minute. I pulled her by the collar to the water's edge, but she steadfastly refused to put her paws into it.

"You'll drown if you don't come with me now, you silly dog," I screamed.

She just wouldn't budge. I realised then I had no alternative but to carry her. In case I had to swim for it, I removed my coat and put it under one arm, while with the other I picked her up. The icy water reached up to my chest. Some moments passed before I could get my almost paralysed limbs to move. To add to my misery, Peter kept struggling to get away from me. The claws of her flailing and powerful hind legs went deep into the skin of my unprotected back and drew blood. Just when I'd nearly given up any hope of either of us getting out of the freezing sea alive, Peter cut loose from the hold my numbed arm had on her and began to swim towards the shore. Now unimpeded, it wasn't long before I reached shallow water. I stood for a while shivering on the sea front, soaked to the skin, with my teeth chattering uncontrollably, before I could muster up enough strength to walk back in the biting wind that cut right through my wet clothes.

As I entered the school, one of the teachers spotted me.

"What on earth have you been up to? Just look at the state you're in."

Desperate to go and dry myself, I gave her the briefest account of what had happened.

"Your foolishness might well have ended up with the poor dog drowning!"

"I nearly did, trying to save her, miss."

"It would have served you right if you had, you stupid boy. Whatever possessed you to go out that far with the tide on the turn? Go up at once and change your clothes, you're dripping water all over the floor."

After giving Peter a good rub-down, we both sat crouched in front of the fire for a long time, thankful to be still alive.

Shortly after this experience, I became very ill. I felt so terrible that I had to be carried by Tom and Eddy up to Miss Minter's room. She thought my condition was sufficiently serious. Dr Mallinson should be called, five shillings or no. He took a long time in coming, and when he did, he seemed to be in a great hurry. He put a cold stethoscope to my burning chest, and felt my feverish forehead. Then, loud enough for me to hear, he said:

"The boy has double pneumonia, there's not a lot you can do for him, I'm afraid. Wrap him up well and get him to drink as much hot milk as possible. If he survives the night, the worst will be over."

With that alarming prognosis off his chest, he put on his coat and left. Despite my raging temperature, I tried hard to stay awake as I wanted to be fully conscious when the angels appeared by my bedside to escort me to the Heavenly Gates, but try as I might, sleep eventually overcame me. Hours later, when I opened my eyes and saw the daylight, I remembered what the doctor had forecast and knew I'd soon get well, because I had survived the night.

By summer I was fit and well, so Peter and I could do all the things we used to do before my illness. On warm days we'd go down to the sea front and play on the long jetty that pleasure boats used to take on board their passengers. The jetty had two levels, one for the high and the other for the low tide. On the top level, I'd do a sprint along the whole length with Peter yapping at my heels, then we'd both take a flying leap off the jetty into the sea, which on low tide could be twenty feet below. We'd do this time and time again, only stopping when we were exhausted. At weekends, day trippers gathered in small groups to watch a dog that could repeatedly hurl itself off the high jetty into the water. I had a notion to pass a hat round, so that they could show their appreciation of my performing animal by parting with a penny. I never did, because I couldn't summon up the nerve.

A man who worked locally was allowed to park his motorbike and sidecar inside the gates of the school's back garden. He and I became quite friendly. He lived ten miles away at Hockley with his wife and two children. I think he befriended me because I was an orphan. One Saturday, after he'd finished working, he asked me if I'd like to go for a ride with him along the coast to Shoeburyness.

Excitedly I wriggled myself into the boat-shaped sidecar. Peter jumped in on top of me. At first she was frightened by the noise of the engine and struggled to get out, but after a while she settled down and, like me, began to enjoy whizzing along out in the open, suspended on one wheel. The force of the wind blew back her furry, pointed ears and parted the long brown and golden hair that covered her magnificent head. The faster we went, the more she loved it. In fact, she enjoyed herself so much that when we got back, I had quite a job persuading her to leave the sidecar. The man who took us told me that he worked at a small engineering factory that manufactured ball-bearing metal wheels for manoeuvring heavy machinery about.

"With our wheels, you can easily push two tons across a factory floor with one hand," he said proudly. He contemplated for a moment. "Tell you what, lad, over the weekend I'll knock up a cart for you and put on it four of the wheels we make at work. Would you like that?"

The look on my face answered his question.

"The one I'll make will whizz along at a fair pelt, it'll go faster than skates and keep up with a bicycle downhill. I'll bring it with me on my way to work on Monday, I promise."

On Sunday night I was so excited that I barely slept a wink. Next morning I was waiting by the back gate and half an hour early. As soon as I spotted the cart in the sidecar I knew he hadn't just knocked it up. The man must have spent the whole of his well-earned day off making it. He lifted it off his bike and put it on the ground beside me. This cart wasn't remotely like any others I'd seen, for they were crudely made out of two planks of rough wood and had four old pram wheels that wobbled as they turned. The one he'd brought had a floor made out of new wood that had been varnished and highly polished. To make steering easy, he'd put on a loop of cord and fixed it securely to the front axle that swivelled on a pivot. The heavy metal wheels had a six-inch diameter and a three-inch hole in the centre, through which they were attached to the axle. Big nuts and bolts held them firmly in position. The wheels had three iron rings that were separated by ball-bearings the size of glass marbles. The cart looked professionally made as if it had been produced in a factory.

"Do you like it, lad?" he asked as he looked down admiringly at his own handiwork.

Like it! Whatever I said by way of a reply would have been an understatement. I did manage to say:

"I can't believe it's really for me! Nobody in the whole world has got a cart like this one."

"Yes, you're most likely right. And because it's so different from the others, there's something you should know before you use it. Unlike a motor car that runs on petrol, ball-bearings run on oil. So every time you take it out, make sure that you put plenty of oil between the rings. If you forget, the bearings will soon seize up and the wheels won't go round."

He handed me a can with a spout and showed me how to use it.

"Let me know when that's nearly empty and I'll refill it. I'd better get moving now or I'll be late clocking in."

"Thank you very much for the cart. I think your children are lucky to have a dad like you," was all I could think of to say to him.

When he left, I just stood and gazed at what I'd been given. I got to thinking, that for today at least, I could be counted amongst the richest boys in all England. Out loud I said, as my fingertips glided over the polished wood:

"Hayden, it's yours, it's only yours, you don't have to share it with anyone."

As soon as I'd done my morning chores, Peter and I took our four-wheeled chariot out through the gate and onto the street. With one leg I knelt on the shiny wood and with the other I gave a hard push. The cart sped along for a good twenty yards before slowly coming to a halt. Its iron wheels made a lot of noise as they went clinkety-clank over the paving stones. People out for an afternoon stroll looked anxiously round to see what on earth it was that made such a din. Sparks, caused by the friction of metal rolling over stone slabs, shot out from under the wheels. In the dark you could see me coming from a long way off. Peter, who preferred to run rather than walk, liked me being on the cart because I could keep up with her. Whenever I went down a slope, she'd hop on just for the fun of the ride.

One day I took her to the top of Pier Hill. The hill was over a mile long, and very steep for the first half; after that it became a gentle slope before finally flattening out. From then, your own momentum would hopefully carry you along the sea front to the Kursaal Amusement Arcade, which was a mile and a half away from the start.

I sat on the cart like a motor-racing driver, waiting for the start flag to drop. "Jump on, Peter," I said.

She tucked herself in between my bent legs. I held her in a tight clamp with my knees, pushed on the road with my hand and we started to roll. Very quickly we were moving at such a pace that if a car had overtaken us it would have been exceeding the speed limit.

"Yoohoo, whoopee," I yelled as we pelted down the steep hill at the speed of a toboggan skimming over frozen snow. I knew Peter liked it because her upper lip was curled slightly. She only did this when she was enjoying herself. We didn't have to worry about cars coming out of the side roads, as there were none. Just as I'd anticipated, the impetus gained from our speed kept us going all the way to the Amusement Arcade.

At the end of our fourth run on that wonderful day, we came to a halt right by the highly polished boots of a very tall policeman. I smiled slyly up at him.

"Are you trying to kill yourself and the dog, or what?"

"It's quite safe, sir, we've done it lots of times."

"Quite safe, eh?"

"Oh yes, sir."

"Tell me then, when you're travelling without brakes at such a speed, how would you stop in an emergency?"

"I don't know, sir."

"And what's more, you never will find out, because if I ever catch you doing this lark again, I'll run you into the station. Then, lad, you're going to have to face your parents when they arrive. You can imagine the whacking your dad will give you when I tell him what you've been up to."

"I haven't got a dad, sir."

"All right, your mum then."

"I've not got a mum either."

"I'll have none of your cheek, boy. Now be off with you or I'll give you a whacking myself."

Tell a policeman the truth and he wants to give you a good hiding, I'd better remember that, I thought. I kept away from Pier Hill for a few weeks, but the thrill of whizzing down it drew me back there many more times.

Temporarily frustrated by the policeman's warning, I devised an alternative way of propelling myself without effort. On the beach I found a length of cord about fifteen feet long. I tied one end to Peter's collar and the other to the cart.

With its well-oiled wheels it was no strain at all for her to pull me along. What she didn't understand was that it was she who was pulling me. I think she thought I was trying to catch up with her, so the faster she ran to get away from me, the quicker we travelled. I, on the other hand, could sit there like Lord Muck, envied by all the other boys I passed, who were laboriously pushing their crudely made carts along using their feet. The only thing I had to watch out for was if my 'husky' unexpectedly stopped to sniff a lamp-post or pass the time of day with another dog. Then I'd have to brake by slamming both my feet onto the ground to stop myself careering into her hind legs. On other days Peter and I still went for walks along the shore and onto the mudflats, so that she could indulge in her favourite sport chasing seagulls.

Peter mostly mated with a brown and white cocker spaniel called Boy, who lived in the next street. He hung around day and night by the back gate when she was in season. He was particularly a nuisance after they'd mated, as then he'd get locked back to back with her. To speed up their separation, I'd frogmarch them down to the jetty and push them into the sea. With both swimming in opposite directions, they soon became uncoupled. It wasn't easy getting them there, because Peter's legs were about three inches longer than Boy's, so while she could go forward on all fours, he had to walk backwards with his hind legs suspended in space.

Some months had passed by, and Joyce still hadn't given birth to the baby doll she so desperately wanted. I found out why when Tom told me that an older boy at his school told him what really had to happen to give a girl a baby. To stop Joyce from fretting, I repeated to her what Tom had said. At first she was very disappointed, but after contemplating it for a moment, she said:

"Well, Hayden, we'll have to do it like that then, won't we?"

Having readily fallen in with the bathroom charade, what she was asking me to do now worried me a little. So to duck out of it, I came up with the bright idea that Ian would be just right for the job.

"Why Ian and not you ?" she asked.

"Well, errr I know, because he's got a bigger winkle than I have, also I could be standing by if things didn't go right. I mean, Tom's school friend could be wrong, you know."

"Will you ask Ian then?"

"Yeah."

I didn't so much as ask him, I told him what he'd be doing in the dormitory after supper that night. Because Joyce was afraid the others might laugh, she took Ian and me into the bathroom and locked the door. My first step as Master of Ceremonies was to have them standing naked facing each other. When Ian put his limp penis in the position I told him to, it just crumpled up and couldn't do a thing. Once again, I thought, I've been told another silly story about how babies are made. Tom's friend must have been telling him fibs. I was just about to call the whole thing off when Ian's penis began to show signs of life. It ended up quite a lot bigger than I'd remembered. I got on my knees ready to act as referee. On his second attempt, Ian entered Joyce without a hitch. He'd barely started on his journey into the unknown when Joyce let out a little gasp. I shouted up to Ian: "Stop, don't move!"

Seconds later, Joyce countermanded me by telling him to get on with it.

When their pelvises met, an alarming thought flashed through my mind. What would I do if they became locked together like Peter and Boy? I could see me, in the dead of night, having to carry them both on my back all the way down to the jetty and tipping them into the sea. Oh dear, oh dear, what if the tide was out? Thankfully my panic was short-lived, and when Ian withdrew and then went back in again, it didn't seem to bother Joyce at all.

When it was all over, Ian confessed to me that his mother got him to do that to her when he went home.

"But Ian, your mum is an old lady, you told me she was thirty-two, I remember."

"I know she's old, but she's still lovely."

"If you had told me about you and your mum before, I wouldn't have been so worried."

From that night on, a whole new vista of sexual play opened up to us all.

CHAPTER FIVE

I was twelve when the headmaster of St John's Preparatory School sent his five-year old daughter to St Margaret's. Because he did, my daily routine changed irrevocably.

An exchange agreement was made between him and Miss Minter, whereby she would take in his child, and in return he'd have me. This was now possible because a sixteen-yearold Swiss girl called Ulrike had been engaged as a domestic. My only chore now was to light fires and bring up the coal. Relieved from all the other duties, I was free, for the first time in my childhood, to begin my education.

Attending St John's meant I had to wear a school uniform. This I didn't like at all, nor did I relish being shut up in a classroom full of boys and girls, who'd had the advantage of having been to a primary school. As most of the lessons were way above my head, I spent a lot of my time staring up at the ceiling waiting for the bell to go. I made no friends amongst the middle-class pupils who were my classmates. They instinctively felt that there was something not quite right about the new boy in their midst. One thing that set me apart from them was that they were all given money each day to spend in the school tuck shop. Never once did any of them offer me so much as a single sweet, on the contrary, they took a sadistic delight in making sure that I could see them as they munched away.

At this school I was lonely and bored. I would have much preferred to be back doing my chores. The teachers had been warned by the headmaster that I was educationally a non-starter and their way of dealing with the problem was to ignore me. As far as they were concerned, I wasn't in the classroom. Once I realised this, I responded by absenting myself as soon as the morning register was taken. In the summer, I'd sometimes bunk off as often as three days in one week, and as I was never taken to task, I assumed that nobody cared or minded.

The only light on the horizon in this school was a very beautiful and well-developed girl of thirteen called June. I sometimes chose to go to school so as to be able to gaze at her sitting at her desk.

Unfortunately, one insurmountable obstacle prevented me approaching this beauty. She charged to bestow her favours on you. For a Milky Way you got a kiss. A Mars Bar got you a longer kiss, and you could put your arms around her lovely body. For a half-pound bar of Cadbury's Milk Chocolate, you could put one hand up her knickers. As this cost sixpence, even the well-off boys could rarely produce the price.

To buy even a kiss was out of the question for me, until I had a stroke of luck. One Saturday, when I was in the local sweetshop pondering what to spend my penny on, the man behind the counter removed a faded dummy half-pound bar of chocolate from the display and replaced it with a new one.

"Could I have that, please, if you don't need it any more?" I asked hopefully.

"You can, but it's not much use. It's only cardboard."

It's of use to me, I thought, as he handed it over. Armed with bait, I could barely wait for Monday to come.

At breaktime on that Monday morning, I slipped the dummy bar into my jacket pocket, making sure that the shiny silver paper was clearly visible. When June came out into the playground, I made a beeline over to her, in order to be quite sure I got to her before any of the other boys did. I stood in front of her, and with my finger I pointed to the fake bar in my pocket. Her eyes grew wide and told me, she'd taken the bait.

"How about a knickerbocker glory?" I said in a feeble attempt to be amusing.

"Come with me to the alleyway, we can't be seen there," she said.

With my heart beating faster, I followed her. When we got there, she leant with her back against the wall and asked:

"How can you afford to buy a sixpenny bar of chocolate all of a sudden? You never even have one penny to spend in the tuck shop?"

"I found sixpence lying in the gutter," I replied.

"Then you went and spent it all on me?"

"Yep," I said.

"Give it to me, then you can start with a kiss."

"I'd rather give it to you afterwards. Then it won't be so hard for me to part with it," I said, thankful that I'd managed to think up a reply.

She bent forward and pressed her full lips onto mine. I felt a tingly sensation go all the way down to my toes. I put my hands around her and let them slowly run up her tunic before sliding them under the elastic of her knickers.

"You're only allowed to put one hand up there," she said.

"Let me have both, please June," I pleaded.

"All right, but not for long."

With my hands gliding over the fleshy part of her beautifully rounded bottom, I was at last doing what I had yearned to do for a year. A minute of sheer bliss went by, then she said firmly: "That's enough."

"Just a little longer, please!"

"No, stop now or I'll scream."

I pulled her even closer to me and held her in a tight grip.

"If you scream, you won't get any chocolate, and what's more, I'll tell the teacher what I had to promise to give you before you'd let me do it."

My blackmail paid off. She let me continue for quite some time before I finally deigned to remove my hands. The moment I did, she snatched the fake bar out of my pocket and began to tear off the wrapping.

"You-you-" was all she said.

Now one would have expected that a thirteen-yearold girl who had the benefit of a very expensive education, would do better than that. Words like cheat, scoundrel, fraud, villain, and rogue would have been more appropriate, but to say just YOU...well! Not that I would have minded what she called me, for I had got what I'd lusted after in exchange for a totally worthless piece of cardboard.

The August carnival I always looked forward to. Flags were strung across the streets and decorations clamped to lampposts festooned the main thoroughfares. The highlight of the festivities was the parade. Local stores and big businesses were represented by horse or motor-driven floats, all competing with each other to make theirs the most spectacular. The dray horses, all groomed and feathered, with their brasses and bridles highly polished, were a delight to see. Leading the parade was a column of smartly turned-out, white-gloved policemen. Behind them the firemen sat motionless in their shiny fire-engines. Then came the nurses and ambulance-men from the recently built General Hospital. When those on foot had passed by, the first of the floats came into view carrying Miss Southend, dressed only in a swimsuit and sitting on a golden throne. A garland of trailing flowers hung down from her pretty head. The Michelin Company had a real man squeezed into layers of tyres, and as he went by he waved his tyre-clad arms at the crowd that lined the route three-deep. Palmolive had a girl in a bath up to her neck in bubbles. Every now and then she lifted a shapely leg out of the suds, much to the delight of the male spectators. An enormous bottle angled across the float with two bagpipers blowing away, was Coca-Cola's contribution.

The very last item, when all the floats had passed, was an entry from Madame Tussaud's. First to appear was a line of soldiers banging a slow, awesome roll on their drums. They preceded four sturdy-looking men on foot, who carried on their shoulders a rigid stretcher with a wax figure of a black man, swathed only in a white sheet, sitting on it cross-legged. As the bearers passed, the mood of the bystanders suddenly changed. Men and women, who only moments before were happily throwing streamers at the floats, began to hiss, boo and shake their clenched fists at the effigy.

"Excuse me, sir, why is everyone getting so angry?" I asked a welldressed man standing by me.

'Because that's Gandhi, my boy. He's the rabble-rouser who wants to snatch India away from our Empire. He can't now, thank heaven, because we've got the evil blighter where he belongs ... behind bars, lad."

I'd never before set eyes on a black man. Despite what the man had told me, I instinctively felt that it was wrong for the crowd to be hurling obscenities onto this gentle and intelligent-looking wax effigy. Their anger frightened me, and spoiled some of the enjoyment of an otherwise memorable day.

At the end of August, when the nights began to draw in, the illuminations were switched on. Like Blackpool, Southend was famous for its lights. Chartered trains and coaches brought hordes of Londoners up for the evening, just to marvel at them. High poles, sunk into the mud some distance away from the shore, had battened onto them Mickey Mouse, Pluto and Popeye. When the electric bulbs flickered to and fro, the cartoon characters became animated. Fixed onto trellises were cascades of star-shaped lights that exploded like fireworks, their image reflected in the sea below. The spacious floral gardens that sloped down to the promenade at Westcliff had flower beds, bushes and trees floodlit.

The illuminations gave a lot of pleasure to the many thousands of ordinary people who travelled a long way to see them.

Even though I'd still not managed to master the questions and answers of the catechism, in my twelfth year I was confirmed. From now on most Sundays I was compelled to take Communion before breakfast. There was, however, one consolation: Father Gould, who took the service, could put nothing more innocuous into my mouth than the Body of Christ, miraculously compressed into a thin wafer.

As a reward for our confirmation, thirty of the less well-off boys in the parish were taken on a five-day holiday to the Church of England camping site at Angmering-on-Sea in Sussex. Father Gould, aided by four lady parishioners, ran the camp for the month of August.

Early one Monday morning, Ian, Tom, Eddy and I met up with the other boys who were standing outside our church. Father Gould ran up and down the churchyard like an agitated hen checking on her brood.

Once he'd decided that all his boys were accounted for, we boarded the coach. Our route took us through London from east to west spanning the entire width of this sprawling city and giving us some idea how vast it is.

It was late in the afternoon before the coach pulled up at the camping site. Dotted about the field were a dozen or so bell tents. There was one for each adult and we boys were put four to a tent. I shared mine with my three friends. The tents were equipped with straw palliasses, ground sheets, and a pile of blankets that by the feel of them had seen better days. When we'd made up our beds, we went over to the marquee for tea and jam sandwiches.

We were each given sixpence to spend in the village store. After tea, my pals and I made for the sea. The only way to get there was through a derelict field of wheat. Growing in profusion amongst the neglected crop were poppies, thistles, and cornflowers. The field was a rich canvas of red, blue and yellow. As we walked through it, trampling underfoot the colourful patchwork of wild plants, I couldn't help feeling that in some way we were violating the beauty of nature. The sea here was different from that of the Thames estuary. From this shore, you could look out to the horizon and see nothing but a vast expanse of water. I'd never seen the sky meet the sea before, and it puzzled me as to how it could. I asked my friends if they knew, but all I got from them was, 'Don't know and don't care."

Then they left me and went off back to the camp to join in a game of cricket. I stayed on, gazing out to sea until sunset, then I walked along a country lane that led to the village of Angmering. It was deserted. The only sound was of my own footsteps walking over the pebbled pavement. Feeling a little uneasy, I went back to the campsite.

The highlight of the holiday was when we all went by motorboat from nearby Littlehampton up river to visit Arundel Castle. It was a big treat for us all as none of us had ever set foot in a real boat before, even though we lived by the sea. I was having the time of my life and my only regret was that my dog wasn't here with me to enjoy it as well.

Every day before breakfast, we went for a swim. Father Gould came too, and had us running naked through the cornfield down to the sea. On the last day it was overcast and a cold wind blew. None of us felt like swimming, but the priest said we must.

As there was an ebb tide, we all had to go a long way out in the mud before reaching water deep enough to swim in. Nobody stayed for very long in the freezing sea, including Father Gould, who was well on his way back by the time any of us got out. In an effort to keep warm, we ran back to the camp as fast as our legs would carry us. As I passed the priest's tent, he poked his head out of the flap and called me in. When I entered, he was standing naked with his back to me, drying himself.

"Dry off, Hayden, use the towel that's hanging over the chair."

While I did, he put on his cassock, then turned to face me.

"I want you to kneel, my son."

Still shivering a little, I did as he asked. I assumed that he and I would pray to God to thank Him for the wonderful holiday that the church had given me, but we didn't. Instead he stood in front of me and laid the palm of his hands on top of my wet hair.

"Close your eyes and open your mouth, boy," he said in a priestly tone of voice. Strange place to take communion, I thought, but I opened my mouth wide and stuck out my tongue in readiness to receive the Holy Wafer. It was no wafer that penetrated my mouth and slid down to the back of my throat. I felt as though I was going to suffocate, and I struggled to free myself, but Father Gould held my head in a vice-like grip. His penis went back and forth a few times, then made a jerky movement that sent a gluey substance down my throat. A few moments passed before the priest released the tight hold he had on me. I responded by vomiting all over his bare feet. I stood up and wiped my lips on his towel, then looked up at the priest. My tearful eyes must have shown such loathing and disgust, that he could have been left in no doubt that I had, without ceremony, defrocked him. As I ran out of the tent, he called after me.

"Hayden, come back, I'm so sorry, please forgive me."

"Never, never," I shouted back at him.

I kept on going until I reached the marquee. Once there, I made for the water-tub and then repeatedly dipped my head deep into it. I gulped down in rapid succession three glasses of fresh water in an attempt to cleanse my throat from the sticky globules of semen that still lingered in my gullet. I thought of telling one of the ladies who were preparing breakfast what their beloved priest had just done to me, but didn't, as I knew she'd never have comprehended or believed what I was saying to her. As I ran back to my tent, cold and naked, an unholy rage overcame me. This vile man had made what should have been a memorable holiday into a nightmare.

I felt quite ill by the time the coach arrived back at Westcliff. Maybe I'd caught a chill swimming in the freezing sea, but more likely it was my reaction to the outrageous behaviour of the priest. Miss Minter took one look at me and decided I'd got one of the inexplicable high temperatures that dogged me through my childhood. She sent me straight off to bed. I'd not been in it long when Joyce appeared with a bowl of bread and hot milk in her hand. Miss Minter believed that this was the panacea for all ills. I only managed to swallow a couple of spoonfuls of the milky slop. Feeling hot and feverish, I got under the blankets and was soon fast asleep.

During the night I dreamt I'd entered an enormous cylindrical sloping tube made out of shiny new steel. In it, floating in air like fish in an aquarium, was a bevy of beautiful young girls whose long flowing hair trailed behind them. Weaving in and around these naked nymphs I began to believe I had died in my sleep and was now in heaven. The girls, smiling angelically, beckoned me to follow them down into the depths of the tube. I felt as though I was being led into the very bowels of the earth. After a long flight, we came up against a brick wall. I turned to go back up, but couldn't because a column of girls was gliding towards me. I was pushed back onto the ones behind, and no matter how hard I struggled to break through the sheer weight of numbers made it impossible. Wedged between wads of flesh, I ceased to breathe. Just when I was about to suffocate, I woke up in a cold sweat with an even higher temperature.

I was jolted back to reality by the sound of Joyce telling me that she'd brought up more bread and milk.

"Hayden, you look very hot, are you all right?"

"I don't want slop, Joyce, I want to feel you."

"You're ill, you should eat, then you'll get better."

"Lie on top of me, please!"

"Not while you're unwell, I won't."

"I'll get better quicker if you do!"

"If I do, will you promise to eat your bread and milk afterwards?"

"I promise, Scout's Honour!"

She lay down on top of the blankets, and I put my hands up her tunic and slid them under the elastic band of her knickers. When I squeezed her buttocks, I became aware of a feeling that I'd never before experienced. The beat of my heart quickened as the pleasurable sensation increased. My ecstasy was magnified by my raging temperature. In my delirium I thought this is it, Hayden, you're about to meet your Maker. In the distance, I heard Joyce's voice.

"You're hurting, stop holding me so tightly."

Her plea was lost in space for I was all set to enter the Kingdom of Heaven. Sitting on a throne in front of the Golden Gates was Jesus surrounded by angels. His arms were raised and the palms of his hands faced outwards.

"Come unto me, my son, come."

As Our Lord spoke, I felt the very substance of life itself pumping out between my legs. Seconds later, an awareness of serene peace came over me.

I released my grip on Joyce and then, as I had promised, I ate the bread and milk. By evening, my fever had subsided and I was up and about again.

CHAPTER SIX

The next morning, I felt well enough to take Peter for a run on the mudflats. When we entered the alley that backed onto the playground, Peter started to bark and growl at a shabbily-dressed, stubbly-faced, thick-set, middle-aged man who was standing near the back gate. I'd seen him before, working in the gardens of the local small hotels.

"Hold on to your dog, will you? I want to ask you something."

Not liking the look of him, I pretended I'd not heard. I opened the gate and was about to follow Peter in when he shouted out: "How would you like to earn sixpence?"

"I don't know anything about gardening, mister," I said.

"I don't need help doing that, I want you to find me a little girl who won't mind if I touch her. I'll give her sixpence if she lets me."

"You'll pay all that just to touch one?"

"Well, a bit more than just touch, boy."

"How much more?"

"Get me a girl that'll let me squeeze her bum."

"I don't think any of them would."

No sooner had I said it than I realised that my chances of getting some easy money were dwindling fast, so I added: "I could ask them, I suppose."

"You do that, I'll be back here this time next Saturday. Remember now, sixpence is yours if you bring me one."

The man then picked up his wheelbarrow and trundled off down the alley.

Six weeks' pocket-money in one lump, that was tempting. With that amount I could have a glorious binge eating three Mars Bars in one session. There's no harm in asking, I decided, after all, they can always say no.

When I put the proposition to Stella, Avril and Daphne, they said no. Joyce, who was game to try anything once, said she'd do it, but only on condition that I stayed with her.

The following Saturday afternoon, as she and I sneaked out of the back gate, Joyce said nervously: "All the man wants to do is squeeze my bum, that's what you told me, isn't it?"

"Yep," I replied with unfounded confidence.

"It's a lot of money just to do that, don't you think?"

"Suppose it is. Maybe he gets paid a lot working for the posh hotels."

"You will stay right by me, won't you, Hayden?"

"I said I would, and I will," I replied, though I couldn't imagine what use I'd be if things turned nasty.

When we stepped into the alley to wait for the gardener I took the opportunity, as her manager, to spell out our terms of doing business.

"Now, Joyce, you mustn't let him touch you until he's given us both sixpence."

"I won't," she said.

As it turned out, I needn't have worried. The first thing he did was to press sixpence in our hands.

"You've brought me a pretty little girl, haven't you, boy!"

Then, lightly stroking her hair, he said to her: "Don't worry, I'm not going to hurt you. All I want is for you to turn round, lift up your tunic and pull down your knickers a little."

She did what he asked. He unbuttoned his flies and rubbed his penis against her exposed bottom. The whole thing was over in seconds. Then he mopped her up with the same piece of rag that he used to clean his gardening tools.

When Joyce had adjusted her clothes, he said to her, "That didn't hurt you, did it, dear? Will you be here again next Saturday, eh?"

"Yes, for another sixpence, I will."

"You'll get that all right, only next time there's no need to bring the boy along with you."

On hearing that, alarm bells went off in my head.

"If I don't come, she won't be coming," I said as convincingly as I could.

"I'll tell you what, I'll give you a threepenny bit and you can earn it by keeping watch at the end of the alleyway. See you both next week then."

When the gardener was out of sight, we made a beeline for the sweetshop and bought three Mars Bars each.

"It doesn't seem fair that you're only getting threepence," Joyce said as she took a large bite into one of the bars.

"We'll share the ninepence between us, fourpence-ha'penny is better than nothing, isn't it?"

"That's a good idea," she said, her voice muffled by the half-chewed toffee, malt and chocolate that made speaking almost impossible.

Making sure that Daphne and Stella were watching, Joyce slowly unwrapped her third bar.

"Give us a bite," asked Stella.

"Why should I, it was me who stuck my neck out, not you scaredy-cats."

"Your bum, you mean."

"Yeh, and that's why I'm eating a Mars and you're not."

"What did you have to do to be given sixpence?"

When she told them, they said it would be only fair if they got a go. To stop any bickering, I decided they should take it in turns. These Saturday afternoon meetings with the gardener went on unhindered for some time, until one Saturday he failed to turn up and was never seen again in the vicinity.

One Friday, when the daylight was fading, I was walking down the road when a woman in one of the small hotels, that catered exclusively for Jewish people, stuck her head out of a window and called out:

"Hey you, boy, how would you like to earn a penny?"

"What do I have to do for it?" I asked.

"Turn all our lights on."

Puzzled why she couldn't do that herself, I nevertheless agreed. Five minutes later, she gave me the promised penny.

"Sonny, if you go to the other two hotels in the road, they'll give you a penny as well. Tell them Maureen from the Kiora sent you. And come back here next Friday."

Pleased I'd recouped the threepence I'd lost by keeping a lookout for the gardener, I turned up at the Kiora the following week. A maid answered the door and shouted up the stairs what sounded to me like: "Maureen, it's only the shabby boy."

Not liking how I'd been described, I said boldly: "I'm called Hayden. It's not my fault if I look shabby. These are the only clothes I've got."

By the look on her face, she'd obviously hadn't understood a word I'd said.

I was an adult before I found out that a Shabbes Goy was a gentile who could do the jobs which their religion forbade Jewish people to do on the Sabbath.

A week before the autumn term began, I was standing on the edge of a calm sea, throwing flat smooth stones onto the surface of the water in an attempt to make them bounce more than three times, which was my previous record. I'd not been doing it for long when I noticed a man watching me. To show off, I put even more of a spin on the stones. Eventually I ran out of the ones in my hand and began to look for more.

"May I help you find some?" asked the stranger. He spoke in an accent I'd not heard before. He had quite a belly on him and was rosy-cheeked. I guessed him to be the same age as Father Gould. He wore a pullover and baggy trousers and perched on his head was a wide-brimmed floppy hat.

While we searched for stones, he told me his name was George, and that he was an Australian who now lived in London. He said that he'd come with a friend to Westcliff for the weekend to take in the sea air. He was interested to know all about me, who my parents were and where my home was. I told him I had neither a mum nor dad, and that I lived in a small school run by an old lady.

"Does she know you're out on your own?"

"She never knows what I'm up to."

"Has she ever told you not to speak to strange men?"

"No, why should she?"

"Because there are men who find some young people very attractive, and in return for a bit of cuddling they are only too happy to give them ice creams, sweets, or even take them to the pictures."

Any moment now I thought, just like the old gardener, he's going to ask me if I can find him a girl who will let him put his hand down her knickers. As it turned out I was wrong, he never mentioned girls once. All he said was that his friend would very much like to meet me.

"Are you staying near here?" I asked.

"Yes, just up the hill at the White Cliffs Hotel."

"That's the poshest hotel in Westcliff."

"Is it? My friend is the man standing up there on the promenade. Come with me, and I'll introduce you to him. Then we can all go and have tea and cakes at the hotel."

For those, I'd have followed this man to the ends of the earth.

The Australian's friend was very different from him. He was older and slim, and he had a full moustache and bushy eyebrows, both beginning to turn grey. By the way he was dressed, I knew that he was a real gentleman. In his left hand he held a bowler, and hooked over his right arm was an umbrella. He gave me a shy smile when I was introduced to him.

"This is my good friend Conny, and this, Conny, is - oh dear, I never asked you your name."

"It's Hayden."

"Now that's a nice name for a boy, don't you think, Conny?"

"Yes, it is. Shall we have tea now, or would you prefer to have an ice cream first?"

"An ice cream first, please, sir," I replied.

We entered the foyer of the hotel. I'd never seen such grandeur under one roof before. High marble pillars propped up an ornately painted ceiling. At intervals on the deep piled carpet were broad-leafed plants housed in over-adorned pots. Men in black suits and white fronts flitted silently about, carrying large silver trays laden with pots of tea, delicately-cut sandwiches and delicious, mouth-watering cakes. A man who looked as though he was in charge came over and asked if we wished to be served in the lounge or the conservatory.

"The conservatory, please," said Conny. Perhaps he thought that with me being dressed the way I was, I'd be less of an embarrassment if I were discreetly hidden from view by the vegetation.

Over tea, George told his friend all that he knew about me, but his words fell on deaf ears. The old man was totally absorbed in gazing at me. After tea George said he was going up for a nap, and suggested that I should go with Conny to his room.

"You could tell him all about yourself, Hayden," he said with a smile.

I agreed to go with Conny as he seemed to be such a gentle and kindly old man. I didn't think he would try to do to me anything as vile as the priest had. If all he wanted was to stroke my legs and bum, then that was the price I'd have to pay for all the lovely things I'd been treated to, and who knows, I might be able to wheedle a bob or two out of him as well.

Conny's room was massive. It had its own bathroom and toilet. The dormitory I shared with ten others was half the size. I settled down into one of the huge armchairs, and the old man sat on the bed. For some time we just looked at each other in silence. Finally it dawned on me that it was up to me to start a conversation, so to put the old gentleman at ease I chatted away nineteen to the dozen, telling him all about my life so far. He seemed quite content to let me go on jabbering away for ever.

Just when I was running out of things to say, he got over his shyness and spoke to me:

"You've had a hard childhood, haven't you? It's amazing how you got through it. If you'd been my little boy, I would never have parted with you."

Not wishing to go on talking about myself, I asked: "Where did you grow up?"

He said he was brought up on the family estate in Sussex. At eight he was packed off to a posh prep school, much to the relief of his mother who couldn't cope with any of her three children. He said he disliked both his parents, particularly his father, who was forever complaining that he'd missed becoming a Lord because he had the misfortune to be born the youngest son.

"I thank heaven that he was. Otherwise, I'd now be burdened with all the trappings that go with a title, attending the House and sitting on the boards of companies in whose activities I would not have had the slightest interest."

He went on to say that at fifteen he left Eton, which he hated, and was sent to Harrow, where he was even more miserable. When it was time to embark on a career, his father gave him three choices: the army, the city or the church.

"I didn't fancy any of 'em. Business horrified me, and as for religion, by my late teens I was disillusioned with that. So I reluctantly opted for the army. I preferred horses to most people so I told my father I'd only enter it on condition I was allowed to train as a veterinary surgeon first.

"People of my class who go into the army are expected to take a commission in one or other of the guards regiments. I chose the Life Guards. I served with them in the Boer War and then on the North-West Frontier, where I was promoted to the rank of major. By the time the Great War began, I'd already retired from the service. And to keep the distance between my parents and myself, I farmed in Canada, where I stayed until they died. Now I live in a flat in St John's Wood and spend a little of my otherwise useless existence helping my friend, Basil Henriques, do the good work he does at Toynbee Hall for the poor children of London's East End."

Most of what he told me was beyond my comprehension. 'Attend the House', what house? Why would he have to sit on oards - were there no chairs? The North-West Frontier could have been anywhere for all I knew. I did know something about the Great War, because every year on 11 November we children had to attend a service at Southend's Cenotaph. Ill clad, in a cold wind with noses dripping, singing 'Abide With Me' through our sniffles, accompanied by weeping people who had lost their loved ones only a few years earlier.

Because of what he told me about his life, I couldn't help feeling a bit sorry for the old man, so to cheer him up I crossed the room and sat beside him on the edge of the bed and put my arm around him. He turned towards me and said, so quietly that I only just heard what he was saying: "My God, Hayden, you are a beautiful boy."

"Can't only girls be called that?"

"No, dear boy. May I feel your lovely legs?"

"If you want to. I don't mind."

Unlike the priest, his lips never so much as touched me. All he did, was run his hand lightly up and down my thighs. Then suddenly, with his feet still on the carpet, he lay back on the bed and hurriedly pushed down the waistband of his trousers with a handkerchief that he'd swiftly pulled out of his pocket. Then, as if he was writhing in pain, he called out: "Oh oh oh, my God."

I thought the old man must be ill, and was just on the point of running down to the entrance to get help when he sat up and looked and behaved as though he'd completely recovered.

"Are you all right?" I asked.

"Oh yes, sweet boy, oh yes."

He bent down and buried his head in my lap. To comfort him, I stroked the curls on his head. How strange it was, I thought, that here was I, who had nothing, comforting a person so rich that he could have bought a Mars Bar whenever he felt like it. To bring things back to normal, I asked him what time it was. He sat up and pulled out from his waistcoat pocket a fob watch that was attached to it by a gold chain.

"My goodness, it's already five and twenty past six. How time flies when you're in pleasant company."

"I'd better go. I might be missed if I stay out much longer."

"Hayden, I really must see you again tomorrow. Can you come here after breakfast or do you think it best if I met the woman who runs your school and get her permission to take you out for the day?"

"It might be," I said, not really caring one way or the other.

"Hayden, when you go back, tell her that you spent the afternoon with me and that I would very much like to come and talk to her about you. Say that I work a lot with disadvantaged boys in London. Where is your school?"

"It's just down the hill from here. If you come with me now, I'll show you where it is."

Before Conny left me, he told me to tell Miss Minter that he'd be calling on her at ten, and that in the meantime, I should think of things we could do.

"Could we go to the Kursaal or take a trip on a pleasure boat?"

"We can do both and more if there's time."

With or without permission, I'll be going with him, I decided.

When I told Miss Minter that I'd spent the afternoon with a retired major whose brother (I lied) was a Lord and that he'd be coming to see her in the morning at ten, she was most impressed.

"I can't imagine why he wishes to see me," she said.

"He told me he helps poor children in London. I told him you'd taken in children from poor homes as boarders so perhaps that's what he wants to talk to you about. He did say that with your permission he'd like to take me out for the day."

"Of course I'll allow it, but you're not going about with a fine gentleman looking like a street urchin. Tomorrow you're to wear your school uniform. I'll tell Ulrike to wash and iron a shirt for you. Go right now and scrape the mud off your shoes and give them a good polishing. Have a bath and wash your hair. It's a disgrace the way you keep it all tangled like that."

I was about to get into bed when I remembered I'd not collected my shirt from Ulrike, so I went down one flight and knocked on her door.

"Who's there?" she called out in her funny accent.

"It's me, Hayden, I've come to fetch my shirt."

"Come in, the door isn't locked."

When I entered, she was sitting on a chair in a nightdress, brushing the long tresses of her light-brown hair.

"Sit on the bed, Hayden, I'll only be quick."

"You mean, you'll only be a moment."

"Oh yes, English is so difficult for me. I am glad you have come because I like you best of all the boys."

"I like you too, Ulrike," I said, parrot-fashion.

"Do you like me enough to give me a kiss?"

"Yes."

"Come on, then kiss me."

"I can't. You're too tall, I'd have to stand on the bed to reach your lips."

"I'll lie on the bed, then we can kiss and cuddle."

Ulrike sat on the bed and pulled her nightdress over her head. Then, lying on her side with open arms, she invited me to join her. I got my first-ever look at pubic hair, and was so attracted by what I saw that a full five seconds passed without me making a move.

"Are you really too shy to take off your nighties?" she asked.

"Not nightie, boys wear pyjamas," I replied as I shed them. I lay on the bed close to her and buried my face between her large breasts. I could have stayed there for ever, if I hadn't had to surface for air every half minute. I wallowed in her soft and giving body as my hands explored her curves. A long time passed by before Ulrike took my hand and placed it between her legs. My fingers instinctively knew what to do as they wove in and around the warm and moist opening nestling in a triangle of silky hair. Ulrike became very excited and held my bottom in a tight grip before she rolled over on her back, taking me with her. Within a second, I was inside her and four seconds later it was all over as far as I was concerned.

"Oh, Hayden, so quick, I wanted more."

Seldom one who is at a loss what to say, I said as casually as one might if help was needed to shift heavy furniture: "I'll go and get the other boys, I know they'd love to lie on you. We do it all the time with some of the girls."

"How? Without getting caught?"

"One of us keeps watch."

"Which boys?"

"Tom, Eddy, Bunty and Ian. It's best to leave him till last. He can keep going for as long as you want, because he can't ... you know, yet. Also, his willie is much, much bigger than any of ours."

"If you're quite sure it's safe, go and get them," she said, as she covered herself with a sheet.

A minute later we were all patiently waiting at the end of her bed while Tom had the first go. When the other two had done their little bit, Ulrike invited me to try again. This second time, I managed to last a little longer. One by one, we left her room to go to bed, leaving Ian behind to continue where we'd left off. This was the first of our wonderful group sessions. Sadly they didn't last very long. A few weeks later Ulrike's year as a domestic came to an end, and she returned to her parents' farm in the Swiss mountains.

Punctually at ten next morning, the largest saloon car ever seen in the road stopped outside the front door of the school. Conny got out of it and rang the bell. Miss Minter, who was peering out through a chink in the curtain, got into such a tizz that she had to ask me to let him in.

"Hallo," I said as he stepped into the hall.

"My goodness, Hayden, you do look smart. Does your principal expect me?"

"Yes, she does, I'll take you to her."

All I heard of their conversation as I closed the door behind him was:

"Good morning, allow me to introduce myself, my name is - "

Not long after Conny emerged with Miss Minter flapping obsequiously by his side.

"Goodbye, Miss Minter, so glad to have made your acquaintance, we will talk again about ways to help Hayden."

"Goodbye, major," said Miss Minter. "Now, Hayden, you be on your very best behaviour. You should be grateful that the major is taking you out for the day."

"It is I, Miss Minter, who should be grateful to you for allowing me to take him out. He was so well behaved yesterday that he did you and your school great credit."

I sank down onto the cushioned all-leather front seat and looked round at the luxurious and spacious interior.

"What sort of help were you talking about with Miss Minter?" I asked when Conny was seated.

"I asked if she would permit you to come and stay with me over the half-term holiday. She thought it was a splendid idea. I told her that in my opinion it would broaden your horizons if I took you to some of the historic sites in London. What do you think?"

"Me, I wish it was half-term already."

Starting the car, he said:

"Now Hayden, where shall I tell Mr Buick to make for?"

"Who is Mr Buick?"

"That's the maker's name for the car."

"Oh I see. It looks very new. Is it?"

"Yes it is, I only acquired it last month."

"I bet it goes very fast."

"With thirty horses under its bonnet, it ought to."

"Are you saying that it can pull something that needs thirty horses to move it? But as one horse can run just as quickly as thirty. That wouldn't make the car go any faster, would it?"

"That's true, but try to imagine the strength and speed produced if they were all crammed into the body of one, and then you will get some inkling of the enormous power the engine has. Now, sweet boy, where would you like to go?"

"To the Kursaal Amusement Park, please. If you drive along the sea front, it's just past the pier. I'm so looking forward to going, I've never been inside it because it cost a whole sixpence just to enter."

"Today is your day, Hayden. You can do and go anywhere you want to, no matter what the cost."

Whoopee, I thought, as the car purred its way along the front. Conny proved to be a man of his word. Without so much as a murmur, he waited patiently while I went on the Big Dipper so often that the thrill of whizzing up, down and round bends at breakneck speed began to wane. With him as my passenger, I crashed bumper-cars head-on so many times that finally the old man's bones could take the pounding no longer. I went on the Big Wheel, the Helter-Skelter and the Waterchute more than once. I screamed with laughter when we saw our reflections in the Hall of Distorted Mirrors. On that memorable morning, I went on everything that in previous years were way beyond my reach. I think Conny's pleasure came purely from watching a poor boy have the best time of his life.

At my bidding, we had a fish-and-chip lunch in one of the many little restaurants that line Southend's Golden Mile. I doubt if Conny had ever been inside such a place before. He looked totally out of place amongst the cloth-capped Cockneys who were eating there.

Stuffing yet another greasy chip into my mouth, I asked: "Didn't your friend George want to come with us today?"

"Oh, er, he was unexpectedly called back to London, on business."

I knew I wasn't being told the truth, because today was Sunday. I only found out why when I stayed with Conny in London at half-term. It seems that George made his livelihood almost exclusively as a procurer of innocent young boys, delivering them into the hands of aristocrats - generals and rich businessmen. Conny was very useful to George because of his connections. This explained why George wasn't with us. He'd done his job when he found me, and I think, as far as Conny was concerned, he'd done it well.

When I'd polished off my fish and chips and nearly all of Conny's, we boarded a small pleasure boat that did trips around the Nore Lightship that was permanently anchored far out in the Thames Estuary. All my life I'd seen it beaming away in the distance, and longed to go out to it. I squatted on the slatted wooden seat with my head peering over the side, fascinated by the parting of the waves as the bow sliced into them. At one point we were so far out that the mile-and-a-half long pier looked as though it only jutted out a few yards into the sea. On the other side of the estuary, Sheerness, on the Kent coast, which when viewed from Westcliff could only be seen on a clear day, was now easily visible. It took over an hour to get to the lightship; then to my delight, we didn't just go round it but tied up alongside its gangway until a man came down to pick up some provisions and post that our boatman had ferried out. Before we pulled away I touched the side of the ship that for so long had only been to me like a mirage.

Whenever I glanced at Conny, his eyes were focused not on the view but on me. Why he was so enamoured of me, I couldn't begin to comprehend.

By the time we got back, the sea had receded beyond the jetty on which we should have disembarked and the poor boatman had to carry his passengers one by one, piggy-back fashion, over the squelchy mud to the dry sand. Conny said he'd not had a ride like that since he was in India on the back of a camel.

It was almost dusk by the time we arrived at the White Cliffs Hotel. Conny, by now, was so exhausted that the first thing he did when we got into his room was phone down for a double whisky and soda for himself, and a pot of tea with a slice of chocolate-layered cake for me. No sooner had he downed the whisky than he recovered enough to ask me to join him by the bed. Just as I was about to sit on it, he said: "Hayden, have you enjoyed yourself today?"

"Yes, very much," I replied truthfully.

"Then would you make an old man extremely happy by allowing me to touch your lovely body?"

To say no to his request after he'd given me such a wonderful day would have been very mean of me, I thought. In any case, I didn't think I was so precious that I mustn't be touched by an old man who'd said it would make him so happy. I undressed and stood naked next to him. He rested his head on my chest while his hands travelled up and down my body but not for long. As on the previous day, seconds later out came a handkerchief that was once more pushed in haste down his trousers, and after a few oh's and ah's everything returned to normal.

When it was over and done with, Conny suddenly realised that he was very hungry. By seven, we were amongst the first diners to be seated in the hotel's lavishly adorned restaurant. I was introduced to food I never knew existed. Pea soup, with a sprinkling of crispy croutons that floated for a while before submerging into a thick green mash of fresh peas, followed by fillets of Dover sole, dusted down with golden breadcrumbs, and curled from having been deep-fried in oil. The chips were incomparable, quite unlike the soggy and greasy ones I'd had at lunch. I ended up by wolfing down two helpings of trifle and cream, the delicious taste of which, to this day, still lingers in my memory.

Towards the end of our meal, Conny was looking decidedly glum. He knew the moment had come for us to part. He told me that every so often he'd phone, and once a month he'd send me a five-shilling postal order as pocket money. Although unhappy about him leaving for London in the morning, his generous offer cheered me up no end. Before we parted, he pulled out of his wallet a brand-new pound note and gave it to me.

"See you again, Hayden, in your half-term holiday," he said, waving goodbye as I left through the revolving glass doors.

Out in the street, I looked furtively first left, then right, to make sure no one was watching before neatly folding the precious note and tucking it securely into the inside pocket of my blazer. My goodness, two hundred and forty weeks' pocket money in one lump! What on earth had I done to warrant being given such a huge amount, I asked myself? Absolutely nothing, I concluded. I felt so immensely rich that the next day I went and bought a whole box of Mars Bars and gave them all away, barring two, to the boys in my dormitory and the girls who joined us in the evenings. The two that remained were gobbled up in quick succession by my one and only real love - Peter.

When the autumn term started, I was no longer the poorest one in the queue at the tuck shop. Quite the contrary for with my new-found affluence I could now spend more on sweets than the others. I presumed I could also buy more frequently than them, the favours of the delectable June. However, I presumed incorrectly. She never forgave me for the trick I played on her with the fake bar of chocolate, even though I assured her that I was now a reformed character. Twice weekly I'd bunk off in the afternoons and go to the Gaumont or the Rivoli to watch cowboys the likes of Tom Mix fighting it out with the Indians. Or I would have Frankenstein's Monster scare the life out of me as he roamed aimlessly about the countryside, shrouded in swirling mist. These escapist activities of mine made half-term come a lot quicker than if I had just sat in the classroom twiddling my thumbs.

CHAPTER SEVEN

On the first day of the half-term holiday, Conny collected me and we drove to his home in St John's Wood. He lived on the top floor of a modern block of luxury flats. His was one of the smallest.

"It's all I need living on my own. Another huge advantage is that, if any of my family unexpectedly arrived at the door, well, there'd be simply nowhere to put 'em, so they'd have to bugger off and find a hotel."

What he described as a small flat was, in my eyes, quite roomy. The front door entered straight into a spacious sitting room that spanned the width of the building. It had a large double bedroom and a small spare one. The bathroom was adequate and the toilet separate. The kitchen was tiny. The minute fridge could only just accommodate two bottles of milk or wine and a few slabs of butter, its only redeeming feature was that it could make six ice cubes. As far as I know, no meal was ever cooked on that stove.

When I got to know Conny well, one thing became apparent - he was a creature of habit. Normally his day started at eight-fifteen when he got up and bathed. By eight-thirty he was in the toilet, you could set your watch by his bowel movements. At eight-forty, Mrs Blaber, the daily, brought his breakfast into the sitting-room. By nine, still in his dressing-gown, he'd be in his armchair reading *The Times*. Before dressing, he shaved with one of the seven ivory-handled cut-throat razors he'd inherited from his father. At ten-twenty he had his first whisky and soda of the day. Twice a week promptly at ten-thirty, he'd leave for Toynbee Hall in the East End to do his charitable work. On the stroke of one p.m., he'd be leaning against the bar of the RAC or the Naval and Military Club, downing a half pint before lunching.

After lunch he'd adjourn to the lounge and discuss *The Times* with other leading members. By four p.m. he was back home, sitting in his armchair having a nap. Precisely at four-thirty, he had his second whisky. Buoyed up by that, he'd sit at his bureau and write letters to businesses, asking if they had any vacancies for unskilled fourteen-yearold boy school leavers. At six p.m. he'd tune into the BBC news. Sharp at seven p.m., he'd be dining at one of his clubs. Home by nine p.m. to listen to the radio until eleven, when he retired for the night.

On my first visit, this rigid routine was set aside. The morning after my arrival I was whisked off to Harrods, fitted out in duplicate with all the clothes, including shoes, that a boy of Conny's class would have, and had the most expensive haircut of my life. By the time I left the store, I'd been transformed from a boy of the street into a Little Lord Fauntleroy. As one of my fantasies was to become a film star like Freddie Bartholomew, to play the part of an upper-class twelve-yearold didn't bother me at all. Now I was suitably dressed, I could accompany Conny anywhere without eyebrows being raised. When I was introduced to his cronies at the clubs, he passed me off as his nephew. Whether it was due to this, or because he thought I ought to have one person I could call a relative, I don't really know, but he told me that I could call him Uncle. And that's what he was to me, until the day he died many years later.

In the first week I stayed with him, we went to the Whispering Gallery in St Paul's, the Tower, Mme Tussaud's, Hampton Court, Windsor Castle and a trip up river to the Nautical Museum at Greenwich. While I gazed at a model of the Battle of Trafalgar, Uncle explained who Nelson was - just as well, as I'd never heard of him. In the evenings, we'd dine out at a restaurant. During my stay, I slept in the spare room, but by the time I left it was referred to by Uncle and Mrs Blaber, the daily, as Hayden's Room.

In the space of a week, I had acquired a well-off uncle and a room in a smart part of London that I could call my own. The only price I had to pay for this dramatic change in my fortune was a couple of brief and ineffectual sexual sessions with my benefactor.

Before leaving, I put all the clothes I'd been bought into my chest of drawers, to be worn again on my return. When Uncle waved me goodbye in Westcliff, I imagined he'd be so exhausted by all we'd done in the past week, that he'd be glad to see the back of me, but by the sad look on his face as we parted I knew that he wasn't.

It was quite a shock for me to be confronted with reality. If it hadn't been for Peter and the girls, I'd have run away back to London. The very next day after my return, when Peter and I were belting down Pier Hill on the cart, I realised that no matter how tempting it was to live a comfortable life with Uncle, I could never leave my beloved dog for long.

From now on, a few days of every holiday, except Christmas, was spent in London. Christmas was the one and only time in the year that Uncle felt duty-bound to be with his family. He divided the holiday between his sister in Hampshire near the New Forest, whom he hated, and his brother's family, who farmed in Norfolk and bored him.

The summer after I met him, Uncle took me to stay with one of his friends who had a manor house and estate north of Aberdeen. Under no circumstances would he sit behind a steering wheel for more than four hours in any one day. After three days touring in the Lakes, and one in Edinburgh, with overnight stops in five-star hotels, it took over two weeks before we finally arrived one day at about four p.m.. Our host, Sir Arthur, wasn't there to welcome us. His butler said he'd gone down to London to see his dentist and wasn't expected back before six. Uncle was so tired that he retired to the rooms set aside for him to have his afternoon nap. I was put into a vast room with a high ceiling and tall French windows that opened out onto a balcony. It overlooked the magnificent gardens and gave a panoramic view of the surrounding countryside. The room had a four-poster bed complete with canopy and a separate bathroom and toilet.

I decided to go for a walk in the grounds. The immense acreage was cut in half by the river Don winding snake-like through the lush meadows. At intervals, sturdily-built wooden bridges spanned the fast-moving river. Standing on one of them, I saw a dinghy moored a short distance away on the opposite bank.

I went over to it, jumped in, and cast off. The current took me effortlessly along at quite a pace. It never crossed my mind that I'd have to row back against it. I'd drifted some considerable way before it dawned on me that perhaps I should make a start at rowing back. Never having handled oars, I made the mistake of putting the blades too deeply into the water. With me pulling frantically on them, whenever they surfaced, the oars jumped out of the rowlocks sending me backwards with a thump onto the floor of the boat. This happened time and again until I vaguely got the hang of it. It took me over an hour plus a few blisters to get back. On my return to the manor, I found Uncle in the lounge sipping a whisky.

"My goodness, Hayden, you have been away a long time, what were you doing?"

I told him and showed him my blisters.

"You poor boy, but don't worry, in a day or so they'll be gone. I do hope Arthur arrives soon. I'm beginning to feel a little peckish."

No sooner had he said it than a tall, slim, grey-haired man came into the lounge.

"Conny, old friend," he said, shaking him warmly by the hand, "I'm so sorry I wasn't here to greet you, but the blasted train broke down and it took them over an hour to find a replacement engine."

Looking down at me, he said: "So this is the young boy you mentioned."

"Arthur, meet Hayden. Through no fault of his own, he's had no education whatsoever, so almost everything you show him or tell him about will be new to him. It's one of the reasons I so enjoy his company."

Sir Arthur placed his hand on my shoulder.

"Tomorrow, my boy, while Conny stays here and relaxes, I'll show you some of the sights of Aberdeen."

"Thank you, sir," I replied, not really relishing the prospect.

"Arthur, your man said that you went to London to see a dentist. Have your teeth been bothering you?"

"My teeth stopped bothering me long ago. It's the false ones that were the problem. They didn't fit properly and hurt like hell. When I phoned him to complain, he said: 'All that's needed is a tiny adjustment. Pop in, it'll only take a moment.' Pop in, indeed, where, pray, did he think I lived - in bloody Mayfair? After travelling some five hundred miles to his surgery, I did 'pop in'. The incompetent fool did such a bad job on them, that on the way back, I wound down the carriage window and flung the ill-fitting things out. Perhaps I should have hung onto them, then, when his hefty bill came, I could have returned the teeth and told him to shove them up his Harley Street arse sans Vaseline. For the time being, I'll have to manage with my old set."

With that off his chest, he said we should follow him into the dining room as the meal was about to be served.

The three of us sat down at one end of a very long table and were waited on by the under butler and two serving maids. As we ate, Sir Arthur told Uncle that he'd bought the Mansion from a laird, who, due to persistent gambling and philandering, was forced by his creditors to sell his ancestral home in a bit of a hurry.

"That's why, would you believe it, I got the place for a paltry eight thousand. When I acquired the estate, it was in an appalling condition, but because of the massive unemployment up here I was able to hire a regiment of skilled craftsmen for virtually a crust. Fifteen months later, the outhouses and the main building were restored to their former glory."

"You're to be congratulated, it's in an absolutely splendid shape now. By the way, Arthur, that salmon was superb. Was it caught in the Don?"

"It certainly was, I have exclusive fishing rights for a mile. During the season, every able-bodied man, woman and child on my estate stands in waders waist-high in the water, and literally scoops the salmon out with hand-held nets as they swim up river to spawn. The catch fetches in the markets almost enough money to run this whole estate for a year."

"You are to be envied, Arthur."

"You could have done what I did, Conny."

'Oh no, I like the uncomplicated life I lead in London. To oversee a large estate is not an occupation for an idle person like me."

"If you're content, it's all that matters, dear fellow."

The next morning, Sir Arthur and I left in his chauffeur-driven Rolls to go on the sightseeing tour he promised. With me alone in the spacious back seat and Sir Arthur sitting next to his good-looking young chauffeur, who, I got the impression, had more than just a working relationship with his employer, we drove through the countryside to Aberdeen. Our first stop was St Andrew's Cathedral. I found it to be a little disappointing because unlike St Paul's, it had no Whispering Gallery. Thankfully we didn't linger there for long but moved on to a lighthouse, built on the harbour wall. Sir Arthur persuaded the keeper to take us up to the tower and see the prismatic lights that beam across the sea at night.

At lunch, because of my age, I had to stay outside the pub to eat my sandwiches while they had theirs inside. I'd not been there for long when a gang of boys started peering through the windows of the Rolls, and one asked me if the owner was in the pub. Not wanting to be associated with all the wealth that goes with such a car, I said I didn't know. They tried to open the doors, but found them locked. This annoyed them, so to vent their frustration, four bent down and began to unscrew the caps on the valves of the tyres with the intention of letting the air out. Thinking quickly, I shouted:

"Run for it, the chauffeur is coming!"

It worked, and they beetled off at some speed.

Our next stop was a museum, where I saw pictures that graphically portrayed scenes of Scotland's glorious past. Sir Arthur stopped in front of every canvas at great length, explaining to me what they portrayed. Most of what he told me went in one ear and out of the other. However, one exhibit did stick in my mind - a human foot, pickled in a glass jar. Why it was on display, I can't imagine.

On the way back, Sir Arthur spent most of the journey stroking his chauffeur's thighs. I was relieved that it was the chauffeur and not me who was the object of his desire.

For the remainder of my three-day stay, I spent a lot of my time with the stable boys. Because of their strong dialect, I could hardly understand them. They had no such problems with me. I loved being in close contact with the horses, but though the boys urged me to, I couldn't summon up the courage to mount one. When I wasn't in the stables, I'd be out in the dinghy.

The trip back to Westcliff took only three and a half days, as Uncle used the most direct route. When I arrived, Peter, who'd not seen me for nearly a month, went crazy with excitement. Tom had promised that for five shillings he'd take her every day for a run and keep her well-groomed. By the look of her shiny coat, he must have done it. I gave Miss Minter a box of Edinburgh rock and Windermere fudge that Uncle had bought for her. God only knows how she tackled eating them with her ill-fitting false teeth.

I gave each of the girls who came into our dormitory that night a tartan scarf. They made such a fuss of my small gift, I think it was the best present any of them had ever received. By way of their appreciation, they put on a mock fashion show. Stella wound hers round her head into the shape of a turban, Daphne slung it sash-like across her body, Monica made a bra from hers. Avril skilfully turned hers into knickers and Joyce tied the scarf around her waist, looking very sexy with half her bare bum showing beneath the improvised skirt. As I'd not brought anything for the boys, to make amends, the next day I purchased a whole box of Mars Bars. This expensive gesture put me back in their favour.

At half term, when I was back with Uncle, I asked him if he ever kept in touch with any of the boys he'd liked when they were young.

"Once they've lost their boyish charm and hairs start to appear on their legs, I no longer find them to be attractive."

"But don't they want to keep in contact with you?"

"Some do and that can be quite a bore. Most of them grow up into very rough and rather unpleasant adults. They imagine that by coming to see me and making a nuisance of themselves, I'll be persuaded to part with a sum of money. But unfortunately for them, I have a good friend who is the superintendent in charge of a police station in the East End. He knows precisely what to do, if they become a problem. He calls on them and tells them what can happen to a young man who even contemplates blackmail, let alone carries it out. His visit puts paid to any nasty schemes they may have in mind."

"Will you want to dump me when hairs begin to show on my legs, Uncle?"

"Oh no, Hayden, you're very different from any of them, you're my adopted nephew after all, and will, I hope, remain so for the rest of my life. My only fear is that the day might come when you have no need of me."

"I'll always need you. You're the only family I've got, and anyway, I love you."

"Sweet boy, come here and sit on my lap," and holding me close, he said, "in all my long life, you're the first person who's ever said they loved me."

"Surely your mum must have."

"No, never, not once," he said, dabbing his eyes with a clean handkerchief.

The day before returning to Westcliff, when I got back to the flat after spending the afternoon rowing in Regent's Park, Uncle was on the phone. I overheard him say: "I'll ask him, I'm sure it will be all right, if it isn't, I'll phone you back, so if you don't hear from me, I'll expect to see you around six. Goodbye."

He put down the receiver and saw me standing by the door.

"Hallo Hayden, did you enjoy your row?"

"I did, but it was spoilt a bit because I accidentally bumped into a swan."

"Was it hurt?"

"I don't think so. It swam away quite normally."

"You're lucky it didn't attack you, they can inflict a lot of damage with their powerful wings. When you came in, I was speaking to a very dear and long-standing friend of mine who wants to drop in here tonight, en route to a reception. He's coming here because he'd very much like to meet you."

"Why?"

"Because I've told him what a charming boy you are."

"Can't he find a boy of his own then?"

"It's very difficult for him to meet any because the poor fellow is married, and he has to be very circumspect."

"Circum what?"

"Cautious because," Uncle lowered his head and whispered into my ear, "he's very high up in the Scouts."

Barely believing what Uncle had told me, I asked: "Does he prefer boys to his wife then?"

"Not just any boy, only the ones that can be trusted, like I told him you could be. He's a very kind man and won't harm you in any way. All he would like to do is cuddle and caress you, nothing more than that, I promise. I'd really appreciate it if you let him."

"I don't mind if that's what you'd like me to do. I don't suppose he's that different from you, eh, Uncle?"

"We both went to Eton and then on to Harrow and have been good friends ever since."

At six I was looking out of the window and saw a taxi draw up. A man in evening dress got out. He must have told the driver to wait, because the cab didn't move off after his passenger had entered the flat. When Uncle opened the door to his friend, I was quite surprised at his appearance. I'd expected, as they had been school friends, to see someone of roughly Uncle's age. This man looked a lot younger. His full head of hair had not a trace of grey, nor did his tanned face show any signs of wrinkles.

After introducing me, Uncle poured out a whisky for his friend. I sat silently on a chair while the two of them talked. What I gathered from hearing bits of their conversation was that Uncle's friend had recently returned from South Africa where he'd attended a Jamboree. While speaking, he hardly ever took his eyes off me. Just when I was beginning to feel a little uncomfortable at being constantly stared at, Uncle suggested I should take his friend into my room.

Within seconds of getting there, he had removed all my clothes and started to shower me all over with passionate kisses. His three-inch paintbrush moustache tickled me as his lips went rapidly up and down my body like an accomplished harmonica player. He only stopped for a moment to remove his dinner jacket and trousers. Clad only in a white frilly shirt, bow-tie and ankle socks held in place by suspenders, he looked so comical I had trouble stopping myself from giggling out loud. As his hands travelled over my body, he kept murmuring, more to himself than to me:

"Oh my God, what a beautiful boy you are, Conny was so right, you're a delightful and wonderful creature."

As for me, I was more concerned about the taxi-meter ticking over than what was happening to me. However, I didn't have to worry about it for much longer, because the whole performance came to an end after he'd rubbed his penis against the cheeks of my bum for a few seconds.

I'd been back in the lounge with Uncle for some time before his friend appeared, all dressed up once more in his finery. He went straight over to Uncle and shook him warmly by the hand:

"I can't thank you enough, Conny, your boy was just wonderful. I do hope you'll let me come and see him again some time soon."

All he said to me was: "Goodbye, sweet boy."

I got the feeling that Uncle didn't like to be cast in the role of a procurer of boys for his friends. Before we left to dine, Uncle handed me a five-pound note that his friend had asked him to give me, and said:

"Hayden, I promise never to put you in that situation again. Please forgive me."

"Five pounds! I must be the richest boy in all England."

Back in Westcliff with a small fortune in my pocket, I immediately shared out my ill-gotten gains with my friends. I didn't want my wealth to set me apart from them. I did keep a few shillings back so that I could get my beloved dog the most expensive collar that money could buy.

In September 1937, when I was fourteen, Uncle decided that it was time something was done about what he endearingly called his 'little ignoramus', so he enrolled me at Leigh Hall College, a boarding school which was considered to be the best in Essex.

I wasn't happy about the plan as it would mean parting from Peter, to say nothing of being separated from Joyce and the other girls. I told Uncle my dog needed me to look after her and take her for a run every day. Anyway, I said, he'd be wasting his money because I was too far behind to ever catch up with the others in my class.

"Hayden, although the college is called a boarding school, it is not in the strictest sense of the word. The boys go home at weekends and are free to go out every day when school finishes until supper-time. The college is only a short walk from Miss Minter's place, so you'll be able to care for your dog throughout the week. As for wasting my money, I doubt if I will be, because I've arranged for you to have additional private tuition. You're a bright boy and I'm sure that with the extra lessons you'll catch up with the rest in no time at all."

"Do they know that I can barely read and can't spell for toffee?"

"When I explained to the principal exactly why you are so far behind, he was very sympathetic and promised that his staff would do everything possible to help you."

What Uncle failed to understand, and no doubt the teachers at the college would soon find out, was that I'd always taught myself everything I knew and had never been trained to digest anything said to me within the confines of a classroom. Any extra help would be futile. This proved to be the case within the first few weeks of my being at the college.

As at St John's, I spent most of the lessons at sea with what was going on, and as at St John's, the teachers soon despaired of getting anything through to me. The extra tuition was a total waste of time, both for myself and for the teacher who'd been lumbered with the task. At my suggestion, after only a few sessions, we sensibly spent the hour-long period in his room listening to the radio.

Despite being so backward in the classroom, I was nevertheless quite popular with the other boys, particularly the older ones, when I told them I'd had frequently had sex with girls. Many times I was asked to repeat the larks my friends and I had got up to with Ulrike. Being the only one amongst them who wasn't a virgin elevated me to a position that no amount of academic prowess could ever have done. I soon discovered that by embellishing my stories, I not only held the attention of my audience, but learned to become more articulate.

The principal of the college had a passion for anything new that came on the market. Leigh Hall College was in all probability one of the first schools in England to install television so as to receive the educational programmes beamed out from Alexandra Palace. Probably in advance of its time the whole college was wired up with a two-way public address system which the principal controlled from a room in his living quarters. His eavesdropping was hated as much by the staff as it was by us boys. At the flick of a switch, he could listen in to the classrooms, corridors, dormitories, and even the bathrooms. We soon found out that when he was speaking into the microphone he couldn't hear the abuse we hurled back. We always made sure that when we needed to fart loudly, we were standing right under a speaker. In the dormitories, we became adept at disguising our voices to sound like one of Walt Disney's characters. But sadly, this little ruse of ours didn't last long. Two nights later, the principal's voice boomed out: "All you boys in dormitory four will forfeit your free time for the rest of the week!"

Now, whenever we wanted to communicate, we had to jump out of bed and whisper into one another's ears.

After technical innovations, dearest to the principal's heart was that the school should do well at games. To this end, he employed the best sportsmen that money could buy to coach the school teams. It was, of course, good publicity for the college whenever we beat a team from another well-thought-of school. In this respect, I was no help at all, for when it came to sport I was a total washout. I never did grasp the most rudimentary rules of cricket. Congenitally incapable of either catching or hitting any missile hurled at me, I hadn't a hope in hell of striking the ball with a bat nor catching it when fielding. If ever I was foolish enough to try, the hard ball would either hit me on the face or give me a bone-shattering blow on my finger tips. To avoid being a target for longer than was absolutely necessary, I made sure that the bowler's view of the stumps was not obscured when i was put in to bat. I was just as hopeless when it came to football.

On one day in late December, our senior football team was to play against a formidable eleven from the Billericay Grammar School. They had beaten our team for three years running. It was hoped that this was the year they would get their comeuppance. The match was to be held in the park opposite our college.

Unfortunately, two days before the game, a calamity befell our eleven. Four of the best players came down with 'flu. After a lot of searching, replacements for three were found. To find a fourth was not easy. Finally, in sheer desperation, the coach was left with no other alternative than to enlist me.

"But coach," I said, "I don't even know the rules, you'd do better using only ten than have me in it."

"You don't have to do anything, just try and look as though you could."

That's exactly what I did on that Saturday afternoon, when the ground was frozen hard and an icy wind blew. Before long my my legs began to turn blue and my cheeks became almost immobile. To keep warm, every so often I'd run down the length of the pitch. Towards the end of the game with only a few minutes left to play, and the score was a draw, I was on one of my runs when, out of the blue, the ball hit my knee with an awful thump and rebounded straight into the other side's goal. The next thing I saw was three of the older boys running towards me. Oh dear, now I'm for it, must have broken one of the rules, I thought as I prepared to defend myself from a torrent of blows. But to my surprise, all they slapped me heartily on my back and hugged me.

"Well done, Hayden," said one.

"Jolly good show, you've won the game for us!" said another.

Minutes later, when the game was finally over, I was lifted shoulder-high and carried triumphantly off the pitch.

At assembly towards the end of my first term, the principal asked the twins Keith and Robert Clark to come up onto the platform.

"Today, I have a treat in store for you, " he announced. "These two boys were seen after school yesterday smoking outside the gym. So for your edification, I'm going to get them to show us how delightful and satisfying smoking can be."

He then pulled two long cigars out from under his gown and lit them.

"Now boys, take a deep draw and then puff away to your heart's content," he said as he handed one to each of them. After only a few sucks they both began to cough violently.

"They're too strong for us, sir, and they make our throats sore," said one of the brothers.

"Nonsense boy, these cigars are made from the finest tobacco, much better than the cheap cigarettes that you and your brother were caught smoking yesterday."

"We really can't smoke them, sir," he said, trying his best not to cry.

"Oh but I must insist that you do. Down to the butt if you please."

Between fits of coughing, the boys took small puffs at the long cigars. Eventually they both turned pale and then slightly green and ended up vomiting all over the footlights.

The principal was also keen that his college should perform well in the gym. His enthusiasm for physical training was one of the reasons why he so admired Germany. The high regard he held for Hitler was why he invited a group from the Hitler Youth to stay at the school. When the tanned young Germans arrived, there was no getting away from it, they were a lot healthier than most of us, and physically superior. As they all had blue eyes and blond hair, we decided that they'd been handpicked to represent their beloved Führer. Their undoubted skills in the gym put us all to shame. One thing about them did have us laughing behind their backs - after cleaning their teeth at night, they put on hairnets before getting into bed.

CHAPTER EIGHT

In July 1938 when the College broke up for the summer holidays, Uncle phoned Miss Minter. He asked her if she would allow me to accompany him to the South of France for a month's holiday.

"How nice of you to invite him, major. It will be the treat of a lifetime for the boy."

"I'll need his birth certificate in order to get him a passport."

"Oh dear," said Miss Minter. "When Hayden came to me as a two-week-old baby, the person who brought him didn't give me one."

Armed only with my names and the date of my birth, Uncle went to Somerset House to try and obtain a copy. This wasn't as straightforward as it should have been, because Miss Minter had given him the wrong date. I'd always been told it was on 12 March, and that was the date I got my much-looked-forward-to birthday egg. However, when the copy was finally located, it turned out that I was born three days earlier, on the ninth.

The night before I left to catch the train to London, Peter had a litter of four. I was glad about this, as it meant that she'd be so occupied with her puppies that she'd hardly notice that I wasn't there.

After Uncle picked me up at Fenchurch Street Station, we went to have my passport photo taken. Apart from a snapshot that was alleged to be me as a baby, this photo was going to be the only picture ever taken in my entire childhood.

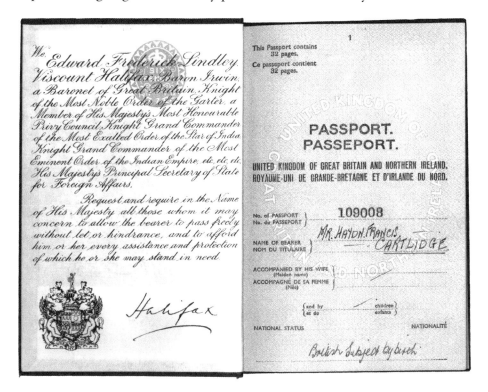

When the man behind the counter at the Passport Office handed me my passport, I held the stiffly covered navy blue book in my hand and read that no less a person than the King of England thought me important enough to be assisted and protected whenever I travelled abroad. It was signed by '*Viscount Halifax*'.

For the first time in my fifteen years, I realised that I had a document that officially recognised that I existed.

At five p.m. the next day, with Paris in the midst of a heatwave, we stepped out of the Gare du Nord and followed the porter carrying our baggage across the road to the Grand Hotel Terminus. Standing by Uncle's side while he checked in, I heard French spoken for the first time. I liked the sound of the language coupled with the expressive movements of hands and face. These people, I decided, seemed a lot livelier than us English. When the page boy arrived, he took us up in an ornate, glass-panelled lift to our rooms on the fifth floor. Judging by the broad smile on his face when he left, I knew that Uncle had tipped him handsomely. After what he considered to be a long and arduous day, Uncle collapsed into an armchair and sipped away at a large whisky and soda. I stood out on the balcony and gazed in wonder at the hustle and bustle of the strange city beneath my feet. Looking down on the streets something worried me, about the way the traffic flowed. It was some time before I realised that the vehicles were driving on the wrong side of the road. Could be dangerous, I thought, until I finally worked out that provided they all did so, it was no more risky than driving on the left. From five floors up, the green single-decker buses, that had the excess of passengers standing all tightly packed on an open platform at their rear, looked like mechanical toys. I would have been content to have stayed out on the balcony, taking in the atmosphere and the unfamiliar smells of Paris, until my legs gave way, and would have done, if Uncle hadn't decided that it was time to go and dine.

When we left the comparative cool of the hotel, with all its fans whirling away, and stood in the hot stuffy street, I was glad to be only wearing an open-necked shirt and shorts. Uncle's only concession to the warm and airless evening was to leave behind his bowler hat and umbrella in the hotel.

A taxi took us through the narrow streets, then went up a winding hill before putting us down in a square packed with people. Standing in front of easels were artists dressed in blue smocks and black velvet berets, angled rakishly over their bearded faces. Some did paintings of the surroundings, while others painted portraits. Mingling amongst the sightseers were musicians, playing jolly tunes on an assortment of hand-held instruments.

To me the whole razzmatazz was like a carnival and I loved it. After a while, the aimless movement of the crowd began to tire Uncle, so he took refuge in a small restaurant. I liked the intimacy of the place more than the spacious restaurants that he normally preferred. I had the French equivalent of fish and chips. It tasted a lot better than in England. They didn't have Tizer, my favourite drink, so Uncle suggested I tried grenadine.

"I think you'll like it, it's made from pomegranates, it's very sweet."

It was that all right, but I missed the fizz and the bubbles of Tizer.

During the meal, Uncle said he must teach me a few short sentences of French just in case we ever got separated.

"I don't think I could learn another language," I told him.

"It's important that you do at least try. Only a few words could get us both out of a lot of trouble, you know, Hayden."

"I'll try, but you'll have to be patient with me."

"I will. If you get lost, hail a cab and say to the driver: 'Pardon, Monsieur, je suis anglais, je ne parle pas français, l'Hotel Terminus, s'il vous plâit'."

"I didn't know you could speak French, Uncle."

"I can't really, even though it was drummed into me for some years at Eton. All I can say is is: 'Où est le cabinet ?' (where is the lavatory), and 'l'addition s'il vous plâit' (the bill please)."

By the end of the meal, I had off pat the couple of sentences Uncle taught me. When we left the restaurant, we strolled along a narrow cobbled street that ended in a large forecourt with a long stone balustrade overlooking most of Paris. Behind the forecourt, up a flight of wide stairs, was an imposing white cathedral-like church dominating the skyline. Uncle rested his arms on the smooth stone slabs that lined the top of the balcony and looked contemplatively at the view.

"The last time I stood here was two years before the Great War. In twenty-six years, Paris has hardly changed."

"Was that very high iron tower built down there by the river, when you were here last?"

"Yes, it's the Eiffel Tower, built for the Great Exhibition of 1889. Until the Empire State Building was erected in New York it was the tallest structure in the world. Tomorrow I'll take you up on it."

"Whoopee," I replied enthusiastically.

We stayed gazing down on Paris until dusk, then watched the city as it gradually became illuminated. On our way back to the hotel, Uncle pointed out a theatre that was festooned with neon lights in a variety of colours.

"That's the Folies Bergère, where leggy and large-busted ladies cavort about on stage practically in the nude. The last time I was here, I was persuaded by a young officer friend to see the show. It didn't amuse me at all."

That's a pity, I thought.

The next morning, after I'd dragged Uncle up and down the Eiffel Tower twice, we went on a whirlwind tour of all the sights. We saw the Arc de Triomphe, and kept the taxi waiting while we walked past the long frontage of the Louvre. We didn't go in because Uncle said that museums bored him.

"In my view, works of art worth looking at are of beautiful boys or thorough-bred horses."

Being a soldier, Uncle felt duty-bound to make a quick visit to Napoleon's tomb. After lunch we took a boat trip along the Seine. As we cruised up the winding river, past Notre Dame, I looked in awe at its sheer majesty and would have liked to have gone inside it, but the boat didn't stop there.

When the heat of the sun had subsided, we took a leisurely stroll in the Luxembourg Gardens before dining. By bedtime, Uncle was completely exhausted. I had the feeling that the old man wouldn't be sorry to leave the hurly-burly of Paris in the morning. For my part, I'd have been more than happy to stay on a few more days in this exciting city.

By lunchtime the next day, I was eating in the dining-car of a train bound for Avignon. To be having a good meal while looking out of a wide window at the ever-changing countryside was sheer joy. I saw men with the baking midday sun beating down on their bare backs. I just couldn't imagine how they could work in the scorching heat with only the shade of their wide-brimmed straw hats to protect them.

It was early evening when the train pulled in at Avignon station. Waiting in the forecourt to take us to the hotel was a very old coach.

"My God, they must have used this old charabanc in the war to ferry troops to the front," was Uncle's comment as he sat down on the bare wooden slatted bench seat.

We'd not been travelling for long, when we went through an arch cut into an ancient wall that surrounded the city.

"Did the Romans build it?" I asked.

"I'm afraid I don't know. Nowadays, Avignon is one of the country's garrison towns, a bit like our Aldershot."

After checking in at the hotel, we went for a stroll in the hot evening air. We passed many cafés that were packed with shabbily dressed soldiers. They made a tremendous noise as they talked and argued amongst themselves.

"The town is full of soldiers, Hayden, because France is anticipating another war with Germany. It has started to mobilise, and that's why there are so many soldiers lolling about. The town must be bursting at the seams trying to billet all the reservists that are reporting back for duty. Personally I think the French Government is typically over-reacting. Only last week, when Neville Chamberlain came back to England after meeting with Hitler, he assured us that he had secured peace in our time. Mind you, Hayden, if the prime minister is proved wrong and war does break out, all I can say is, God help us, if this scruffy-looking lot are to be our allies."

Our hotel was nearly as ancient and run down as the rest of the town. I liked its fading grandeur, but I don't think Uncle did. However, he had to put up with it as it was the only reasonable accommodation available.

The next day, after we'd visited a very old bridge that spanned a dried-out river, Uncle hired a taxi to take us to the Roman arena in Arles. The old building fired my imagination. I could almost hear the bloodthirsty crowd screaming with delight when the hungry lions bit into the flesh of Christian martyrs. I could visualise the governor of the province surrounded by his entourage, sitting in the shade of the balcony, giving the thumbs up or down to a victorious gladiator.

It was with some reluctance that I let Uncle lead me away from the ancient stadium to a waiting taxi.

In broken English, our driver persuaded Uncle to let him drive us up the mountain that was visible from the town.

"Ah, monsieur, very belle, the view!"

"More likely the sight of his meter ticking over, is why he's so keen to take us there," said Uncle.

We drove up a steep, snake-like road that was cut into the side of the mountain and got out at its highest point. The view was spectacular. It overlooked the landscape for miles around. The earth varied from shades of brown to red. Trees, the likes of which I'd never seen before, grew despite the relentless heat from the sun bearing down on them. Vines covered most of the well-cared-for soil. I asked Uncle if I could take a photo of him standing on the edge of the mountain, with the panoramic view in the background.

"I'd rather you didn't. I don't know why, but I've never liked being photographed."

After I'd pleaded with him not to be a spoilsport, he grudgingly agreed. I took out the Box Brownie camera, which Uncle had bought me before we left England, and held it waist-high. Looking into its little square window, I could only see his face and shoulders.

"Please, go back a few steps, Uncle, so that I can get the whole of you in."

"If I do, Hayden, all you will see on the photo is the soles of my shoes as I fall head first over the mountainside. I'd feel a lot safer if you took a few steps back and I moved forward a little to put some distance between me and the edge."

With one click I got the picture that I still treasure to this day.

In the morning, the old coach took us to the station, just in time to catch the train for Cannes. When we were nearly at the end of our journey, I got my first sight of the Mediterranean. Unlike Southend, the sea wasn't grey but blue and translucent. Anchored, and in motion on the calm water, were boats very different from any I'd seen before. I saw large luxurious yachts and speedboats that threw up huge streams of spray as they sliced their way through the still sea. Magnificent three-masted sailing ships were floating listlessly in the windless air. I didn't see one working vessel, so I assumed that the fishing boats must be far outr at sea. I longed for the train to come to a halt so that I could escape from the heat and dive into the sea.

Peering out of the taxi window that was taking us to our hotel, I felt as though I'd arrived in another country because it was so different from the north. Lofty and leafy palm trees, interspaced with exotic flowers in vast earthenware pots, lined the sidewalks. Almost everyone we passed was dressed in the lightest of clothing: I even saw men strolling leisurely along the promenade, in their bathing costumes.

As soon as we'd checked in and dumped our luggage, I persuaded Uncle to take me to the beach just across the road. With him seated in a deck chair under the merciful shade of a parasol, I went to the bathing huts that lined the back of the beach, put on my swimming trunks, then, at the speed of a greyhound leaving the trap, I made a dash for the sea. To my surprise, the water was almost tepid. It was so clear that when I stood up to my neck in it, I could see my feet resting on the firm rippled mud of the seabed. I would have been content to stay submerged in this enormous swimming pool until dusk, and would have done, if only Uncle hadn't beckoned me to come out because it was time to have lunch. As I stood by him drying myself, he said:

"I've been told by my friend Eric - who, by the way, will be joining us in a few days - that the best place for meals in Cannes is the Carlton. It's just a short walk from here. When you're dressed we'll make our way there."

"Will they have eggs on the menu?" I asked.

"It's the sort of place that has everything, even eggs," he said.

The Carlton was without question a grand hotel. It shone brilliant white in the bright sunlight. It was set back from the promenade and had a splendid garden as its frontage. Within the lush garden was a restaurant, where tables, beautifully laid with sparkling silver cutlery, were spaced well apart and shaded by palm trees and vines entwined in wooden arches.

Uncle was about to give his order to a white-jacketed waiter when a commotion started up on the pavement outside the hotel. People were jostling and craning their necks in an effort to see an elegantly dressed lady who had just stepped out of a white Rolls. She was signing autographs as she walked towards the hotel entrance.

"What's all the fuss about?" Uncle asked the waiter.

"They all want to see Marlene Dietrich, sir, she is staying here in our hotel for a few days."

"Who is she, Uncle?" I asked.

"Oh, she's a famous film star."

"Is she as famous as Jessie Matthews or Gracie Fields?"

"Darling boy, this lady has an international reputation as a film actress."

"She does look beautiful, doesn't she?" I said, unable to take my eyes off her.

"Yes, she does, but given the choice, I'd much prefer to see Freddie Bartholomew." For the next few days after breakfast, I'd set off for the beach, leaving Uncle to amuse himself. He joined me in the afternoons, when he'd sit in a deck chair, seemingly content to watch me revelling in the water. Not once during the holiday did he so much as put a toe into the sea. I did manage to persuade him just once to come with me on a pedalo, but when the wake of a passing speedboat made us rock a little, he said he wanted to go back to the beach. Alone out at sea, pedalling away, I really wished that Peter was sitting beside me. She would have been in her element, diving after me into the water.

We'd been in Cannes for about a week when Uncle's friend Eric joined us for lunch. He was in his middle forties, slim and very tall. His blond, wavy hair, slightly bleached by the sun, was parted to one side. His intelligent, finely chiselled face with blue eyes made him attractive to almost everyone. In addition to his good looks, was the timbre of his voice. If he'd only read out loud from a telephone directory, the velvety sound of his words would be a pleasure to listen to. He was cultured and witty and could charm the birds out of the trees.

Uncle told me later that his friend had inherited a fortune, along with a penthouse in New York, a large house in Mayfair and a villa in the South of France. Before that, his golden voice had made him a comfortable living. He had been a broadcaster for the BBC and a regular commentator for Movietone Newsreels. After explaining to me what a bisexual was, he said that Eric had had many affairs with people of both sexes.

"But," he said, "in the end it was a middle-aged American multi-million-dollar heiress who, after pursuing him for nearly a year, finally got him to marry her. The story goes that after they had been married for six months they went to stay on her ranch near Los Angeles. Eric, who didn't at all like to be surrounded by horses or sombrero-hatted, straw-chewing rancheros, very soon became bored. He put up with it for a while to please his wife, then suggested that as they were so near Mexico they should take a driving holiday there. So they set off in her Rolls, chauffered by Eric's valet who had been with him for many years.

One afternoon they left their hotel to go on an excursion up a rocky and remote mountain. Near its summit, the dusty and unmade road came to an end, and they stopped to look at the view. Eric, who is a keen amateur botanist, saw growing amongst the rocks a rare and exotic flower. Aided by his valet, he clambered down a craggy, steep slope to examine it more closely while his wife remained in the car. Unfortunately for her, the handbrake of the Rolls slipped and sent the poor heiress hurtling over the mountainside to her death.

It took the distraught Eric and his man more than twenty-four arduous hours to walk back to their hotel. When the police visited the scene of the accident, they never so much as asked how it came about that the handbrake of such a new Rolls- Royce had unhitched itself when no human hand had touched it."

"Uncle, you don't really believe it was an accident, do you?"

"I'm quite sure that Eric did not, and could not, commit murder, it's just not in his nature. What's more than likely is, that his valet, who worshipped him, intentionally failed to apply the brake in the hope that a sudden gust of wind would send his employer's wife to her death. He disliked her intensely."

"Did Eric dismiss him?"

"No, he's still with him. To be fair, it's just possible, that a powerful gust of wind could have sent the car over the mountainside, one will never know the truth of it."

For the remainder of the holiday, Eric was our constant companion. Uncle thought it was because he'd taken quite a fancy to me. This didn't bother me a lot as he was such amusing company to be with. In his open Rolls, he drove us to

Nice and to the casino in Monte Carlo, where I lost the money he gave me to play the tables. We visited his friends who had villas in the hills behind Cannes and on the coast. One, in Juan-les-Pins, was built on stilts and jutted out over the sea. From a springboard attached to the balcony, you could dive straight into deep water. The architect, whose place it was, took me out for a spin in his speedboat. As we sliced through the waves at a tremendous pace, I pinched myself to make sure that all the fun I was having wasn't a dream.

Down the road from our hotel was a garage that hired out miniature racing cars. They were easy to drive because they had no gears or clutch pedal. To move off, you simply pressed on the accelerator. When you removed your foot, the car slowly came to a halt. For emergencies, they had a brake pedal. Anyone with or without driving experience could take them out onto the open road.

I persuaded Uncle to let me hire one. I drove it just like a dodgem car in a fairground. I crisscrossed the busy road from side to side and wove in and out of cars going in both directions. The fun stopped when a policeman stepped out into the road, frantically blowing his whistle and gesticulating madly. I pulled over, and he began shouting at me. I waited for him to calm down, then, by the use of the few words Uncle had taught me, let him know that I couldn't comprehend what he was saying. Indicating by a hefty shove that I should move over to the passenger seat, he got in and sat behind the steering wheel. In the station yard, he held me by the wrist, marched me into the reception area, and sat me down on a chair.

Over an hour passed before anyone was found who could speak English.

"Where are you staying?"

"At the George V Hotel."

"With your parents?"

"No, my uncle."

"His name?"

I told him.

"I will phone him and when he comes, I'll tell him that you're lucky that I'm not charging you with dangerous driving. You are not to hire one of those cars again, do you understand me?"

"Yes, sir," I replied meekly.

Two hours went by before Uncle turned up to collect me.

"You got yourself into a spot of bother, didn't you, Hayden?" he said, as we left the police station.

"Yep, I think I'll stick to going out to sea on a pedalo, there's no rules to break out there."

"Good idea," he agreed, and that was the end of the matter.

For the last few days of the holiday, Eric invited us to stay at his villa. It nestled in the hills above Grasse and was by far the most grandiose of any of the others I'd visited. The villa had about fifteen rooms and was built on one level. The rooms facing front had a magnificent view that overlooked the hills and the distant coast. Two gardeners tended the beautifully landscaped garden and maintained a swimming pool that was almost as big as the public pool in Westcliff. Three servants, a cook and Eric's valet, saw to it that everything ran smoothly. His valet was very definitely in charge. He behaved with his employer more like an intimate friend than an employee. Uncle didn't like his overtly camp behaviour, and let him know it.

One morning, Eric took me round the perfumeries in Grasse. All the places we visited squirted a cocktail of perfume at us, so that by the time we left the last one, we smelt like a couple of cheap working girls. The only way I could get rid of the pungent odours was to have a shower and hang my clothes out to air.

On my last night during dinner, Eric casually asked me if I'd like to go with him to a brothel.

"You're fifteen, Hayden, it's time you lost your virginity, and there's no better place to lose it than a good old-fashioned French brothel, don't you agree, Conny?"

"No good asking my opinion, dear fellow, never visited one nor do I intend to."

"How silly of me to even ask. Anyway, how about it, Hayden?"

I thought to tell him that I stopped being a virgin when I was thirteen, but said instead:

"Will they let me in when they see how young I am?"

"On the contrary, you'll be a welcome relief to a poor girl who normally has to put up with some boring old pot-bellied codger lying on top of her."

As soon as we'd finished dinner, we drove to the outskirts of Cannes. The house we stopped at had a red light above the front door. One knew at a glance that the woman who opened it would stand for no nonsense. However, her severity quickly faded when she smiled. She obviously knew Eric. She ushered us into a dimly lit room, the walls of which were concealed by carnation pink velvet drapes. Three men were seated on buttoned and cushioned high-back armchairs. In the centre of the room was a square table with a vase of flowers. Eric and I sat down on a small settee. We'd not been seated long when a pretty topless young girl came in carrying glasses of champagne on a silver tray. When she bent down to offer me one, the closeness of her breasts got me so excited that I lost my voice. All I could do to indicate that I didn't want one was to shake my head.

"Come on, Hayden, take a glass, even if you don't like it, you'll find the sensation you get when it's down is very pleasant," Eric said as he handed me one. "Now drink up and be merry," and with that raised his glass to his lips.

I took a sip and decided it tasted better than the sickly-sweet grenadine I'd been drinking in France. As no alcohol had ever passed my lips before, that first glass went straight to my head. Soon I felt so relaxed that when the lovely girl offered me another one, I took it without any hesitation and gulped it down. That one made me so tipsy that when four ladies came into the room, wearing open negligées, I only just managed to stop myself from applauding. Their entrance was the cue for the regulars to place a small coin on each corner of the table. Without a word spoken by anyone, the girls stood by the coins and picked them up with their vaginas, as deftly as an elephant takes a bun from the palm of your hand. Though I was a little shocked by what I'd seen, the two glasses of champagne I'd drunk transformed the whole distasteful performance into a farce.

When the girls left the room, Madame came in. She unrolled a screen from the ceiling, then turned off the lights. In the darkness, Eric whispered:

"Hayden, you're going to see a film that would never be shown in a cinema."

"If it's in French, I won't understand what's happening."

"This sort of film needs no dialogue. You'll see why in a moment."

The film started and as I watched my jaw dropped and my eyes almost popped out of their sockets. I had no idea that things like this could happen.

When the lights came on, Eric said: "I've arranged a much better entertainment for you now, Hayden."

"What's that?" I asked.

"You see that sweet young girl who came round with the champagne? She's going to take you up to her room."

"Thank you," I said, feeling nervous about what was in store for me.

Four ladies came into the lounge and collected their customers, including Eric, leaving the girl and me alone in the room. While she went round to pick up the empty glasses, I got my first opportunity to really look at her. She couldn't have been more than two years older than I, and had not yet got the hard look some of the older women had. She put down the tray on the table and came over to me, then, leading me by the hand, took me to a room upstairs. When we entered it, my heart began to beat faster. Pointing to herself, she said:

"Je suis Yvette."

"Je suis Hayden," I replied.

She came and stood by me and very slowly removed all my clothes. Then she untied the tapes of the apron she had on, and let it drop to the floor.

Just the sight of her naked body made my heart pump even faster. With my eyes following her every step, she moved over to the bed and sat down.

"Hayden cheri, ici," she said beckoning me to join her.

We sat close together for a while without touching. I think she perceived that I felt apprehensive. She started to stroke me with the tips of her fingers, running them very gently over my body with a light touch that helped me to relax. I found her so desirable that I could hardly summon up enough courage to lay a hand on her. I think she sensed this too, because she took hold of my hand and placed it on her breast, then guided it over the firm curves of her beautiful body. Afterwards we lay kissing and locked together for a very long time, finally parting because I think she was worried that Madame would start to wonder what it was that kept her for so long.

"My goodness, Hayden, you did take your time, didn't you?" said Eric when we entered the downstairs lounge.

"Sorry," I said sheepishly.

"Did you have a lovely time?"

"Oh yes, I did, thank you."

"Splendid, that's all that really matters."

As we left to go, I blew a kiss across the room to Yvette. She responded with a wave and a little smile as she led an elderly gentleman by the hand out of the lounge towards the stairs. That momentary glimpse of her saddened me.

Back at the villa, Eric plied me with yet another glass of champagne. While I drank it, he said:

"Hayden, as it is your last night here, would you mind very much spending it with me in my bed?"

Under the influence of all the champagne, I might well have agreed to sleep with a crocodile if it had asked me nicely. With his hand round my shoulder, he led me to his bedroom.

"You know, Hayden, from the moment Conny introduced you, I had to restrain myself from touching you. However, I did because I thought it would upset him."

"Uncle wouldn't have minded, we're only together because I love him and he me."

"That's wonderful. I think you must be the only person in his whole life that he has felt great affection for."

My answer freed Eric from any of the guilt he might have had about deceiving his friend. I undressed and lay down on top of his bed. With my mind firmly fixed on the lovely Yvette, I was hardly aware of him as he helped himself to my body. After a while, he sat up in the bed and asked:

"Hayden, has anyone ever had anal intercourse with you?"

"Had what?" I replied.

"Has a man ever put his cock into your gorgeous bottom?"

"No, nor would I let anyone either. It would hurt me."

"Without doing it to you, I can prove it wouldn't."

"How?"

"Clench your fist, then try to push into it the thumb of your other hand."

I did what he asked.

"You can't, can you, Hayden?"

"No," I replied, relieved that I couldn't.

Eric picked up an open jar of Vaseline and liberally smeared it over the tip of my thumb and the top of my fist.

"Now try again," he said.

This time, my thumb penetrated my tightly clenched fist as easily as a knife cuts into butter.

"Now, darling boy, do you see why it won't hurt? It would give me a lot of pleasure if you would let me."

Reluctantly I agreed, but only on the condition that he stopped if I told him to. He was right, it didn't hurt me at all. In the middle of the night, while I was still under the influence of alcohol, he did it again.

When I told Uncle what had happened, his comment was: "Oh dear, oh dear, I do so wish he hadn't."

Over breakfast, Uncle said that he'd arranged to give me a special treat. As the whole holiday had been one treat after another, I just couldn't imagine what else there was left to do that would be so special.

"In half an hour Eric will drive us to Nice Airport where we will board a small plane that will fly us along the coast to Marseille. There we will get into a much larger aircraft that will, in one gigantic hop, land us in Paris. Do you approve of the plan?"

Approve ... the mere idea of it got me so excited, I was unable to finish my breakfast.

"Have you ever been up in an aeroplane, Uncle?"

"Only once. It was just after the war when I was farming in Canada. A friend persuaded me to go up for a spin in his biplane. When we'd climbed about a thousand feet the engine started to splutter before it finally stalled. My friend shouted back at me: 'Conny, I think we've had it, old boy!' Miraculously he somehow managed to land it on its side with a god almighty thump right in the middle of my neighbour's wheat field. From that day until now, I've not really relished the idea of flying."

"Do you think it's still so dangerous?"

"No, nowadays I believe, planes are just as reliable as motor cars," he said convincingly.

When we pulled up outside the entrance of Nice Airport, I got my first look of a plane on the ground. I could hardly believe that within the space of a few minutes I'd be airborne.

We said goodbye to Eric whose parting words were:

"Hayden, you'd be most welcome to come and stay with me again next summer. I'd be more than happy to pay his fare, Conny."

It was sheer joy being lifted up from the runway into a cloudless sky. I spent the entire flight in the ten-seater monoplane with my face pressed against the oval porthole taking in a bird's eye view of the magnificent Mediterranean coastline. The ever-widening patterns that the wake of the boats made as they moved through the shimmering blue and turquoise sea, fascinated me. I got a wonderful view when we flew low over Cannes and the little fishing ports dotted between St Raphael and Marseille. I would have been content to stay in it all the way.

The plane we changed into for our flight to Paris was much bigger. It had two huge propellers mounted between its dual wings. Lined in pairs, either side of a wide gangway, were comfortable seats with plenty of legroom. The plane was half full but we were told that it could seat sixty. A big improvement on the last one were its large square windows.

After flying over Lyons, we were served with freshly cut sandwiches and a choice of champagne or fruit juice. Nearing the end of the journey, I took pictures of the ripe wheat fields that covered the land for miles on my Box Brownie. I was just about to click down the lever when a stewardess tapped me on the shoulder.

"The taking of photographs is forbidden," she said firmly, pointing to a notice above the pilot's cabin.

"Why on earth can't he?" asked Uncle, peeved by her abrupt manner.

"Military fortifications, sir," she replied.

"What utter nonsense. Hayden, your little camera is incapable of taking a picture that would be of any use to a potential enemy. Tell you what, when she's got her back to you, click away, my boy."

This I did. As it turned out, the French Generals could continue to sleep peacefully in their beds. When they were developed, my photos were an unrecognisable blur.

The next day, back in Paris, Uncle took me to the Palace of Versailles. The ostentatious look of the Palace and the Grand and Petit Trianons amazed me. How people could live in such a place was beyond my comprehension. I didn't really take in much of the information the guide imparted, but one thing did stick in my mind. He said that the Palace was ransacked by a raging mob during the French Revolution. No wonder, I thought, the mass of ordinary people must have taken a terrible revenge on the aristocracy when they saw the extravagant and opulent life-style they had while many of them and their families starved. But as the guide pointed out, all that was past history. Now, two hundred years later, the buildings have been restored to their former glory by the very descendants of the revolutionaries who almost demolished them. The following day, we were back at the flat in St John's Wood.

CHAPTER NINE

As the autumn term didn't begin for another three weeks, Uncle asked me to stay on with him for a further fortnight, but as I was pining to see my dog, I told him I could only stay a week longer. Peter's puppies would by now be weaned and she'd start to fret if I wasn't there.

Four days later, I felt a rawness between the cheeks of my buttocks. I refrained from mentioning it to Uncle until it became almost too painful to walk.

"Oh dear, oh dear, oh dear," he exclaimed, "now you know why I was so concerned when you told me what Eric had done to you."

"What that's got to do with my sore bottom?" I said.

"The damn promiscuous fellow has in all probability given you clap, that's what."

"Clap, what's that?"

"It's a sexually transmitted disease that is one hell of a job to cure. Jesus Christ, what on earth am I going to do about it?"

"Take me to see a doctor, I suppose," I replied, as casually as one might, if it were a sore thumb that needed medical attention.

"If only it were that simple, Hayden! What of course you couldn't know is that what Eric did to you is a serious crime, and might well end up with both him and me going to jail for a very long time. Now do you see why I can't take you just to any doctor?"

"Maybe it will go away by itself. Then no one will need to know about it," I said, trying my best to console him.

"I'm afraid it'll only get worse if it isn't treated. There is just one hope of avoiding a calamity - I think George knows of a doctor who is prepared to stick his neck out and treat people in this sort of trouble. For vast sums of money he will risk being struck off the medical register, and face the possibility of a spell in jail."

"What do those people do, who can't afford that kind of doctor?"

"The only place they can be treated is behind bars."

"That's most unfair, don't you think?"

"I suppose it is, but it's largely their own fault, because they just don't take the precaution of using a rubber. If only Eric had, we'd not be in the situation we now find ourselves. All practising homosexuals know perfectly well that what they do, unlike in France, is illegal in this country."

"If I can only be treated in London, I won't be able to go back to college when term starts, will I?"

"Under no circumstances could you."

"What will you tell Miss Minter?"

"I haven't the remotest idea. My first priority is to find a doctor who can begin to treat you without delay. You see, Hayden, in your present condition, you're like a primed powder keg that could blow up in all our faces at any time."

"Uncle, I'm sorry to be such a nuisance, please forgive me."

"Sweet boy, it's not your fault that Eric took advantage of you. "

That very afternoon, Uncle and I were seated in the waiting room of Dr Gadd's Harley Street practice, when the receptionist ushered us in. Uncle told me to stay behind while he had a few words in private with him. When Uncle returned, I was shown in. Dr Gadd was tall, well-built and very handsome. Although in his early forties, there was something boyish about him.

"Well, my boy, you've got yourself into a spot of bother, haven't you? But don't worry, within a couple of months you'll be cured. Now, I'm going to show you the instrument I'll be using to examine your inside."

He picked up a steel object shaped like a penis. He must have seen the look of horror on my face, because immediately he said: "Don't be frightened, I promise you won't feel a thing. Before I insert it, I'll lubricate it. When it's in place, I'll remove the knob and with a swab on the end of this probe, I'll paint the lower part of your colon with a substance that will start the healing process. Within a few days, your pain will subside and you'll be able to resume a normal life once more."

The doctor proved to be right. I hardly felt any discomfort while he carried out his preliminary diagnosis. But when he began to paint the affected area with the long probe, and rattled it about inside me just below my navel, it did feel a bit weird. When he'd finished, he said:

"You've been very brave. A lot of my patients make a tremendous fuss on their first treatment. For the next few weeks, with the exception of Sundays, I have to see you daily. Four times a day, you must take two tablespoonfuls of a laxative called Petrolarger. It looks like Brylcreem, and I fancy may well taste like it. Nevertheless, it's most important that you persevere with it. Now, Hayden, there is to be no hanky-panky while you're infected."

Thinking that he was warning me not to go with men, I decided to put him right.

"I only have sex with girls at my boarding school. I can go with them, can't I?"

"Most definitely not," he said.

When I came out of the surgery, the relief on Uncle's face was obvious.

"You know, Hayden," he said as we went down in the lift, "money does not necessarily make you happy, but by God, it does come in handy when you're trying to solve a problem of this kind!"

Now that the medical side was solved, Uncle had to think what he should say to Miss Minter. He paced up and down the carpet agonising for some time.

"I've got it, I'll tell her that you are suffering from colitis, and that you caught it from something you ate in France."

"But won't she ask why it can't be treated in Westcliff?"

"I'll tell her that the specialists who deal with this particular complaint only practise in Harley Street. I will also tell her I will pay the medical fees."

"What will you do about my college?"

"That's no problem, I'll just pay for one term in lieu of notice and that will be that."

Whoopee, I thought, now I wouldn't have to go back to the school I so disliked.

The next day we drove down to see Miss Minter, who believed all the pack of lies she was told.

Now, with the problem behind him, Uncle could at last relax and resume his regular routine. While he carried out his charitable work with Basil Henriques at Toynbee Hall, and then lunched at one or other of his clubs, I spent my mornings with Dr Gadd. Afterwards I'd go walking in Hyde Park or take a boat out on the lake in Regent's Park. Most afternoons I'd go to see a film.

By late September 1938, it was almost certain that war would break out before long. Men in their hundreds were bussed in from far and wide to dig deep air-raid shelters in all the parks and any open ground in London. You could not but admire these men and their families, who throughout the years of the depression had lived on the meagre handouts of the dole, yet could now summon up the physical strength to do such back-breaking work. Buildings such as fire stations and hospitals that would have to function somehow during an air attack were sandbagged in depth and often to a height of more than twenty feet.

I took lots of photos, including a picture of Uncle's daily wearing one of the gasmasks that were hastily distributed to the civilian population. After my treatment on Saturdays I left all the electrifying atmosphere of London behind me, so that I could go and be with Peter, whom I was pining to see.

Joyce told me that while I'd been away Miss Minter had once again got into debt and that the local tradespeople now refused to make deliveries unless they were paid cash on the doorstep. Some teachers had left because they'd not been paid for a long time. The worst news of all was that in a week's time the school was having to move. Miss Minter was being chucked out because of all the rent she owed.

"I don't understand it, Joyce, when I left everything was fine."

"A teacher told me that the trouble is Miss Minter has no head for business."

"Didn't all those day-pupils bring in quite a lot of money?"

"I've been told that she didn't charge anywhere near enough. It seems St Margaret's was the cheapest private day school in all Westcliff. That's probably why the posh people sent their kids to it."

"Will you be sorry to leave here?"

"No, in February I'll be sixteen, then I'll be free to go and do whatever I like."

"Where will you go?"

"I don't know, hitchhike to London, I suppose. I won't go to my mother. I've only clapped eyes on her twice in the last ten years. As far as I'm concerned, she's dead."

"May I come with you and bring Peter?"

"I'd love you to, but we'll need to wait until March when you're sixteen. Hayden, do you know how I can earn a living when we get to London?"

"You're not sixteen until February, so you'll not have to wait for long, will you?"

"I'm sure my uncle will find me some sort of job, he's doing it all the time for boys like me, who live in the East End."

"Will he be able to find a job for me?"

"He might, anyway it's easier for girls, they can always work as nippies at Lyons or stand behind the counter in Woolworth's. With us both in jobs, we could afford a nice place to live in."

"I'd really like that, Hayden, I really would," she said enthusiastically.

On my first night back in the dormitory, Ian, Tom, Eddie and Bunty, and the girls who regularly visited us, sat in a semi-circle around me while I regaled them with an account of my holiday. The luxury I'd tasted was beyond their comprehension. But what they could relate to was what went on in the brothel and about the films I'd seen. My graphic description got them so excited that it sparked off a sexual romp the likes of which I've never again witnessed. While Joyce and Stella did their version of a lesbian couple, Tom, Eddie and Monica portrayed fairly accurately the farce of the irate husband who caught his wife astride the page boy. As Dr Gadd had told me that until I was cured I was under no circumstances to indulge in what he called hanky-panky, I could only be an observer to all this frivolity.

When I got back to Westcliff the following weekend, St Margaret's had already moved. It saddened me to see Miss Minter now having to come to terms with the reality: that within the space of a few years, her lifelong dream of being the principal of a private school for girls had collapsed. Only a handful of the day-pupils turned up when the autumn term began. Once again, with virtually no money coming in, the poverty returned. As there was no longer any domestic help, I think she hoped that once I was well Uncle would pay her for my upkeep, while I went back to doing all the chores that I'd done so well before Ulrike was taken on.

It was early December when Dr Gadd declared me cured. It was a relief, not having to take four daily doses of the revolting Petrolarger. If it hadn't been for Peter, I'd have asked Uncle if I could have stayed on with him until I was sixteen, because then Joyce, Peter and I would be able to find a place of our own. Uncle told me he was quite concerned how I was going to earn my living when I left Miss Minter's.

"You see, Hayden, because you are educationally so behind, to place you in any worthwhile occupation will be almost impossible."

"I could do unskilled work like navvying or be a porter in a railway station, couldn't I?"

"You could, but one thought had crossed my mind. The Army can give opportunities to boys like you that are not normally available to civilians. You could learn to do a skilled trade, so that when you leave it would be easier for you to find a job."

"How long would I have to stay in it?"

"Six or seven years. Now that may sound like a long time, but you know, Hayden, by the time you leave, you will only be twenty-three."

"I don't think I'd like to join. I wouldn't be happy if I were separated from you and Peter."

"I can arrange for you to serve in a regiment whose barracks are in London. Then we would be able to meet at weekends, and you could stay with me when you are on leave."

"What about Peter?"

"She's getting on a bit and won't be around for that much longer, you know."

The very thought that one day I'd be without my lovely dog upset me. For most of my life, she'd been the only creature on earth that I'd loved and who, in turn, loved me.

"Will the Army take me before I'm sixteen?"

"No."

"So I don't need to make up my mind just yet, do I?"

"That's right, you don't. All the same, I'd like you to think about it."

"I will, I promise," I replied, being fairly certain that I would go ahead with my plan to live with Joyce.

Almost the moment I entered the front door back in Westcliff, I was put to work as the school drudge. This time, however, there was one important difference - I had money in my pocket because Uncle sent me every month a one pound postal order. All the other boarders were back once again to a penny a week, and even that wasn't guaranteed.

Joyce, who was fed up with the return to dire poverty, said to me, "I'm going to bunk off, Hayden. When I've found a place to live, I'll write, then when you're sixteen you can join me."

"How will you manage for money until you've found a job?"

"Maybe I'll go and work in a place like the one you went to in France."

"I don't think you'd like it, Joyce. Nearly all the men who go to brothels are old and fat, and most of the money the girls earn is pocketed by the women who run the place."

"Then I'll just pick on men who I like the look of, and let them put their hands down my knickers for a couple of bob."

"Don't, whatever you do, let them put their thing into you. I know that you can get a nasty disease from men who pick up girls in the street."

"Don't worry, I'll only let them rub their cocks against my bum."

Her reply did nothing to reassure me. She then left and went upstairs to her dormitory, and a few minutes later came down again carrying a brown paper bag.

"In this small bag, Hayden, are all the personal possessions that I've collected in all my life - pretty miserable, don't you think?"

"Yep," I said.

Before she left, I gave her all the money I had.

"No need to hitchhike, now you can go by train and still have enough left over to stay in lodgings for a few nights."

She kissed and hugged me. "I'll write, Hayden, we'll meet in London soon. Goodbye, and thanks for the money."

She never did write, and that was the last I ever saw of the poor girl who, not for most but for all of her sixteen years had been so terribly neglected.

CHAPTER TEN

I'd just brought up a bucket of coal from the cellar and was on my way to light the fire when I bumped into Stella.

"Oh, there you are, Hayden, Miss Minter wants to see you."

Normally, when I was summoned, it was either because I'd done something wrong, or to have another chore heaped onto me. I built up the fire, lit it, and went to her room. She was sitting in her armchair with her head rested on a lace doily, and her hands clasped together across her lap. The depressing circumstances she now found herself in had taken their toll on the old lady. It was upsetting to see her looking so frail and worn out.

"You wanted to see me, Miss Minter?" I said cheerfully.

"Yes, come over here and sit opposite me."

She paused for a moment as if she were trying to think what to say.

"Hayden, I'm afraid the time has finally come, when I can no longer afford to keep you. Last week I spoke with the major and asked him if he had any ideas about what could be done with you. He told me that he'd already discussed with you the possibility of your going into the Army, and that you weren't that averse to the idea, is that correct?"

"I've not thought about it a lot."

"I was hoping you had. However, yesterday he phoned me to say that he'd made an appointment for you to go tomorrow morning at ten to the recruiting centre in Southend. Because he has some influence as an ex-military man, he has persuaded the recruiting sergeant to enlist you to a regiment based in London."

"May I phone him?"

"I'm afraid you can't, the phone company are only allowing incoming calls until I've settled their bill. In any case, it would be of no use, because the major told me that as from today he would be away for three weeks."

"I suppose I'll have to go then," I said, somehow resigned to my fate.

"Don't sound so glum, you can't be made to join, but it might be a good idea if you at least go and see what is being offered."

"I will," I said.

"Hayden, I think you should know that I'm quite ill, and don't expect to live for very much longer. It would please me if I knew before I die that you have a roof over your head, and aren't just out on the streets."

After I left her, I began to wonder if putting me into the Army was Uncle's way of dumping me. After all, I was no longer the innocent boy of eleven that had so appealed to him. But then I decided that he was keen for me to join, because he genuinely believed that it would be in my interest to do so.

The recruiting centre was a small place that looked more like a shop than an office. Stuck on the front window were posters. One read: 'Join the Army and see the World', with a drawing of two young soldiers on camels, admiring the pyramids as they rode by. Another one was of a soldier standing to attention with a rifle on his shoulder. Written in large letters across his chest was 'It's a man's job'. Seeing the world appealed to me, as I'd so enjoyed being in the South of France. Buoyed up by the placards, I went inside.

The man sitting behind a desk was in uniform and had three stripes sewn on the sleeves of his tunic. He was reading a newspaper and didn't realise I was there, so I gave a little cough.

"Hallo, lad, can I help you?" said the man, looking up.

"I was told to be here at ten."

"Oh yes, you're the young man the major phoned me about. You want to volunteer, that's right, isn't it?"

"Well, I -" I was about to say I'd like to think about it when he interrupted me.

"Provided you pass your medical, there's no reason why you can't join up. First of all, I have to fill in this little form, your name and present address please?"

I gave him my name and the address of the school.

"School? How old are you, lad?"

"Sixteen years and one month."

"You're too young, you have to be seventeen before you can join."

"Oh, well, that's that then, isn't it?" I said, a little relieved that I had been rejected.

"I've had a thought, you're a good strong-looking chap, and can easily pass for seventeen, so that's what I'm going to put you down as."

What I didn't know at the time, was that the sergeant got a guinea for every man he enlisted.

"The major mentioned that you would prefer to be stationed in London. Well, you're in luck, because I've found a place for you with the Middlesex Regiment, which is based in North London." He handed me a piece of paper.

"Hand this voucher into the ticket office at the station, it's a free journey to Fenchurch Street, and here's a shilling that will more than cover you for the Underground and bus fare to the barracks. Go by tube to Golders Green, then jump on any bus that's going to Mill Hill. Ask the conductor to put you off at the barracks. Have you understood all that?"

I nodded. He stood up and held out his hand for me to shake.

"Well, good luck, young man, I'm sure you're going to do well."

"Thank you, sir." I said as I released my hand from his strong grip. If all the soldiers are as friendly as he is, maybe Army life won't be so bad after all, I thought.

Miss Minter was very pleased that I had been accepted.

"Come back and visit me whenever you can, I'll always be glad to see you."

"I will, and thank you for looking after me all these years."

"I have to admit it's not always been easy, nevertheless I'm glad I did. You will come and say goodbye before you leave, won't you?"

"Of course I will, Miss Minter."

She didn't look at all well. Every Christmas for as long as I could remember, she always said 'Children, this may be the last I'll be with you'. This time I felt that her annual forecast might well be realised.

I told Tom how he could best look after Peter, and said I'd come and visit her whenever possible. By way of an incentive, I told him that I'd get Uncle to post him the monthly pound he used to send to me.

"Hayden, I looked after her perfectly well when you were away. I like her and she's quite happy when she's with me, so don't worry."

The next morning, after a sad farewell to my beloved dog, I left Westcliff. It was the thought of leaving her that upset me most of all.

When I arrived at Mill Hill Barracks, a soldier on duty by the gate took me into the Guard Room, where a man checked my name on a list.

"OK, son, you are in Block H. Tea is at four, and supper at seven. If you walk around a bit, you'll soon find your way about."

The barracks were built right on top of a hill mostly surrounded by countryside - in the distance you could see London. Built around a large parade ground were buildings (probably erected when Queen Victoria was on the throne) two storeys high, by using an outside iron staircase, you could get from the ground floor to the one above. Scattered about the barracks were larger structures. These, I found out later, were the assembly hall, the cookhouse, the dining room, and the gymnasium.

After familiarising myself with the general layout, I found Block H. A soldier, with one stripe on his arm, was standing in the doorway.

"Excuse me, sir," I said, "I was told to report here by the Guard Room."

"Not 'sir' - 'Corporal' is what you call me. Now, as you're one of the first to arrive, you have a choice. You can take a bed up or down."

I opted for the ground level.

The barrack room had twenty beds, a line of ten each side. In the middle of the floor were two trestle tables with wooden benches on either side of them. At the far end was a large coke stove. The wash-house and lavatories were attached but outside in the open, with only a roof as protection from the weather. All the walls were painted brown.

I picked myself a bed near the door and put the few things I had brought with me into the locker next to it. At four o'clock, I made my way to the dining hall. This was a huge place, it could seat about eight hundred men. I looked around for somewhere to sit down, and eventually saw a table right at the end of the hall where men in civilian clothes were sitting.

"All right if I sit here?" I asked one of them, who was stuffing a thick slice of bread and jam into his mouth.

"Sure, mate."

I sat down on a bench next to him and helped myself to a slice of bread and covered it with margarine and some tinned jam. The tea was in a large urn and the milk was in tins dotted about the table. It was sticky stuff that poured out like glue.

"Are you a rookie too?" said the ma, "You look to me like you should be in the Boys' Army. How old are you?"

"Sixteen," I said.

"I suppose it's because it looks like a war is coming, that they are taking them in young nowadays. You sound a bit of a toff to me. You're not going to try to become a fucking officer, are you?"

"Oh no, I couldn't anyway, because I can't spell and even find it hard to read."

"Nor can the rest of us, mate! Take my advice, get rid of that posh way of speaking, if you want to 'ave any mates."

"I can't help the way I talk."

"Well, I've warned yer, 'aven't I?"

As he had dropped the 'H', I knew that from now on, when I told anyone my name, I would end up being called 'Ayden'. I supposed I'd just have to get used to it.

After tea, I went back to the barrack room. By now, it was full of men. All of them were four or five years older then I. With the exception of two from the North, the rest were Cockneys. As I hadn't heard the Cockney accent before, I had great difficulty in understanding what they were saying. A lot of the swearwords they used were new to me. They seemed to sprinkle them about within a sentence like confetti. They realised very quickly that I wasn't one of them.

I was lying on my bed, wondering what would happen tomorrow, when a man walked over to me.

"Hey, pretty boy, this bed is going to be mine, so fuck off and go and take the one at the other end."

"Excuse me, but I bagged this bed before you'd even arrived."

He turned his head and called to a friend:

"Alf, cunty here says it's his bed."

"Oh dear," said Alf, joining his mate.

"Well, Jack, I'd say it's the old one-two-three routine, wouldn't you? 'ere goes, ONE-TWO-THREE- "

One of them grabbed my legs and the other my head. I was dumped onto my back on the floor. One sat on my chest while the other pulled off my shoes.

"Leave me alone," I screamed. In seconds they got my trousers off, and then my pants.

"Cor, look at that tiny prick, that won't be much use to the Judys, will it? We'll have to brighten it up a bit, won't we, Alf?"

He went over to the bin holding the coke and picked up a tin of polish, and a brush used to blacken the bin.

"This will do it, eh Jack?"

He opened the tin and put the brush deep into it, then knelt on the floor and pulled at my penis with one hand and with the brush in the other, rubbed away as hard as he could.

"There, pretty boy, that's better! Mind you, you're gonna have to wank all night long to wear the polish off."

I didn't know what that meant, but the others did, because they all burst out laughing. I tried my best to fight back my tears and somehow managed to.

"Now, be a good little darling, and go and get your fucking things out of my fucking locker."

I got dressed and did as I was told. I took my towel and went outside to the wash-house, but no matter how much soap I used, I couldn't get the black stuff off.

For the rest of the evening I kept myself to myself. Having had their fun, left me alone. Lights out was at ten o'clock. I went under my blankets and pulled the sheet over my head. Feeling frightened and very miserable, I eventually fell asleep.

I was awakened by a loud voice shouting 'Wakee wakee - show a leg me beauties!' It was the Duty Sergeant. If anyone didn't respond immediately, he prodded them with the stick that he carried under his arm.

When everybody had got their feet on the floor, he said very loudly:

"First you go and wash and shave, then at six-thirty go and 'ave your breakfast, and at seven-fifteen sharp you will form up in the passage outside the barrack room. Your Squad Sergeant will take care of you from then on."

There were eight hand basins with twenty men needing to use them, so there was a lot of waiting around outside in the cold before one became free. Washing and shaving in cold water wasn't pleasant. Breakfast consisted of bread, margarine, and a hard-boiled egg.

At seven-fifteen we all hung about in a disorderly group waiting for the sergeant. He arrived a few minutes later. He was a fierce-looking man, about six feet tall and thickset. His face was almost square and above his thin mean-looking lips was a neatly trimmed moustache. He stood so upright that you couldn't help wondering if he had a plank of wood up his back.

"Right, men, face me and form a line."

We made a wavy line in front of him.

"My name is Sergeant Bulldock, and when you address me, you call me sergeant. Now this morning, what you will be doing is as follows: first it's to the MO for your medical, and if any of you fail that, out you go. Then I take those of you that remain, to the quartermaster's stores, where you will be fitted out with everything you will need for the time that you are a squaddy. When you've done all that, it will be dinner time. At two p.m. sharp, you will assemble at the parade ground, and I will give you your first taste of square bashing. Now follow me to the Assembly Hall for your medical examination."

Once in there, we were told to make a line and take off all clothing from the waist up. After standing around for about twenty minutes, the doctor arrived.

When it got to my turn, I received the same routine as the others. First the stethoscope was placed at points on my back and chest. Each time it was put anywhere, I was told to take a deep breath. A small torch was shone into my eyes, then I had to open my mouth so that my tongue and teeth could be seen.

"Drop your trousers, lad."

I didn't want to because of the black polish on my penis. The medical orderly repeated the order.

"Drop 'em now and make it snappy."

So I did.

"What's this black thing all about, eh?" inquired the doctor.

"It was a prank, sir."

"Well, do you mind NOT larking about before a medical in future? Now turn round and bend down."

He opened the cheeks of my buttocks.

"Very good, you're A1."

"Get dressed, and stand over there with the others," said the orderly.

Only two out of the twenty men were rejected. We were told to line up outside and follow the sergeant to the Quartermaster's Stores. When it was my turn at the counter, a man with a tape measure sized me up. My measurements were given to the store man. He handed me a large kitbag.

"Right, son, as I hand you the gear, put it in the bag."

All the items were stacked in rows made of slatted wood, three tiers high. The man went up and down them, and came back to the counter with an armful.

"Now, son, make sure I give you all the things I call out. First: three shirts, three vests, one gym vest, three pairs of pants, two towels, one tunic, one pair khaki trousers, one white belt, one denim jacket and pair of trousers, two rolls of puttees, one pair of boots, one pair of plimsolls, three pairs of socks, one peaked cap, one forage cap. Right, that's all the clothing. Now come to the other end for the equipment: one three-o-three rifle, one bayonet, one webbing harness, and the last thing - one billycan. Now, lad, have you checked all that?"

I hadn't, but I said yes.

So with all that in the kitbag and the rifle slung over my shoulder, I staggered back to the barrack room. By the time I had unloaded everything and put it into my locker, it was twelve-thirty, time to go to the dining hall for dinner. As I didn't eat meat, all I had was the over-cooked vegetables. I decided that when I had settled in I'd tell the Duty Officer that I was a vegetarian.

At two o'clock we all sauntered over to the parade ground to face the awesome Sergeant Bulldock. He was waiting for us.

"Right, you men, I want you to get yourself into three straight lines."

I made sure that I got into the back row, so as to be as far away as possible from him.

"Well, first of all, you're not in a straight line. The way to get one is to raise your right arm sideways until it reaches the man next to you. If you all do that, we'll have made a start. Right, you can rest your arms and put them clasped together behind your back, and at the same time put your feet eighteen inches apart. You will then be in the position of standing-at-ease. You lot are now rookies in - not the males, nor the females - but the MIDDLESEX Regiment. I can bloody promise you, that when I've finished with you in six weeks' time, you will be real MEN."

The rest of the afternoon was spent trying to get us to know the difference between our left and right. Before he dismissed us, he told us that at seven-fifteen a.m. sharp, we were all to turn up in our 'denims' outside our barrack room.

Lying on my bed that evening, I reflected on what type of men were in my squad. I came to the conclusion that most of them were, like me, educationally sub-normal. Some of them couldn't read at all, none could spell, and apart from a huge stringing together of numerous swearwords, they could hardly communicate. In the spoken word, I was way ahead of them. This was, of course, the main reason why I wasn't liked. I found out that quite a few of them had joined up under a false name and were on the run from the civil police, and some were deserters from other regiments. It seemed that the best way to avoid getting caught as a deserter was to join the army.

For the following six weeks, apart from a break for dinner, we did nothing but drill from seven-fifteen a.m. to three-forty five p.m. The huge parade ground was filled with squads of rookies, having orders bellowed at them. Sometimes, if the Sergeants weren't paying attention, one squad would be on a collision course with another, only to be saved in the nick of time by the order 'About turn'. Every fifty minutes, the voice that had been shouting orders to you, bawled out 'Fall out for a smoke'. Even if you were a non-smoker, that order was obeyed along with the rest.

The last two weeks of square bashing had to be done in full uniform. That meant goodbye to most of your spare time because it was now spent polishing the many buttons on your tunic with Brasso, or blancoing the white belt that went round your waist. But the longest job of all was polishing your boots. They had to be so shiny, that they could almost have doubled-up for a mirror. The worst job was doing the toecaps. You had to put the cloth over one finger and dip into the tin, then in tiny circles go round and round until the cloth was worn through. Anyway, it was all a complete waste of time, because very often the first thing you did in the morning was a route march through muddy fields. The three-quarter length khaki trousers had to have a knife-like crease, which had to be ironed in daily. Some of the men cheated by getting their mothers to stitch in a crease. The cap badge had to become so bright that it glittered in the sunshine. I presumed that all this shining of brass must have made it easier for the enemy to see us coming from a long way off.

All this nightly cleaning and polishing was a piece of cake compared to the Commanding Officer's fortnightly kit inspection. This happened at seven-fifteen a.m., immediately after breakfast, and as it took hours to prepare, everything was done the evening before. All the kit you possessed had to be laid out in straight lines on your bed. Starting from the head end, three of the blankets had to be folded in a special and precise way, the final fold reinforced by a three-inch wide wooden slat. All three blankets were then piled one on top of the other. You had to make sure that no edges were protruding. The fourth one was tightly wrapped around the other three. Your tunic with brightly polished buttons had to be laid out flat and uncrumpled, and the three-quarter length trousers had to be pressed with razor-sharp creases; any shirts, vests or pants you were not wearing had to be ironed and put into neat piles. Your boots had to be placed on the bed with the laces removed, and the soles uppermost. These had to be blackened with boot polish until they were shiny, and the metal studs dotted about their surface had to be burnished. By the side of each boot, a shoelace was put, rolled up like a Catherine wheel. The puttees, washed and ironed, were then rolled neatly up and placed by the leg of your trousers. The belt had to be blancoed snow-white with the brass clasp gleaming. The cloth of the peaked cap had to be brushed in ever-diminishing circles, the regimental badge was polished until your arm gave out. When all this was done, came the worst job of all: the webbed harness with its numerous straps and sewn-in pockets had to be scrubbed with a green mixture. This harness had dozens of brass studs and buttons. Trying to put Brasso on these, without getting any of the polish spilling onto the green webbing, nearly drove you insane.

Your rifle barrel had to shine for its entire length. This was done by using a cord which had a piece of cloth on the end of it, and if you pulled it through about thirty times, the barrel shone brightly for about a day. With all this kit laid out on your bed, the only way to go to sleep was to lie on the floor with a pillow under your head.

By the end of May, our squad had done its six weeks basic training, and real Army training began. They thought that they had made men of us, now they would hopefully turn us into soldiers.

On the first day of the new regime, we were taken to the firing range. We were all handed ten rounds of live ammunition, and told to lie down on the ground on our stomachs and point our rifle at the target area. The order came to put a round into the breech, and aim at the target, but we were not to pull the trigger until given the order to fire.

All my life, I'd never been able to squint with my left eye, which meant that in order to aim, I had to rest the rifle butt on my left shoulder. When the sergeant saw me, he shouted:

"What the fuck do you think you're doing?"

"I'm waiting for your order to fire, sergeant," I replied.

"Put your bloody rifle on the other shoulder, you can't fire like that."

I told him of my problem.

"In the British Army, we fire from our RIGHT shoulder, so fucking well put it there now."

"But, sergeant, I won't be able to see the target!"

"I don't bloody care, just obey my order."

When the order to fire came, I just pulled the trigger. Everyone managed to hit their target, but my bullet couldn't be found anywhere. The sergeant called out to me:

"Hey, you, get up and come over here."

I went over.

"Right, private, from the standing position, using your right shoulder, aim the rifle down the range."

I did.

"Now, squint your left eye, and that's an order!"

I pushed and pushed with my left cheek, but no matter how hard I tried, my eye wouldn't close.

"You're fucking me about, aren't you, boy? Do you think you'll work your ticket with this caper?"

"No, sergeant, it's that I just can't do it."

"Oh yes, you will do it. You're going to meet me in the gym tonight and every night at five o'clock until you fucking well can."

I assumed he was going to give me a bashing in the boxing ring. So when I turned up at five o'clock, I felt a little uneasy.

He was standing at the far end. As I walked across to him, I thought, this man is going to half kill me. He was over six feet tall, and brawny with it, and certainly twice my age.

"Reporting to you as requested, sergeant."

"What's your name, private?"

"Cartlidge, sergeant."

"Right Cartlidge, stand to attention!"

I stood rigid in front of him.

"What we are going to do now is some eye drill. So on the command 'Right Eye Squint', you do that, and on the order 'Left Eye Squint', you will do that. Have you understood, Cartlidge?"

"Yes, sergeant."

"Right eye squint!"

This I could do easily.

"Left eye squint!"

I repeated the performance I had done on the range, and no matter how I contorted my left cheek, my eye wouldn't close.

"Right eye squint!" and then again, "Left eye squint!". He repeated the order "Left eye" then "Right eye" many times. Then he came over to me, put the flat of his hand over my right eye and shouted an inch away from my ear:

"Left eye squint!" while at the same time pushing my cheek up with his other hand until my eye closed.

He alternated this shouting and pushing for a few minutes until he went red in the face with anger. Finally he stopped and took one pace back.

"Right, Cartlidge, I'm going to give you the order one more time, then, if you don't carry it out, I'll have you put on a charge for malingering, and that would end up with you doing three months detention in the Glasshouse. So you'd better fucking well get it right. Now, right eye squint! Left eye squint!"

Despite his threat, I was unable to do it. At this point, the sergeant was beside himself with rage. He threw himself at me and knocked me backwards onto the floor and sat on my chest, then he turned my face very roughly sideways and started shouting as loud as he could into my ear.

"You fucking bastard, fucking well do what I order." He pulled my head up a little and repeatedly banged it back onto the floor. No matter how much I struggled, I couldn't free myself from this powerful man. He carried on shouting abuse into my ear. In the end I started to cry. Seeing this, he got off me.

"Jesus fucking Christ, a soldier, a British soldier, fucking crying. What the fuck were they doing, letting babies like you into the Army."

I got up from the floor and dabbed my tears away with my sleeve.

"For Christ's sake, stop snivelling and behave like a man, and stand to attention when I'm talking to you."

I stood rigid with my head bowed towards the floor, then in a much quieter voice, because perhaps he thought he may have gone a bit too far, he said:

"On second thoughts, I'm now fairly convinced that you really can't squint with your left eye. So in future, when you go to the range, you're going to have to wear an eye patch. With that at least, you will be able to fire off your right shoulder, which is the way the British Army has done since before Waterloo. I'll see that you are issued with one. Dismiss."

I began to recover a little as I walked slowly back to the barrack room and even allowed a funny notion to enter my sore head. What, I thought, would happen when I'm facing the enemy, and I shout out 'Pax - hold your fire while I put on my eye patch'? That thought made me smile.

The next day our squad was taken out into a field for bayonet practice. Lined up in front of us about a hundred yards away, were straw dummies. The order came 'Fix bayonets'. This had to be done by numbers. Number one, you bent your legs and put the rifle between your knees. Number two - the bayonet was pulled out of its sheath with your right hand, and Number three, you attached this lethal weapon, which was eighteen inches long (and still the type they used in the First World War) to the muzzle. Then, on the command 'Charge', you ran towards the straw man, yelling and screaming as loud as you could.

Orders were to thrust the blade into the belly as far as possible, then give it a twist so that when the bayonet was withdrawn, the guts of the real victim would come out with the blade. The very idea of this sickened me. Just doing this a few times that day convinced me that I was never going to be much good as a soldier.

CHAPTER ELEVEN

In the middle of June 1939, the Prime Minister, Neville Chamberlain, announced that conscription would start immediately. Five days later, gangs of workmen appeared and started to build large huts, which were to accommodate the big influx of conscripted men. The huts were being erected in the fields surrounding the barracks and took up a large chunk of our training area.

A few days after the building work started, I woke up one morning with a terrible pain just above my right groin, so I reported sick. After standing at ease outside the sick bay for one hour, the M.O. arrived. He decided that I had a problem with my appendix. An ambulance was ordered and I was taken to Millbank Army hospital, which was by the Thames in Chelsea.

On arrival, I was put into a large ward. Some of the patients came from the Guards Regiments, most of them hospitalised for 'Observation', because they were complaining about pains here, there and everywhere. One of them told me that they were just 'swinging the lead' to avoid the Trooping of the Colours on the Horse Guards Parade, which was to take place in a couple of days.

"Why, what's so terrible about it?" I asked.

"Oh mate, it's bloody awful. You have to spend days polishing your uniform and grooming the horses and all the fucking brass that they have dangling all over them. Then the parade itself - standing to attention for hours in the heavy red tunic with a busby on. If it's a hot day, a lot of us just keel over from exhaustion. If you do, the bastards put you on a charge. They accuse you of getting pissed the night before, or going out with a girl, when you should have been resting."

"What happens, when the doctors find out that there's nothing wrong with you?"

"Oh, they can't fucking prove you're faking, the worst they can do is to prescribe some foul-tasting medicine and make you drink it three times a day. By the time they chuck you out you've dodged the fucking parade."

Most of the patients were, like me, genuine cases. The man in the next bed was also in for an appendix operation.

In the evening before my operation, a very pretty young nurse came and shaved off all my pubic hair, and any more that would get in the way of the surgeon's knife. Then she went to the man in the next bed, and did the same to him, but when she started to move his penis about from side to side, it very quickly became erect. The nurse reported him to the sister. The poor man was put on a charge for 'Dumb Insolence'.

In the morning, I was taken down very early to the theatre. The Sister in Charge lifted my gown to just above my knees.

"Why hasn't this man been shaved?" she asked the orderly.

"I don't know, sister."

"But I have been, sister," I interrupted.

I pulled up the gown and showed her where I had been shaved.

"You've brought down the wrong patient, the one we want is for the cartilage operation. This man is to be done later and have his appendix removed. Now take him back and bring down the right one."

"I'm sorry, sister, I was just told to get the 'cartilage case', that's what was written on the tab at the end of his bed."

The next day, after breakfast, when I'd only just come out of the anaesthetic, the ward was smartened up and got ready for the CO's Inspection. All the blankets were straightened up and everything on top of the locker was put out of sight. The CO was a full-blown colonel. The sergeant who accompanied him gave the order:

"Ward - lie to attention!"

This hurt because it made me laugh. 'Lying to attention' meant that you had to put your arms outside the blankets in a straight line close to your body, at the same time, pull in your chin, and look up to the ceiling.

When the colonel got to me, he asked:

"Everything fine with you, lad?"

The way the question was put, you knew what the answer had to be.

"Yes, sir," I replied.

"Good!" said the colonel and then moved on.

As soon as any patient was well enough, work was brought to you even though you were still bed-ridden. Pots and pans had to be burnished. I was given a large brass fireguard to polish. All the silverware from the Officers' Mess was brought into the ward for cleaning.

It was three weeks before I got out of hospital. I was given a note informing the Squad Sergeant that I was to be on light duties for a month. When I gave it to him. He tore it up.

"Fucking light duties. They should have kept you in until you were fit. You will fall in with the rest of the squad in the morning, understood, Cartlidge?"

The next day was a ten mile route march, carrying full pack plus rifle. Not the best way to recoup. Nevertheless I survived. The frantic building that had started before I went to hospital had made progress. Dotted about all over the surrounding fields were large huts, most of them near completion.

Within a few days the first batch of conscripts arrived. They were all twenty-one years old. I found it refreshing to see normal-looking people going about the barracks, as up to now I'd made no friends with anyone in my squad.

I first came into contact with one of them in the NAAFI. One evening, while I was sitting by myself, having a cup of tea and eating a sticky bun, a slim, fair-haired man asked me if it was all right to sit at my table. This sort of politeness I had not experienced for all the weeks I'd been in the Army.

"Of course, please do."

He had the voice of the upper classes, but the more he spoke, the more I became aware that his manner of speech was affected. Affected or not, he was royalty compared to the morons that I had had to associate with up until now.

I told him my name and he said his was Victor Blake.

"You look too young to have been called up, so what made you join the Regulars?"

I gave him a brief account of how I came to be in the Army. He told me that before being conscripted he had been studying engineering, and lived in Winchester, and also went to school there. I think I was supposed to believe that he had been educated at that famous public school, but I guessed it was more than likely that he had attended the local grammar school. By the end of the evening, the seeds of a friendship had been sown. From now on, most of my free time was spent with my new friend.

As far as I was concerned, the more I got to know Vic, the more I liked him. I found out that he was an all-round athlete. He had come second in the 'Round Britain Cycle Race', only having been beaten by a few yards by the champion, Reg Harris. He was also a long-distance runner, and was always way ahead in any cross-country race that the regiment put on. But best of all, although he was of slim build, he could knock the hell out of anyone who was foolish enough to take him on. He told me in confidence that he was a member of the British Amateur Boxing Association, and became one of their stars in the middle-weight class. He didn't like anyone to know, because it took away the element of surprise when he was involved in a brawl. His prowess in the ring was very useful, because other men often ridiculed the way he talked, but they did it only once. As I was known to be his friend, his fame as a pugilist protected me as well.

I told Vic about the men who had debagged me and then smothered me with black polish, and he said: "If the louts had a go at you because you weren't like them, let's see how they react to me."

When we entered my barrack room, both of them were there. Vic and I began to talk to each other, very loudly, in an exaggerated posh accent.

One of them swallowed the bait immediately.

"Oh look, Alf, our pretty boy has found a little friend."

"Are you referring to me as 'a little friend'?" said Vic.

"Sit down, you posh cunt, before I knock you down."

Well, all I can say is, that before you could say Jack Robinson the man had five or six of the quickest punches I had ever seen delivered to the top half of his body. He was on the floor in no time, with Vic sitting on his chest, pounding away.

"Let me know when you've had enough, old chap."

"Enough, I've had enough, mate!"

Vic got off him.

"There's only one thing, old boy, I'm NOT, nor ever will be, YOUR mate, so don't forget it."

The fact that Vic had settled this old score of mine gave me immense pleasure.

Having Vic as my protector gave me much more confidence in the company of men in my squad. However, to make myself a little more acceptable to them, I did incorporate into my vocabulary most of the swearwords they used.

One day, using a word picked at random from my new and extended vocabulary, I called someone who'd said something that annoyed me: "You bastard!"

The man stood up to all his full and considerable height, and said: "Did you call me a bastard?"

Foolishly, instead of apologising there and then, I said: "Yes I did."

He pointed to his clenched fist and said: "Right, cunty, I'll see you in the gym at six o'clock, and you'd better fucking well be there!"

Oh dear, I thought, he'll make mincemeat out of me. As I had been the transgressor, and not the transgressed, I couldn't in all fairness call on the services of Vic. But I did tell him about my six o'clock appointment.

"Don't worry," he said, "I'll come along with you."

I asked Vic if he could explain to me why the man got so upset when all I did was call him a bastard?

"It was because you used it in the wrong context. If you had said, they are bastards, or he is a bastard, talking about absent persons - that would have been all right. But you mustn't say 'you' are, because then you're calling into question his legitimacy, and more importantly, casting a slur on the good name of his mother. You left him with no alternative but to fight for her good name, especially when you've called him that in front of all his mates."

"So I suppose, if someone calls me a bastard, my retort must be: How did you guess, you clever chap?"

We arrived at the gym some time before six.

"Now Hayden, I have a plan which might just save you from being slaughtered. It's called psychological warfare, you defeat the enemy by undermining his confidence. Animals do it all the time, they make themselves look bigger than they are. There's even a fish that can blow itself up to four times its normal size, just to frighten off any predator. I've brought my boxing trunks with me for you to wear. Printed in large letters is 'British Boxing Association', but first, old boy, I'll show you how to shadow-box."

Vic and I ran around the gym many times with me trying my best to imitate him. He told me as I pranced about, that when breathing in, I should purse my lips and make a sort of snorting noise, then every three or four steps do a scissor-like movement, like we do when you change step on the Parade Ground, he said.

"What's the idea of that?" I asked.

"It confuses your opponent as to which fist will land on him next."

"I see," I said, but didn't.

The man arrived dead on time and saw Vic and me doing our stuff.

"I've not come here to fight you," he said to Vic.

"Oh no, old chap, I'm only here to have a workout with my friend. You see, we both belong to the same boxing club. My friend is considered to be one of our most promising young members. In fact, old boy, we had quite forgotten that you were coming. Still, now that you're here, let play begin, eh what?"

It was then my turn to say something.

"First of all, I am really sorry for calling you what I did, I didn't really know what it implied. I do apologise."

"Well, mate, seeing as you've said you're sorry, I suppose we could call it off."

"Oh good," I said, "that leaves me free to give my friend here a good thrashing."

The man left the gym looking quite relieved, but not half as much as I was.

Pleased that our bluff had worked, on the way to the NAAFI I told Vic that when it came to sport of any kind, I was hopeless.

"What you must do is to make yourself look more formidable than you actually are."

"How do I achieve that?"

"Press-ups, they very quickly build up your arm and chest muscles. A daily three-mile run would also be a good idea. To 'get the fuck out of harm's way fast' can be very useful if all else fails."

From then on, every weekday, rain or shine, Vic took me to the gym to make sure I did the exercise plan he had set out. I must say, it did work, for after a few weeks, my arms and chest were measurably bigger and my confidence increased at the same rate as my muscles.

One day in mid-July sergeant Bulldock told our squad to go to the barrack room as he was going to give us some training with our gas masks. When we had all assembled, he ordered us to put them on. On the table laid out three capsules.

"When I smash these in a few seconds the room will be filled with tear gas. You, Cartlidge, go and shut the door and close all the windows."

When I'd done this, he continued:

"Now if any of you think that your mask is letting in gas, put up your hand and leave the room."

We all put on our masks, then the sergeant broke the capsules with the knob of his cane. The room soon filled up with a thin white smoke, which disappeared almost at once. No more than thirty seconds had gone by, when I felt or imagined that gas was getting under my mask. So I put up my hand and left the room. When the test was over, the sergeant told the squad to line up outside and said he'd be out shortly. A minute later, he joined us, saying to me:

"Cartlidge, give your mask to the man next to you, then go and pick up my cane, I've left it on the mantelpiece - at the double, boy!"

Halfway across the room, I realised that it was still full of tear gas, so coughing madly, I retreated back to the door. But it was shut, I tried to push it open, but it wouldn't budge. I banged on it as hard as I could with both my hands and shouted 'Help' as loud as I could between coughs. Tears started to stream down my face and the coughing got worse. Any moment now, I thought, my lungs would come out through my mouth. In the end I was on my knees, still hammering on the door. Just when I began to think that I was about to die - the door opened, and I fell out. Sergeant Bulldock was standing by it.

"Now, soldier, you really do know what gas smells like, don't you? Take half an hour off to recover, then join the squad."

You bastard, I thought, you fucking, sadistic bastard, you won't see me in half an hour. In fact, you'll be lucky if you ever see me again.

When I felt well enough, I took off into the fields and sat in the long grass. I stayed there for the rest of the day, looking at London bathed in the summer sunshine.

Although the Middlesex Regiment was supposed to be a machine-gun outfit I had not as yet even seen one let alone handled one. The day came when five open trucks equipped with machine-guns were waiting for us on the square. A whole morning was spent drilling us in assembling and disassembling the guns.

In the afternoon, we were taken out into the fields for training.

A machine-gun crew consisted of three men - Number One fired the gun, Number Two fed the belts of ammunition into the breech, Number Three kept Number Two supplied with boxes of ammo. The drill was that when the truck pulled up, Number One jumped out with the barrel, Number Two with the tripod, and Number Three with the boxes of ammunition. We were considered to be proficient when the machine-gun was set up and ready for action in thirty seconds. To fire, you had to sit on the ground bolt-upright with your legs stretched out in front of you, then look through the adjustable sight, aim at the target and press the button. If the gun jammed, you had to (without looking), slide back a metal strip which was placed under the barrel, and by using your middle finger release the part that had become stuck.

This I never managed to do. I'd spend forever fumbling about trying to free the bloody thing. One day, the Sergeant shouted out:

"Cartlidge, use your fucking courting finger, boy!"

What my middle finger had to do with courting, I didn't understand.

After a week of constantly doing the same drill, it was decided we were advanced enough to be taken to the Firing Range. When it came to my turn, the target didn't receive one of the twenty or so bullets I shot off. In the end, the Sergeant thought I'd be useless as Number One. In real war, this could work to my advantage, because the man whose hand was on the firing button would be taken out first.

CHAPTER TWELVE

The day after the August Bank Holiday, I was getting ready for morning parade, when the Squad Corporal told me that Sergeant Bulldock wanted to see me. On my way over, I wondered with some trepidation what sort of horror he had dreamt up for me this time. I knocked on his door.

"Come in, Cartlidge. Sit down, boy, I'm afraid I've got some sad news for you, lad. Your mother has passed away, boy."

I guessed he meant Miss Minter, but I didn't correct him.

"You're getting compassionate leave starting straight away. If you go to the Guard Room, they will give you a railway pass. You must leave in uniform and carry yourself like a soldier, no matter how upset you are. You're to report back to barracks by lights-out Sunday night."

While I was sorry to hear of her death, the thought of six days' leave cheered me up. Best of all, I'd be able to spend a few days with Peter. When I returned to the barrack room, the Corporal was waiting for me. I think he expected that I'd be in tears. When he saw that I wasn't, he said:

"There's a good lad, taking it like a man."

I supposed he was telling me, that soldiers aren't expected to weep when they hear that their mothers have died. He offered to help me polish and clean my uniform. I was glad he did as it would have taken me a very long time.

When I was finally dressed, the Corporal stood back a couple of paces and looked at me.

"Well, lad, you look very smart, a real credit to the Regiment. Off you go, and remember, keep a brave face on it."

The Corporal's help was the first kind act that any of the regulars had ever shown me.

I arrived at Westcliff about midday. What I saw shocked me. Parked outside the school were two large removal vans. Men came out of the house carrying furniture which they put without much care into the waiting vans. All the items being carted off were things that had surrounded me all my life - wardrobes, large tables, school desks, even sheets, blankets and cutlery. The house was being emptied. I made my way past the removal men and went inside.

Jim and Eileen were there, distant relatives of Miss Minter - so distant, in fact, I'd only ever seen them half a dozen times. They were packing Miss Minter's prized possessions into suitcases. When Jim saw me standing in the doorway, he paused for a moment.

"Hallo, Hayden. Look, Eileen, Hayden's arrived, doesn't he look smart in his uniform?"

"What's going on?" I asked.

"What do you mean?"

"All those vans? Where are they taking the furniture?"

"An auction room, I presume, the money they get for them will go to the tradespeople she owed."

"Did she owe you money as well?"

"Oh no, Hayden, she'd want us to have her personal possessions," said Eileen.

"Then she would have left them in her will to you, wouldn't she?"

"Unfortunately she didn't leave one. So now, as we are here, it's easier for us to take them with us. You do understand, don't you, dear?"

"I understand," I said sardonically. "Where are all the boarders?"

"The last of them left yesterday."

"When is the funeral?"

"It's on Thursday."

"Will you be staying for it?"

"Can't, dear, we have to get back to our work in London, you see."

"I see," I said.

They'd managed to get time off from work to come here and plunder Miss Minter's belongings, but couldn't spare the time to pay her their last respects.

"Where's Peter?" I asked.

"We had to shut her up outside, in the shed, while the removal men are here. And talking of Peter, I've arranged with the vet to have her put down this afternoon. I wonder if you'd be a good chap and take her there. I'll give you the five shillings for his fee."

This news went into my side like a knife.

"Is there no other way?" I asked.

"No, I'm afraid not. We don't want a dog and you certainly can't keep her, so there's no alternative."

Jim reached into his pocket and gave me two half-crowns, and wrote down the vet's address.

"The receptionist said that you are to be there not later than four o'clock."

I left the two vultures and went to the shed to get Peter. When I opened the door, she went berserk, yelping madly and leaping up at me time and time again. When she had exhausted herself, I knelt down in front of her. She rested her front legs on my shoulders, and with her long tongue kept licking my face. I put my arms around her golden body and hugged her tightly for a long time. Eventually I let her go, and then clasped her beautiful face in my hands.

"Peter, my darling, Hayden's back, your Hayden's back. Do you know what we are going to do? You don't, do you? Well, I'll tell you, I'm going to take you on your favourite walk. We're going down to the beach, and if the sea is out, we'll go out into the mud and you can chase the seagulls, would you like that, Peter? You would, I know you would."

I walked out by the garden entrance onto the street. Peter raced at full speed down the road. After a short distance, she stopped, turned her head round to look at me, then barking with joy came running back again. Once on the beach, we did what we had done many times before. We ran along the beach and at every breakwater, I climbed while she jumped over them. We kept this up until both of us had to stop and rest for a while. I lay down on the sand and Peter spread herself across my chest I put my hand on her head and just kept on and on stroking it. Every now and then, my hand slid down her long soft and silky, half gold and half brown ears. Oh Peter, my darling, I'm going to miss you. Please, please, forgive me for what I'm going to have to do. I had to stop thinking about it, because tears started to run down my face. I stood up.

"Come on, let's walk out on the mud path and you can chase the gulls."

Out there, it was just her and me, like it used to be. She was a wonderful sight, running across the hard mud at a tremendous speed, her ears flapping in the breeze, trying as always in vain, to catch a gull. Her golden-coloured hair silhouetted against the clear blue sky, was a picture that I knew I would never forget.

I could see by the angle of the sun - it was time to leave.

"Come on, Peter, we have to go."

As we made our way back to the beach, she reluctantly followed me. I stopped at one of the little shops on the sea front and got her a big bar of Cadbury's Milk Chocolate, her favourite. I sat on the bench and fed it to her. She ate the whole bar.

"You liked that, didn't you, Peter?"

I knew that she must be thirsty by now, so I took her to a drinking fountain and let her drink out of my cupped hands. We left the promenade and walked to the vet's premises. When we got there, I took hold of her collar and we went in. There was no one in the waiting room, but a few seconds later a woman came through some swing doors.

"You're a quarter of an hour late," she complained.

"I'm sorry," I said, "but I don't have a watch."

"Have you got the five shilling fee?"

I gave the money to her.

"Give me your dog, there's no need for you to stay."

"Please be gentle with her, would you stroke her a little before you..." I couldn't finish the sentence. So far the woman had seemed quite callous, but seeing that I was obviously very distressed, she changed her manner and the tenor of her voice.

"Of course I will, I'll stroke and pet her up to the last. She will feel no pain, no pain at all, I promise you."

I gave Peter one last hug and kiss, then she disappeared through the swing doors. I just managed to make it to the outside before I collapsed. I sat down on the front door step, buried my head in the palm of my hands, and howled my eyes out for a long time.

When I had recovered a little, I stood up and walked slowly back to the beach. My throat was dry so I made my way to a little café, where I'd worked sometimes, clearing the tables. Mrs Collins, who ran it with the help of her daughter, had always been very nice to me.

"Hallo, Hayden, how lovely to see you. We wondered what had happened to you. Seeing you so smart in your uniform, we know now, don't we?" Then, noticing my red eyes, "What's up, lad? You look as though something has upset you."

I told her why I was in Westcliff, and what I had had to do with my beloved dog.

"There, there, boy, you sit here and I'll go and make you a nice cup of tea. And what about some scrambled eggs on hot, buttered toast?"

"I'd love some tea," I said, but although I hadn't eaten anything since breakfast in the barracks, I just didn't feel hungry. "Nothing to eat, thanks, Mrs Collins, just a cup of tea."

"Nonsense, Hayden, I bet you haven't eaten all day, I'm going to make some scrambled eggs. If you feel you can't manage, then you can leave them."

Sitting there in the sunshine facing the sea, which by now was coming in quite fast and covering the mud that Peter and I had been on a little more than an hour before, I began to feel a little better. Mrs Collins' kindness helped me a lot. She came to my table carrying a tray with a big pot of tea, plus a plate with two slices of toast covered with butter, and scrambled eggs. It was well-known locally that Mrs Collins' scrambled eggs were the best in Westcliff.

"Now, Hayden, you try and eat something, there's a good boy."

I wish I'd had a mother like her, I thought.

After drinking two cups of tea, the sight of all that butter melting on the hot toast, and the look of those fluffy eggs tempted me to try and eat. My appetite began to return, in the end I ate it all.

Seeing that the cafe was beginning to fill up with customers, I thought it was time for me to get out of her way.

"What do I owe you?" I asked.

"Oh, nothing, Hayden, I mean you can't take money from a man who's serving his king and country, can you?"

"No, really, Mrs Collins, I do want to pay."

"I won't hear of it, and that's final."

"Thank you very much, Mrs Collins. I'll come and see you again when I'm next in Westcliff."

"I'd like that, Hayden, now mind how you go, and look after yourself."

I crossed the road and went and sat on the beach. By now the sea had almost reached the edge of the sand. It was getting deep enough to float the boats that lay on their sides. I liked to watch the sea gradually put them upright. I stayed looking at the boats and at the sea until sunset, then left the beach and made my way along the sea front as far as the pier. I didn't take the little tram to the other end, but walked. As it was by now dark, all the lights, suspended between the white posts on the iron railings, were switched on. Their bright glow reflected in the sea below like strung pearls.

The pier's end was very wide and had three levels. The bottom floor was only covered by the sea at high tide, and was used by the big paddle steamers to take on or disembark passengers that came up from London for a day's outing. On the top level was an enclosed area with a bandstand. This was surrounded by deck chairs. Mostly the old people came here to listen or sleep while the military bands, rigged out in their colourful uniforms, played familiar tunes. Behind the stand was a large restaurant, serving fresh fish and chips and pots of tea, and sticky buns or cakes for the kids.

On the top level was a small version of Mme Tussaud's waxworks, and an amusement arcade. For a penny, by winding a handle, you could see flickering pictures: 'What the Butler saw', when he looks through the keyhole of a lady's boudoir. Or you could gamble another penny on a machine with a clock-face operated by pressing a lever, which whizzed around the big hand. You hoped it would stop at twelve o'clock, because if it did, you would be twelve pennies richer, but mostly it would come to a halt on the minutes between the hours and would pay out nothing.

Late into the evening, two large paddle steamers arrived to take the day trippers back home. As most of them came from the poverty-stricken East End of London, this day's outing with their families was most likely the only holiday they could afford all year. With sleeping kids in their arms and silly paper hats on their heads, with 'Kiss me Quick' or 'Come up and see me sometime' printed on them, they got on board. The men had bottles of beer stuffed in their jacket pockets, and tucked under their arms, big sticks of Southend Rock. With all the hundred or so passengers on board, packed like sardines, the paddle steamers pulled away and moved off down the Thames, bound for Tower Bridge. With hundreds of voices singing the old Cockney favourites like 'Knees-up Mother Brown' or Gracie Fields' popular song 'Sally', you could still hear them when the boat was out of sight.

The time had come for me to get off the pier before it closed. Looking at the twinkling lights of Southend in the distance, I knew that I had to say goodbye to this town of my childhood. Now that Miss Minter and my wonderful Peter had gone, there was nothing for me to return to.

I left the pier, and went back along the sea front to Westcliff. Opposite Mrs Collins' cafe was a jetty, it was from here at high tide, that Peter and I ran along and took huge leaps into the water. I went down to the beach beside the jetty, and as it was a warm night, I lay down on the sand, and looked up at the stars. Gradually my eyes closed and didn't open again until morning.

When I woke up, I dusted the sand off my uniform, set off for the railway station and caught the train back to London.

By nine o'clock I was ringing Uncle's doorbell.

"Hayden, my boy, how nice to see you."

I told him that Miss Minter had died and about the unhappy day I'd spent there, and what I'd had to do with Peter, and asked him if I could spend the rest of my leave with him.

"Of course you can, dear boy, I'm so sorry to hear about your dog. I know how much you loved her. I don't suppose you've had any breakfast yet, have you?"

"No, I came straight here."

"Well, then I suggest you go and have a bath, then put on your own clothes which I know Mrs Blaber has washed and ironed, and while you do that, I'll ask her to make us breakfast."

I filled the bath up to the brim, got in and wallowed in the sheer luxury of it all, and thought how wonderful it was, that I didn't have to go back to the barracks for three whole days. And how nice it was to be with someone that you cared for and who cared about you.

For the next three days, I hardly left Uncle's side - wherever he went, I went. Each day we lunched at the RAC. I really enjoyed going there. To sit in its peaceful and spacious restaurant, served by waiters who knew everyone by name, was somehow very comforting. The club for me, and I think for Uncle, was a little oasis of sanity protecting you from the hurly-burly of the real world outside. It had a large swimming pool, made almost entirely of marble. I swam in it every day. Mostly I was the only one in the pool. While I was swimming, Uncle would be in the long bar upstairs having his second whisky and soda of the day. After lunch, we went into the lounge and sat, or rather sank, into the huge leather armchairs. Here club members quietly chatted to one another or read *The Times* or *Telegraph*. I don't remember ever seeing anyone with the *Daily Express* or *The Mail*. I think you would have been banned from entering the club, if you had a copy of the Daily Mirror tucked under your arm.

Looking back I think these three days were the last time that I felt entirely comfortable in a totally conservative atmosphere.

For the three evening meals, Uncle took me one night to Frascati's in Tottenham Court Road, the next to Oddenino's in Shaftesbury Avenue, and on the last evening to my favourite, the Strand Palace. Here I had green pea soup with croutons, followed by fillets of Dover sole and chips. The sole was dusted in fine breadcrumbs and then lightly deep fried. For a sweet I had the thing I loved most of all - trifle covered with whipped cream. When I thought of what I'd be eating the next day back in the barracks, a cold shiver went down my spine.

When I got back into my uniform I hoped the Duty Corporal in the Guardroom wouldn't examine me too closely: after a week without any spit and polish, I looked anything but smart. I thanked Uncle for all his kindness and he gave me ten shillings to tide me over until the next pay-day. It was typical of him to realise that I must by now be penniless.

I arrived at the barracks a couple of minutes before lights out. Luckily, the Duty Corporal didn't even notice the untidy soldier standing in front of him. I undressed and got into bed just as the last post sounded. In the morning, my few days of luxurious living were over and I was now back in the real world, heralded by the blowing of a trumpet.

CHAPTER THIRTEEN

By mid-August it was becoming more and more apparent, even to Neville Chamberlain, that his policy of placating Hitler was doomed to failure. It became a top priority to prepare for a war with Germany that could break out at any moment.

To this end, workmen building the huts to accommodate the ever-increasing flood of young conscripts worked round the clock including weekends. Our regiment suspended all leave until further notice, even at weekends. We were confined to barracks except for Saturday evenings.

On my first day back from leave, my squad was detailed to report to the munitions dump. The dump was a maze of long tunnels, dug deep into the hillside under the barracks. In shifts, day and night, we loaded into a never-ending queue of Army trucks, hundreds upon hundreds of anti-aircraft shells, urgently needed by the ack-ack sites being hurriedly set up in and around London. We were handed two shells at a time. These were placed one on each shoulder, and as they weighed over fifty pounds each, and often had to be carried the length of the tunnels to the waiting trucks, it was exhausting work. By the end of the eight-hour shift, I hadn't enough strength left to pick up a box of matches. It took the whole week before the arsenal was cleared. By then, I ached in every part of my body.

On my first day off, I went to the new buildings to find Vic. I hadn't seen him for nearly two weeks. He now had his meals in the new dining hall, and that's where I found him.

"Hallo, Hayden, where have you been all this time?"

I told him about working all week at the munitions dump.

"Not sorry I missed that little party." He told me his company had been on manoeuvres on Salisbury Plain for five days.

"It was a total botch-up, old boy, I must say I never really managed to work out who was friend or foe. Being confined to barracks is a bit of a bore, isn't it?"

"It is, but frankly, I'm so wiped out after all the lifting and humping that I don't think I could muster up the energy to go out anyway."

"Apropos of nothing, do you still want to change your name?"

"I do, I'm really pissed off with being called 'Aden'."

"How about Derrick? Even cockneys can pronounce that."

I just couldn't understand the connection between me lifting shells and the name he had chosen.

"A derrick is a small crane used mostly on boats for hoisting small but heavy weights, do you get it?"

"OK, Vic, from now on, Derrick it is."

As most in my squad had either called me 'Posh Boy' or, when they were in a friendly mood, 'Mate', I didn't bother to let them know I'd changed my name.

98

By the time I'd been in the army for five months, I'd not only got a new name but also the status that raw recruits gave to what they called the Regulars. As Vic had finished his basic training, he was also someone the Rookies looked up to. So, conscious of our new elevated position, we worked out a plan that would make us a few pounds over and above our measly army pay of ten shillings a week. We would run a raffle. It would be easy to relieve these innocent draftees of at least one sixpence. There was one problem, however: neither of us had enough money to buy the prizes. We decided the first prize would be a bottle of whisky, the second of sherry, and the third a hundred cigarettes.

"How the fuck are we going to be able to buy them?" asked Vic.

"We don't have to buy them - well, not at least until we've collected enough money selling tickets."

"Nobody will buy a ticket unless we can show them the prizes. They are not that gullible!" he said.

"What I'll do, is: on Saturday night I'll go and see my Uncle. He uses everything we need for the prizes. I'll get an empty whisky and sherry bottle, and ask him to lend me a box of a hundred cigarettes. We'll fill up the empties with water and then buy the real thing when the money comes rolling in. How's that?"

"Very good, Derrick, my boy, very good indeed!"

So at six o'clock the next day, I arrived just at Uncle's and explained to him why I had come.

"Oh dear," he said, "I don't keep empty bottles. Mrs Blaber just throws them out."

My brain went into top gear.

"If you wouldn't mind, Uncle, I'll empty the contents of the bottles you're currently using into clean milk bottles."

"Well, I suppose it would be all right. After all, the drinks will still taste the same, won't they? I'm afraid I have to leave you to it, otherwise I'll be late. I'm meeting Eric for dinner at the Club. Come again soon, Hayden, won't you?"

"I will, and thanks a lot, Uncle."

I got back to the barracks and showed Vic the empty bottles.

"Well done, Derrick. Tomorrow we're in business."

As the next day was a Saturday, the afternoon was free, but as only evening passes were possible, all our likely punters were trapped in the barracks until six p.m.

Our method for selling the raffle tickets was simple but dishonest. We told those who bought one that the raffle was exclusive to whatever company they were in.

By six o'clock the next day, we'd sold about three hundred tickets which, at sixpence each, added up to seven pounds and ten shillings. We told everyone that the draw would be held in the NAAFI the following Saturday at seven p.m. We also went to where the workmen were building the huts and sold them a fistful of worthless tickets. This worried me a little, and I mentioned it to Vic. It didn't seem to bother him.

Eventually we replaced our dummy prizes with real ones. By mid-week, almost everybody we had approached had bought a ticket. At the end of the week Vic calculated that we had made a profit of eight pounds each. "Sixteen weeks' Army pay!"

In the midst of all this self-congratulation, a nasty thought came into my head.

"Vic, what will we do if all the companies and some of those beefy building workers turn up at the NAAFI to witness the draw tomorrow night? They'll know immediately that the raffle was a huge swindle - they'll have our guts for garters, won't they?"

"Don't worry, dear boy. Why do you think I said the draw will be at seven o'clock Saturday night? It's because on Saturday the fucking NAAFI closes at four o'clock. There is nothing to worry about."

"That's a load off my mind. So where shall we have the draw?"

"Well, we don't have to have one really."

"Oh no, Vic, three of the participants have to get a prize, we've taken them for enough of a ride as it is. It would be going too far to keep the prizes as well."

"All right, we'll put into my tin hat only the tickets we sold to our Company. The first three numbers we take out will be the winners."

And that way my conscience was satisfied.

By the end of the month, soldiers in the Reserve were being told to report to their regiments within eight hours. They piled into the barracks at an alarming rate while the normal intake of conscripted men continued to arrive.

The result was utter chaos. If there was a space of 6 ft x 3 ft anywhere, somebody slept there. The floors of the gym, the Assembly Hall, and at night even the NAAFI, were covered with palliasses. Some slept squeezed between beds in the barrack rooms. Somebody, somewhere, should have cried 'Halt', but nobody did.

However, one good thing did come out all this turmoil. Spit and polish was put on hold for the foreseeable future. Some of the reservists really did look a sorry sight for any Commanding Officer's eyes. A lot of them, particularly the men over thirty, had put on quite a bit of weight. They experienced considerable difficulty squeezing their newly acquired paunches into their old uniforms and had to walk about in unbuttoned tunics with a string around their trousers to hold them up. Due to the lack of washbasins, within a few days most had a stubble and ended up looking more like Mexican bandits than soldiers serving in the British Army.

Any semblance of normal catering completely collapsed. To get a meal, you had to join a long queue, and when you eventually arrived at the cookhouse, you were confronted by a long line of shiny new dustbins full of steaming spuds. The only way to get them was to dip your arm and pull out as many as you could cram into your billycan. Each man was given one thick slice of bully beef. With no cutlery around, eating was a hand-to-mouth affair.

This menu was not varied for over a week. For the next three days, my squad was put on cookhouse fatigue, and all we did all day long was peel potatoes. We sat on benches out in the open, basking in the late summer sunshine, endlessly hacking away at ton after ton of them.

"I didn't join the army to do this fucking old women's work," said one of them, "I enlisted to be a soldier."

"Don't worry," I replied, "it looks like within a day or two, you'll be able to soldier away to your heart's content."

On the morning of 2 September, the CO gave the order that guards should be placed every few yards around the perimeter of the barracks. Perhaps he thought that German saboteurs were hiding in the long grass that grew in the fields surrounding us, waiting for a coded message from Berlin that war had been declared, and that they should move forward and take the barracks. My squad was taken off the boring potato-peeling chore and put on guard duty. We were given eight rounds of live ammunition and had to stand on guard with tin helmets on our head, and gas masks slung round our necks. The duty was four hours on, four off, all day and throughout the night. This, of course, meant that you never got more than three and a half hours of uninterrupted sleep at any one time.

Sgt Bulldock placed me in position and told me that if I saw anyone approaching from the fields beyond, I was to challenge them with the words 'Halt, who goes there?'. If there was no answer, I was to repeat it, and if there was still no response - ;Shoot to kill, boy' he said with some glee.

'Who goes there?' must have been the way sentries called out before the battle of Agincourt.

I had decided to modernise it with 'Stop, put up your hands, or you're dead.' Better still would have been to shout out: 'Halt, Kraut, or you're kaputt'.

The next day I was standing at ease and well into the third hour of my morning guard duty when Sgt Bulldock came running up the hill towards me.

"It's war, it's war, Chamberlain has just announced it over the radio," he shouted excitedly.

Then, putting his heavy hand on the top of my tin helmet, he looked me straight in the eye.

"Now Cartlidge, I expect you to be extra vigilant, and if you see so much as a blade of grass move, aim your rifle onto it and get ready to fire it."

The sergeant reached into a bag and pulled out a huge wooden rattle, and from his tunic pocket a piece of paper. He handed me the rattle and pushed the paper onto the sharp end of my bayonet.

"This is litmus paper. You keep an eye on it, and if it changes colour you'll know that a gas bomb has exploded. Don't panic, just hold your breath and put on your mask, and with the other hand rattle like fuck. Do you understand all that, boy?"

Then he ran off in the direction of the next sentry.

I had to make a quick decision: should I keep a sharp eye on the fields in front or gaze down at the litmus paper? It was certainly not possible to look at both at one and the same time. I opted for the latter, for it seemed to me that there was more likelihood of a gas attack, than any of the enemy popping their heads up out of the long grass.

A few minutes passed, and the first air-raid warning of the war made its fearful wailing sound. My stomach twisted itself into a tight knot, and my imagination ran wild. I thought I knew what to expect. After all, I'd seen in newsreels horrific pictures of the carnage and devastation when German bombers dropped their load onto defenceless Spanish towns. Any moment now I imagined the sky would be almost blacked out by waves of enemy aircraft, carrying loads of gas and explosives to drop on London.

As I stood there on top of the hill, all by myself, I began to feel as if I was the only person left in the world. Everything went silent. There was no sound of the big city that sprawled out in a panoramic view in front of me, no sound at all from the barracks: as the whole regiment had been sent at the double into the safety of the now empty underground tunnels of the munitions dump. The only sign of human life was another sentry some distance away, doing the same as I was, standing on guard.

I began to wonder how long this war would last, and if I would survive it. One thing I knew for sure was that I would rather die in it than come out maimed, the way some of the poor men did in World War I. I had seen these helpless men begging on the kerbsides minus one or both legs, or blinded by mustard gas. I had been dwelling on these morbid thoughts for some time, when suddenly I heard the long note of the 'All Clear'. You could almost see the sound waves looping their way up and down the rooftops and church spires in the motionless town. Then, imperceptibly at first, the hum that is the heartbeat of a big city returned. For me at that moment, there was no sweeter sound.

My sombre mood changed dramatically. I made up my mind that never again in this war would I allow myself to get into such a state of fright, and that from now on I would live for the day and to hell with the uncertain future.

A half-hour later my relief arrived. It was Alf, the man I hated most in my squad.

"Thought you might like to change your pants, pretty boy!" he said with a smirk on his face.

"You'll shit yourself long before I do!" I replied from a safe distance.

I walked down the hill to the cookhouse. Vic was sitting outside on the ground, mixing corned beef into the boiled potatoes with his bare hands.

"Jesus, Vic, doing that with your filthy hands!"

"If I'm expected to behave in a civilised fashion, I should be given a fucking fork. It tastes so much better when it's made into a hash, old boy."

Then, to change the subject, he said:

"What do you think of that little drama this morning, eh? I mean to make us run like frightened rabbits into an underground shelter. If the officers giving out orders are going to panic every time things look a bit dangerous, we might as well throw in the sponge. In any case, the whole thing was a false alarm - I heard it on the radio. It seems that some idiot on the coast mistook a small private plane for a German bomber, when all it was doing was flying back from France to England so as to be on our side of the channel before war broke out. This sort of hysteria (which incidentally managed to paralyse the whole of London for nearly half an hour) had better stop pronto, wouldn't you say so, Derrick?"

"Yes, I would say so, Vic."

I left him eating his hash and went to the barrack room to have a little nap before my next guard duty. This four on four off was starting to wear me out. The devil could have had my soul in return for eight hours' uninterrupted sleep. I had by now been doing this ridiculous sentry duty for five days and nights, and was starting to fall asleep standing up even when on guard duty, despite Sgt Bulldock's threat, that I could be shot if I did.

Four days into the war, the CO hadn't been seen. He had been conspicuous by his absence ever since the reservists had arrived. But now he came out like a raging bull and started to give a whole range of commands, so quickly that it was difficult to keep up with them.

No more were men going to be allowed to walk around unshaven. If they did, they'd be put on a charge. Also, if the quartermaster didn't get off his arse and have those old uniforms replaced within forty-eight hours, he too would be for the high jump. No more were men to eat out of dustbins. They were to be given proper army fare in the dining halls.

This was to be achieved by having several sittings. It resulted in some of us having dinner as early as eleven a.m. and others as late as three p.m. As far as men sleeping on the floor were concerned, this was solved by those with beds having to give them up every other night and take their turn on the floor. Top priority was given to get the reservists to look and behave like an efficient fighting force. To achieve this, they were sent out onto the barrack square and drilled every day for hours on end.

This was of great benefit to me, as Sgt Bulldock was given the job of drilling them. Our squad was broken up into little groups. I decided to take full advantage of the general muddle by not bothering to report to anywhere I'd been assigned to.

Now to skive off was one thing, but to do it successfully was quite another. It was essential to look and behave as though you were engaged on matters of some importance. That meant that whenever I ventured out of the barrack room, I always walked briskly with a folder tucked under my arm. I never went about in denims, only in uniform. My tunic buttons gleamed, my boots shone and my blancoed belt was whiter than white. Any officer I passed was given an exaggerated salute. The only journeys I made were to the dining hall or the NAAFI, and in the afternoons I'd go and have a nap in the long grass above the arsenal. I knew this lark would be short-lived, but while it lasted, I enjoyed it thoroughly. For once the Army was paying me ten shillings a week for doing absolutely nothing.

In my second week of dodging the column, one morning after breakfast, a hell of a hubbub started up. The older regulars and the reservists were all running about with packed kitbags on their shoulders. They appeared to be making for the parade ground.

"What's all this frantic activity about?" I asked one of them as he struggled to put on his equipment.

"We're moving out, to join the froggies, mate."

He could see I didn't understand what he said.

"France, mate."

He put his kitbag on his shoulder and hurried off. I followed him to see what was going on. There, lined up in one neat row after another, were over a hundred of our trucks, with their crews of three or more drivers and machine guns mounted on their tripods. An officer with his driver in a scout car went up and down the lines, making sure that each vehicle was complete with men and equipment. When he was satisfied that everything was in order, he moved to the front of the lines and stopped. Then, standing up in his open car, he faced the impressive formation of trucks, with a wave of his arm he shouted:

"Forward!"

One hundred engines started up and moved in single file through the barrack gates onto the main road to Dover. From there a ferry would take them across the Channel to Calais and thence to a destination unknown, which was always known throughout the war as 'somewhere in France'.

The effect on the barracks when some four hundred men had suddenly left was dramatic. Very quickly things returned to something like normal. It became apparent that my little game wouldn't last much longer. Still, I made my mind up to carry on with it until fate decided otherwise, which, as it happens, was the very next day.

I was making my mid-morning way over to the NAAFI when from some distance away Sgt Bulldock spotted me.

"Cartlidge," he bawled, "come over 'ere, at the double, boy."

I ran over to him.

"You called, Sergeant?"

Not that there could be any doubt that he had. When he shouted, the whole barracks could hear it.

"What are you on, eh boy?"

"I'm er, I'm er..." Then, with a flash of sheer brilliance, I said: "I'm waiting to be posted, sergeant."

"POSTED, P O S T E D, what do you think you are, a fucking letter? I can tell you where you're posted right now. You will report on the parade ground tomorrow morning sharp at o-seven-thirty hours."

The Sergeant's newly-formed squad had, as far as I was concerned, one good thing going for it - my friend Vic was in it. This made the endless days of square bashing a lot less boring.

We couldn't do any training with machine guns and trucks as they had all been taken by the lot that went to France. However, this was no obstacle to Sgt Bulldock. He marked out the approximate dimensions of a truck on the gravel.

"Right, men," he said, "this is the truck, now four of you get in."

Vic and I went forward and stood within his lines. Vic was No. 1, and I was, as usual, No. 3. Another two men joined us to make up the four.

The sergeant ordered us to sit on our seats and we all bent our knees, folded our arms and sat on the imaginary benches. The soldier acting the part of the driver bent his legs, and with his arse sticking out, put his hands on the make-believe steering wheel. Anybody passing at that moment might have thought we all had taken leave of our senses.

The sergeant must have thought differently, because he said:

"Fine, lads, you're doing fine. In a moment, I'm going to give the order 'Truck Halt', so you, driver, slam on your brakes while Nos. 1-2-3 go through the normal drill for setting up the gun."

"Yes, Sarge," we shouted in unison.

"Right then, 'Truck Halt'."

We all stood up and casually walked out of the scratched out area.

"No, fucking NO," yelled the Sergeant. "Get back into the truck and remember to step into it."

We resumed our lunatic positions.

"Now, lads, when I give the order 'Halt', you don't just stand up and walk off. What 'appens when a truck suddenly slams on the brakes? You're jerked towards the front of it. Then, you, No. 1, pick up the barrel and make it look like it's 'eavy, and you, No. 2, do what you fucking well always do, put the tripod on your shoulder. You, Cartlidge, grab the ammo boxes. Then don't just walk off the truck, jump off it. Finally put the bloody gun into its firing position, just as you would if it was a real one. Right, now let's do it all again, and only this time use your imagination."

Vic and I overacted like mad, and found it hard to suppress the urge to burst out laughing. Because the other two didn't see the funny side of this charade, it increased our desire to laugh all the more.

Five times that afternoon, we went through this crazy routine, until in the end we were all so good at mime that Marcel Marceau would have been proud of us. Who knows - perhaps if Sgt Bulldock hadn't made the army his career, he might have ended up as a choreographer - but that taxed the imagination too far.

The next few weeks were just devoted to square bashing, or long route marches. The kit and barrack room inspections came back with a vengeance. A barrack room inspection was an awful chore, because it entailed 'bumpering' the floor. A 'bumper' was a long stick with a square brush attached to the handle by a swivel. To start polishing you had to move all the beds from one side of the room to the other. Then, with a huge tin of yellow polish in one hand and a small stick in the other, you had to drop big dollops of the frightful smelling stuff onto the floor. A full swipe on the bumper covered about twelve feet of floor space. It had to be swung with an outstretched arm as far as you could to the right, and then to the left. This was kept up until all the polish disappeared into the wood. It wasn't considered to be done until the floor had a skin on it hard enough to withstand the blades of an ice-skater's boots, without leaving a trace.

The ancient black coal bin was polished until it looked like new. Trestle tables and benches were scrubbed until they were almost white, and of course, not a speck of dust must be seen anywhere.

On one such inspection, when the CO came in, the RSM ordered us to stand to attention by our beds. The CO didn't look at the room at all. He just stood by the doorway and turned his back on all the hard grind we'd done, then he ran his fingers along the lintel above the door. It was the one place we'd not thought to clean.

"Disgusting, absolutely disgusting!" he said. He clapped his hands together, making a small cloud of dust. "Sergeant Major, I shall inspect this room again in four days' time!"

When he and the RSM were well out of earshot, one of the men shouted after them: "You fucking shits, you fucking smart-arsed bastards!"

It was the opinion of us all.

By early November, the war had been going on for two months. The Germans were busy digesting the slice of Poland they had grabbed, and also letting the inhabitants of Czechoslovakia know, what sort of people they had more or less invited into their country. Apart from the blackout at night, you could have been forgiven if you forgot that we were at war.

There was no sign in Europe of any movement by the opposing armies facing each other across the Franco-German borders. Jerry manned his Siegfried Line of fortifications while the French in their Maginot Line stayed buried in the labyrinth of underground tunnels, that linked one big gun emplacement to the other. Both were confident that their line was impregnable. One had to presume that the British Army was stationed exposed out in the open in the countryside behind the well-protected French.

At a cinema I saw a newsreel interview with Lord Gort, the Commander-in-Chief of the BEF (British Expeditionary Force), in which he said confidently:

"We are ready to engage the enemy - so let them come!"

Very comforting words. I'm sure Lord Gort would never have thrown down the gauntlet, if he had known that the French military planners hadn't extended the Maginot Line beyond their frontier with Germany. Any foreign power, attempting to invade, would, of course, attack from the border with Belgium, in the same way as they did in World War I. It was like over-protecting the front of your home against burglars while leaving the side door wide open.

Meanwhile, back in the barracks, life went on in its monotonous way. There was, however, one little break in the daily routine. Our company was detailed to go thirty-five miles out of London to the Rifle Range at Bisley for small arms training. Coaches were hired to take us. We were to stay there for one night, sleeping under canvas, and on the next day bang away on the range for as long as daylight lasted.

The journey down was pretty awful, for it seems that when a pack of men get together in a coach, an urge comes over them to start singing. At least five times Vic and I were treated to the current popular songs like 'Roll Out the Barrel' or 'We'll be Hanging our Washing on the Siegfried Line'. The only break in the sing-song was whenever we passed a policeman on point duty. He got the full blast of thirty-six men shouting through the open windows:

"All coppers are cunts...", then, when the poor man time looked angrily round, the word "...tables" was added.

This was quite amusing done once or even twice, but ten times it wasn't.

It was typical mid-November weather, when we arrived at Bisley, cold, damp, and overcast, with, to add to the gloom, a biting wind.

"Grim, isn't it, Vic?" I moaned.

"Yes," he agreed, then added "I think I'll strike this dump off my list of places to return to."

Good old Vic, he always found a way to make me smile when I felt a bit low.

In the evening, as we sat on the grass in the draughty bell tent under the dim light of a tilley lamp, to pass the time away we played pontoon, using a blanket as a cardtable. When I'd won a few shillings, it became my turn to be the banker. Very rapidly I started to lose not only what I had won, but also the sum I had started with. Suddenly the blanket was pulled up from the ground, making all the cards and the stake money tumble into the grass. In the next second, Vic had a man flat on his back and started to give him a terrible thumping. The rest of the card-players disappeared through the tent flap at speed. Vic picked up the man who had been at the wrong end of his fists, and bundled him out of the tent.

"What was that all about?" I asked.

"The scoundrels were swapping their cards, that's why you were losing. Pick up the money and keep it. It's rightfully yours."

Vic must have really frightened the card-sharpers, because they didn't creep back into the tent until lights out.

I woke up the next morning to the sound of heavy rain hitting the canvas.

"Oh shit," said Vic, when he heard the downpour.

"Maybe they'll call it off. It'll be nigh impossible to see the bloody target, let alone hit it."

"That would be the sensible thing to do, but on the other hand, the Army's reasoning could be that in the heat of battle, you can't really shout at Fritz across no-man's-land 'sorry chaps, there will be no fighting today because it's raining cats and dogs.'"

After breakfast, the whole company was lined up in three columns and marched off to the rifle range. Waiting for your turn to shoot was very unpleasant. The pouring rain bounced off your tin helmet and cascaded down in such torrents, that it was almost impossible to see anything at all. In minutes, my trousers were soaked through. Eventually I was called up onto the firing platform with eight others. The first practice was to learn how to load and fire a Colt pistol. I was surprised how weighty it was and what a kickback it gave when it fired. In the end, because of the terrible conditions, it was completely useless to show me anything, as all I did was raise my arm and without even trying to aim, emptied the barrel, God only knows where they ended up. Lying on the rain-sodden ground, squaring up to the rifle and then attempting to look down its sights, was almost impossible. So once again, I didn't even try. Vic, who was a much better marksman than I, did no better.

When our turn had finished, we were told to go back to the end of the line and wait there until we were called. It wasn't hard to work out that we would be standing around in the wind-driven rain for at least half an hour before it was our turn again. We realised nobody would notice if we absented ourselves altogether. On our journey down, I had seen in a country lane an old Tudor cottage, with a sign saying it was open for lunch and tea. I reckoned it to be about a mile away.

"Wonderful, Derrick, fuck hanging around here getting soaked."

Making sure we were not seen, we broke ranks and made off down the road in the direction of the café. The moment we stepped through we went from hell into heaven. A big log fire burned brightly in a large open grate, making the room warm and cosy. A few small round oak tables were neatly spaced on the highly polished floor, each with four sturdy old captain's chairs. The walls were lined with panels of dark wood, and the low white ceiling had oak beams.

We hadn't been in the room very long when a woman of about fifty came in. She had straight grey hair, which was pulled back into a bun behind her round, rosy-cheeked face. Over her long black dress, she wore a flower-patterned apron which was tied around her ample waist. When she saw us standing there in our muddy boots and with water dripping from our capes and clothes onto her polished floor, she threw her arms up into the air and said: "Oh you poor, poor boys, get those wet things off and dry yourself by the fire, while I go and make you a big pot of tea."

"Looks like we've landed on soft ground, eh Vic?" I said as we peeled off as much of our soaking-wet clothes as was decently possible. She came back with a big pot of tea on a tray and put it down on the table nearest to the fire.

"Are you boys up at Bisley?" she asked.

"Yes," I replied, then thinking up a good excuse as to why we were in her café, "the practice was cancelled because of the rain."

"Oh, of course, you wouldn't be able to see the target in this downpour, would you?"

"She's got more sense than the idiots running the show!" Vic whispered.

"Now you make yourselves at home and let me know when you would like lunch."

That angel of a woman let us stay in her place until she closed at four-thirty. Apart from umpteen pots of tea there was a lunch of sausages, eggs and chips for Vic and Welsh rarebit with poached eggs for me, followed at teatime by sandwiches and home-made cakes. The bill she gave us on leaving was, I'm sure, nowhere near what it should have been.

When we left the café, the rain had stopped and we arrived back at the camp all glowing and dry. The poor sods who had been out in it all day were in the big tent standing around paraffin stoves, trying to dry themselves out.

The next morning the coaches came to take us back. Thankfully this time (perhaps because their spirits were low and their clothes still damp), there was no singing or policeman-baiting.

CHAPTER FOURTEEN

By the end of November, the number one priority was to get the factories on a war footing. This meant that they should work flat out, producing fighter planes and bombers for the RAF and guns, tanks and trucks for the Army. The factories were expected to keep going day and night, seven days a week. They therefore needed all the skilled or semi-skilled men they could lay their hands on, and because of this the number of men being conscripted began to slow down considerably. There was no point at all in increasing the size of the armed forces if, when the recruits had finished their training, there was no equipment to give them. Not only did they stop drafting in men with any skills, but some were sent back into civilian life, if it was thought they would be more useful on the production line.

Vic was one of those. Before being called up, he was a very skilled spot-welder. When he told me he was to be released, I was stunned. To stay on in the Army without my friend and protector was very depressing. He could see that I was upset.

"Don't worry, Derrick, we'll see each other all the time, there'll be the evening, and Sundays."

He obviously didn't know, as I did, that he'd be working round the clock including Sundays. The chances of seeing much of each other were pretty remote. Still, to make it easier on him, I said:

"Yes, of course we'll meet up. I'll give you my uncle's number. Let him know how I can get in touch with you. You certainly know where the fuck I am, don't you?"

I went over with him to his hut and stayed with him while he changed into his civvies. He looked very different in his grey flannel trousers with neatly pressed turn-ups. He put on a clean white shirt, and his prize possession, an Old Boy's tie from Winchester. God knows where he got it; he certainly wasn't entitled to wear it. I helped him carry his equipment to the Quartermaster's stores, where he handed everything in, including his uniform.

The corporal behind the counter checked all the items off.

"Where is your billycan, private?"

"Not private, old boy, Mr Blake to you. I've mislaid it, I'm afraid, corp."

"Well, Mr Blake, you're going to have to pay for it."

"Not possible, old chap, bit short of the ready at the moment, so you'll just have to bill me, won't you?"

"All right, you toffee-nosed git, fuck off."

"Bad-mannered lout," mumbled Vic as we left.

I walked with him to the barrack gates and waited until his bus arrived. When his bus pulled up, he stood on the platform and waved as it went down the hill towards London.

With the phony war continuing through December, nothing happened to relieve the boredom of my daily life. As by now I had been in the Army nearly nine months, there was no point in me doing any more square bashing. I knew all the drill backwards and could have done it with my eyes closed. Like others with a similar degree of overtraining, I was put in a squad that did fatigues around the barracks. This work was unbelievably tedious. It varied from latrine and washhouse cleaning to sweeping paths, peeling potatoes and washing up greasy pots and pans in the cookhouse. Some days we polished the huge floors in the gym and the assembly hall, or whitewashed dozens of little posts placed short distances apart along the edges of the paths. The chains that linked them had to be painted black. What all this had to do with the war effort, only our Commanding Officer knew. Our working party was nicknamed the 'Shit Shovellers' or the 'SS' for short.

We went on doing this chore right on up to Christmas, when we were given three days' leave. It was wonderful not to have for three whole days a mop, or a broom, or a filthy cloth, or a whitewash brush in your hand! Early on Christmas Eve morning, I turned up at Uncle's - he had not seen me for some weeks.

"I've been given Christmas leave and don't have to report back until ten o'clock in the evening on Boxing Day," I said with a smile.

He stroked his moustache with one finger, which is what he always did, when something worried him.

"Anything wrong?" I enquired.

"No, not exactly, Hayden, the problem is that I promised my sister I'd spend Christmas Day with her. I told you she's in that expensive home for well-off old ladies in the New Forest, and because she is such a cantankerous old thing nobody will sit at the table with her. She begged me to come so she'd have someone to pull the other end of her Christmas cracker. So I'm afraid I have to go, but you, of course, can stay here."

"Thank you, Uncle, I was hoping we'd have had Christmas dinner together."

"I would have much preferred that, my boy. But I just can't bring myself to let the poor old thing down."

Although disappointed, I told him I understood.

Oh shit, I thought, because that unsociable old woman needs someone to be at the other end of her fucking cracker, I'm going to be all on my own over Christmas.

At lunch I asked Uncle if he was going to stay at the Old Ladies' Home.

"Good God, no, I'm booked into a nearby hotel, I'll be there to-night and Christmas night and only join my sister for lunch on Christmas Day. I should be back home by mid-day on Boxing Day. Then, with a bit of luck, we can be together until you have to go back to your barracks."

While I was eating my sweet, which was, as usual, trifle with lashings of whipped cream piled high on top of it, Uncle gave me a brand-new five-pound note.

"This is a small Christmas present for you. A fiver should cover a few good meals and maybe a film or two."

"Thank you, Uncle, thanks a lot - it's the best Christmas present I've ever had."

I went with the old man to the station and stayed with him until his train pulled away. I left the station and walked briskly (so as to keep warm in the cold December air) over Waterloo Bridge. The Thames looked grey and uninviting, some of the moored cargo ships were unloading onto the jetties of the warehouses that lined the south bank of the river. The stevedores were working quite quickly, perhaps it was because they wanted to unload the boats before daylight ended and the black-out regulations came into force.

I crossed the bridge and entered the Strand, where I passed my favourite restaurant, The Strand Palace. I went up the Haymarket towards Piccadilly, and by the time I stood in front of Eros, daylight had almost faded. When I reached Leicester Square, night had fallen, and the square was in total darkness. I decided to go and see a film, but the only way to see what was showing was to go through the swing doors and into the lit-up foyer. In the end, I went to see Charlie Chaplin's *Great Dictator*. Chaplin played Hitler and Jack Oakey Mussolini. It was a very funny, and at the same time, serious film. It ended by Chaplin stepping out of character,and talking straight to camera. As far as I remember his speech ended:

"Don't be like sheep going to the slaughter, rise up and resist your Governments when they order you to go to war. They want you to fight to protect what they, and their bosses, the ruling class, have. There is no reason for you, the ordinary men and women, to obey them. You have nothing to gain but everything to lose."

With that, he stepped back into character and fell through the floor - then the film ended. I had never heard anything like that before. Up until then, my king, my country, and those in authority, were law to me. That they, or what they stood for, should be brought into question, was unthinkable. Chaplin's speech gave me something to think about.

I left the cinema and made for the Coventry Street Corner House. Just before I got to the restaurant, a voice called out from a doorway:

"Good evening, darling, want to have a good time?"

I stopped to look and see who had spoken, but in the dark, I could only make out the vague outline of a woman. She was about my height and slim. She had an accent that I'd never heard before. She stepped out from the doorway and took my hand.

"It'll cost you a pound. You've got a pound, haven't you, dear. Well then, we'll take a taxi to my place, it'll cost you two bob, including the tip?"

Before I had time to even think about her proposition, she hailed a passing cab and more or less bundled me into it. Just the thought that soon I'd be lying close to a naked woman got my heart beating faster. While the cab travelled through the back streets of Soho, she put her hand between my legs and gently rubbed up and down.

"My goodness," she said, "you're raring to go, aren't you, dear?"

Thankfully, the cab pulled up, for if it hadn't, it would have been all over for me before we'd even got going.

"Give the driver two shillings, dear, and follow me."

With me close behind her, we entered the hall and felt our way up two flights of narrow and unlit stairs. We went through a door and she turned on the light, a bare bulb hanging down from a low ceiling. When I saw her standing there under the bright light, my heart sank and so did my erection. She was as black as the ace of spades, but it wasn't the colour of her skin that bothered me. She looked old enough to be my mother, maybe even my grandmother. She, I think, was equally surprised at the young innocent she had picked up. Oh Christ, I thought, what on earth do I do now?

"Get undressed and sit on the bed while I go in the bathroom and have a wash-up," said the lady, pointing to a grubby old divan in the corner of the room.

As soon as she was out of the room, I made a dash for the door and ran down the two flights as fast as I could. Once out in the street, I didn't stop running for a long time.

Looking back on this little adventure, I'm sure that the good woman gave me the opportunity to bunk off. She probably laughed out loud when she saw the back of me, going hell-for-leather down her stairs. When I had got my breath back, I returned to the Coventry Street Lyons Corner House. It was surprisingly empty - I suppose most people were at home decorating their Christmas trees and wrapping up presents. As I was going to be left out of all the festivities, I consoled myself by eating a much bigger meal than I needed.

After I left the restaurant, I kept close to the kerb, well away from any lady in a doorway. Because it was Christmas Eve, the Underground had shut down earlier than usual and there were no taxis. There was nothing for it but to walk from Piccadilly to St John's Wood.

It was nearly midday before I woke up on Christmas morning, so I skipped breakfast and thought about where to go and have my Christmas dinner. I opted once more for one of the Corner Houses. I knew there would be no public transport, so I decided to pick the nearest, at Marble Arch.

When I stepped out into the cold crisp morning, the streets were bathed in winter sunshine - London can be beautiful sometimes, I thought, as I walked down Baker Street with all its shops closed, and not a soul in sight.

The Corner Houses were built at the beginning of the twentieth century for ordinary working- and lower middle-class people, who went there as a special treat. The ground floor was a huge shopping area. Displayed on big mahogany counters were packets of tea, coffee, cakes and confectionery. A curved marble staircase led up to the three restaurants on the floors above. On every landing were toilets of such ornate design that royalty would have felt at home in them.

Large, gleaming white hand basins were set into marble slabs, each with freshly laundered and ironed hand towels piled neatly by their sides. The floors were laid with beautifully patterned square tiles and the lavatories were so spacious and spotlessly clean that you were tempted to sit there longer than you needed. Ordinary people must have felt like lords and ladies, sitting in all that splendour, for most of them had their toilets outside in a little shed at the end of a narrow garden.

I went up to the dining hall on the first floor, and a frock-coated waiter came over to me.

"Just for one, sir?"

He must have said that to everyone, because almost all the tables were occupied by single customers, most of them were elderly women. It was a sad sight to see these lonely old people all on their own on Christmas Day.

I, too, felt a bit low all on my own. On previous Christmases with Miss Minter, Mary, Joan, Ian and Joyce, I had at least company. I would have been very happy if Vic could have been with me, but he hadn't let Uncle know his phone number or address. I presumed that if he had got time off over Christmas, he'd most likely spend it with the parents he never talked about.

Sitting all by myself at a table laid for four, for the first time in my life I became aware of what being an orphan really meant. While I was wallowing in all this self-pity, a pretty young waitress came over to my table.

"Do you want to have the set Christmas dinner, Sir?"

"Yes, please, but I don't eat meat so could you wangle me a little extra gravy instead of the turkey?"

"I'll do more than that, what about two fried eggs? How would that be?"

Her friendliness cheered me up and made the meal more enjoyable than it might have been otherwise.

What shall I do now, I thought, as I left. Across the road was a cinema called The Pavilion. A poster outside announced that today there would be only one performance, at three p.m. As I had three-quarters of an hour to kill, I went for a walk in Hyde Park. This, like Baker Street, was totally deserted, even the anti-aircraft batteries seemed to be unmanned. I knew, of course, they weren't, because I could hear the gunners in the Nissen huts enjoying themselves. A little bit of me would have liked to have been with them.

The film I saw was a Western, starring John Wayne. Unlike Chaplin's 'Great Dictator', I got no lasting message from this saga.

By the time I left the cinema, virtually everything had closed down, even the Corner House. There was nothing else to do but walk back to Adelaide Court. Looking back it's almost impossible to imagine leaving Oxford Street, walking down Baker Street, then crossing the usually busy Marylebone Road on into Park Road, and passing Lord's Cricket Ground to St John's Wood, without seeing a single person or car, or taxi. I knew why there were no cars: all privately owned vehicles had been taken off the road for the duration of the war. Only doctors and others on essential work were given a petrol ration, but walking through London without the hustle and bustle of everyday life was like being in a city that its citizens had deserted. The silence was uncanny.

I got back to the empty flat as darkness fell, but before switching on the lights, I remembered to pull all the curtains so that not a chink of light would show through into the street. I knew that if it did an air-raid warden would soon be banging on the door and accuse me of helping the enemy. Not that there seemed to be any signs of them about on this Christmas Night in 1939.

The next morning, about midday, Uncle returned. He made straight for the whisky and soda and poured himself double the usual amount. He drank it all down without stopping.

"Hayden, please remind me to never, but never spend Christmas with my sister again. She never stopped complaining the entire time I was with her, and to cap it all, she didn't even want to pull the damn cracker (which after all, was the sole purpose of my visit). She didn't want to, because she said, the bang frightened her. So I got hold of a waiter and jerked it apart with him. I then absolutely insisted that she put on the ridiculous paper hat that came tumbling out. She refused to, so I just bonked it on her head and made sure it stayed there for the rest of the meal."

He helped himself to another drink.

"Ah, now at last I'm beginning to feel normal. Well, enough of my woes - how did you pass the time, Hayden?"

I told him briefly how I had spent my Christmas, including the fiasco with the prostitute. This seemed to cheer him up because he laughed so much that his upper, ill-fitting false teeth dropped down to his lowers.

"Well, my boy, you certainly fared better than I did the one and only time I went with a prostitute. I was a couple of years older than you are now. Most of my friends had been with a woman and then boasted about it, so, not to look out of step, I went down to Half Moon Street and picked up a lady. She was not that much older than I was and I'm sure most of her clients thought she was highly desirable. But she wasn't to me, I'm afraid. When she had removed all her clothes and lay naked on the bed, I was completely repelled by the sight of her. Those bulbous protuberances sticking out from her chest made me quite nauseous, and all that hair covering her quim filled me with revulsion."

To hear a woman's body described in such a way shocked me to the core.

"So you see, Hayden, under the circumstances there was nothing I could do but to leave as quickly as possible. So I said to the young woman, I'm terribly sorry, but I'm afraid I've made an awful mistake so I hope you will pardon me if I take my leave. I must say, she looked pretty angry when I put my coat on and left, foolishly without paying her. As I went downstairs she hurled a torrent of abuse at me. Suddenly I felt something whizz past my right ear. It hit her front door and broke into small fragments. It was a huge china chamberpot, fortunately empty at the time. That was the first and only attempt I ever made to go with a woman. You, dear boy, got off quite lightly, compared to me."

The way Uncle related this incident made me understand for the first time what being a homosexual was all about. Up until then I had assumed that they went with their own sex because they didn't want all the responsibilities that came with being married.

The rest of the day passed as expected - lunch at the Club and dinner at the Trocadero. I got back to the barracks just in time for the ten o'clock deadline.

The next day I was back in 'SS'- squad.

CHAPTER FIFTEEN

At the end of January, I was still doing this soul-destroying job, most days in freezing weather. There was one small consolation. The loos didn't stink as much as they had before Christmas, because without heating, the over-powering smell that pervaded was almost neutralised by the near-freezing air. Oh God, I thought, when will I be relieved from this terrible work? It had been my daily occupation for nigh-on two months. There was nobody in the squad with whom I had the slightest rapport. The only conversation was one humourless and crude joke after another. They seemed to have a never-ending supply of them.

After breakfast one day, in the first week of February, our squad was lined up in the usual way, armed with brooms, mops, buckets and bumpers, when the corporal in charge of our work party, told us to stand easy.

"I've been ordered to find one man, who is intelligent and can speak the King's English, to go and work as a clerk in the Rationing and Billeting Office. Looking at you gormless lot, I'd say I've been given an impossible task. None of you qualify on both counts, but you, Cartlidge, do on one. I've 'eard the posh way you speak, and as far as intelligence goes, you'll just 'ave to try and look as if you 'ave it. So fall out and go and report to a Captain Kitchen in the Regimental Offices at ten a.m. The rest of the squad, Attention, right turn and quick march!"

Watching them fade into the distance, in the direction of the latrines, I just couldn't believe my luck. Two hours later, on my way over to the Captain's office, an awful feeling of doubt crept into my mind. What will happen, I thought, when he finds out that I don't even know the alphabet and can only spell the simplest of words? I was sure he would never take me on. I resigned myself to being back on the shit-shovelling job the next day.

When I got to the Captain's office, I knocked gently on his door.

"Come in, please!"

Please? that was a new one on me. Nobody from one stripe upwards had ever used the word before. I entered the room. The officer was sitting hatless behind a desk at the other side. I marched smartly over, stood to attention and saluted him.

"Private Cartlidge reporting on the instructions of Corporal Hawkins, sir!"

"At ease, private. Ah yes, I was told you were the most likely candidate. Now, before we go any further, do you happen to know the nursery rhyme 'Mary had a little lamb'?"

"Yes, I do, sir." I couldn't, for the life of me, think why he wanted to know.

"Good, very good, would you mind reciting it to me?"

I did.

"Excellent, what about Humpty Dumpty, do you know that one?"

"Yes, sir."

"Well, go ahead then."

By the end of that, I had used the letter H three times and was pretty sure that I had passed the test as far as the King's English was concerned. Had I not wanted the post, all I needed to do was say 'umpty just once, and I would have been out of his office within seconds.

"I'm well satisfied with you, private, the job is yours."

I had to restrain myself from jumping with joy. It was only when I relaxed a little that I was able to have a real look at my new boss. He was about five and a half feet in height, and in his early forties. I think he had allowed himself to become quite flabby in the twenty-odd years that must have passed since leaving Sandhurst. Probably being a naturally lazy man, I was pretty sure that he was very content with the cosy desk job that he now had. His face was chubby and had rosy cheeks and had a friendly look about it. His hair was beginning to recede. The captain looked up at me from behind his desk.

"I see your first name is Hayden, so that's what I will call you."

"Excuse me, sir, but I've changed it to Derrick."

"Oh, what a pity, it's a nice enough name. Why did you do that?"

"Well, sir, a lot of the people I mix with have a problem with their aitches."

"So Derrick it is then."

He outlined the duties I was to perform, most of which consisted of handing out railway passes and ration cards to men going on leave. Why anybody had to be particularly intelligent to do that, I never did find out. The captain told me to follow him into an adjoining room where there was a small desk.

"This is yours, Derrick, all the ration cards and railway warrants are in the drawer under the desk. Make sure you check their leave passes before handing anything out. We work from ten a.m. until three, with one hour off for lunch. So you see, it's not too hard, is it? You can have the rest of the day off and I'll see you tomorrow morning."

When I left his room, I just couldn't believe what had happened. No more out in the freezing cold doing a lousy job, but from now on inside, all snug and warm, and working the sort of hours that I imagined only the top people did. If I'd still believed in God, I would have got down on my knees and thanked him. For the next few days, I was like the Cheshire Cat, grinning right through the short working day.

Nobody came in, wanting anything. The only time I had to leave my desk, was to take the captain a mug of tea at eleven o'clock. Friday afternoons were a bit hectic, as all those with weekend leave needed attending to.

Sometimes I had to work until five o'clock, but as I'd done hardly anything all week, I really couldn't complain about that. The first Friday in my new position, as I hadn't seen Uncle since Christmas, I persuaded the captain to give me a weekend pass. After all, I thought, there should be some perks if you do such a responsible job.

Uncle was pleased when I told him about my new situation. He knew how miserable I'd been in the fatigue squad. He had a bit of a guilty conscience, having been instrumental in putting me into the Army in the first place. He told me, that if only the war hadn't started, he would've gladly paid the forty pounds it would have cost to buy me out.

The Monday morning, after my weekend leave, a heavy snowfall had covered the barracks during the night. I didn't care, as I knew I'd be dry and warm sitting at my desk all day. At ten, I trudged ankle-deep through the snow to my office. An hour later Captain Kitchen arrived.

"Good morning, Derrick, brew me up a mug of tea, lad," he said, stamping the snow off his boots.

When I took it in to him, he was standing in front of the coal fire, warming his bum.

"Thank you, put it down on my desk, please. Derrick, I've got a little job I would like you to do for me in a personal capacity. My poor wife is snowbound indoors. I only just managed to get our children to school. I thought it would be a good idea to drive you over to my house and get you to clear the snow from the driveway. You wouldn't object doing that little service for me, would you, Derrick?"

"No, sir."

Shit, I thought, today I was really looking forward to being nice and warm, sitting at my desk.

Captain Kitchen lived in a large three-storey house in a road leading off Mill Hill Broadway. He made no attempt to drive up the wide, long path to his front door.

"Wait here, please, while I go and find you a shovel."

He came back with the most enormous one I'd ever seen.

"What I would like you to do is make a pathway through the snow, about four feet wide from the gate here to the front door. Do you think you can manage to do that?"

"I'll try my best, sir," I said, wishing I had a couple of people to help me.

"Right then, I'll leave you to it, but just before I go, I'll have a word with my wife and arrange with her to give you lunch. She will call you when it is ready."

As I'd not brought my greatcoat with me, the only thing I could do to stop myself from freezing was to start shovelling away. Within minutes I was so hot that I had to take off my peaked cap and was almost tempted to remove my tunic. It took me nearly three hours to clear a pathway to the front door, and by then I was very hungry and dying for a big mug of tea. I stood by the door, trying to make up my mind whether to ring the bell or not, because the captain had said his wife would call me when lunch was ready. After a few minutes of hanging about, I began to feel cold, so I thought, to hell with this - I'm going to ring the fucking bell. Very promptly, Mrs Kitchen opened it. She was wearing an overcoat.

"Do please come in, I'm sorry, I'd quite forgotten you were working out there. Poor boy, you must be starving. Come through with me to the kitchen, and I'll see what I can rustle up."

Oh dear, I thought, that doesn't sound too promising. I had hoped I was going to get a good hot lunch.

The captain's wife was at least ten years younger than he. She was tall and thin. Her straight brown hair was cut in a bob, with a neat fringe. No make-up disguised her haggard looks and she spoke loudly as the upper class do when speaking to the lower orders. I followed her through to the kitchen where I could see thin layers of dust on every surface. It was obvious that she thought she was far too well-bred to do anything as menial as housework. The kitchen sink was piled high with dirty plates, cups, frying pans and saucepans. The long refectory table was littered with half-used pots of jam and marmalade. Where she told me to sit there was an open tin of sardines looking definitely off.

Trying to find a space to put a plate down was difficult. Her idea of rustling up something was two slices of bread and butter, accompanied by a chunk of hard cheddar cheese. Her lunch was a generous measure of gin and it, poured into an unwashed tumbler.

"I suppose you'd prefer tea to this?" she said, raising her glass.

Not trusting her to make it, I said:

"If you'll show me where it is, I'll make it myself, save you the bother."

"Splendid, you'll find it on the table somewhere, if you look hard enough. I'm sorry everything is in a bit of a shambles, but trying to manage on a captain's pay precludes being able to afford servants. If only you knew how difficult it is to look after this large house and two completely wild young boys without any help whatsoever."

I wondered how she'd cope if her husband had the income of a lance-corporal.

She took another large gulp from her drink and continued:

"I blame Frank, you know, my husband, your captain. He's got no ambition whatsoever. He ought to be a major at the very least by now. If he were, we'd have been posted to India. Life there, would be entirely different. Servants galore, and an ayah to look after my unruly brats. But no, Frank just wouldn't even try. Said he didn't like hot climates. I met Frank at my coming-out ball, I was eighteen. He looked so handsome in his regimental dinner dress, to this day I don't know how he wangled an invitation. I became absolutely besotted with him and ignoring Daddy's advice, I went ahead and married a penniless officer, to my cost, I must say."

I remained silent, believing it wiser not to agree or disagree while she bemoaned her fate. The only response she got from me was an occasional nod.

"If it wasn't for Daddy," she went on, "we wouldn't even have this house. He, bless him, bought it for me, knowing full well, if it were left to Frank, we'd spend the rest of his Army service in some ghastly Regimental Married Quarters. Mind you, right now we'd be better in them - they, at least, have central heating. This house has ten spacious rooms, all heated by coal fires. Neither Frank nor I can possibly cope with that. If it hadn't been for this bloody war, Daddy would have paid for us to have central heating installed. Now, of course, it's too late, one can't get hold of any heating engineers for love or money, not that we have a surplus of either. All I have now is a fire in the lounge, which Frank lights before he leaves in the morning. The rest of the house is like a refrigerator. That is why I'm forced to live in my overcoat."

When she had finished her drink and was pouring herself another, I made a near-fatal mistake - I offered to do the washing up.

"Would you really? I'd be eternally grateful, I feel a headache coming on. I'll go and lie down on the couch in the lounge and be in the warm. You'll find lots of dishcloths in that drawer over there."

She left me, carrying her glass in one hand and the other on her forehead. Oh Derrick, you twit, what have you let yourself in for, it'll take for ever to do this lot. Well, it didn't take for ever, but it did take two hours and the bottom of the sink saw daylight for the first time in weeks.

I decided to be nice to the poor 'suffering' woman and clear the long dining table. I threw in the bin all the empty jam jars plus the revolting half-eaten tin of sardines. Anything still edible, I put away into the cupboards. The surface of the table was in a terrible state, even when I had scrubbed it down with very hot water and a bar of soap.

When I'd done, Mrs Kitchen popped her head through the door. She now wore a large fur hat and a long, woollen scarf.

"I'm off to fetch the children from school, er - I'm so sorry, I'm afraid I don't know your name."

I told her.

"My God, Derrick, what a transformation! I haven't seen the kitchen look like this in ages. How can I thank you enough?"

You could try by offering me a half-a-crown, I thought, so that I could buy myself a hot meal in the NAAFI when I got back.

"Now when you leave, just give the front door a good hearty slam. And once again, thank you so much, I shall tell Frank all about you. Goodbye - oh, just one more thing, would you mind putting some coal on the fire before you go?"

I did as she asked, then put on my peaked cap and went out into the cold. I really did wish I had brought my greatcoat with me. Coming over to the captain's home by car had only taken ten minutes, but to walk back through the frozen snow took a good half hour. It was after five when I got back to the barracks, too late for tea. I had to wait until supper before I could get anything to eat.

Next morning, the first thing I did was look and see if any more snow had fallen during the night. It hadn't. So there would be no need to use me as a snow-plough today, thank heavens! By ten, I was sitting all warm and comfortable at my desk looking forward to doing absolutely nothing all day. A few minutes later the captain arrived.

"First of all, Derrick, I have to say my wife was absolutely delighted with the way you helped her yesterday - so delighted in fact, that she would be very happy if you could go there again today. Well, as we both know, there's sod all to do here except on Fridays, so I told her I'd send you over."

"Sir, do you mean every day except Fridays?"

"Yes, I suppose that's about the score, until further notice anyway. The drill is, every weekday, Monday to Thursday, you report to my wife at ten a.m."

He could see from my face that I was pretty fed up with the prospect of doing domestic work at his home 'until further notice'.

"Derrick, try to remember, it's me you are helping, not Mrs Kitchen."

"I understand, sir."

"Good, so off you go then."

Shit, fuck and blast, I said aloud when I'd left his presence. Because he hasn't got the guts to tell his wife to put the gin bottle down and get off the couch and do her own bloody housework, I've got lumbered with the fucking job. So this was to be my reward for being kind to the upper-class slut! I cursed myself all the way over to her house for being such a stupid twit.

As I walked up the drive, I could see Mrs Kitchen peeping out of her front-room window.

"Good morning, Derrick, so glad you could come," she said, knowing full well I had no alternative, "If you'd start please by lighting the fires in the lounge, the kitchen, and the master bedroom - that's the large one on the second floor - you'll find coal and some wood in the shed. When you've done that, it would be simply marvellous if you would work the same magic in the kitchen as you did yesterday. A good sweeping everywhere is well overdue. The boys' bedrooms are on the top floor. After you've made their beds, put all their toys away in their lockers. I think I've given you enough to be getting on with. I'm just off to do some shopping - I'll be back in about an hour."

" Mrs Kitchen, I do have to leave here at eleven-thirty so as to be back in the barracks in time for the midday meal. You see, it's the main meal of the day."

"Oh no, that would be a complete waste of time, it'll take you a half hour to get there and another to come back. What I'll do is bring back heaps of tinned beans, then you can cook yourself as much as you want. Must be off now, see you later."

She waved me aside and left, leaving me no time to protest even if I had the nerve.

So that's it - I've got this lousy job as a houseboy (as far as she is concerned) for the duration of the war. The only way out of it would be to start fucking everything up, but if I did that, I'm sure that the captain would put me back into the shit-shovelling squad the very next day. Now I'd gone full circle and was back doing all the chores I'd had to do as a child. Still, who knows, with a bit of luck, the real war would start up and the captain and I would both be shipped off to France. By the end of the week, baked beans were coming out of my ears.

I was sitting in the NAAFI on Saturday morning, wondering how I would ever get out of all this domestic drudgery, when world events came to my rescue. For there, on a notice board, printed in big letters, was:

'VOLUNTEERS WANTED TO MAKE UP AN EXPEDITIONARY FORCE TO GO TO FINLAND AND ASSIST THEM IN THEIR FIGHT AGAINST THE INVADING RUSSIAN ARMY. THOSE WISHING TO VOLUNTEER CAN GET A FORM FROM MAJOR RATCLIFFE'S OFFICE.'

I hadn't the slightest idea where Finland was, except that it probably shared a border with Russia. But one thing I knew for certain - it was a long way away from the captain's wife, and Mill Hill barracks.

I downed my tea quickly and beetled off at speed to the Regimental Office. Major Ratcliffe wasn't on duty but his clerk was.

"I've come to get the form about going to Finland."

The way I put it, one might have thought I was at a travel agents.

"The major will be pleased, you're the only one who's turned up so far."

He gave me a form.

"Fill it in, and bring it back on Monday, mate. We open at nine-thirty."

That same afternoon I went to see Uncle.

"Hayden, I'm not at all sure volunteering to go to Finland is a good idea. Apart from the obvious danger, it will be a lot colder there than here. The whole country will be up to its neck in snow until late spring."

Snow or not, I still wanted to go. I asked him to show me on his atlas where precisely Finland was.

"It looks like to get there is a long journey by sea, doesn't it, Uncle?" I said.

"It is, and this time of the year, the sea will be very rough."

"Maybe it is, but I just can't stand being a houseboy for the rest of the war. Anything would be better than that."

He found my birth certificate and handed it to me.

"Tell them that it's the original and you want it back when they've had a look at it. I'll keep it for you until the war is over."

At nine-thirty on the dot the following Monday, I was at Major Ratcliffe's office, and handed in my form.

"When will I know that I've been accepted?" I asked the clerk.

"In a day or so, mate."

Wonderful, I thought, perhaps by Thursday I'll be out of Mrs Kitchen's clutches, and shortly after that out of England altogether. Only the young and naive could feel pleased about the possibility of going off to a snowy grave in a foreign land, but that's how it was for me at that time.

I worked at the captain's house all Monday and apart from the normal household duties I had to do the snowploughing job again. I was about to leave when Mrs Kitchen arrived back, having picked up her two sons from school.

"Derrick, I'm so glad you are still here. Frank and I are going to the pictures this evening and we want you to sit in with the brats."

"I'm afraid I can't, Mrs Kitchen, I have to be back before lights out at ten."

"Don't you worry about that, Frank has already told the guardroom that you won't be back until about eleven-thirty."

What a bloody liberty, I thought, this had all been arranged without even asking me.

"When Frank arrives at six, we'll be off and come back about eleven. If the boys give you any trouble, just give them a good clip around their ears."

So the captain didn't get home until six. I wondered why, because he always finished work at three. I suppose he whiled away his time in the Officers' Mess before summoning up the courage to face the chaos of his family.

When the captain arrived, he made straight for the cocktail cabinet and poured himself a large whisky.

"Can I give you anything, Derrick?"

"No thank you, sir, I don't drink."

"Splendid, my boy, keep it that way if you can, all it does for you is to make life a little easier for a short while."

Mrs Kitchen came into the lounge all togged up in a full-length fur coat with matching hat and gloves. She looked more like she was going on an arctic expedition than to the local cinema.

"Get your coat on, Frank, we'll be leaving soon, and Derrick, if you'd give the boys for their supper some of those beans that you are so expert in cooking, they will be your friends for life. See you later!"

The boys spent most of their time arguing or fighting or rampaging through the house. The tidying up I had done during the day was a complete waste of time. I remembered that I had promised their mother to make them some beans on toast. 'They will be your friends for life' she had said. When I bawled up the stairs and told them that their supper was ready they didn't even reply, let alone come down. Well, I thought, fuck those bad-mannered posh little bastards, I'll eat mine and they can do what they like about theirs.

After I had eaten, I went into the lounge and spent the rest of my child-minding time listening to the radio. Just before eleven, I tiptoed upstairs and looked into the boys' bedrooms. Thankfully they were both fast asleep.

"Everything been all right, did the boys behave?" asked Mrs Kitchen as she entered the front hall.

"Oh, they were no bother at all, Mrs Kitchen."

That was after all the truth. I had hardly seen them all evening. I was hoping the captain would drive me back, but when he started to take off his overcoat, I knew that wasn't even going to be offered.

"Thanks a lot, Derrick," he said, as he let me out of the front door, "Good-night!"

He shut the door behind me and I was left to slog my way back through the snow to the barracks.

I had worked from ten in the morning until eleven at night for that family, all for the princely sum of two shillings, which is what the Army paid me.

The next morning, at breakfast, Corporal Hawkins came over to my table.

"Cartlidge, you are to report to Major Ratcliffe's office at ten o'clock."

I jumped up and just restrained myself from hugging him.

"Wonderful, wonderful!" I cried out loud.

"What's so fucking wonderful, mate?" said one of the men sitting at the table.

"I've most likely been accepted to join the volunteer force going to Finland!" I said excitedly.

"You must be a bigger cunt than I took you for, wanting to go on that fucking outing," said the man.

I didn't bother to argue with him. Before ten, I was outside the major's office, waiting for him to arrive. A few minutes later, he did and went straight into his office. I gave him a short time to settle down, then knocked on his door.

"Private Cartlidge reporting, sir."

"Stand at ease, please, private."

The major reached across his desk and took out my application form with my birth certificate pinned to it and put them in front of him.

"Well, Private Cartlidge, a bit of a problem has arisen regarding you. It's to do with your age. According to your birth certificate, you are not yet seventeen. Under NO circumstances could I send you off to the Finnish campaign. You can imagine the rumpus if anything happened to you there! I'd get into an awful lot of trouble, and rightly so. So Finland is absolutely out. Now I know you're probably disappointed, but I'm afraid there's worse to come."

Oh hell, I thought, he's about to tell me I'm to be put on a charge for lying about my age when I joined up.

"The main worry is that legally you're not supposed to be in the Army at all. Now on that score, I can do one of two things: either turn Nelson's eye for a few weeks by which time you will be seventeen, or discharge you immediately. The decision is yours."

I just couldn't believe what I was hearing. It took me a moment or two to pull myself together enough before I could answer him. Whatever you say, I thought, be very careful how you say it.

"Well, sir, as I've already served almost a year before I needed to, I wouldn't mind a short break until I'm drafted officially."

"So, you'd like to be discharged, is that it?"

"Yes, sir."

"Well, if that's what you want, so be it. I hope, Cartlidge, when you rejoin the colours, you will ask to be sent to your old regiment."

"Oh, of course, sir, I wouldn't want to be with any other." (Surely, I thought, he must be able to see through my monumental lie.)

"That's the spirit, lad, it's good when an old soldier stays loyal to his regiment. I'll take you to Captain Gilbert and he will draw up your discharge papers."

I was so elated when I followed the major, that my feet hardly touched the ground.

"Good morning, Gilbert," said the major when we entered the captain's office, "this man is being discharged - reason: under age. Do the necessary, will you?"

The captain took a little red book out of a small safe, entitled *The Regular Army Certificate of Service*.

"What we have to do is fill this in, so if you would just answer the questions I put to you, the whole thing will take but a couple of minutes."

He asked what was the last thing I had been doing. I told him I'd been clerk to Captain Kitchen.

"Oh, you're the chap Frank told me about. He thinks very highly of you. I'm sure he'll be sorry to see you go."

The captain went on writing in the little red book, and then read to me what he had written.

"This is what I've put down under 'Assessment of Conduct and Character on leaving the Colours' : For Military Conduct, I've put 'very good', and as a testimonial, I've written 'he is a clean, honest and sober man, possesses good intelligence. He has been clerk to the billeting officer and has done well. Is only being discharged as he is under military age.' That, my boy, should help you get a job in civvy street."

The captain closed the little book and handed it to me.

"Now my advice is to look after your discharge paper and keep it on your person when you are out and about. Young men in civilian clothes often get stopped by the military or civil police and asked why they are not in the services. Right, that's all done, so you are now free to go."

I thought it would be the polite thing to do to go and see Capt. Kitchen and tell him the good news about me and the bad news for his wife. He was sitting at his desk when I entered his room.

'Hello, Derrick, what are you doing here? You're supposed to have been with my wife an hour ago?"

When I told him what had happened, he looked crestfallen for a moment.

"My wife, you know, will be very disappointed when I tell her that you've been discharged - but there you are, Army regulations can't be ignored. So, Derrick, all the very best in your new life and I can't thank you enough for all the good work you did in my home."

In seconds I was in my barrack room, stripping to my underwear and putting on the clothes I had arrived in from Southend eleven months before. I stuffed my uniform into my kitbag, picked up all the equipment that I'd so hated polishing, and slung it over my shoulder, grabbed my rifle off the wall and took the whole lot over to the Quartermasters' stores and dumped it on their counter.

"I've never seen a uniform and equipment brought in here in such a mess!" grumbled the store man.

"Sorry," I said, "but I've a train to catch."

"Train or not, mate, all this gear has got to be checked off in the proper fashion."

He took for ever before he finally gave me a receipt. I walked quickly over to the guard room to check out. The Duty Corporal asked to see my pass.

"Haven't got one, Corp. But I can show you my discharge papers if you want!"

"Discharge papers? How did you swing that this early in the war?"

"It's all written down there, corporal," I said as I handed him the little red book.

"What I need now, sonny boy, is the receipt from the stores."

I gave it to him.

"You didn't think I'd want to keep any of it, did you, corp?"

"OK, wise guy, hop off!"

So that's what I did. I didn't just walk out of the barracks that as far as I was concerned had been a sort of open prison for the last 314 days, I hippity-hopped. I was free, free to do I did not know what nor did I care.

That evening at Uncle's, when I was listening to the six o'clock news, the announcer said that contingent of volunteers would not now be leaving for Finland. British Intelligence had discovered (just in time) that the Germans had already dispatched a whole division there to help the Finns fight off the invading Russian Army. This made it impossible for our troops to go to the aid of the hard-pressed Finns. Christ, I thought, what a fiasco it would have been, if our secret agents hadn't found that out in time. It would have ended up with Tommy, who was at war with Fritz, standing shoulder to shoulder with him, firing at Ivan. If this situation had become known a week earlier, I couldn't have volunteered, and the question about my age would never have arisen. I would still be the captain's wife's houseboy. The very thought of it sent a shiver down my spine.

CHAPTER SIXTEEN

After a couple of weeks being bone idle, I began to get a little bored, so I asked Uncle if he had any suggestions about finding work. He gave it some thought, and then remembered that George knew an old queen, who ran an agency for film extras.

"But I can't act," I told him.

"You don't have to be able to act, extras are used only as part of a crowd. One time you might be a person in a pub, or another a pedestrian walking on a pavement. Whatever happens, you would never be in the limelight or need any acting ability."

To be in films, no matter in what humble capacity, appealed to me, and so it was arranged that I should introduce myself that afternoon at five to a Mr Archie Wolf at his office in Soho.

The building was almost derelict: I had imagined that anything to do with films would be housed in smart premises. Eventually, I saw a small notice pinned by the side of the door: 'Archie Wolf Agency, first floor, come up please'.

If the outside had shocked me, the office looked even worse. There was no carpet covering the grubby floorboards, and crumbling plaster protruded through the cracks of the faded wallpaper. Three people were squeezed into the tiny room. Two of them middle-aged women, were seated behind a table, answering a battery of phones. The dialogue from both of them was the same:

"Nothing for you today, dear, try again tomorrow!"

The third person, who I took to be Mr Wolf, was sitting at a desk that had certainly seen better days. He was a short, fat, bald-headed man, wearing an open-necked shirt and an unbuttoned cardigan.

He looked up at me and I could tell by his eyes that he liked what he saw.

"Hello, duckie, what can I do for you?"

"George Greaves phoned you this morning about me. I'm Hayden Cartlidge."

"Yes, dear, so he did, pity you're so young-looking, but still, the studios sometimes ask for young people."

At this point one of the women called over to him:

"Archie, he's ideal for Denham tomorrow, remember?"

"Of course, he's perfect," then turning to me, he said: "You're in luck, dearie, be at Denham Studios at eight in the morning and go to the *Love on the Dole* set. I think there may be a few days on it for you. Now, duckie, go and give Margaret over there all your particulars, and when you've finished your days at the studios, come back here and pay your commission. It's ten percent. And remember, my pet, no commission means no more work until you pay, understood?"

"No fear of that, Mr Wolf, I'd like all the work I can get."

"Oh, they all say that, duckie. Call me like everybody does, by my first name - Archie."

That night I was so excited I hardly slept a wink. By seven-thirty I was at Denham, and although it was such a short train journey from London, I was surprised how much in the country it was. Walking through the little Buckinghamshire village, I had the feeling that London was a hundred miles away. There was no problem in finding the studios as I could see their big hangar-like buildings dominating the skyline about a quarter of a mile away, silhouetted in the dawn light across the fields.

When I reached the main gates, there was a queue of people. Eventually it was my turn, a security man asked me what film I was to be on. I told him.

"You want Studio B, just follow the signposts, you can't go wrong."

At the reception desk, I handed over the piece of paper the agency had given me.

"You're called for *Love on the Dole*. Go to the wardrobe department down the corridor on the left, and pick up your costume."

Costume, I thought, why would I need one? I knew it couldn't possibly be a period piece as there was no dole for the unemployed until after the Great War. Still, I was told to go there, so that's what I did. A man behind a long counter looked me up and down and disappeared into the rows of shelving crammed full with every type of costume, ancient and modern. Within a couple of minutes he was back with clothes slung over his arm.

"One grey shirt, one pair of black trousers, and one cloth cap. Sign here please. The changing rooms are just across the passage and the make-up room is next door to that."

Make-up? I didn't like the sound of that, that's for girls. The changing room was full of men of different ages in various states of undress. Once everybody had donned the clothes, we were all transformed into working-class men in the thirties. When I was dressed, I put on my cloth cap and followed the others into the make-up room. I was plonked into a chair facing a large square mirror with bare electric lights surrounding it. A woman dipped a huge powder puff into a big bowl of light-brown cream and dabbed it all over my face.

"Why do we need all this?" I said to her as she slapped this awful stuff all over my face.

"If we didn't, the camera would hardly see you," she replied.

I followed the others out of the make-up room to the set. Under a huge roof, an entire street of smart houses had been recreated. As if by magic I had been transported to a small town in the north of England. For a long time I gazed in wonderment at it all. The whole set was teeming with people, carpenters banging and sawing away, painters touching up the outside of the houses. Real cobblestones were used for the road surface, the pavement slabs and kerbs were painted on wooden boards, as were the bricks on the outside of the terrace houses, yet everything looked realistic even from a short distance away. The two-storey house at the end of the street had no side-wall, leaving it exposed to view. All the rooms were furnished in the style of the early thirties.

Up to now, the studio was lit by ordinary lights suspended from the high ceiling, but when a man shouted "LIGHTS", the whole set became brighter than daylight. A man walked around with a little meter in his hand and directed the electricians, who were standing some twenty feet up on scaffolding, as to how they were to aim their beams.

Although I, and the other extras, had been called for eight o'clock, it was after eleven before anything happened. Then, all of a sudden, the big lights went out and a small cluster of spotlights lit up the end house. Two actors were rehearsing a scene in the upstairs bedroom, which was divided in half by a white sheet. Judging by the dialogue, the room was shared by a brother and his younger sister. The girl looked about eighteen and was very beautiful. The two were having a conversation through the sheet as they got dressed. The actress could only be seen as a shadow appearing on the sheet.

They were filmed doing their little bit of action at least five times before the director said: "Very good, print it."

As far as I was concerned, they could have repeated the scene for the rest of the day, as I had totally fallen for the actress. I was told she was new to films, and this was her first day on a set. Her name was Deborah Kerr.

At twelve-thirty, a voice shouted: "Break for lunch."

The canteen was packed with people from other sets, all dressed in different costumes. You knew who were the workmen or technicians - they were without make-up. I was hoping that the beautiful actress from my set would come in, then maybe I could sit next to her. But no such luck, as all the stars and the directors had their own restaurant.

After lunch, things got moving. The assistant director stood on a raised platform, and through a hand-held megaphone, explained what the scene we would be doing was about. We were men from the local mill who had been locked out because of a dispute with the owners. One of the workerswould stand on a small box and incite us to follow him up the street to the mill to smash down the locked gates. However, at the end of the street six mounted police with batons raised would confront us, coming towards us, first at a trot, then at a gallop. We would turn about in panic and run back down the street. No harm would come to anyone, as these were real mounted police whose horses were highly trained. When the actor asked us to follow him, we had to shout our approval. We were to do a couple of run-throughs, then attempt a take.

We went through this routine many times, mainly because a lot of the crowd turned and ran long before they should. I didn't altogether blame them. Those policemen on horseback coming at speed towards you did look menacing. By the end of the afternoon, no shot had been taken, and we were all told to be back at eight in the morning.

"Where do we get paid?" I asked someone.

"Come with me, I'll show you. Is this your first time here?" he asked.

"Yes, it is. Do you know how much we get paid?"

"One guinea a day plus rail-fare."

"One guinea?" I echoed.

"Were you expecting more then?"

"Oh no, I didn't think it would be as much as that."

Crumbs, I thought, that was more than two weeks' army pay, all earned in just one day.

When I handed back the studio clothes to the wardrobe department, I was given a receipt.

"Hang on to that," said the man who gave it to me. "Without it, you won't get paid."

I was paid one pound and three shillings. I felt very rich.

When I got back to Uncle, I told him I had earned so much money that I wanted to treat him to the evening meal for once.

"That's very nice of you, Hayden, but I think we will wait for a while before you start throwing your money about. If this keeps up for a couple of weeks, then I'd be delighted to take you up on your offer."

The next morning at the studios was a repetition of the previous afternoon, the only difference being that after one rehearsal, filming started in earnest. That morning, we rushed down the cobblestoned street many times before the director was satisfied. By the end of the day, everything was 'in the can'. The Assistant Director told us how much he appreciated our co-operation.

"Thanks everyone," said the assistant director. "Tomorrow we'll only need three of you."

I was one of the three he chose.

"You three, be on set at eight, wearing the same clothes, please."

The next day the set was a hill covered with synthetic grass. It must have been built overnight, as it wasn't there the day before. Looking down from the crest of the hill, you could see a part of a town in miniature.

I was glad to see the lovely young actress was back. The scene that morning was her talking with her boyfriend as they slowly walked arm-in-arm up the hill. I was told to sit halfway up the slope and as the couple passed by me, I was to say to the man "Allo 'Arry", with a northern accent. The Assistant Director got the actor to say it to me a couple of times.

To get the accent right, I rehearsed those two words many times in my mind before shooting started. When the realisation of what I had been asked to do dawned on me, I got nervous.

I felt very important. Who knows, I thought, when the director hears me, maybe I'll be discovered as a new young star and have a career in films. That dream was short-lived, for on the word "Action" the actors walked up the hill, and in my anxiety to get it right, I said my two words before I should.

"Cut, cut, cut," shouted the director, "NO, you don't say hallo until they are level with you. You cut right across their dialogue. Now let's do it again."

I felt terrible, being told off in front of everyone, especially the beautiful actress. So this time I lined up the hillside as if I was looking through the sight of a rifle and only said my words when they crossed my line of fire. The next time, when it went wrong, it was the actor's fault, but on the third take, all went well. I was glad. I don't think my nerves would have stood up to a fourth go.

Before lunch, we three extras were told we were no longer needed, and we could go and be paid off.

Oh dear, I thought, that means we only get a half day's pay. But my fears were unfounded, for not only did I get my full day's pay, but an extra ten shillings for the two words I'd spoken. Five shillings a word! I assumed that was also the rate by which the main actors with all their dialogue were paid.

On the following day, I went to the agency and paid my ten percent commission.

"Good boy, paying us so promptly," said Archie.

"You did say, to come when I'd finished, didn't you?"

"Yes, duckie, I did, but hardly any of them do. It's put you in my good books. How about having dinner with me tonight at my flat?"

Jesus, I thought, I wouldn't like to be alone with this man in a football stadium, let alone in his flat.

"Thanks for asking, but I've promised to take my girl to the pictures. Shall I check in tomorrow?" I asked.

"If you wish, provided your girlfriend doesn't mind."

He's not only an old queen, I thought, but a catty one as well.

I checked in every evening for the next ten days, but always got the same answer ,

"Nothing today, dear, thanks for calling". It occurred to me that turning down Archie's dinner invitation had probably cost me my career as a film extra. Still, if that was going to have to be the price paid, plus commission, maybe it was all for the best .

Uncle said he was sure he could find me something else to do, and a day or two later he found me a job at Marks & Spencer. He had spoken to a friend who was very high up there, and who Uncle said was very nice, even though he was a Jew. I'd never heard of anyone being spoken about like that before, and wondered what Uncle would think if somebody said about him 'He's very nice even though he's English'. According to the friend, I would only work in the storeroom for a few months, after which he would see to it that I got promoted to floorwalker. If I did well at that, in a couple of years I could become an assistant manager. My God, I thought, my whole working life has been planned out until I reach pensionable age.

I turned up at the Camden Town branchat eight-thirty the following Monday. No less a person than the store manager greeted me.

"You must be Mr Cartlidge. Mr Green from Head Office told me you would be starting today, and that I was to take good care of you. Are you a relative of his?"

"No, sir, he's a friend of my uncle's."

"Oh, I see, not everyone who gets sent to us is personally recommended by one of our directors. Now, if you would please come with me, I'll introduce you to our head storeman. His name is Harry."

"Harry," said the manager, "this is Mr Cartlidge, you remember, he is the young man I told you about. He's been sent by one of our directors."

I think the poor man had a hard fight to resist the urge to address me as 'Sir'.

"Pleased to meet you, Harry, my name is Derrick."

When the manager left us, I knew the only thing for me to do right away, was to let Harry know who I really was. I told him I was just seeking temporary work until I made up my mind what I wanted to do with myself. Harry was a short barrel-shaped man with narrow shoulders. Long hair from the side of his head looked as if it was glued across the bald patch on top in a vain attempt to hide it. He was a timid little chap, who never looked at you when he spoke. You just knew that no smile had creased his rounded face for years.

"Have you been here long?" I asked.

"Since I was a boy of fourteen, and that was over thirty years ago."

"Didn't you ever want to become a floorwalker or an assistant manager?"

"Oh no," he said, looking down to the ground, "that's not for the likes of me, I'll go on working as a storeman until I'm retired or get the sack."

"That seems a bit unfair, you never getting promotion, I mean."

"Maybe," he replied, "but that's the way things are. I'll take you round the back to meet Jack, he'll be your mate while you're here and he can show you the ropes."

I followed him into the back of the storeroom.

"Jack, this is Derrick, he's got Brian's old job. Show him what to do, will you?"

As we shook hands, I knew at once that we were going to become friends. Jack was about two years older than I, and very different from Harry. For a start, he was over six foot, and had a strong and athletic build. His thick brown, wavy hair was brushed back from his handsome, narrow face and unlike Harry, he smiled a lot. He looked straight at you with his blue eyes, which had unusually long eyelashes for a male.

"Why did Brian leave?" I asked.

"The poor sod got called up, and that will be happening to me before long."

I told him I had only just got out of the army after eleven terrible months, and why I was discharged.

"So you're only just seventeen. That means you've still got two more years of freedom before they want you again."

I agreed, then added, "Who knows - the war may be over by then."

"Perhaps," he said, "but it's got to get started before it can end, hasn't it?"

"You're right. Tell me, how much pay will I get at the end of the week, and what are the hours?"

"They are Monday to Wednesday 8.30 – 6 p.m., Thursday is a half-day, Fridays and Saturdays are the long days, from 8.30 a.m. to 8.30 p.m. A total of fifty-seven and a half hours, all for the measly pay of one pound, seven shillings and sixpence - or, if you prefer, sixpence ha'penny per hour. We get one hour off for lunch, and a short tea-break morning and afternoon."

"You may moan, but the pay is almost three times more than I got in the army."

"But you got full board there, didn't you? I give my Mum fifteen shillings a week for my keep. So I'm not left with a lot after that, am I?"

I didn't tell him that where I was staying cost me nothing.

The work was more or less as I had anticipated, mainly consisting of replenishing the stock sold at the counters. For the first two hours, I followed Jack about. All the goods were pushed around the store in large wicker trolleys. When we weren't doing that, we swept the long corridors between the rows of counters. This wasn't as easy as one might think as a lot of the time was spent scraping off chunks of squashed chewing gum.

When we weren't doing either of these jobs, we were in the yard, helping van drivers unload their deliveries. At ten-thirty, Jack stopped working.

"Tea-break, mate, come with me up to the canteen. For tuppence you can have a big cuppa and a huge jam doughnut, and I'll introduce you to some of the girls. You know, you're in luck, because forty girls have only six men to chose from, and four of those don't get a look-in, because they're either too fat or too weedy, so that leaves the field clear for you and me."

When we entered the canteen, about twenty women with ages ranging from fifteen to thirty, were seated at small tables.

"Ladies," said Jack, shouting over the hubbub of their chatter, "this is Derrick, my new mate."

"Cor, look what Jack's brought in," said one of them.

"You've got competition now, Jack," remarked another.

"No," he replied, "not competition, just a helping hand with you sexy lot."

"Leave off, Jack, we're all good girls."

"Yes, I know how good you are," he said sarcastically.

He put his arm around one of them and whispered into her ear loud enough for most of us to hear:

"You haven't forgotten you're going to the pictures with me tonight, have you?"

"How could I forget something as important as that, Jack, I'm the envy of you all, aren't I, girls?"

"Oh, yes, Mary, you are," said one of them who then turned to me. "Come over here, Derrick, and sit next to me."

She was a very pretty blonde of about twenty. I felt a bit shy in the company all these grown-up women. They, on the other hand, appeared to be quite confident. I suppose it was because they had nothing to fear from two young males who were outnumbered by ten to one.

"Is this your first job?" said the pretty blonde.

"Yes, in civilian life. I was in the army before."

"You mean, the boys' army?"

"No, the Regulars."

"How did you get out?"

"Well, that's a long story, I'll tell you some time."

"Do you think you'll stay in this job long?"

"That depends on how I get on with girls like you," I said.

"Well, in that case, you'll be here for a very long time, because we are all so gorgeous. I'm Stella."

Jack beckoned me to leave, so I downed my tea and stood up to go.

"See you again, Stella."

"It's impossible not to, in this place."

As I walked down the stairs behind Jack, he warned me not to get too involved with her, because she was married.

"Oh shit, she's lovely," I said.

"Yeah, that's what her old man thinks. But don't worry, there are plenty more delicious fish for the catching."

"Maybe, but I felt at ease with her."

"You'll see, Derrick, you'll be at ease with all of them once you get to know them."

On that reassuring note, we both started work again. During the rest of the week I got to know Jack really well. He told me he had been working at Marks & Spencer's since he was sixteen. His home was in a street that backed onto the store, this meant that he could tumble out of bed at 8.25 and be at work five minutes later. He also had the advantage of being able to pop back there during the day unnoticed by Harry. His father worked as a plasterer with a local building firm and his mother did a part-time job up the road at the Black Cat factory which made Craven 'A' cigarettes. Jack had no ambitions other than to get paid as much as he could for doing as little work as possible. As he said to me:

'After all, Derrick, that's what the upper classes do, isn't it? All I'm doing is my best to imitate them."

By remarks like that you knew that he had a natural intelligence and had not yet been ground down into subservience, like Harry. It seems he spent a lot of his spare time doing gymnastics and weight training, which was the reason for his broad shoulders and slim waist. It was because of his obsession with body-building that he was unable to take full advantage of making it with the girls who fancied him. He had some weird notion that having sex drained his strength. I knew that Samson was weakened when his hair was shorn off, but your strength leaving you via your cock was a new one on me, so I said to him:

"It seems pointless to make yourself attractive to girls, only to reject them when they want you."

"I don't reject them," he said, "I just limit their numbers. I never allow myself to have a fuck more than twice a week."

Jesus, I thought, he's rationing himself to twice a week when I've not been with a girl since I went to the brothel in France.

Jack was a great clown and practical joker. One of his favourite tricks was to pretend to trip when he was carrying on his head a large wooden tray packed full of delicate meringues and chocolate eclairs. A gasp would come from the customers as the tray tipped perilously first one way, and then the other, before he regained control of the sliding pastries. He did this with such expertise that not a single cake was damaged. Sometimes, he got a round of applause from the admiring audience. The girls behind the counter, who had seen this performance many times, just gave a little yawn.

There was another trick he liked to play on poor old Harry. Just to make doubly sure he'd locked all the many doors at closing time, Harry's habit was to check all of them two or three times. Jack, unseen by him, would unlock a few of them, so that when he came round again, he found some open that he was quite sure he had locked.

One of Jack's traits I liked a lot was his 'Robin Hood' behaviour to those less well-off. At the end of the day, instead of throwing away the leftovers as he was told, he'd keep them overnight. Early the next day, he left the trays of cakes on the pavement outside the back gates, so that all the poor kids of the neighbourhood could come and help themselves. Generally there was a whole crowd of them waiting, and the stale cakes would vanish within seconds. He also helped a lot of the girls working in the store by stealing things they wanted. At the end of the day he would take from the counters what the girls asked for and stuff as much as he could under his shirt, and a whole lot more down his baggy trouser legs, securing them with a pair of bicycle clips. Padded out this way, he got past Harry's beady eyes as he left by the staff exit. Items missing from the counters were put down to those shoplifters. He justified this by saying that all he was doing was supplementing their meagre wages, and like Robin Hood, he only stole on their behalf, never for himself.

Well, if Jack was to play Robin, I decided to become one of his merry men. Before long, I too was concealing goods up my shirt and down my trouser legs. The girls we stole for told us lists of things they wanted, ranging from sweaters and blouses down to camiknickers, bras, petticoats and stockings. When you gave them a nod or wink they would meet you after work in a side street round the back of the store to pick up the loot. This made Jack and me very popular and it often ended up by me taking one of them out for the evening. As I was two years younger than Jack, the girls that I dated were the fifteen to sixteen-yearolds. So an evening spent with them was nearly always at the pictures, where a lot of kissing and cuddling was all that was expected or indeed permissible. When I complained to Jack that I didn't get as far with my girls as he did, he told me it was because they were all virgins and that the older ones thought I was too young.

"With the exception of Gloria. She's about twenty-one, and not much to look at, but she's got one hell of a lovely body and just likes to fuck. After you've been with her a few times, you'll be experienced enough to go with the older girls. Apart from not being much to look at, Gloria has one other drawback: she's not very bright. Conversation with her is impossible. If you want, the next time we're in the canteen, I'll introduce you to her."

"Will you really?"

"Sure I will."

The same afternoon, in the tea-break, Jack saw her sitting by herself at one of the tables.

"This is a good moment to meet her," said he, as he took me towards her, "Gloria, this is my friend Derrick, he thinks you're smashing and said he wanted to meet you."

"Hallo Derrick, I've seen you around."

I sat down next to her: "I suppose a beautiful girl like you is already married?"

"No, I'm not," she replied.

"Really? I'd have thought you'd have been snapped up by now. I think you're lovely - so lovely in fact, that I was wondering if you would come out with me this evening. We could go to one of the Corner Houses and have a meal, and then do whatever else you fancy. Shall we meet in the alley round the back after work then, Gloria?"

She got up to go.

"See you there then!"

When she had gone, Jack came and sat next to me.

"How did you make out?"

"I'm going out with her tonight."

"Take my advice, keep your boots on. They are the only thing that will stop her swallowing you up completely."

I couldn't imagine what he meant by that, but for some reason it worried me, especially as I was already feeling a bit nervous.

Luck was on my side that evening as Uncle had gone to visit his brother in the country, which meant that I had the flat all to myself for the night. My plan was that after we had eaten, I would suggest that she came back there with me. I just hoped that she didn't live with her parents and have to be back by midnight.

CHAPTER SEVENTEEN

It was only when Gloria met me that I took a really good look at her. She was my height, and very well built, but not fat. I think she weighed more than I did. Her face had no distinguishing features. Her brown hair was curly and reached half-way down her back. She had full and generous lips, and small eyes.

The first thing I asked her, was: what time did she have to be home by. She said her home was in Buckinghamshire, where her father had a small farm. She lived in Chalk Farm, in a furnished room that had an absentee landlord who only came round on Friday nights to pick up his rent.

As far as I was concerned, things were looking better by the minute, for, if she didn't want to go to Uncle's flat in Adelaide Court, we could go to her place. I gave her the choice of where to eat: either the Corner House in Tottenham Court Road, which was nearer to her place, or the one in Marble Arch, which was closer to mine. She opted for Marble Arch.

I could tell that Gloria hadn't been to many restaurants before, as she seemed to be overawed by the pseudo-splendour of it all. I also saw why she was such a big girl as she ate like a horse. Apart from the first two courses, she ended up with two helpings of trifle. All this food was washed down with four glasses of beer. A couple of times during the meal, I tried to make conversation, but without success, for whenever I did, the response was "Oh really?" or "My goodness!"

I decided to leave her in peace to enjoy her food and gawp at the diners. As we got up to leave, she did manage one sentence.

"Oh thank you, that was lovely."

"I'm glad you enjoyed it." Then I asked her the question I'd been waiting patiently all through the meal to put: "Shall we go to my place?"

"Yes," she replied without any hesitation.

The green light flashed in my head, and to give her no chance to change it to red, I hailed a passing cab.

"I've never been in a taxi before," she said as she seated herself close to me, and I've never paid for one before, I thought.

Gloria was very impressed by the smart façade of the block of flats and enjoyed going up to the top floor in its cosy little lift. Once through the front door, I took her on a tour of the flat. Her only comment was: "Cor - it's quite posh, isn't it, Derrick?"

The last room I showed her was my bedroom. She made straight for my bed and sat on it. She patted the top blanket, indicating that I was to sit next to her, which I did. I gave her a kiss on her full lips, which lit the touch-paper of a fireworks display that was to go on throughout the night. She pushed me onto my back and lay beside me and slowly undid all the buttons of my shirt. Kiss after kiss landed on my bare chest in quick succession. Then she got off the bed and took off all her clothes, folding each item neatly before putting them on the back of a chair. As for me, I just sat on the edge of the bed, and with wide-open eyes watched her do this strip-tease in slow motion. Jack was so right about this girl, she certainly did have the most unbelievably sensuous body.

While she lay on the bed I tore off my clothes and dropped them in a crumpled heap on the floor. I got on the bed beside her and started to feel every part of her beautiful body. There was, however, one big drawback. Whenever I said something like 'What wonderful firm round breasts you have!' or 'How velvety your skin is!' she only replied with the same three words: "Oh, thank you!".

Now in most other circumstances, this would have had been like a bucket of cold water, but I was so sexed up, I wouldn't have cared if she had started to chant the Lord's Prayer. I thought that if I didn't get cracking soon, it would all be over as far as I was concerned before it had even begun. I lay on top of her, and put the palm of my hands under the cheeks of her well-rounded buttocks, then, with all my strength, raised her a few inches up from the blanket and entered her. Within seconds it was all over. She won't be saying 'Oh thank you' for that pathetic performance, I thought. I felt so embarrassed, I just couldn't come up with anything to say or do.

Finally I did manage to say: "I'm sorry!"

Her response was to hold me close to her and say softly into my ear:

"Don't worry, Derrick, it will be all right next time, you'll see."

She stroked my back like a mother consoling a baby, then she rolled me over and sat astride me. With her legs folded under her thighs, she bent down and slowly rubbed her breasts up and down my chest. I felt a tingling sensation going down my spine that recharged my sexual batteries. Before long Gloria had shown me that you could do more with your tongue than lick a lollipop.

That night, we hardly slept at all. By dawn we had both dropped off into a deep sleep, only to be awakened by Mrs Blaber, knocking on my door.

"Your breakfast is ready, Hayden," she said through the closed door.

"Thank you, Mrs B., I'll be out in a moment."

I'd meant for us to be out of the flat before she arrived, but forgot to set the alarm. Gloria began to panic.

"Keep calm," I whispered, "just stay in here and get dressed while I'll go and gulp down my breakfast."

"What shall I say if she comes in here?" she said, a little agitated.

"Don't worry, she never does, but in the unlikely event that she does, just say good morning ."

It took me less than two minutes to bolt down my bowl of cornflakes and have a cup of tea. I refilled my cup and buttered two slices of toast and took them in to Gloria. While she ate them, I got dressed.

When Mrs Blaber was safely ensconced in the kitchen, I shouted out my goodbyes as we walked out of the flat.

"Cor, you're a calm one, aren't you, Derrick!"

"Not really. There was nothing to worry about. The old dear would never have said or done anything, even if she had seen you. Servants are trained to be discreet. If they weren't they'd lose their jobs."

When we got in to work and before Gloria left to go to her counter, I thanked her for the wonderful night she had given me. She replied the way I knew she would: "Oh, thank you."

One day, I said to myself, I must teach her another response.

"How did you get on?" asked Jack when I got into the storeroom.

"Oh, all right, I spent most of the night sleeping."

"That's right, never let girls drain your strength away."

"I was only joking, Jack, I was at it all night long, and hardly slept a wink."

"It's up to you, mate, but it's not good for your health."

"Don't worry about that, Jack, I've never felt better in my life."

That was the first of many nights with Gloria. Since nothing succeeds like success, the older girls were starting to show some interest. Somehow they must have sensed that Gloria had broken me in.

Stella was one of those. Anything sexual that might happen with her would have to be within the working day, as she had to go back to her husband after work. Jack, who had met him, told me he worked as a bank clerk and was as boring as the job he did - and according to Stella, he was no good in bed either. It seems they had got married three years ago, when she was seventeen and became pregnant. Her parents forced her to marry him. It was very bad luck, because a few weeks later, she had a miscarriage, so now the poor girl was stuck with him. Her only hope now was that soon he would be called up.

Jack told me how Stella and I could get together during the lunch-break. He knew that it worked all right as he had done it a few times with her. The idea was that when Harry went off to the local caff for lunch, I could take Stella into the goods lift, then press the button for the next floor and stop it halfway up. He said that nobody would bother us as only he and Harry and I ever used it.

"How can you lie down on that dirty floor?" I asked.

"You don't."

A stand-up fuck wasn't exactly what I had in mind, but first I had to find out how Stella felt about it. I put it to her during the tea-break, and to my surprise she agreed. I spent the rest of the morning giving the lift a spring-clean.

"That's what I like to see - you and Jack doing something useful without having to be asked a dozen times first," said Harry when he saw it.

The moment he left for lunch, I covered the lift floor with a whole load of flattened cardboard boxes. When Stella saw what I had done, she was delighted.

"Oh, Derrick, how clever you are, you've transformed the lift into the largest double bed that ever was. This is going to be more fun than with Jack."

I pressed the lift button and stopped it halfway up. Within seconds, we were both naked, our clothes thrown into a corner. I took a step towards her, and she darted away to the other end of the lift and said provocatively:

"If you want me, Derrick, you'll have to catch me first."

Right, I thought, so this is the way she wants to play, is it? It wasn't new to me, for I had played this game many times before with Joyce when chasing her around the dormitory. However, now there was a difference, because this girl was very nimble on her feet. Every time I lunged out at her, she made a step sideways with the dexterity of a toreador. This would end up with me crashing into the wall of the lift, and her screaming with delight. Every time I tried to grab her and missed, she would taunt me like a child.

"Derrick can't catch me!" she chanted.

She kept repeating this until finally I beat my chest like Tarzan and with a roar took a flying leap at her waist, a tackle which brought her down on the cardboard floor.

She struggled, I retaliated Dracula-like, by biting deep into the lower part of her slender neck. Eventually my superior strength won the battle. She was now, I think, where she had wanted to be all along - at my mercy. Finally her lovely, slim body relaxed. At last, I could tenderly caress and kiss her beautiful face.

When all the huffing and puffing, ooh-ing and aah-ing was over, exhausted, we lay on our sides facing one another with our bodies entwined. We kissed and cuddled for a long time, oblivious to the outside world. I could have stayed with her pretty little face cupped between my palms, and her elf-like body bonded to mine, for the rest of the day, but Harry might have needed the lift, and he would be shocked to the core if he saw the two of us huddled together naked on the floor. We dressed and after one last long kiss I took the lift up to the store level. Stella went back to her counter and I back down to the storeroom.

"Well, mate, how did you make out?" asked Jack when he saw me.

"What I don't understand, Jack, is why you need to go in for all those gymnastics when all you need to do to keep fit is chase Stella around the lift two or three times a week?"

"What do you mean, chase her around?"

"If you don't know, there's no point in me telling you."

"All right then, keep your little secret. Nothing will alter my opinion, working out in the gym is the best way to keep fit."

"I believe you, but I'd rather take it easy and live for the day. Who knows, Jack, by the time this war is over, we could both be dead. I'd much rather go to my grave knowing that I took every opportunity to hop on a bed with a wonderful girl than be buried with bulging muscles that I'd had only got by weight-lifting."

"Ah, but I intend to survive this bloody war."

"I really hope you do, Jack." And I meant what I said.

For the rest of March and all of April, my sex life settled down into a routine. Twice a week I'd spend the night with Gloria in her bedsit, and twice a week with Stella in the goods lift. The three days off were spent looking forward to the other four. Although I was totally besotted with Stella and would have been quite content just to go with her, I didn't stop sleeping with Gloria. I reckoned that putting all my eggs into one basket was a bit risky.

Stella was my favourite because of her inventive imagination. I sometimes wondered whether she had hidden away somewhere a bumper-fun book on sex, as with her you rarely played the same game two days on the trot. I had the feeling that if she had such a book, we were going through it chapter by chapter. One day she'd have me on all fours with her sitting upright in the middle of my back, going round and round like a circus horse, with her whacking my bum when she wanted me to go faster. The only way to get her off was to shy up high enough, making it impossible for her to stay mounted. Then, once she was on the floor, and after the usual struggle, her make-believe stallion would take her.

Another day, she'd want to be a slave girl who would have to do everything her lord and master commanded or suffer the consequences. The next time, everything was reversed, she the Queen and I her obedient servant. Sometimes the menu of the day was a number of positions needing (mainly from her) some acrobatic skills. This was possible because she was so light and agile. I can't imagine how a girl with her spirit ever managed to live with such a boring man as her husband.

With Gloria, things were very different. There were no games, only good down-to-earth sex.

Everything was going along splendidly until one day, Stella and I had just finished one of our lunch-time sessions, and I was giving her a kiss as she left the lift, when the assistant manager saw us. He took her up to the manager's office and she was sacked on the spot. I went straight up to see him, and told him I was just as much to blame, and therefore he should dismiss me also. He said that as she had worked in the store longer than I, and was older, she should have known better. I knew that the reason only Stella got the sack was that I had the protection of a director.

Quite unexpectedly, Stella didn't seem upset at all.

"Don't worry, Derrick, it's not like before the war. It's not so hard any more to get a job."

"But Stella, darling, what about us?"

"You'll see, we'll soon see each other again, perhaps quicker than you think. I'm sure it won't be long before my old man is drafted, and then you'll be able to come and see me as much as you like. You could even move in if you wanted to."

"I certainly want to, my lovely," I said.

I gave her Uncle's phone number and walked with her out of the store. Had I known then, as I watched her disappear down Camden High Street, that it was going to be the last time I'd ever see her, her leaving would have been more painful.

CHAPTER EIGHTEEN

A few days after Stella had left, the weather changed from a cool spring into warm summer. The sky was blue from sunrise to sunset. At lunch time Jack and I would buy cheese rolls at the Express Dairy and eat them by the lake in Regent's Park. Lying there on the grass bank with our shirts off, soaking up the first of the summer sun, it took tremendous willpower to return to work. It was then that I realised that to work shut up in a building wasn't going to be for me much longer.

On 10 May, with the sun beaming down on most of Europe, you felt that the Almighty himself gave his blessing to anything that might happen on that day. The German High Command must have thought the same, for they unleashed their Panzer Divisions to move forward on the first stage of their plan to conquer Europe. That day the phony war came to an abrupt halt. There was an air of excitement everywhere. People were either glued to their radios or queueing up to get a copy of the latest newspaper editions. Some felt a sense of relief now that the war had started in earnest. We could at last give the Bosch a sound thrashing, and have the whole show wrapped by Christmas. We would soon get our boys back and continue once again with normal life. However, that illusion was shattered within days. As for me, on that fateful day, I went to work as usual, and Jack and I spent our lunch-hour (blissfully unconcerned with what was happening) lying on the grass in the park eating our cheese rolls and sunbathing.

By the middle of June 1940, with most of Europe in German hands, only England stood alone to carry on the fight. Uncle, who had, of course, something to conserve, thought that as there seemed no hope in hell for us to win the war, Britain should come to some accommodation with the 'Hun', rather than us lose everything. He wasn't alone amongst his aristocratic friends to think like that.

"After all, Hayden, as far as I know, Herr Hitler is much more against Bolsheviks, Socialists, Jews, and the like, than ordinary people. I'm sure that the gentry in the countries already occupied are reasonably well treated and allowed to keep their estates."

"But Uncle, what about the ordinary, decent working people? What would happen to them?"

"Oh, they'll hardly notice any difference, provided they don't do anything silly like going on strike."

Well, I thought (but didn't say), if living under German rule wasn't going to be so bad, why on earth are we fighting this war? In the end, thank God, the defeatist and misinformed notions of Uncle and his friends didn't prevail. Now that Europe was cut off, everything England needed had to be imported from the other side of the Atlantic by boat. Rations, which before the

fall of France had been quite generous, were cut to the bare minimum almost overnight.

At the beginning of July, Jack gave in a week's notice.

"Why did you do that?" I asked.

"Because I'm fed up with the bloody job - I'm going to be called up at the end of the summer, and I want to spend my last few weeks of freedom enjoying myself."

"How will you manage without any money?"

"I've enough saved to give my mum her fifteen shillings a week until I go into the army."

"But won't you need some extra spending money if you are going to enjoy yourself?"

"Hardly any for what I have in mind."

"What doesn't need money?" I asked.

"Hampstead Heath. I'm going there TO swim in the ponds and sunbathe for all the hours of daylight. I won't waste any time chasing girls, because I can go and see Gloria a couple of times a week."

"You might well bump into me, Jack, as I go and stay with her twice a week for the night."

"OK, Derrick, I'll do the evening shift and you can do the one at night."

"That's all right with me, Jack, if you don't mind being the soup and me the main course."

Then I said, "Jack, I'm going to join you."

"Join me - where?"

"On Hampstead Heath, that's where. I'm going up now to the old man and give in my notice. Now that both you and Stella have gone, I don't want to stay on here any longer."

The manager, I think, was relieved when I told him I was going. But Harry wasn't, as now he would have to break in two new boys at the same time.

As I hadn't told Uncle that I'd chucked in my job, it meant leaving in the morning at the usual time. What might have given the game away, was (if he had noticed, but he never did) the way I filled myself up with huge bowls of cornflakes at breakfast. For with no money coming in, it was all I was going to get to eat until I got back late at night, when I'd slam into the cereal again.

My day started with a five mile walk going via Jack's house in Camden Town to the men's pond on Hampstead Heath. Most of the day we spent swimming and larking about in the muddy water, or sunbathing on the grassy slopes outside the bathing enclosure. Every day Jack went inside the fenced-off pool to do weight training. The men in there exercised and sunbathed in the nude, but that wasn't the reason I didn't join him - it was because the place attracted a lot of homosexuals, who languished on their flower-patterned towels ogling the weightlifters. Some of these athletes were magnificent specimens, particularly if they were six foot or over. Although they looked as if they could snap you in half as easily as breaking a twig, most of them were gentle giants and vegetarians. There were some, however, who had the misfortune to be born with small heads. No matter how long they pushed the weights up and down, nothing would increase the size of their skulls, so they ended up with arms and legs the width of tree trunks, and perched on top of their thick necks were these little heads, making the rest of their bodies look absurdly out of proportion.

After three days I got fed up with this male only preserve, so I told Jack that I wasn't coming to this pond any more but would go instead to the mixed swimming pool in Parliament Hill Fields.

"You're missing the girls around, is that it? But do you know that the mixed pool costs sixpence a day? Where are you going to get that from?"

"I'm going to steal it from my uncle. It'll be easy, as he always empties the loose change from his pockets onto the bureau before going to bed, and he only remembers how many pound notes he's got in his wallet."

"In that case, Derrick, I'll come and join you in the afternoon and stay with you until it closes, how's that?"

"That's fine."

For the rest of July and into August, the weather remained as near perfect as anybody could wish for an English summer to be, and while the Germans were busy consolidating their ill-gotten gains in Europe, Jack and I continued to spend every day on Hampstead Heath. As for me, I had never had such a wonderful time. The memory of my most unhappy childhood years, and the more recent experiences in the army, began to fade as I enjoyed my new freedom. Jack, who had never had any time off since leaving school at fourteen, was also wallowing in what were to be his last weeks before being conscripted. Both of us in that long, hot summer could hardly stop smiling.

One day, when we were drying off after a swim, Jack told me about an idea he had on how we could play a practical joke on old Harry.

"What sort of joke?" I asked.

"You know what a mania he has about locking up, checking all the doors three times over. However, he forgets to close the toilet window that opens out onto the back yard. I suppose it's because he's such a titch, he can't reach the catch. Our little lark will be to climb over the back yard gates when the store is closed, get in through that window and unbolt all the front swing doors, then walk calmly out onto the High Street. What do you think about that?"

"I think it's a great idea, when shall we do it?"

"How about this evening?"

By seven-thirty, by which time we knew even the manager would have left, we were in the side streets leading to the back entrance of the store. Some of the kids for whom Jack used to leave out trays of cakes were playing football in the road. One of them spotted Jack and asked him why they didn't get any cakes any more.

"It's because I don't work here any more, I left a few weeks ago."

"If you don't work 'ere, what yer 'ere for?"

"We're going to play a joke on old Harry, so mum's the word, eh?"

"Yeah, Jack."

The boys watched as first Jack, then I, climbed over the gates into the yard.

Just as Jack had said it would be, the toilet window was unlocked and we were inside the store within seconds. To make it hard on the cops to fathom out how anybody broke in, he bolted the window from the inside. It was quite eerie, walking about in a place that was normally full of staff and shoppers. We walked casually through the store, lit only by the rays of the setting sun, to the front swing doors and unbolted all six of them, then stepped out onto the High Street.

"Come across the road, Derrick, in a few minutes you'll be able to watch all the fun start. At about eight, regular as clockwork, a copper on his beat walks by, testing all the shop doors. Let's see what happens when he pushes against the lot we've have opened up," Jack said with some glee.

Sure enough, the copper got to our store, pushing his baton against the first set of double doors, which promptly swung open, as did the next two. He pulled a large whistle out of his tunic pocket and blew on it frantically. Very quickly another policeman arrived and stood on guard while our copper ran down the road to the nearest phone box. Five minutes later two plain-clothes officers arrived in a police car.

"Time for us to move off, don't you think, Jack?"

"Well, that was a bit of a lark, wasn't it, Derrick?"

"Certainly was," I said.

Jack went on home and I made a beeline for Gloria's.

When I looked out of the window next morning, it was raining for the first time in weeks. No going on the Heath today, I thought. I finished the tea and toast Gloria had left for me before she went to work, and walked down the road to Jack's place.

"Suppose we can't grumble," said Jack, "after all, we've had it good up to now, haven't we?"

"If your mum doesn't mind, Jack, I'll sit around here until lunchtime, then, as it's Thursday and half-day closing at the store, I can go back to my place, quite legitimately, and perhaps get myself invited to eat out with my uncle this evening. I can't remember the last time I had a square meal, I'm sick to death of cornflakes."

When I arrived back at Adelaide Court that afternoon, Uncle was sitting in his favourite armchair.

"Hello, Hayden, back so soon?" he said, looking up.

"Yes, it's hal-day closing today."

"Oh, of course, it is." Then he added, "Louis Green phoned me this morning."

"Oh, how is he?" I asked.

"Well, he's a bit upset."

"Upset about what?"

"You, Hayden."

Oh dear, I thought, here it comes, he's told Uncle that I left Marks & Spencer weeks ago.

"Yes, he was told that you and another employee, broke into the store last night. What have you got to say about that?"

I told him that I had only deceived him because he and Louis had been so kind in getting me the job - I just hadn't been able to bring myself to mention that I had left. The lark last night was just done as a joke on the over-zealous storeroom manager. If they checked their stock, they would find out nothing was missing.

"You could have told me you wanted to leave. I wouldn't have objected to you playing around in the sun for a few weeks."

"How did they find out it was us?"

"The investigating officers accused some boys who play around in the streets at the back of the store, and said they saw you climbing in over the gates."

"What happens now, Uncle?"

"I think I can explain everything satisfactorily to Louis, I'll just tell him all that you've told me, I'm sure he will understand. You're lucky, you know, that he is my friend, for if he wasn't, you and your chum might well have ended up in prison. Judges don't take kindly to young men who break into shops, even though you did it as a prank."

A little later, Uncle told me that he had spoken to Louis, who had assured him that no charges would be made against either of us.

"I reminded him that when he and I were undergraduates, we were never charged with anything when we went on the rampage during rag week, smashing up cafés and bars and terrorising local people. If any one wanted money for the damage done, well, naturally, our parents would pay up."

With everything forgotten and forgiven, he invited me to join him at his club for dinner. When he saw the ravenous way I devoured the food, he asked me what I had been eating while I wasn't working.

"Cornflakes," I said.

"Oh, poor boy, you must be starving," then with a wave of his hand, he called the waiter over. "Give my young friend another portion of trifle please."

The next day, the sun was shining again, and as I no longer needed to pretend that I was going to work, I joined Uncle at breakfast. I told him that I didn't care very much for any work that meant me being shut up in a building all day long, and would prefer to find a job in the open air.

"How do you feel about working on a farm?" asked Uncle.

"I think I'd like that. Do you know a farmer then?"

"No, I don't, but some of my friends have tenant farmers on their land. There's one with a large estate not far from Coventry. I'll phone him and see if he has any ideas."

"Working on a farm does appeal to me. I promise not to let him or you down again."

I got up from the table and prepared to join Jack. As I was going out of the door, Uncle called me back.

"Hayden, how did you manage to pay for bus fares all these weeks without any money?"

"I walked everywhere."

"Well, there's no need to do that any more. I'm going to give you half-a-crown a day until you've found another job. Do you think that will suffice?"

"Oh,yes, Uncle, that will be more than enough."

When I got to Jack's place, I told him how our little escapade had backfired and that one of the boys had spilled the beans. He was furious.

"Fucking bastards - after all I've done for them, feeding them with trays of stale cakes every day. I'm glad they don't get them any more."

"Jesus, Jack, what were the poor kids to do when the police accused them of breaking in - say yes, we did it?"

"You're right, there was nothing else they could have done. Now I suppose the cops will be round here any moment to nick us."

"No, they won't," and I told him why.

"Cor, Derrick, it's bloody useful having a friend who knows toffs, isn't it?"

"It is, but it shouldn't be."

"Maybe, but all I can say is, when you're born like we were, on the wrong side of the track, you should take any fucking help that's offered."

We left Jack's home to have yet another day enjoying ourselves on the Heath, only this time we could take a bus.

Next day Uncle told me his friend with the estate had rung back and said that one of his tenant farmers needed an extra hand to help bring in the harvest, and I could start as soon as I liked.

"I hope it's all right with you, Hayden, but I suggested next Monday. I thought that would leave you the weekend free to say goodbye to your friends."

"Yes, that's fine, I'll spend today and tomorrow with Jack, and tonight with Gloria."

"I suppose she'll be very upset when she hears you're going?"

"Oh no, I don't think so, I share her with one or two others, I think she'll hardly notice that I'm gone. If anyone is going to be upset, it'll be me."

"Well, Hayden, I don't think it will be very long before you meet a buxom wench that you can romp in the hay with."

On that hopeful note, I left for Jack's place.

That last weekend together, he spent the time with me in the pool at Parliament Hill Fields. I think he was unhappy that he was going to lose his friend, but understood when I told him I couldn't go on sponging on my uncle for much longer. Gloria, on the other hand, surprised me. She was, quite upset, so to console her I said I wouldn't be away for very long and would leave the farm after the harvest. She could be sure that one day when she returned from work, I'd be standing on her doorstep waiting to be let in. I told them both that I would write and let them know how I was making out.

CHAPTER NINETEEN

By now it was mid-August, the sun was shining, the skies were blue. In these perfect flying conditions, our pilots were in the cockpits of their Spitfires, engaged for all the hours of daylight in dog-fights with the Luftwaffe, who with their superior numbers were trying to gain air supremacy prior to launching a full-scale invasion of Britain. What I did while all this was happening was board the eleven o'clock train bound for Coventry. Uncle told me that the farmer, a Mr John Napier, would meet me and drive me to his farm, some ten miles south of the town.

I stood outside the station and waited to be approached by someone, who I imagined would look like your typical Farmer Giles. It was over half an hour before a man in a pork-pie hat came up to me.

"Are you Cartlidge?" he said gruffly.

"Yes, I am, pleased to meet you, Mr Napier."

I held out my hand for him to shake but he ignored it.

"I've got my truck over there," he said, pointing to a vehicle that looked so decrepit that one couldn't help but marvel how it ever managed to travel the ten miles into town. The passenger door almost fell off as he opened it, for it was only attached to the body by one of its two hinges, the other having rusted away.

"Get in," he said.

The seat I had been invited to sit on was a loose wooden box with an old sack folded double for upholstery.

"I was told a man, was coming, not a boy," said the farmer as we drove out of the station precinct.

"Sorry," I replied, "but my uncle did tell his friend how old I was."

"His name, boy, is Lord Upton, and had his Lordship told me your age, I would have said no thanks."

"In that case, sir, would you prefer it if I returned to London on the next train?" I hoped that the unfriendly old bugger would say yes.

"Now you're here, you might as well stay, I suppose, but I'm warning you, if you're no good I'll send you packing soon enough."

With that off his chest, he set his eyes on the road ahead and said no more for some time. This gave me an opportunity to have a sideways glance at the man. He appeared to be about my height, and in his early forties. His face was almost square and had thin, mean lips. A pencil-line moustache neatly trimmed grew precisely halfway between his nostrils and his upper lip. But one feature that worried me most was his piercing dark-brown eyes. His very muscular, short neck was almost the same width as his face and therefore didn't really exist. The hands that now had a tight grip on the steering wheel were the strongest pair I'd ever seen - rough and weatherbeaten, and covered with skin so hardened by years of manual work, that I'm sure if you struck a match and held the flame close to his palm, he'd smell the burning flesh long before he'd feel the pain.

At one point, as we drove along the leafy country lanes, we had to stop and let a herd of cows cross the road. Immediately the engine stalled and despite repeated turns with the ignition key, wouldn't start up again. The farmer banged his fist onto the dashboard with such force that he made a crack in it. Although he said nothing, you knew he was in a God-Almighty rage because of the way his veins bulged out from his neck. He got out of the truck and opened the bonnet. After a minute or two tinkering about, he put his arm through the window and turned the key, but the motor didn't respond. Then he opened the truck door and pulled out a crank handle from under the seat. He strode round to the front of the truck and rammed it into the engine. He swung the crank with such vigour that I think the front wheels were literally lifted a couple of inches up off the road. Thank God, it did the trick and the engine started.

When we had done a mile or two, the farmer opened his mouth and spoke to me for the first time.

"At this time of the year, boy, we work from sunrise to sunset, every day except the sabbath, when after milking the cows, my wife and I attend the morning service. You will, of course, want to join us there. You are, I hope, a Christian and God-fearing man?"

He didn't wait for me to answer but it crossed my mind that when the good Lord saw this frightening man enter his house he probably ducked. Anyway, I couldn't muster up the courage to tell him that I'd finished with all that hocus-pocus long ago.

"You will be paid fourteen shillings a week and board." The farmer continued: "My wife is a good plain cook and does nothing fancy. If you don't agree with my terms, now's the time to say so."

"Agreed," I said.

I had the distinct feeling that if I hadn't, he'd have stopped the truck and thrown me out, suitcase and all, leaving me to walk the eight miles back to Coventry. Still, on the plus side, he was paying four shillings a week more than the army had.

A little further on, we turned off the lane onto an uneven and rutted earth track. After a couple of hundred yards we stopped in front of a broken down, old wooden gate. A notice nailed to it read in big letters 'KEEP OUT'. I thought it should also add 'AND BEWARE OF THE FARMER'. The gate, like the door on the truck, had only one hinge.

The farmhouse I had imagined was a picture-postcard kind, with rambling roses climbing up old walls laced with oak beams, but this one wasn't anything like that. A child could have designed a better one. It had two storeys and was completely square, with four large, flat windows evenly spaced on its front-facing wall. The front door was placed precisely between the two windows on the ground floor. Nothing pleasing to look at embellished any part of the exterior. Under the sloped and slated roof was a small attic window on one side only. I guessed that the house had been standing for about a hundred years or so, and from then on had been allowed to crumble. However, it had one redeeming feature, a large lawn extending from the front of the house down to the farm buildings some twenty-five yards away. A small vegetable plot was tagged on to one side of the lawn.

The farmer went through his front door and beckoned me to follow him, shouting
out: "Meg, I'm back."

Within seconds, his wife appeared. I was quite shocked when I saw her. She looked pale and worn out. Two fading black eyes were distinctly visible, as were bruise marks on both arms. These only showed because it was a very hot day and she was wearing a sleeveless dress.

"Meet my wife," he said, not looking at me as he spoke. "This boy is called, I've forgotten your name."

"Call me Derrick, Mrs Napier, it's my middle name but the one I prefer to be called by."

I put out my hand and gently shook hers. I felt a slight tremble when I held her hand in mine. Then, like a beaten dog with its head bent, she said almost inaudibly, "I'll show you to your room."

I followed her up the stairs to the next floor. It had three doors all of which were closed. She opened one of them and showed me where the combined bathroom and toilet was. I fully expected her to open another one and say 'This is yours', but instead she took me to the end of the landing where a ladder led up to a trap door in the ceiling.

"Your room is the attic up there. I'll leave you to make your own way up. When you've unpacked, come down and I'll make you some tea. And please remember to bring your ration book with you."

I went up the ladder sideways, lugging my suitcase with me. What hit me as I stepped into this tiny attic was how unbelievably hot it was. The sun was beating down on the sloping roof a few inches above my head. I went straight to the small dormer window and opened it wide but it made no difference at all. I decided that I wouldn't spend much time in this tiny, stuffy attic, not while the sun was shining, that's for sure.

It was furnished with the bare minimum. A divan not more than two foot six wide was pushed against the wall. I made a mental note to remember not to sit up in bed, because if I forgot I'd give my head a hell of a bang against the sloping roof. A little table was by the side of the bed, and put conspicuously on it was a Bible. I would have much preferred to have seen an electric fan there.

At the other end of the room was the smallest chest of drawers I'd ever seen: you could only get to it by shutting the flap of the trap door. The only space I could stand upright in was in the centre.

I unpacked the few things that I'd brought with me and went down to join Mrs Napier for tea. I found her in the kitchen, standing by the stove waiting for the kettle to boil.

"Sorry your room is so small, but it's the only spare one we have, I'm afraid."

"Please don't apologise, it's quite cosy, just a bit hot at the moment, but no doubt it will cool down once the sun has set."

She made the tea and poured me a cup.

"Mr Napier not joining us?" I enquired.

"No, he's out bringing the cows in for milking."

I was relieved to hear that, for as far as I was concerned, the less I saw of him the better. It also gave me chance to observe his wife. She was probably about thirty-five, but looked older. Her long, curly hair that showed a few strands of grey was parted in the middle and hung down each side of her face, almost screening it from view. There was a sort of beauty about her sad and worn-out face. Looking through the thin summer dress that she wore I could see that she still had a good figure, which I'm sure was totally wasted on her God-fearing husband. He probably took more care of the animals than he did of his wife.

Although she had poured herself a cup, she didn't sit down at the table and relax while drinking it, but instead pottered about the kitchen doing things. I could see she wasn't used to indulging in idle conversation, but I decided I would let her know that in me at any rate she would have a sympathetic friend. So, with that in mind, I got a conversation started.

"Do you mind if I smoke?"

"No, I don't, but my husband regards smoking as sinful."

Well fuck him, I thought, it's a pity he doesn't think it's a sin to bash his wife about. Then I looked pointedly at the large bruises on her arms.

"How did you get those bruises on your arms, did you fall?" I asked. I was fairly sure that I wasn't going to be given a truthful answer.

To my surprise she said: "My husband made them," then added the lie I had expected, "I bruise very easily. A gentle squeeze leaves marks on me."

Did the bastard give a gentle squeeze to her eyes, I wondered.

"In future he'll have to make his squeezes even more gentle, won't he, Mrs Napier?"

I hoped that my sarcastic answer let her know that I didn't believe what she had told me for one moment. To change the subject, I told her I didn't eat meat.

"It has one advantage though, Mrs Napier, you can have my ration, and please don't bother to cook anything different for me, I'll just eat what you and your husband do minus the meat."

"I'll do the best I can for you, Mr - "

"My name is Derrick."

"Derrick," she repeated, and then looking for the first time straight at me, said, "And mine is Meg."

"Well, Meg, thanks for the tea. I'll get out of your way now and go and look around a bit."

"Supper's at seven," she said.

Knowing that the farmer was in the shed milking, I decided to avoid him by walking about in the surrounding fields. Most of the acreage I saw was given over to the growing of wheat. It was lovely to see the stalks standing erect and golden, swaying a little in the slight breeze. Standing there and admiring the scenery all around me and inhaling the fresh country air, I felt nothing but pity for all those people whose only view was a factory wall. I stayed there for a long while, gazing in front of me, with my mind a complete blank. Then, from the position of the sinking sun, I guessed it must be getting on for seven, and was time to go back to the farm for supper.

Mr Napier was in the front room, sitting in the only armchair, reading a newspaper. He didn't look up when I came in nor did he say anything. Getting the distinct feeling that he'd rather be left on his own, I went and joined his wife in the kitchen. She had already laid the table and was slicing up a loaf when I came in.

"Hallo, Derrick, did you enjoy your walk?"

"Yes, it's very beautiful around here, but then you're used to it, I suppose."

"Yes, it is lovely but I don't get out much except to church on Sundays. I'm sorry I can't offer you a glass of wine or cider, John doesn't agree with having anything alcoholic in the house."

"Sinful," I said.

"Yes, that's what he thinks."

"You don't have to worry about me, as I don't drink, but not for the same reason as your husband, I just don't like the taste of any liquid except tea."

"Oh, I'll be making tea," then, pointing to a chair placed on one side of the table, "if you'll take a seat I'll go and tell John supper's ready."

When he was seated - and as I hadn't eaten since breakfast and was very hungry - I reached out to pick up a slice of bread. The farmer's hand shot out and grabbed me by the wrist.

"In this house, boy, we say grace before we eat," he said with one of those piercing looks of his.

Jesus, I thought, if I don't watch out this religious zealot will force me onto my knees and make me say my prayers before getting into bed. He let go of me and clasped his hands together, then closed his eyes, bent his thick neck as far as he could and said grace. I looked at his wife, and as she had only bent her head but not shut her eyes, I made a point that she could see me defying her husband by folding my arms and staring at the ceiling.

The meal was eaten in silence. 'Meal' perhaps was the wrong word to use, for all that was on offer was bread and cheese with pickles. I would have liked to have spoken to Meg but decided against it, for I think it would have only made her feel uneasy.

When we had finished eating, I would have loved to have said out loud my version of grace after meals: 'We thank thee, oh Lord, for the meagre meal we've just had', but I didn't. After tea, I thought I'd test the reaction of the lord and master by lighting up a cigarette. His response was immediate and predictable:

"There's to be no smoking in this house, boy."

"All right, Mr Napier, I'll go outside."

As he didn't protest, I presumed that as far as he was concerned, it was OK to sin provided you did it outside the four walls of his house.

As it was such a hot night, I sat in the middle of the lawn puffing away for some time, then had a stroll. When I went back although it was not yet nine o'clock, neither the farmer nor his wife was anywhere to be seen. I supposed they must already have gone to bed. Oh well, I thought, I might as well do the same. I went into the bathroom and cleaned my teeth, then climbed the ladder that led into the attic. It was still very hot in there, so I quickly stripped down to my underpants and pulled the blankets off the bed. I lay on top of the sheets and was soon fast asleep.

In the morning, I awoke feeling a hand touching my bare shoulder. As I opened my eyes, it was withdrawn. Meg was standing by the side of the bed, holding a cup.

"Good morning, Derrick, I've brought you a cup of tea."

She put it down by the Bible on the little bedside table. She took a furtive glance at my almost naked body and asked me where I'd got so brown.

"On Hampstead Heath in North London," I told her.

"But you look so tanned, I thought you must have been on holiday at the seaside. Who would have thought you could get a tan like that in smoky old London."

"London isn't always smoky, it's only like that when all the coal fires are burning."

She disappeared through the trap door and descended down the ladder. How on earth she ever managed to bring up a full cup of tea without spilling any was a mystery to me. When I went into the kitchen, there were only two places laid.

"Isn't Mr Napier joining us?" I asked.

"No, he's out milking right now. He has tea before he goes off, then comes back for his breakfast after he's done with the cows."

Good, I thought, there'll be none of that grace nonsense. However, what Meg gave me I wouldn't have minded thanking the Lord for. First I got a big bowl of steaming hot porridge with fresh milk and a large spoonful of golden syrup plonked on its surface. This was followed by a boiled fresh egg, and to finish off, there was buttered toast with home-made marmalade spread generously over it.

"Do you have many chickens?" I asked.

"About a dozen."

"They certainly give you wonderful eggs."

"Yes, they do, but you can't rely on them, especially when they go all broody."

I didn't know what 'going all broody' meant, I presumed it was that sometimes they just wanted to be difficult. Thinking of chickens and then chicks prompted me to ask Meg if she had any children.

"No," she said abruptly.

This stopped me pursuing the subject any further. I was just taking the last sip of tea when Mr Napier came in and sat down at the head of the table.

"Good morning," I said cheerfully.

He responded by just nodding. Meg put a bowl of porridge in front of him.

"Be by the truck in ten minutes," he said, looking only into the bowl. This I took to be his way of saying 'piss off and leave me in peace while I eat. So that's what I did.

When he came out, I was having a smoke.

"You can put that out and get into the truck."

I kept him waiting while I took a couple more draws, then got in beside him. Turning to me, he said: "Today, boy..."

"My name is Derrick," I said firmly.

Ignoring my interruption, he went on:

"We are going to follow the hired men with their harvester as they cut the wheat, then, as the sheaves are bundled and flung out, we pick them up and stook them. Watch me and you'll see how it's done!"

On the way to the fields, he stopped at the barn and picked up two scythes and their cone-shaped sharpening stones. When we arrived, there was no sign of the harvester or the men.

"Perhaps they've forgotten to come?" I said.

"They'll not be here until the sun has burnt off the dew. In the meantime, I'll show you how to use a scythe."

He picked up the implement and turned it upside down, so that the end of the handle was on the ground and the blade shoulder level. Holding it firmly in one hand, and the honing stone in the other, he looked at me for once and said:

"We use the scythe to cut the edges of the field where the machine can't reach, but before you cut one stalk, you must spend some time sharpening it. Now, boy, pick up your scythe and when it's sharp enough, get cutting."

I found the honing procedure quite unnerving as the blade seemed to act like a magnet, drawing my fingers ever closer to its razor-sharp edge. The farmer was getting more and more irritated with the timid way I wielded the stone, until he shouted out:

"That's enough of that, next time do it with a bit more vigour, otherwise you'll spend all day just sharpening the thing. Now, get on and do some cutting."

Thank God, at that moment the harvester arrived, and he went off to meet the men. This gave me a chance to practise a little without being supervised. I'm always at my worst when someone is standing over me, watching and criticising every move I make.

My first swing was a disaster. The pointed tip of the blade sank into the ground and hit a large stone with some force. It dawned on me that the best way to learn was not to try and do any cutting until I'd got the feel of swinging the long blade evenly, two inches above the ground. After a bit of practice, I felt confident enough to have another try. To my delight, I managed to cut a few stalks. Just as I was beginning to enjoy myself, the farmer returned. He looked at what I had cut and said:

"That's better, keep it up and maybe soon you'll get the hang of it, but for now you must stop it and come with me and help with the stooking."

By now it was quite hot, so I took my shirt off and followed him.

The driver of the harvester started up the engine and moved off along the edge of the field. Protruding from the side of the machine was a wide wheel interspaced with wooden slats that, as the harvester went along, rotated, pushing the standing stalks against the fast scissor movement of the blades. The cut wheat went up a conveyor belt to two men standing on a platform behind the driver. They tied up handfuls of stalks, heavy with ears of ripened wheat, into large bundles and then threw them onto the stubbled ground behind the slow-moving machine. I watched the farmer for a bit and saw what I had to do. You had to pick up two sheaves at a time, put one under each arm, then prop them up against each other. When three pairs were placed together, you had made one stook.

With the top half of my body uncovered, I bent down to pick up my first sheaf, then slung it under my arm against the side of my bare chest Immediately I felt a stinging pain. I gave out a yell and dropped the bundle to the ground. The farmer saw this and just grinned. The bastard could have warned me that growing between the stalks were thistles and nettles, as tall and sturdy as the wheat itself. He was totally protected by his jacket. I pulled out some of the worst prickles that were embedded in my skin, but as there were so many I gave up trying and just put up with the discomfort. I put my shirt back on for some protection, but not much.

The rest of the day was spent following the harvester as it went in ever-diminishing circles round the field. Then, with only a small amount left to cut, it came to a halt. The two men who had been on the platform jumped off and went with the farmer to his truck. They returned each carrying a double-barrelled shotgun under their arm.

"Now the fun starts," said one of the men.

"What are you going to do?" I asked.

"What do you think Mr and Mrs Rabbit have been doing while we've been cutting away? They've been retreating into the uncut wheat with nowhere to go. They'll have to make a run for it across the stubble to the hedgerow, and as they do - bang, bang, we shoot them."

The farmer and the two men took up their positions around the circle of uncut wheat. Within seconds, out came some terrified rabbits, running for dear life towards the nearest hedge for cover. Almost all of them were gunned down only halfway across the open ground. Some were shot when they were only a few yards away from safety. A few clever rabbits did make it: instead of running in a straight line they zigzagged across the field, making it almost impossible for their assassins to get them in their sights. I was overjoyed. After all, as a non-meat eater, I didn't have a vested interest in their death. Unfortunately, one was only wounded in the back leg by the farmer, just as it was about to escape.

"Go and get it, boy," shouted the farmer as the poor creature started to crawl towards the hedge.

Without thinking, I ran towards the injured animal. As I got to it, the rabbit lay motionless, apparently dead. I bent down and picked it up by its bleeding hind legs, when, unexpectedly, they gave a violent jerk. It felt like a thousand volts had passed through my body.

"Oh Christ," I screamed as I released my grip. By using only its front paws, the rabbit dragged itself into the long grass and thankfully disappeared.

"You blithering idiot, you've let it get away," he yelled. But I was too shaken up by the incident to give a damn what abuse he shouted at me. At least, I thought, it died in the familiarity of its own habitat and not at the hands of a human.

Although some twenty rabbits had been slaughtered that afternoon, the farmer gave only two each to the three men on the harvester. The remaining carcasses he threw into the back of his truck, before driving off to the farm. I spent the rest of the day stooking, only stopping when the daylight faded.

By the time I returned to the farm, it was nearly dark. Meg was in the kitchen:

"Hallo, Derrick, sit down. You must be very tired and hungry."

She had guessed correctly. All I had eaten since breakfast was two Marmite sandwiches.

"Have you and Mr Napier eaten already?"

"Yes, some time ago, but I've kept yours nice and hot in the oven."

She had made a rabbit pie, but remembering my aversion to meat, gave me only the pie crust with a big helping of potatoes and carrots, liberally covering it all with gravy.

I felt a bit queasy about eating anything made from the creatures I'd watched being so brutally slaughtered. But as I was so hungry, I overcome my reluctance.

The farmer sold nine of the fourteen rabbits to the village butcher. The other five he gave to Meg, and, rabbit cooked in various ways was the menu every night for a week.

Meg asked me how I'd made out on my first day. I told her how the nettles and thistles had stung me and how the prickles had got stuck into my arm, and into one side of my chest.

"Roll up your sleeve and let me have a look."

When she saw how inflamed they were, she gave out a little gasp.

"Oh you poor boy, stay here while I go and get some tweezers."

When she returned, she put my arm across her lap, and with the help of a magnifying glass, she removed even the smallest thorns.

"Meg," I said, "you're a regular Florence Nightingale, aren't you? Thanks a lot."

"It was no bother, but please do put on your jacket when you're out working in the fields tomorrow."

I stayed there for a bit after Meg had left and bade me goodnight. Well aware that I was breaking a house rule, I lit up a cigarette. Then, feeling very tired, I made my way up to the attic.

It was still extremely hot up there, so once again, I stripped down to my pants, and lay on top of the sheets. I was asleep before my head hit the pillow.

CHAPTER TWENTY

I awoke with the feel of Meg's hand stroking my back. I knew that if I stirred, she would stop, so I didn't. She even gave me a gentle kiss between my shoulder blades. I liked what she was doing, so I let it continue for some time, only opening my eyes when I thought the cup of tea I was sure she had brought up might be getting cold.

"Good morning, Derrick, did you sleep well?"

"Like a log, Meg. It's very nice to be woken up by a lovely lady with a cup of tea in her hand. But it must be quite a bother for you to come all the way up here. It can wait until I come down to breakfast, you know."

"It's really no trouble at all. Anyway, how would you ever get up if I didn't wake you?"

"That's true, left to myself I can easily sleep until midday. Has Mr Napier gone off to the cowshed yet?"

"Yes, he has."

"Good," I said, and by uttering that one word, I let her know that I didn't care very much for her husband.

A few seconds later I was in the kitchen, where once again Meg made me a wonderful breakfast. Remembering the advice she gave me, I fetched my jacket before setting off for the fields.

I preferred to walk rather than go with the old grump in his truck. The whole of that day, and for the next four, was spent propping up the bundles of wheat, the late afternoons ending up as always with the slaughtering of rabbits.

One evening the light faded before they could shoot any, so they had to wait until the next day. Early the following morning, I got to the field before the farmer and the men on the harvester. I ran up and down the small plot of wheat still standing, and clapped my hands while shouting madly. To my relief, this worked: all the rabbits took fright and ran across the field to the shelter of the hedgerow. The farmer and the men on the machine were very puzzled when no rabbits appeared as they cut down the last stalks.

"Maybe they're getting wiser," I said.

"Rabbits don't get wiser, boy, something strange has happened. In all my years, I've never known there to be no rabbits at the end of a cutting."

"Perhaps a fox scared them off during the night," I suggested to divert any suspicion being directed my way.

"Well, something cunning did," he said.

About midday, I saw a man on a white horse coming towards where the farmer and I were stooking. He stopped right by us. The man looked very distinguished on his white steed. He was wearing an open-necked shirt which was tucked into his light brown, twill riding-breeches. Well-groomed, silver-coloured hair was brushed back from an intelligent high forehead and finely chiselled face.

"Good day, John," he said.

The farmer took off his hat, and looking at the ground, replied:

"Mornin', my Lord."

The man on the horse then turned to me:

"My name is Upton, you must be Hayden Cartlidge, Conny's adopted nephew. How are you liking life on a farm?"

"Very much."

"Glad to hear it. Is John looking after you all right?"

Unable to say truthfully that he was, I skirted round the question by saying that Mrs Napier was more than kind to me.

"I'll be speaking to Conny this afternoon, have you a message for him?"

"Oh yes, would you tell him that once the harvest is in, I'll be coming up to London for a few days. That is, of course, if Mr Napier doesn't object."

"I'm sure that would be all right with you, wouldn't it, John?"

"Yes, me' Lord."

Conditioned the way he was, there was no alternative for him but to agree with any request made by his lord and master. God only knows why, because without the tenant farmers like him, scraping a modest living in return for hard work and long hours in all weathers, generations of Lord Upton's family wouldn't have been able to live the grand life they did.

One good thing did come from my meeting with Lord Upton, I now knew I had nothing to fear from my bully of an employer. I was sure he realised that the noble Lord would feel duty-bound to keep an eye on me because of his friendship with Uncle.

By the end of the afternoon, the men on the harvester had finished cutting the four fields of wheat they were contracted to do, and after being paid, they left. The farmer and I went on stooking the remaining sheaves until sundown.

The next day was spent scything the edges of the fields. I really enjoyed doing this once I had got into the rhythm of it, but unfortunately by midday huge blisters had appeared on the palms of my hands. It became increasingly painful to hold the scythe. I asked the farmer if I might go back to the farm and see if his wife had anything she could put on them, or bandage them some way.

"The only thing worth putting on them, you carry within you."

I couldn't imagine what he meant by that.

"You urinate on them. It sterilises and at the same time hardens the skin."

I did what he suggested. It helped a bit, but it was still not possible to hold the handle and I told him so.

"For goodness sake, boy, can't you put up with a little pain?"

"This isn't a little pain, Mr Napier, it hurts like hell."

"Oh very well, then, spend the rest of the day tying up the cut wheat into bundles."

Thank heavens it was Saturday, and tomorrow being Sunday meant I didn't have to work. With a bit of luck, my hands would have healed up a little by

Monday morning.

That evening at supper Meg saw the state the palms of my hands were in and offered to bandage them up.

"Don't fuss over the boy," said her husband.

Then, for the first time since I'd been there, she dared to answer him back.

"I'm not fussing, John, I just think Derrick's hands need a little attention."

The farmer brought his fist down onto the table with such force that all the plates jumped up in the air.

"For goodness sake, all that's the matter with him is a few blisters on his precious hands. I forbid you to touch the boy, do you understand?"

"It's very kind of you, Mrs Napier," I said quickly (I never called her Meg when he was around), "but I think if I prick them, it may be the quickest cure."

The rest of the meal continued in silence, then the two of them retired to their bedroom. I went out and sat on the lawn, had a couple of cigarettes, and then took myself off to bed.

My head had hardly hit the pillow when I heard a lot of banging, shouting and thumping going on downstairs. I could hear Meg calling out: "Oh no, John, please don't ... please no more, John, stop it."

But the bastard just carried on attacking her. It got to the point where I could stand it no longer, so I dressed quickly and climbed down the ladder. Then, knowing I was taking my life in my hands, I mustered up all my courage and knocked on their door.

"Are you all right, Mrs Napier?" I asked with a tremulous voice.

The room went silent, so I repeated my question. The door opened a little and half the farmer's face peered out through the gap. The one eye that I could see had a mad look about it.

"Go back to bed, boy, there's nothing going on here that is any concern of yours. Go back to your bed."

He looked so threatening that I retreated slowly back up the ladder, leaving poor Meg to her fate. In the end, however, some good did seem to come out from my timid intervention, because all went quiet for the rest of the night.

The next morning Meg didn't wake me.

Shit, I said to myself, perhaps that swine of a husband murdered her during the night. I dressed hurriedly and went downstairs. To my relief, Meg was in the kitchen, standing by the stove, facing the wall.

"Good morning, Meg."

"Morning, Derrick," she replied without turning round.

I went over and stood by her side, put my hands on her shoulders and very gently turned her towards me. What I saw shocked me. Both her eyes were swollen and were turning black. She had bruises on her cheeks and forehead, and her arms were badly marked.

"Meg," I said, "this can't be right, can it?"

"I'll be all right in a couple of days, Derrick, now you sit down and have your breakfast."

"Meg, what can be done to stop this sort of thing happening again?"

"Nothing, I married the man and that's that."

"You wouldn't be the first woman to leave her husband if he treats you badly," I said.

"I have nowhere to go. Both my parents are dead."

"Come with me to London, Meg, I'll find you a room. Nowaday's it's easy to find a job. If I were you, I'd rather work in a munitions factory than stay here."

"I can't, Derrick, really, I can't."

Tears started to roll down her swollen face. I drew her close to me, she rested her sore head on my chest and to comfort her, I stroked her hair.

"Oh Meg, dear Meg, please don't cry, but do promise me you'll think about what I said."

"I promise," she said between sobs.

"Where is he now?" I asked.

"He's gone to morning service."

"I suppose he's going to ask God to forgive him for the beating he gave you last night, eh?"

"Oh no, he won't be doing that, he'll be asking the Lord to forgive me."

"And what wicked thing does he think you've done?"

"I contradicted him in front of you last night at supper."

"Oh dear, it makes me feel dreadful that it was because of me that you got so badly treated."

"Please don't blame yourself. If it hadn't been for that, he'd have found another reason. He was in that sort of mood. Now sit down and eat your breakfast before it gets cold."

I was nearing the end of the meal when the farmer came back from church. As he never responded, I'd given up saying good morning long ago. I just gave him a look and carried on eating.

"What sort of a time do you think this is, to be having breakfast?" he asked.

"I overslept. Perhaps it was because I didn't get to sleep until quite late last night."

I hoped that he would ask me what kept me awake, but he didn't. Instead he said to his wife: "In future, if the boy doesn't come down to breakfast at the proper time, don't give him any."

Meg didn't answer him.

"I'm talking to you, woman, did you hear what I said?"

"Yes."

"Are you saying 'yes' you did hear, or 'yes' I will obey you?"

"Both," she said meekly.

This seemed to satisfy him, because he left the kitchen and went into the other room and read the Sunday paper.

"Can I help you with the washing up or the housework? I'm very good at it,

I've done lots of it in my time."

"No, thank you, Derrick."

I took a stroll down to the village to see if there was any life going on there. But everybody must have been indoors, having their Sunday lunch, for I saw not one person as I walked around. The village had three shops, a baker, a butcher and a small, general store, but no pub. If you needed a drink, you had to go to the next village, which was five miles away, and the nearest picture house was in Coventry. God only knows what people did around here for entertainment, I thought, as I left to return to the farm.

For lunch, Meg had made roast beef with golden-baked potatoes, roasted parsnips and my favourite dish - Yorkshire pudding, with lots of gravy, especially made for me. Just to annoy her husband, and at the same time break the silence rule, I told her what a wonderful cook she was. Then, to rile him even more, I asked: "Don't you agree, Mr Napier?"

"What on earth would be the use of a wife if she can't cook?"

I thought, if I were the wife of this bully, I'd inject tiny pinches of arsenic into his food every day until it killed him.

When the meal was over, he said his grace, then left the kitchen.

"I certainly put my foot in it, didn't I?"

"I wouldn't worry about it. He'll vent all his anger on his usual Sunday afternoon nonsense wrestling the bull."

When I went outside, sure enough, I could see the lunatic leading a medium-sized bull by its nose up from the sheds towards the lawn. Halfway across it, he stopped and took off his jacket. Then, standing by the side of the animal, he let go of the rope and took a few paces backwards until he was about three yards away. Suddenly and at great speed, he made a running jump at it. Gripping the bull round its neck with his muscular and powerful arms, he held it in an unrelenting stranglehold. He dug the heels of his boots into the lawn and pushed with his full weight and strong legs against the beast, simultaneously tugging at its neck, trying his best to twist the animal sideways and topple it over. But the bull held its ground. I think it decided that the best way to rid itself of this annoying man was to lower its head down to the ground. This movement nearly put the farmer flat on his belly, then with a quick jerk of its head upwards, it forced the farmer's locked arms to spring open, sending the Midlands toreador flying backwards through the air. He landed some distance away flat on his back, with a tremendous thud which momentarily stunned him.

Having suffered three gruelling rounds which always ended in defeat, and when most normal men would have thrown in the towel, this very strong man was determined to show the animal who was master even if it killed him. So, in round 4, he changed his tactics. This time he clasped the bull around its neck, but unlike the previous rounds, he didn't dig his heels into the lawn, instead he swung his legs in a backwards and forwards motion, like a child swinging from a low branch of a tree. Now, all the farmer had to do when the animal lowered its head, was sit on the ground until he was hoisted up again. At no time did he ever slacken the tight grip around its neck. Up and down he went, like a yo-yo. Eventually the poor beast began to tire. Finally its head went down and stayed there. That was the moment he'd been waiting for. Now he could do what he had tried to do before so unsuccessfully. With his feet firmly dug into the ground, he twisted and tugged at the bull's neck until it very slowly keeled over. The farmer lay across the prostrate animal's neck, triumphant, for a full minute, before allowing the bull to get back on its feet. Totally exhausted, and led by a slack rope, the humbled beast was taken back to its shed.

If the farmer had done all this to impress me, I must admit he succeeded. However, it didn't stop me harbouring the wicked thought, that perhaps one day the bull would be the victor, thereby relieving poor battered Meg of a tyrannical husband. When I told Meg what I had witnessed, all she said was:

"Oh thank God, he's finally done it. This is the first time he's ever managed to bring the poor creature down. Let's hope he can leave it in peace for the rest of the summer."

"Well, surely it's better if he fights the bull than you, isn't it, Meg?"

"What would be best, Derrick, was if he left both of us alone."

With the rest of the day still in front of me, I tried to think up some way to amuse myself. Meg must have read my thoughts, as she suggested that it might be a good idea if I went into Coventry and saw a film.

"They have quite a lot of cinemas there. One of them will have something on that you'd like."

"It's a good idea, but after a week of hard physical work, I don't think I have enough energy left to walk the ten miles there and back."

"You can take my bike, if you like, I won't be using it today. And I'll leave some bread and cheese out for you, just in case I'm in bed when you come back."

I fetched the bike and cycled off. Everything was closed, I couldn't even get a cup of tea, which after my ten-mile bicycle ride, I sorely needed. As there was over an hour to wait before the last complete programme started. I walked about a bit. Compared to London, this Midlands industrial city was a dismal place. There was only one sight worth looking at, and that was its magnificent cathedral. As it turned out, it was a good thing that I did stop to admire this splendid building. A few weeks later it was totally destroyed in one of the biggest air-raids of the war.

All the films that were showing had been on in London two or three years earlier. I ended up seeing *The Lives of a Bengal Lancer*, which was about the British Army in India at the turn of the century. The fact that all the main parts were played by well-known American actors didn't seem to bother the audience, or me, for that matter. The supporting film was a Laurel and Hardy one, which had the whole cinema rolling in their seats with laughter.

When I got back, Meg had already gone to bed, but she had kept her promise and left some food out for me. I made myself a pot of tea, ate up the bread and cheese, then made my way to bed by candlelight.

In the morning, I was sitting on the edge of the bed when Meg brought me up a cup of tea.

"Good morning, Derrick," she said. "Did you enjoy the films?"

"Yes, thank you."

I took hold of her hand and asked her to sit down beside me.

"How are you feeling today, Meg?"

"All right, thank you," she said unconvincingly.

I turned towards her and held her bruised face in my cupped hands, and very gently kissed her swollen cheeks. Suddenly she got up off the bed and said: "Drink up your tea, boy, before it gets stone cold."

I'm sure she felt a little guilty that anything intimate had passed between us. I had no such misgivings. All I was trying to do was to ease some of the pain that her poor battered body must have been feeling. Although I thought Meg was a lovely woman, I fantasised for a moment that she was the mother I never had. It was because I felt that way about her, that it upset me so much to see the brutal behaviour of her husband.

When I sat down to breakfast, Meg, who I think sensed that I was a bit hurt by her abrupt departure, looked at me and smiled. To see a smile on a face that mostly looked so sad cheered me up a lot.

I had almost finished eating when Mr Napier got back from milking the cows. I noticed that he was walking with some difficulty, and looked as though he was in considerable pain. He very slowly eased himself down into his chair, and as Meg started to serve him his breakfast, he bawled at her.

"I've hurt my back, so you and the boy will have to load the cart by yourselves, I'll lead the horse."

I had to stifle a laugh, for he had obviously damaged himself while wrestling with the bull. As he was so unpopular with his neighbours, he could never have asked them to help out. So he was stuck until he got better, with his wife and an inexperienced Londoner to bring in the harvest.

I quickly did the washing up and Meg made the sandwiches, Mr Napier got the horse harnessed up to the cart. Armed with pitchforks, Meg and I jumped into the back of the wagon. With the wounded amateur toreador hobbling along leading the horse, all three of us made our way towards the fields.

Once there, Meg and I pitched the bundles of wheat one by one into the slowly moving cart. Every few yards, I'd jump into it and stack them into layers, to make room for more. Before long, the handle of the pitchfork began to rub against the punctured blisters on my sore hands.

Back at the barn, and under the direction of the farmer, I unloaded the cart and started to make the basis of what was to be the first of many stacks. These stayed outside the barn until all the harvest had been gathered. Only then would the threshing begin.

Meg lent me some gloves, so picking up the sheaves was much less painful, and using the pitchfork protected me from the nettles and thistles. I could work shirtless and take in the last of the late August sun. Meg kept cooler by wearing a sleeveless blouse and a loose skirt. To protect her hair from getting entangled with bits of chaff and straw that floated about in the light wind, she had a small cotton scarf tied to the back of her long, curly hair. Even though the bruises still showed on her face and arms, I thought she looked very beautiful when she twisted her firm body from her slender waist, to swing the sheaves onto the cart. I'm sure it was quite a strain on her to do this work, but I felt that despite this, she was enjoying it.

While we lifted the wheat, we chatted away to each other, totally oblivious of her husband, who was at the nose end of the horse. As far as we were concerned, he was as far away from us as the engine driver on a long train. Probably all he was thinking about, was how many bushels of wheat would the harvest yield. We took three or four loads to the barn before Meg's strength left her and she went in to prepare the evening meal.

I worked on until sunset. I really thought that Meg and I had done a good day's work, but that idea was shattered when the farmer said to me, as I flung the last sheaf from the cart onto the stack: "At this rate, boy, we'll not have the harvest in till Christmas."

There was no point in answering this mean, ungrateful bastard, I decided.

For the next three days, it was left to Meg and me to work out in the fields. As the sun shone all the hours of daylight, Meg was getting quite brown. Gradually, her tan began to camouflage the bruise marks on her skin. To me she looked a completely different woman to the one I had met just a week earlier. What made her look happier and more relaxed was, of course, that for the last three days she hadn't lived under the constant threat of a violent husband, for it took all his strength just to lead the horse. I hoped and prayed that this short respite from the fear of him would give her a little taste of what life could be like if only she'd pluck up enough courage to leave him.

By Thursday, the farmer felt better and could work again, which meant that there was no need for Meg to come out with us any more. I'd have much preferred to be out in the fields by myself than have him for company. Straight away, he showed me that he was twice the man I was by picking up two sheaves to my one.

The next ten days were spent going with full loads from the fields to the barn. The blisters on my hands had healed and my palms were hardening. My arm and chest muscles were visibly beginning to expand, and I began to look more like a young farm labourer than a city dweller. If it weren't for the farmer, I would have enjoyed doing this hard, physical work.

When all the wheat had been gathered, the threshing started in earnest. For the best part of a week I spent my day forking sheaves from the stacks to the farmer who was precariously perched on a small platform attached to the thresher. He fed them into the machine one by one and the ears tumbled down a narrow chute into a sack. Seeing him standing on that small platform, I once again harboured a wicked thought about his demise. If only, when he faced the thresher, I gave him a God-Almighty wham in the centre of his back with my pitchfork, he'd go headfirst into the mechanism and emerge at the other end all minced and sacked up. Then I could run to Meg, and tell her that at last she was rid of him. But sadly for Meg and luckily for him, there's a world of difference between having such an idea and carrying it out.

When the week came to a close, and all the wheat was in sacks, I reminded the farmer that I would be taking a few unpaid days off up in London.

"You can't go, boy, you're needed here to help lift the potato crop."

"Excuse me, Mr Napier, if you remember, I asked you in front of Lord Upton if that would be all right, and you said it was. I'm sure Lord Upton will confirm what I've said."

"I will not go bothering his lordship with matters like that. You can go if you must, but be back in a week."

"I'll be away first thing in the morning."

After breakfast, I set off to walk the ten miles to Coventry. I gave myself two and a half hours to get there, which meant walking at four miles an hour, the speed we went when on a route march in the army. To get the pace right, from time to time, I repeated to myself the refrain that the sergeant bawled out as we marched along. Lep-lep-lep-right-lep. It was wonderful walking down these country lanes, unhampered by a pack on my back, and a rifle slung over my shoulder, wearing just an open-necked shirt with rolled-up sleeves, a pair of thin flannel trousers and plimsolls for shoes.

CHAPTER TWENTY-ONE

I arrived at Adelaide Court in the late afternoon, and being pretty sure that Uncle would be having his afternoon nap, I used my own key to let myself in. I sat down on the settee and waited for him to wake up. I knew I wouldn't have long to wait, because he always awoke at precisely four-thirty. He opened his eyes and saw me sitting there.

"Hallo, Hayden, this is a pleasant surprise. Have you been here for long?"

"No, only a few minutes. I'm sorry, I didn't let you know I was coming, but it's such a palaver getting hold of a stamp and posting a letter that I just took a chance that it would be all right."

"You can always come here, whenever you like."

"Thanks, Uncle. How are you coping? I heard on the radio about the air-raids. Do they bother you a lot?"

"Well, yes, they do, particularly the anti-aircraft battery which is sited very near here on Primrose Hill. They make a terrible racket so that sleeping becomes almost impossible."

"Do you go to a shelter?"

"For the first two nights, I did go down to the basement with all the tenants, plus their wives in their unsightly nightdresses and curlers in their hair, but I prefer to stay up here in my flat. Because I live virtually under the roof, if there was a direct hit I'd be blown to bits, but at least I'd be sleeping peacefully in the comfort of my own bed, whilst those in the basement could be trapped down there for God knows how long before being dug out."

"But at least they'd be still alive."

"Yes I know, Hayden, it's just that I'm not at all sure that I want to go on living through this bloody war – it's beginning to look like it's going to be a long-drawn-out affair. I mean, dear boy, things have come to a pretty pass when the people I've bought my whisky from for more years than I care to remember, informed me that they would have to ration me to one bottle a month. Now that sort of thing, plus the black-out, is beginning to get me down."

He went over to the small cabinet that housed his whisky and, from an already half-empty bottle, poured himself a treble measure. With the month only halfway through, at this rate he'd be lucky if his ration would last another two days. After that, he would have to do all his whisky-drinking at his club, costing him four times the price.

He cheered up a bit after a few sips, and asked me how I was making out on the farm. I told him how much I liked the work and what a nice lady Meg was, but when I told him what a lunatic her husband was he suggested that perhaps it would be wise not to return. I was only going back, I said, because I had promised the wife that I would. I also wanted just once more to try and persuade her to leave, before her savage husband murdered her.

"I understand, Hayden, nevertheless, my advice is not to get too involved. I have an old army friend, more an acquaintance really, who married a woman whose fortune came to her from a tobacco company. They live on a large estate which includes a well-managed farm not far from Stratford-on-Avon. Would you like me to ask him to find you a place on his farm?"

"Not at the moment, thanks."

I had planned to spend a short time with Uncle, have a bath, change into clean clothes, then bunk off and meet Gloria when she left work. If my luck was in, I'd spend the night and most of Sunday morning with her. However, Uncle asked if I would dine with him, and I just couldn't bring myself to say no. I had the feeling that as most of his friends had left London for the safety of their country houses, the old man had been all on his own for some days.

Uncle sat back in his chair and looked at me over the rim of his glass of whisky.

"Hayden, I wonder if you can help me out with something. In a moment of weakness, I agreed to go with Eric Moir and a young friend of his, and the friend's mother, on a picnic somewhere in the Surrey countryside. He will pick me up in his car at ten o'clock tomorrow morning."

"I'm surprised he can lay his hands on any petrol!" I said.

"Ah well, you see, he gets a ration because he is a doctor. Mind you, he's not supposed to use it for this sort of journey."

"Why do you need my help?"

"I was wondering whether you would mind terribly standing in for me. You see, the fact is I'm just not a picnic sort of person. When I was a child, Mother felt duty-bound to take her three offspring out picnicking. It was the only day in the year that she actually spent with us. We hated it, just as much as she did, but she escaped the boredom by drinking glass after glass of bubbly, while the three of us were expected to run around the fields enjoying ourselves. All we children wanted to do was to go back to the house and play in our own nooks and crannies in our private world. By the end of the day, Mother invariably had to be assisted back to the carriage by the footman. I'm afraid squatting on an old blanket, munching cucumber sandwiches, with bits of grass stuck to them, to say nothing of ants and other creatures crawling all over the place is anathema to me."

I didn't know what 'anathema' meant, but I realised I would have to go. Oh shit, I thought, bang goes my hope of spending the night with Gloria. I just hadn't the heart to say no.

That night we dined at my favourite restaurant, The Strand Palace. I was surprised to see how empty it was, considering it was Saturday.

"That's because most of the people who can afford to eat in restaurants like this have left London to escape the air-raids."

At the end of the meal, just as the waiter brought me a delicious-looking trifle, the sirens went off.

"Does that mean we have to leave?" I asked, worried that I would be unable to eat up my sweet.

"No, just carry on as normal. Damned if the Hun is going to make us go without our sweets!"

We went home on the Underground, as a lot of the buses had stopped running. It was quite a struggle, getting through to the entrance of the Tube. Lots of people were queuing up, with camp beds and blankets folded under the arms, to make their way down to the stuffy platforms below, so that they and their children could spend the night in comparative safety.

"Glad we don't have to join them," Uncle said as we boarded the train.

By the time we arrived at St John's Wood, the air-raid had hotted up considerably. The ack-ack guns were sending up shells as fast as they could. Searchlights raked the cloudless sky hoping to pinpoint a bomber in their crossbeams, then hold it illuminated long enough for the gunners to get a fix on them. As we walked along the deserted streets, we heard in the distance the whizzing sounds the bombs made as they twirled their way down to earth.

It was quite late when we got back to the flat, so after listening to the news, we went to bed. All night long, the guns on Primrose Hill pounded away, making a tremendous din, but I was so tired that I slept through most of it.

Uncle's doctor friend Eric arrived as arranged sharp at ten o'clock. As he liked the company of young men, I think he was pleased to hear that I was to go in Uncle's place.

Eric's car was a small, two-door, open coupé. His boyfriend sat in the front with him, and I in the back with the boyfriend's mother. As it was Sunday there was little traffic and we could speed through the streets of Greater London.

Our destination was the countryside near a village called Purley. When we passed Croydon airport, we saw a squadron of fighter planes parked around its perimeter. Some of them had pilots seated in the cockpits with the engines ticking over. They were obviously ready to get airborne at a moment's notice.

"Looks like they're expecting trouble," Eric said as we drove by.

Just before Purley, we turned off into a narrow lane and stopped by a four-barred gate. There was a bit of a problem getting the woman over it with any sort of decorum because of her long skirt.

The field we ended up in was on a hill, so we decided to climb to the highest point so as to have a good view while we picnicked. I helped the woman lay out the food, while Eric and his friend went for a walk. She told me she was the doctor's housekeeper, and said how very pleased she was that he had taken such a keen interest in her son. Thank God, she didn't really know why the good doctor was so keen on her son, I thought. But ignorance is bliss, and her boy, who was at least nineteen, was old and strong enough to say yea or nay if he was asked to do anything he didn't want to.

When Eric and his friend returned from their 'walk', looking very relaxed, we began to eat the food that had been so nicely prepared by the housekeeper. Hardly had we taken our first bite into a sandwich when the sky was filled with fighter planes, weaving and dodging around one another, with their guns blazing away. They spun and twirled with great skill set against the backcloth of a cloudless sky in an aerobatic dance with death. We watched in awe as this spectacular dogfight unfolded above our heads and in front of us. The drama quickly turned into tragedy when first one and then another plane, with smoke belching out from their tails, twisted out of control down to earth, marking where they crashed with a plume of black smoke. There was no way of knowing if it was ours or theirs that had come down, so we didn't know whether to cheer or weep. In the end there wasn't a decision to be made - you can only feel sad when young men, English or German, one fighting for his King and country, the other for his Fatherland, lose their lives, even if they believe theirs is a just cause.

Suddenly I heard something swish past me and bury itself in the earth a few feet behind me. I knelt in the long grass and found the blunt end of a bullet, glittering in the sunlight. I dug it out with my fingernails and discovered it was the same type I had used in the machine gun when I was in the Army.

When Eric saw what I had unearthed, he worked out by the angle it had embedded itself into the ground that if I had been standing three feet more to the left, the bullet would have gone straight through my head. With that sobering thought in our minds, we all took cover behind the trunk of a very large tree, and stayed there until the aerial battle was over.

As we were putting away the picnic things, a man came up the hill towards us, wanting to know what we were doing on his land without his permission. Eric, using his best Harley Street manner, managed to smooth him over and even got him to take a photograph of us all, with me holding the bullet that had so narrowly missed me.

The next morning, I set off to see Jack. His mother opened the door to me, looking distressed.

"Is Jack in?" I asked.

"No, he's been called up. He's now on his way to join his unit and I don't think I'll see him for a long time," she said, weeping.

"Oh, Mrs Harrison, don't worry about Jack, he'll know how to keep out of trouble. Which regiment has he been told to report to?"

"It's not the army he's joined, it's the RAF."

"I hope he doesn't want to be a pilot?" I said, thinking that after what I had witnessed the day before, being a pilot wasn't the way to keep out of trouble.

"No, just as ground crew."

Ah, I thought, that sounds more like the Jack I know, for I was sure that he would find some cushy job well away from anything dangerous.

"Well, Mrs Harrison, if that's what he's going to be doing, I'm certain he will be OK. When you write to him, please tell him I called."

As I left her, I hoped that I had reassured the poor woman. I spent the rest of the day with Uncle and only left him so as to be in good time to meet Gloria when she had finished work.

I waited for her outside the back entrance. Gloria was one of the last to come out.

"Hallo," I said to her as she passed by, and she stopped and turned round.

"It's you, Derrick! Aren't you supposed to be working on the land?"

"I've got a few days off. Could we spend the evening together, go and have a meal somewhere and then see a film?"

"I'd like that, and afterwards we can spend the night at my place - if you want to, that is."

I'd been thinking about nothing else for the last two weeks.

I took her to the Coventry Street Corner House. As we crossed the floor of this enormous dining-room, to Gloria's delight, a small orchestra (average age about sixty) strummed out a Strauss waltz. Gloria studied the drastically reduced war-time menu, with as much concentration as a cat might employ before it pounced on an unsuspecting mouse.

"I have to tell you, due to the new rationing restrictions, we are only allowed to serve one main course per person," said the waiter who came to take our order.

Remembering Gloria's robust appetite, I lied and told her that as I wasn't very hungry, she could have mine if she wanted.

"I'll start with Mulligatawny soup, then fish and chips, and trifle for a sweet, please."

"And for you, Sir?"

I asked Gloria what she thought I should have as a main dish.

"Shepherd's pie with peas," said Gloria.

As I watched her gobble down this huge meal, I just couldn't imagine how she found space for it all. All I had was pea soup and trifle and even that she eyed enviously as I took my first spoonful, so I pretended I couldn't manage it and offered it to her. Once again, she woofed it down.

We went on to one of the cinemas in Leicester Square. The film Gloria chose, starring Fred Astaire and Ginger Rogers, was not my favourite sort of picture, but if it pleased her, that was all I cared about.

After the film we got a cab back to Gloria's. No sooner had we arrived than the sirens went off. Oh shit, I thought, she'll want to go to a shelter for the night, leaving me to sleep in her bed all by myself, but I needn't have worried, for all she said was:

"You don't want to go to one of those horrible shelters, do you?"

"No, I don't. I'll be your shelter for tonight, you'll be quite safe lying under me."

"What about when I'm on top of you? Who's going to protect me then, eh?"

"The good Lord," I said, as we climbed up the stairs to her room.

Within seconds, we were both naked. To the sound of ack-ack guns blasting away, and bombs exploding (sometimes a bit too close for comfort), Gloria and I had sex until the all-clear had sounded. It was only then that we fell asleep.

When I awoke, she had left a note for me: 'Help yourself to some tea. Sorry

I won't be able to see you tonight as I have a friend staying - but it's OK for tomorrow evening."

Jesus, this girl is insatiable, I thought. She'd been fucked silly by Jack the previous night, then by me last night. She's got another bloke laid on for tonight, and she's got me back again tomorrow. I wrote her a note, booking myself in (so to speak) for the following evening, and then made tracks for Adelaide Court.

I arrived there as Uncle was having his mid-morning drink. He looked quite distressed. His whisky bottle was empty and the merchant wouldn't allow him another until next month, and that was ten long days away.

"Don't worry, Uncle," I said. "I'll pop down the road to the pub and bring you one back."

"It's awfully nice of you to offer, but they won't let you leave with one of their glasses, will they?"

"OK, I'll take one with me."

"That's a good idea."

What was the point, I thought, of being educated at Eton and Harrow when you couldn't even think up a simple solution like that.

Uncle had had a message from Vic, saying he would be standing outside the Dominion Cinema in Tottenham Court Road that evening between seven and seven-thirty and really hoped I would
come.

I hadn't seen Vic since the previous December, and hardly recognised him. He looked like a skeleton. His boyish and ruddy complexion had vanished. He looked utterly worn out. I must have looked the complete opposite, for I was still brown from my long summer with Jack on Hampstead Heath and from working in the open air.

"My God, Derrick, you do look well," he said.

"I can't say the same to you, Vic. What on earth's happened to you?"

"Let's go into the pub over the road, where we can talk," he said.

The pub was packed with people having a quick one after their day's work and before facing the journey home. Vic ordered himself a pint, then, remembering that I didn't drink alcohol, got me a lemonade.

'I'll tell you why I look so bloody awful – it's the fucking job I've been doing for the last ten months, that's why. From the time I started work last December right up until last month, they had us welding aircraft bodies together for twelve hours a day, seven days a week, one month on the day shift, the next on nights. We only got a day off when we changed shifts. I hardly ever saw daylight."

"Christ, Vic, you poor chap. I hope at least they pay you good money?"

"Oh yes, I get paid the top union rate plus overtime, but the trouble is, you're left with no time to spend it. If I get hit by a bomb, all those hard-earned pounds I've got tucked under my mattress will be absolutely wasted. You know, Derrick, I didn't even have enough free time to go boozing on a Friday night."

"It sounds like you were almost better off in the bloody army. Has it got any better now?"

"Yes, but only because the workers started to drop like flies, most of them from sheer exhaustion. In the end, production began to fall, so the time we worked was reduced. We still do a twelve-hour day or night shift, but only for five days a week. The whole factory closes down on Saturday morning, and starts up again at six a.m. on Monday. How have you been making out? The major told me you were no longer in the army. How on earth did you manage to work your ticket?"

I told him how and why I got discharged and what I'd been doing since.

"You have been having a right old time, haven't you, dear boy?"

Vic downed his second pint, and said:

"Derrick, my boy, I want to invite you to a meal. There's a marvellous restaurant just round the corner from here called Frascati's?"

"Yes, I'd love to, I've been there once with my uncle, but I must warn you, it's very expensive."

"It'll give me chance to spend some of the oodles of money I've accumulated these past ten months."

Just one glance at the menu of this exclusive restaurant, and you could have been forgiven if you didn't know there was a war on. There was a whole list of game and a variety of sea or freshwater fish, including salmon, and no mention of being restricted to one main dish. There was also a whole range of vegetables with sauté potatoes and creamed carrots, plus a delicious-looking sweet trolley. Vic had two bottles of wine with his meal, so when the bill arrived, he was almost incapable of standing up, let alone settling it. He gave me a fistful of notes and asked me to deal with it.

"I think I'd better see you home."

"It's a slen ...splendid idea, old boy."

"Where do you live?"

"Warwick Avenue," came the slurred reply.

"The number, Vic?"

He didn't answer, so I repeated the question. After a long pause, while he searched his befuddled mind, I heard what sounded like forty-nine. Supporting him with one arm, I hailed a cab with the other. No sooner was he seated than he fell into a deep sleep and remained that way for the rest of the journey.

No wonder the poor chap had passed out. After all, he'd been up since five a.m., then done a twelve-hour shift, and all that before meeting me and consuming all that beer and wine.

The driver helped me get my legless friend out of his taxi and up to the front door. After a frantic search through his pockets, we eventually found the latch key. I asked the cabby to wait, then using a fireman's lift, I hoisted Vic over my shoulder and carried him through the front door.

What on earth do I do with him now, I wondered. Luckily I remembered that he'd mumbled something about the first room on the right. I laid him down on what I hoped was his bed, then scribbled a note on the back of the restaurant bill, thanking him for the meal. I folded his change into the receipt, covered him with a couple of blankets and went back to the waiting cab. As the taxi pulled away, the air-raid sirens went off.

For the rest of my stay in London, I spent the days with Uncle and the nights with Gloria. Before leaving for Coventry, I asked Uncle if he would get in touch with his friend who had married the tobacco heiress, and ask him if he needed anyone to work on his farm.

"I could cycle over there on a Sunday if he wanted to see me. Stratford is only about twenty miles from where I am at the moment."

"I'll do as you ask, Hayden, but twenty miles there and the same back, isn't that too far to go in a day?"

"Not far me, Uncle."

I got him a double whisky from the local, then left for the station.

By the time I'd walked the ten miles from the station to the farm, it was dark. I found Meg and her husband in the kitchen, having supper.

"Oh, you're back, are you?" said the farmer.

"Hello, Derrick, did you have a good time in London?" said Meg cheerfully.

I told her I had, and about my narrow escape when watching the dogfight.

"So we're lucky to see you back at all by the sound of it."

"A near miss with a bullet is as good as a mile, you know."

I went on to tell her about the fantastic meal I'd had at Frascati's with my friend.

"After that, I don't suppose you'll be looking forward to my simple cooking."

"On the contrary, your cooking is very good and I like it a lot." I never wanted to miss an opportunity to bolster up the little confidence she had.

She asked me if I was hungry, and if I was, I should help myself to some bread and cheese. At this point, her husband left the kitchen.

"He can't bear it when anything vaguely resembling a normal conversation takes place," she said as she got up to join him.

"Stay a while, Meg. What's the point of following him, only to sit there in silence when we can talk to each other in here."

"All right, just for a short while."

And that's precisely what it was, as a few minutes later, the old bastard poked his head through the door and said curtly: "Meg, bed now, and I mean now."

Meg got up immediately and left me at the table. Somehow, I thought, I've got to have one more try to get her to leave that brute.

In the morning, Meg came up to wake me. Once again she kissed me between the shoulder blades and very gently stroked my back. I remembered that the last time she did this and I responded, she suddenly bolted off out of the attic. So I pretended to be asleep until she spoke to me.

"Good morning, Derrick, I've brought you a cup of tea, drink it up before it gets cold."

"Thanks, Meg, I'll be down in two secs."

Looking out of the tiny attic window, I could see that the glorious weather had vanished. It was all grey and raining. My first inclination was to get back under the sheets and stay there for the remainder of the day, but the mere thought of facing the wrath of the farmer, made the alternative seem almost pleasurable. Meg, as usual, gave me a substantial breakfast, which I had just finished eating when the farmer returned after having milked the cows. As was his way, he dispensed with any of the normal niceties, such as saying 'good morning' or 'did you sleep well?'

"Today, boy, we're going to do what I've been doing this last week while you chose to be in London."

"And what were you doing, Mr Napier?"

"Lifting potatoes, that's what. Off you go now and leave me in peace to have my breakfast. I'll see you in the truck in ten minutes. Have you brought any clothes with you for this sort of weather?"

"No, only a jacket."

"When you work on the land, you should come properly equipped. Go and see my wife and ask her to find you a mackintosh and some Wellingtons."

Meg found me both.

"I don't feel like going out there," I said.

"It does look miserable, doesn't it? But I'm afraid that the land has to be worked whatever the weather."

I made a dash through the downpour to the truck. Sitting in it and waiting for the farmer to come, I reflected on how in this sort of weather Vic and I had dodged the column when it was pissing down at the Bisley Range and skived off to the warm and cosy comfort of an old café. There wasn't a hope in hell of doing anything like that today. The farmer arrived moments later, looking like a bad joke decked out in a mac and wellies, with a sou'wester (which was too large for him) perched at a rakish angle on his head, instead of his usual battered pork pie hat. We drove off through the muddy fields to where the potatoes were growing.

On arrival, reluctantly, I left the relative protection of the truck. I don't think I'd felt so miserable since cleaning out the latrines in the army.

I was given a metal bucket and a four-pronged fork.

"Now boy," said the farmer pointing to a long row of potatoes and said, "when you dig
them up, push the fork right down until it will go no further, then lever it up by pushing the handle down and make sure you don't leave any in the earth to go rotten. Tear off their foliage and remove as much of the mud as possible. When the bucket's full, go and empty it into one of the sacks that are dotted about the field."

The rain started to trickle down through the badly fitting neck of the mac, making the back of my shirt wet. Oh God, how I hated the fucking situation I was in, but there was nothing for it but to start digging. I pushed the fork deep into the sodden earth and tried to lever the handle back up. This wasn't easy as beneath the thin layer of topsoil lay heavy water-logged clay which gripped the prongs of the fork like a vice. After a lot of tugging and to the sound of squelching noises coming up from under the earth, I finally managed to bring a few potatoes to the surface. After I'd removed the greenery and peeled off as much of the clay as was possible, I threw the potatoes into a bucket. It took for ever to fill the bloody thing, and when I had, I couldn't move because my Wellingtons had become bogged down in the mud. I was only able to free them by tugging hard on their rims with both hands. There was, however, one small consolation in all this drudgery: for with all the heaving and tugging needed just to get the fork out of the heavy soil, I was (despite being soaked to the skin) getting very hot. Thankfully, by lunchtime, the rain had ceased and held off for the rest of the day, making the digging a lot easier. I didn't have to eat my sandwiches sitting in silence with the farmer in the truck. I ate mine perched on an upturned bucket, well away from him, stripped to the waist, so my shirt could dry out.

By now it was into the first week of November, and unlike harvest-time, when it was light up until ten at night, work stopped just after five as dusk fell. I went back in the truck as far as the sheds and helped the farmer bring in the cows for milking, then left him there. As I walked back across the lawn to the farm, I prayed that Meg had lit the stove so that there would be some hot water to have a bath so I could get off all the mud that had stuck to me. I made straight for the kitchen. When Meg saw me, she looked horrified.

"Oh Derrick, you naughty boy," she said, "go into the scullery and take off those filthy Wellingtons, you're treading mud all over the floor that I've just scrubbed."

"I'm so sorry, Meg, I just didn't think."

"That's all right this time, but please do remember it in future! Now go and get them off, then come back here and I'll give you a cup of tea. I'm sure you must be very wet and cold."

"No, I'm not really, but tea - that's what I really need. And then could I have a bath?"

"Yes, but leave some hot water for John in case he wants one, although he very seldom does."

"If he doesn't, how does he get the mud off?"

"He leaves it there until it eventually rubs off."

Another reason, I thought, why it must be hell to have to share a bed with that man.

For the rest of the week and most of the next, rain or shine, I was out for all the hours of daylight, digging up potatoes. I became quite a dab hand at it and lifted almost as many as the farmer. Anyway, I didn't work hard just to please him. I did it purely as a muscle-building exercise.

CHAPTER TWENTY-TWO

One evening, when I got back from working in the fields, Meg handed me a letter from Uncle. He wrote that he had got in touch with the couple who had a farm near Stratford-upon-Avon, and they would be pleased to have me join them for lunch next Sunday at one o'clock. Their name was Gascoyne, and Uncle added that although the chap called himself a major, he was in fact, only a captain when he retired from the army. He was one of those ex-army officers who promote themselves every few years, and might even have pushed himself up a pip to the rank of a lieutenant-colonel by the time I met him. Although Uncle thought the 'Major' was a bit of a bore, his wife was a very charming woman. Well, I thought, I'd much rather work under a twit than the morose and sadistic Mr Napier.

"Good news?" asked Meg, as I put the letter into my jacket pocket.

"No, not exactly, it's just that I've been invited on Sunday to have lunch with friends of my uncle's."

"Where do they live?"

"About three miles the other side of Stratford."

"That's an awful journey by public transport."

"I'd thought of setting off at the crack of dawn and walking there."

"But it's over twenty miles. I think you'd better take my bike."

On Sunday morning, I got up bright and early so as to have time to make myself as presentable as possible. I had a thorough wash, shaved and plastered my unruly hair down with a big dollop of Brylcreem. This, I think, I overdid somewhat when I saw myself in the mirror, I looked more like a gigolo than a farm hand. I just had to hope that as I cycled along, the wind would fluff it up again. I put on the shirt that Meg washed and ironed for me, and my shabby grey flannels.

It was a sunny but cool day when I cycled off, the turn-ups of my trousers folded neatly into my socks. I worked out that, provided I didn't have a puncture, I would arrive at the Gascoynes' by one. As all the signposts had been removed to confuse any German parachutists that might drop down from the sky, the RAC route map that Uncle had sent was essential. The notion that the parachutists would have been given Ordnance maps of the area never occurred to the idiots who ordered that signposts should be uprooted all over England. Some, however, were left standing and were turned in the wrong direction.

The RAC maps pinpointed landmarks instead of place names. For example, they would read something like this: 'After four miles, turn right at the George, carry on for a quarter of a mile and go left at the pillar box. Three hundred yards after crossing a hump-back bridge, bear right at the fork.' It was so detailed, in fact, that you wouldn't have been at all surprised if you were told to turn left where Mrs Smith's large pink bloomers were left hanging out to dry every day except Sundays. But to be serious, one shouldn't poke fun at these excellent maps.

Without one, I would never have arrived at my luncheon date on time.

It was impossible not to find the manor house, because it dominated the skyline at the far end of the village, and overlooked the countryside for miles around. I stood outside these awesome gates for some time before plucking up the courage to open them. Once inside, I hid Meg's bike behind some bushes, then walked up the long drive that was cut through the centre of the very spacious and well-kept lawn to the imposing front doors. I searched everywhere for a bell to press but to no avail. It seemed to me that it didn't look like the sort of place where you shouted to an upstairs window 'is anyone at home?'. Eventually it dawned on me that perhaps you were meant to pull the handle attached to the end of a long and ornate iron rod protruding from the brickwork. This I did, timidly. I stood there for some time, but no one came to let me in. Perhaps I hadn't pulled it hard enough, I thought. So the next time I tugged it, I used all my strength. On this second attempt, the bells made such a din that they could have awakened the dead. A liveried servant opened the front door. He was slightly out of breath.

"I came as quickly as I could, sir, once I heard the bell, as I wanted to make quite sure that you didn't pull it again."

That, I presumed, was his way of rebuking me.

"Sorry," I said, "but the first time I rang, nobody came."

"May I say who's called, sir?"

I gave him my name and told him that I'd been invited to lunch. Sticking close to his heels I went into the main hall, which was large enough to play cricket in, and stood in the doorway of the drawing room while he went over to a lady who was talking to a group of people at the other end of the long room. She came over with her hand outstretched to greet me.

"I'm Margaret Gascoyne. So glad you could make it. Come and be introduced."

I followed this petite and elegantly dressed lady, who looked as though she might be about fifty, to where the others were.

"Everyone," she said, "this young man is Hayden Cartlidge. He is the adopted nephew of a friend of ours."

They turned their heads and gave me a faint smile and nod, then carried on talking to each other. There were eight of them standing about, divided into small groups. They must be the local bigwigs, I thought, all on the same ticket as me, namely a free meal. Amongst them was a man wearing a dog-collar, obviously the parish priest, getting, no doubt, his reward for having delivered an inspiring sermon at morning service. Due to my childhood experiences with priests, his presence made me feel uneasy. It was more than likely that all the other guests had the same feelings about me. As far as they were concerned, I was a fish out of very murky waters.

Mrs Gascoyne led me by the hand over to the other side of the room where a very tall and lanky man was helping himself to a large sherry.

"Hayden," she said, "this is my husband, Major Gascoyne."

"Oh, yes, you're Conny's nephew, aren't you? How's the poor chap coping with all those frightful air-raids?"

I told him he managed quite well, considering he was reluctant to go down into a shelter.

"Don't blame him, my boy, I'd be the same, hate to be cooped up with all that stinking humanity. Conny mentioned to Margaret that you might like to work here on our farm. Have I got that right?"

"Yes," I said.

"Well then, after lunch, I'll give you a guided tour around the farm, and if you think you would like to come and work here, you could start a week from tomorrow. So many of our farmhands are being called up into one or other of the armed services that we are beginning to get desperately short of labour."

We couldn't continue the conversation because a very elderly man, who I thought must be the head butler, came and announced that luncheon would be served in the main dining room.

This was very welcome news as after my long cycle ride, I was getting very hungry. I held back and let the others move forward before taking my place at the end of the small queue. When it came to my turn to enter the room, and I saw how big it was, I thought that to call it a dining room was a bit misleading. You could have easily held a banquet in it.

A mahogany table that could seat at least thirty people, stood out conspicuously in the centre of the enormous parquet and Persian-carpeted floor. Huge tapestries, and probably priceless old paintings hung from the oak-panelled walls. If all this splendour was to impress, I must admit it certainly worked on me.

When Mrs Gascoyne had seated her nine guests, she and her husband sat together at the end of the table. I was sandwiched between the local doctor and his rather severe-looking wife.

As well as two elaborately decorated silver candelabra which were spaced evenly apart in the centre of the table, there was a whole armoury of expensive-looking cutlery laid out. This worried me a bit, as I had no idea which item was used with which course. So I made up my mind not to pick up anything without first seeing which piece the formidable lady on my left used.

When the vicar had done his little bit by saying grace, through the service doors came the same servant who had opened the front door to me. He was carrying a tureen of piping hot soup. Trailing behind him were two servant girls holding silver boats.

"Soup, sir?" he asked when he got to me.

"What sort is it?" I asked, just in case there was meat in it.

"Cream of celery, sir."

"Yes, please," I said.

He half-filled my soup plate, and made to leave for the lady sitting next to me.

"Excuse me," I said, "could you fill my plate before you go away?"

"Of course, sir."

Then I got another rebuke from this toffee-nosed lackey:

"I will be coming round again, you know, sir!"

When he bent over to give me more, I whispered into his ear:

"I didn't know it, mate."

After he moved on, one of the servant girls gave me a liberal helping of croutons and the second girl offered me fresh farm cream.

Because I was so hungry, I had a job to stop myself from doing the unforgivable - to pick up a spoon and get stuck into the delicious-looking soup. It seemed to take forever before everyone was served, and the cue was given by the host to start. Most of the guests took some time to consume their half-filled soup plates, but I bolted mine down in seconds. I had to wait for more until the last person finished eating theirs. Only then did the snooty servant come round again.

"More, sir?" he said, thinking, I'm sure, that I couldn't possibly want any after my first huge helping. So, just to annoy him, I pointed to my soup plate and spoke to him as if he were a petrol pump attendant.

"Fill it up, please," I said.

I had the feeling he was fighting back the urge to pour a ladleful into my lap.

As we were having Sunday lunch, the main course was predictable. Roast beef with Yorkshire pudding, served with Brussels sprouts and roast potatoes. Not wanting the meat, I helped myself to quite a lot of everything else, then got the serving girl to drown it all with gravy.

The conversation going on around the table was mostly about local matters, and bored the pants off me. Major Gascoyne had some pretty strong words to say about the evacuees brought in from London's East End and billeted on the villagers. "Little savages" he called them. He said that to help out the poor women who had to house and feed them, he sent his head gardener round with vegetables from the estate's market garden.

"But," he went on, "believe it or not, he's been told by those long-suffering women not to bring round any more. It seems all the little blighters want is fish and chips. The only fresh food they'd touch is the apples they steal from my orchards."

All the guests agreed that the sooner the evacuees could be sent home the better it would be for everyone. In an attempt to start up a dialogue with the doctor's wife sitting on my left, I asked if she had any evacuees billeted on her.

"Good heavens, no," she said. It was obvious that the very idea filled her with horror. Her response put an end to my little effort to make conversation with anyone present. I decided for the rest of the meal I would concentrate on the wonderful food that was placed in front of me.

I think Mrs Gascoyne must have observed that none of her guests had spoken a word to me, for she very pointedly spoke to me across the table.

"Tell me, Hayden, what have you been doing since you left school or college?"

"I was at neither, I was brought up in a sort of orphanage."

Glancing at the faces of those who heard my reply, I knew that they felt distinctly uncomfortable at having a bastard in their midst.

"But," said Mrs Gascoyne searching desperately for a way out of my embarrassing answer, "I don't quite understand, I am sure Conny told me that you were his nephew."

"That, I would imagine, was because he didn't want to burden you with how or why he came to adopt me. We met because of the voluntary work he did in the schools for under-privileged children."

That, of course, was a big lie, but I could hardly have told her the truth.

"Oh, you poor boy, so you have no idea who your parents are?"

"I'm afraid not, Mrs Gascoyne."

"I must say, I think it's very courageous of you not to try and conceal your misfortune."

Looking at the people around the table, I couldn't help but think that it might take more courage to admit they were your parents than simply to say you were an orphan.

"I'm so glad you found someone as nice as Conny to befriend you," Mrs Gascoyne continued. "Now tell me, when you left this er this er place, what did you do?"

I gave her an abridged account of my short army career, being an extra in films, and working at Marks & Spencer. I regaled her with stories about the farmer, who amused himself wrestlingwith a bull on Sunday afternoons when he was not beating up his wife. By the time I'd finished the whole table listening. It became apparent that I was no longer the outcast that nobody wanted to talk to; now I was the star attraction. They wanted to know more about my childhood, and in more detail what it was like inside a film studio, andhey couldn't get enough tales about the madman I was working for. I couldn't help feeling that I had packed more variety into my last eighteen months than they had in the fifty-odd years of their unadventurous lives. Major Gascoyne said he was pleased to hear that I was a trained soldier, because the local Home Guard (of which he was naturally the commanding officer) needed somebody in the ranks with military experience. He didn't know, and I wasn't going to tell him, was there wasn't a hope in hell of getting me to play soldiers.

After lunch Major Gascoyne drove me in his Rolls around his 3000j-acreestate. He showed me the stables that housed magnificent and well-groomed horses, some used only for the hunt, others for pulling carts. The barns and outhouses were built in brick with concrete flooring, a far cry from the ramshackle wooden and earth-floored barn and cowshed on Napier's farm. One huge building contained machinery that most tenant farmers would have given their souls for. There were tractors, harvesters, ploughs, carts with inflatable rubber tyres, and muckspreaders - nothing was missing that modern farming needed. All the equipment was kept in pristine condition. The dairy was spotlessly clean, as were the Friesian cows who stood in long rows on either side of this enormous shed, their black and white hides gleaming under the electric lights. The Major was obviously very proud of his model farm. Although what he personally had to be proud about, I didn't really know, for according to Uncle, it was his wife's fortune that made it all possible, to say nothing of an army of dedicated and hard-working farm labourers. Surely it was for them, not him, to be proud of anything that had been accomplished. I doubted whether the Major had ever picked up so much as a pitchfork, let alone endured the hard graft of a day's work.

"Come now, Hayden," he said, when the tour of the farm was over, "we will go over to the Clark's cottage, where you could be housed. Harry Clark has been with us since he was a boy, and ought really to be retired by now, but thankfully with the shortage of labour, he's agreed to soldier on."

After a short drive, we went down a path lined with terraces of small cottages. All of them had a little vegetable plot instead of a front garden. When we pulled up, the length of the Rolls was almost the width of the tiny house where the Clarks lived.

The Major left me in the car and went up to the front door of the cottage. It was opened by a man whom I presumed to be Mr Clark. As soon as he saw Major Gascoyne, the old man immediately removed his flat cap and bent his head, taking up the inbred stance of the country working class whenever they were confronted by their squire or any other member of the gentry. The Major beckoned me to follow him in.

"Hayden, this is Mr and Mrs Clark. I've already spoken to them and they would be quite happy for you to lodge with them."

I shook hands with them.

"Pleased to meet you, sir," said the old man.

"Likewise, I'm sure," said his wife.

I liked the look of this old couple, and said that I was looking forward to staying with them.

On the way back to the manor, I asked Major Gascoyne what sort of pay I could expect.

"I'm not sure, to tell you the truth, but I think it's twenty-two shillings a week plus your board and lodgings."

That was eight shillings more than I got now, and the working conditions were, without doubt, much better.

Back at the house, I went to find Mrs Gascoyne and say goodbye to her. She was in the music room, playing the piano. I stood by the door and listened until she finished.

"You do play beautifully, don't you."

"Thank you, Hayden. Do you like Chopin's Polonaise?" she asked.

"Well, if that was what you were playing, then, yes, I do. I don't want to take up any more of your time, I just wanted to thank you for the marvellous lunch and to say goodbye."

"Are you going to come and work on the farm?"

"Yes, I'll be back in a week."

"Tell me, do you like going to the theatre?"

"I don't know, I've never been to one."

"Oh dear, that's a pity. If you would like to, you can have the seat I have permanently reserved at the Stratford Theatre whenever I don't want it. I'll leave a letter of authority with Mr and Mrs Clark."

"That would be very nice, Mrs Gascoyne."

I went to pick up Meg's bike and started on my journey back. As it was mid-afternoon and wouldn't get dark for a couple of hours, I thought I'd just take a look at Stratford. It was only about four miles away, so I got there in no time at all. Stratford appealed to me a lot, for in this mediaeval town, with its old Tudor houses and buildings, you were transported out of the England at war in November 1940 to the rumbustious time of Henry VIII, Shakespeare and Elizabeth I.

I treated myself to tea on the terrace of the Royal Shakespeare Theatre overlooking the river, and sat there for some time, admiring the view and feeding the swans as they gracefully glided by. The difference between this beautiful old town and the drabness of Coventry was enormous. You just couldn't believe they were both in the same county.

The wonderful weather that had been there all day suddenly vanished and grey rain-threatening clouds replaced the blue sky. That was my cue to get on with my journey. I cycled off but I never found my way back on to the RAC route. Before long, daylight faded and it started to rain, then pour. I could find no one about in the deserted country roads to ask the way, and as I was only dressed in a shirt, I began to feel the cold and get very wet. To think that only a couple of hours before, the sun was shining and I was a passenger in a Rolls- Royce. Contrasts like this were beginning to become a feature of my life.

I was hopelessly lost, and my only hope was to find a farmhouse and get help, but this wasn't easy. What with the pouring rain and the blackness of the night, with not a chink of light showing anywhere because of black-out restrictions, I could see myself cycling around in circles until dawn. But just as I had almost given up hope, I saw a small light coming down the road towards me. It was a man on a bike. He could hardly see me as Meg's bicycle didn't have any lights, not even the dim ones that were allowed. I shouted to him to stop. Thankfully he knew how to point me in the right direction.

By the time I got back to the farm, it was after ten and Meg and her husband had gone to bed. Soaked to the skin and trembling from the cold, I went straight up to the attic, put on dry things and my jacket, and got into bed.

When Meg brought me up a cup of tea in the morning, she found me fully dressed and under the blankets.

"Is it so cold up here then, Derrick?"

"No, it's not that, it was the nightmare of the journey that I had last night. It's lucky that I'm not down with pneumonia."

"Oh, of course, poor boy, you were only wearing a shirt, weren't you, and last night was very cold and the rain came down in buckets. Tell me, how did you like your Uncle's friends, were they nice people?"

I told her how my day had been and about the big mansion and the huge estate they lived on.

"Meg," I said, "come and sit next to me. I've got something to say to you before I speak to Mr Napier. I'll be leaving here at the end of the week, and going to work on the Gascoynes' farm. But if you come away with me to London, I won't go there. I'll fix you up with somewhere to stay and I know there will be no problem in finding you a job. You will never regret it, Meg, I promise you that you won't. I've worked it out, we could both bunk off when Mr Napier goes to church next Sunday."

"But, Derrick, he'll insist I go with him."

"You can tell him you can't because you're not feeling well. Say you have a splitting headache, or say any old thing. Do please, think it over."

"I'd love to come with you, I really would, but who would look after John if I left him?"

"For God's sake, Meg! Much more to the point is who will watch over you when I'm gone? While I've been here, he's only beaten you up once. I'm sure he would have done more if it wasn't for my connection with Lord Upton. Please, Meg, come away with me."

"I'll think about it, I promise you I will. Come on now, come down and have your breakfast."

When the farmer came in from milking, I told him I'd be off at the end of the week. I think he was glad to hear it; I had the feeling he was about to sack me anyway. I had outlived my usefulness, now that the harvest was in and the potato crop had been lifted.

It rained for most of the days of my last week while the farmer and I were out in the fields, picking up the wet and muddy sacks of potatoes. The clay that stuck to the sacks made each one weigh over a hundredweight. It was a backbreaking job to lift them high up onto the horse-drawn cart. The sacks were emptied onto the floor and the potatoes hosed down to remove the clay so they were in a fit state to be sent to market. In all that week the farmer and I hardly spoke, which suited me all right.

One evening I went up to the bathroom to have a bath. After days out in the rain and mud, it was sheer joy to soak myself in hot water and feel clean all over. I hadn't been submerged for long when I heard the drone of planes going overhead. Must be our bombers from the nearby RAF base on their way to hit targets in northern France, I thought. A few minutes later, Meg shouted to me through the door.

"Derrick, come and see this, come quickly. It's Coventry, it's being bombed," she said.

I wrapped a towel around my waist and went out onto the landing. Meg was standing in front of the uncurtained window at the end of the corridor. She was looking at a red glow that spanned the horizon. I went and stood beside her.

"It looks like the whole town is in flames, doesn't it?"

She nodded her head. As we stood there in silence, the skyline became even more red. Every so often, a huge cascade of fire shot up into the night sky, when no doubt a gasometer or a mains received a direct hit. The unceasing drone of the German bombers went on relentlessly. I watched, mesmerised by the horror of what I was witnessing.

"Oh, Derrick," said Meg in a whisper, "those poor people. Dear God, how they must be suffering."

"Let's hope that most of them are in the air-raid shelters," I replied, though I thought that with this type of carpet-bombing the shelters would afford very little protection.

"I just can't watch it any more," Meg said, as she turned away from the window and buried her face between my still slightly wet and bare shoulder blades. Imperceptibly I felt her lips brushing up and down my back. Then, with her arms around me, the tender movement of her lips turned into kisses. I thought nothing of it at first, as she had done this many times before when I pretended to be sleeping. But this time it was different. Her hands travelled slowly, then more intensely all over the top half of my body. I just let it happen. The next thing I knew was that Meg was on her knees, frantically kissing me all the way up my legs and thighs, her hands went under the towel and gripped my buttocks. My loosely-tied towel dropped to the floor, leaving me standing there naked. I turned towards her and picked her up off her knees. We kissed passionately and our fast-moving hands explored every part of each other. It made no difference that Meg was so much older than I. She went wild with excitement as her hands were all over me and mine over her. Suddenly a terrifying thought hit me: Jesus Christ, what if her husband came up the stairs and caught me standing naked next to his wife. I became paralysed with fear, and all my sexual ardour left me. I knew for certain what he would do: my head would be tucked under one of those massively strong arms, and Meg's under the other and our skulls would be crushed.

"Meg, darling, we really must stop this now, he might come up at any moment," I whispered. "In the morning, when he's out milking, we can have a whole half hour to ourselves without fear of being caught. It will be so much better."

I stroked her a little and after a final long kiss, she left me and went into her bedroom. I picked up the towel and put it round my waist, and after taking another look at the flaming red sky over Coventry, I made for the bathroom. Just before I got to it, her husband came up the stairs. I pointed out of the window and he took a glance at it, shook his head and said: "Terrible, isn't it?" before going into his room. Jesus, I thought, thank God he didn't come up forty-five seconds earlier.

Up in the attic, with the feeling of fear gone, and my desire for Meg back, it took me a long time to go off to sleep. It was only the knowledge that I'd have her in my bed when I woke up that finally made sleep possible.

I was wide awake when Meg came up with a cup of tea.

"Good morning," she said. "Come on down, your breakfast is ready." She bent over and gave me a kiss on my forehead, like a mother would to her child. Then she left.

Fuck me, what on earth had happened to all that fervour of last night? I'd lain awake for hours in the anticipation of having her in my bed when I woke up. Now, apart from a platonic kiss on my forehead, she was behaving like a chambermaid. For Christ's sake, she'd all but raped me only a few hours previously.

I sat on the edge of my bed for some time before it dawned on me why everything had changed. It was, of course, the old foe that forbade Meg from doing anything that might be at all pleasurable. It was the guilt that had been drummed into her from childhood. As Meg wanted to behave as if nothing had gone on between us, I decided to do the same.

My last days were spent bringing in the remaining sacks of potatoes. I was relieved when Saturday came, and work stopped. Now there was only one more problem to solve before my departure the next day, and that was how to get to Stratford station. I knew that leaving from Coventry would be impossible as the railway network would be out of action. There was only one way out, and that was to ask the farmer if he would take me to Stratford in his truck. I didn't relish the idea much, but I could think of no other way, so plucking up all my courage, I asked him.

"I certainly will not," he replied, without a moment's thought, "I'll take you back to Coventry, which is where I collected you, and that's as far as I'll go."

"But Mr Napier, the railway station there is unlikely to be working after the air-raid, so there would be no point in me going there."

"That's no problem of mine," he said abruptly. Then I had the brilliant idea of using the trump card that I'd played so successfully before.

"Oh, well, if you won't, I'll just have to go and ask Lord Upton if he would send his chauffeur over to pick me up," I said with tongue in cheek, for I gambled that the mere mention of the noble lord would kick the ball my way.

"You will do nothing of the kind, I will not have you bothering his Lordship, that I won't. To save him from being troubled, and for no other reason, I will take you to Stratford after morning service."

Whoopee, my bluff had paid off.

On my last morning, when the farmer was out milking and I was left alone with Meg, I made one more attempt to persuade her to leave.

"Even at this late hour, Meg, I'll cancel going to the Gascoynes'."

"It's no good, Derrick, I just can't."

"So you're saying that you'll stay on here until one day, in a fit of temper, he kills you."

"No, Derrick, that's not what I'm saying. It's just that I can't bring myself to leave him to fend for himself."

Well, I thought, at least I tried. I gave her both Uncle's and the Gascoynes' telephone numbers and told her, that if she ever changed her mind, I would drop whatever I was doing and come to London immediately and make quite sure she'd be all right.

"Derrick, you sweet boy, I really do appreciate your concern. I promise you if ever I do decide to leave here, I'll let you know."

Meg had insisted that I stay to lunch before setting off and for once her husband didn't argue with her. When the meal was over, Meg came with me and her husband to the front door. I would have loved to have given her one last kiss and hug, but with him there, all I could do was say:

"Goodbye, Mrs Napier, and thank you for looking after me so well."

"Goodbye, Derrick, look after yourself."

I shook her hand and gave it a small squeeze.

"Remember what I told you," I said in a whisper, and went over to the waiting truck.

I slung my case into the open back, and for the last time sat on the wooden box that substituted for a passenger seat. As we drove off, I gave Meg a farewell wave.

As always, not one word was spoken by either of us on the twenty-mile journey. When we pulled up outside the station, I jumped out of the truck and grabbed my suitcase.

"Goodbye, and thanks for the lift," I said, not expecting any reply, but to my amazement he actually managed to say: "Goodbye, boy."

I looked for the last time into those fierce-looking eyes of his, and thought I saw for a split second that they seemed to be saying 'sorry I was so unfriendly', but I was probably wrong.

CHAPTER TWENTY-THREE

When he drove away, I went into the station, and as arranged phoned the Gascoynes to say that I had arrived. Fifteen minutes later, the Rolls pulled into the station forecourt. The chauffeur got out, opened the passenger back door and asked: "Are you Mr Cartlidge, sir?"

"That's me," I said.

I sunk into the luxurious and roomy leather seats in the back, and a quarter of an hour later arrived at the Clarks' cottage.

I walked up the garden path and knocked on the door. Mr Clark opened it.

"Afternoon sir, please come in."

"Hallo, Mr Clark," then, to make quite sure he never addressed me as 'sir' again, I said, "My name is Derrick, I'm here to work under you as a farmhand, and nothing more."

"All right, Derrick, I'm Harry. Follow me into the kitchen. Mary will have made a fresh pot of tea, and there'll be some of her home-made rock cakes."

I left my case in the hall and went with him into the tiny kitchen, where Mrs Clark greeted me.

"Come and sit down, you must be very tired after such a long journey."

The contrast between this couple and the Napiers was immense, so much so in fact, that you could be forgiven if you wondered whether or not they inhabited the same planet. The love that you felt flowed between them was almost visible. They had been married for over forty years, yet they behaved like newly-weds. They had a son, who used to work on the estate until last spring. Now he'd been called up but they hoped he would get Christmas leave.

Mary Clark was a well-rounded, motherly type of woman, her straight grey hair combed back and tied into a loose bun. You just knew that her whole life was devoted to making a comfortable home for her family. I think she must have succeeded, for her husband mostly had a grin on his face, and she herself smiled frequently.

After tea, Harry took me up the short flight of stairs to what was to be my room.

"This is my son's," he said. "Where we will put you if he gets Christmas leave, I don't really know."

"Don't worry, I'll be in London by then."

"You don't have to, Derrick. I'm sure we'll manage somehow."

"Harry, I'll be wanting to go anyway, to be with my girlfriend, you see?"

"Will you be marrying her soon then?" he asked.

"Not yet awhile, I think I'm too young to be planning to get married."

"I don't know about that, I just wished I hadn't courted Mary for such a long time. If we'd married sooner, we could have had three more happy years together."

Their son's room was like all the others in the cottage, very small. There was just enough space for a little chest of drawers and a narrow single bed. The almost miniature wardrobe had what was probably their son's Sunday-best suit hanging up inside it. A picture of a young girl had centre place on the mantelpiece. I had just finished putting my few things away when Harry called up to say that Major Gascoyne would like to see me. I leapt downstairs, and saw him standing outside the front door.

"I just called to see if you were settling in."

"I'm fine, thank you, major, and thanks for sending your car to meet me."

He reached into his jacket pocket and pulled out a letter.

"Mrs Gascoyne asked me to give you this. She said it would get you into the theatre in Stratford on Saturday matinees. Now, there is another thing I want to mention - our Home Gguard. We meet every Monday and Thursday evenings, Harry will tell you where to assemble."

Oh shit, I'd hoped he'd forgotten about that.

"I'm afraid I've had enough of the army for the time being, major. Of course, I'll be back in again when I'm called up."

"That's a great pity, you being trained and all. It would have been so useful to have you in, you could show the others what to do, drilling and the like."

"I promise you, major, in an emergency, I'll turn out and fight shoulder to shoulder alongside you and your men."

"Well, let's hope you'll think it over. See you again soon, goodbye!"

When I shut the door on him, Harry came into the hall from the kitchen where he had been hiding.

"He's gone," I said, "but I think he's not too happy about me. It's because I won't join the Home Guard. He wanted me as he knows I was recently in the army."

"Surely you're too young to have already been in and out of the army."

"It's a long story, and I'll tell you about it one day."

"I know why he's fed up that you won't join. It's such a long time ago since he was in, I bet he's forgotten everything he ever knew."

"For fuck's sake, Harry, there's not a hell of a lot to know," then, realising I'd sworn in front of this gentle man, I said: "Sorry Harry, the swearword slipped out."

"I don't mind, Derrick, we all curse sometimes, but not in front of the ladies, mind you!"

"You see, Harry, what I was trying to say was, that men in the country know perfectly well how to handle a gun. All you need to do is aim at Jerry and fire when he comes parachuting down, in the same way as you do to a rabbit or a fox. That's all there is to it, really."

"I must say, you make it sound all very simple, but there's one snag - the rabbits don't fire back at you, do they, Derrick? Now, shall we go to the Village Hall? You can meet some of the other lads, have a pint and play darts or shove ha'penny."

"I'm ready when you are," I said.

The hall was very unpretentious looking. No carpet covered the rough wooden floor and it was sparsely furnished. A trestle table at one end of the room was the bar. Some twenty or so men sat on stacking chairs around the rickety and soiled tables. Most looked as though they were over forty. All of them, including Harry, wore cloth caps. I think they put them on when they first got up, and I'm sure they remained on their heads until they retired for the night. Only their wives would know whether or not they were bald.

Harry manoeuvred me over to the bar, which was self-service.

"A pint or half a pint, Derrick?"

"Not for me, thanks. I only like lemonade or Tizer."

He handed me a bottle of Tizer and a glass, then helped himself to a pint from a barrel that was perched precariously on top of the table. He threw a shilling into an open cardboard box and took out the change due to him.

"You wouldn't be able to have a system like that in London," I said.

"Ah, Derrick, me boy, if anyone was caught cheating here, the very next day there'd be a public hanging on the village green."

I knew he was joking, for this lot looked as honest as the day is long. I played a game of darts and managed to disgrace myself by missing the board completely with every throw. For the first time in my life I tried my hand at shove ha'penny, and did reasonably well at it. I think the men wondered what I, whom they had mistakenly thought to be a 'young gentleman', was doing here amongst them, but it didn't stop them from being friendly. I could see that Harry was very popular.

We stayed in the hall for a couple of hours and after Harry had downed his third pint we went back to the cottage. Mary had prepared supper, and while we were eating, Harry told her all he'd heard whilst chatting with his mates. When the meal was over, we went into the front room and listened to the nine o'clock news. A short while later we all went up to bed.

In the morning, it wasn't Meg's tender strokes and gentle kisses that woke me - it was Harry's big and rough hand touching my shoulder.

"Mornin', Derrick, time to get up."

"What time is it?"

"Six-thirty and work starts at seven."

"But it doesn't get light until after eight, does it?"

"What we'll be a'doing doesn't need daylight. Come down, Derrick, Mary's brewed up the tea."

When I entered the kitchen, Mary was sitting at the table lit only by the soft, cosy light of a single candle. The fire in the small grate was already making a warm glow. On the table were three large cups of tea, and nothing else. The thought struck me, that maybe this old couple didn't eat breakfast.

"Drink up, Derrick, then we'll be on our way."

I think Harry must have noticed my worried look, because he said: "We'll be back here at nine for breakfast. By then you'll have worked up a healthy appetite."

Sitting at the table by candlelight, sipping away at a cup of hot tea, was a very gentle way to start the day.

"What sort of work are we doing today?" I asked.

"We're going on the coal runs in the tipper. We pick up a wagon full of coal for the big house at Stratford station goods yard. We'll be making several journeys as there's some twenty tons of it."

"A whole wagon-load, Harry?"

"Yes, but it lasts them for the winter. They have a lot of rooms to heat, you know."

"I suppose they do, and then, of course, all the farm buildings need heating up, specially in this freezing weather."

"None of it goes there. If you want to keep warm in those buildings, you can only do it by working hard. We'd better leave now, otherwise we won't get our first load back before breakfast."

Harry put on his overcoat and I my jacket. Just as we were about to leave, Mary called out from the kitchen: "Harry, it's very cold today, so put on your scarf."

"I don't think I need it."

"Harry," she said.

"All right, then I will."

"Women," said Harry, as we walked down the garden path, "they're always fussing."

We walked along in the dark to where the tipper truck was parked by the farm buildings. I got in and sat down on the comfortable passenger seat. Fifteen minutes later, we pulled into the station goods yard. Harry showed a man standing by the entrance a piece of paper, and told him what we had come for.

"The wagon is over there in the sidings, mate, you can't miss it because it's the only one loaded with coal."

We drove along the seemingly endless lines of wagons and managed eventually to find ours. Harry pulled up just before it and jumped out of the cab.

"Come on, Derrick, we'll put the flap down first, then I'll bring the truck alongside it."

Harry got into the back of the truck and picked up the biggest shovel I had ever seen. He told me to climb into the wagon and stand on top of the coal.

"Hadn't you better hand me the other shovel?" I said.

"Not yet, Derrick, all I want you to do now is just walk up and down along the top of the heap."

When I did this, an avalanche of coal came tumbling down into the tipper. I think more came rolling down than Harry had expected. I stood still and didn't move again until he had spread the coal evenly across the floor of the truck. Using this simple method, it wasn't very long before we had our first load. After shovelling up the lumps that had fallen onto the ground, and leaving the wagon flap open in readiness for our next load, we made our way back to the farm.

On arrival there, Harry pulled up by the side of one of the farm buildings. He got out and unhitched the back flap of the tipper, then pressed a button inside the cab and slowly the truck floor started to rise at an angle. Within seconds, three tons of coal slid down the sloping floor and made a pyramid of coal on the ground.

"That was easy, wasn't it, Harry?"

"Yes, that it was, but as you'll find out, lad, the hard bit comes later on."

We drove back to the cottage to have breakfast - two slices of fried bread with scrambled eggs. The eggs, Mary told me, were laid during the night by the few chickens she kept. I hadn't tasted scrambled eggs as good as this since last August, when Mrs Collins made some for me the day I had to put down my beloved dog Peter.

By lunchtime we had brought back three more loads. Even then, the wagon was still only half-emptied. The afternoon runs were much harder going, as all the coal nearest to the flap had been moved, and we had to go further and further into the wagon to pick up our shovelfuls before being able to throw them into the tipper. Poor Harry was beginning to feel the strain of it all. His arthritic back was playing him up and I guessed he was in considerable pain. They should have sent us out with another younger man after lunch leaving Harry free to sit in the cab while the man and I did the loading. In the end, I just couldn't bear to watch him suffer any longer, so I insisted that he go and rest in the truck. Although it was nigh on freezing, I began to get very hot running backwards and forwards, carrying a shovelful at a time. The only way I could cool off was to strip down to my vest. The rest of the lugging I did at the double to make up for the time lost by Harry's absence.

When the daylight faded, I got Harry to switch on the truck headlamps and shine them into the wagon; only then could I see where the remaining lumps of coal were. It was well after five when we got into the truck and started to drive back with our final load.

On the way, I suggested to Harry that we should go by his place and drop off a couple of hundredweights.

"After all," I said, "they wouldn't notice a bit missing from the twenty tons we've brought over today, will they? We can consider it to be a small tip for all the hard work we've done."

"Oh no, I couldn't do that, it just wouldn't be right," was his reply.

Oh shit, I thought, once more those fucking Christian morals. The same morals that had prevented poor Meg from leaving her swine of a husband were now stopping Harry from having for once a little bit extra over and above his miserable wages. Religion, it seemed to me, protects the property of the rich far better than any guard dog could.

After we had tipped the load off and were walking back to the cottage, Harry said: "Don't tell Mary that I had to stop working, will you, Derrick? It will only worry her."

"Mum's the word, Harry, but all the same, I think you ought to tell the farm manager not to put you on such hard work in future."

"I mostly manage," he said.

When we stepped into the cottage, Mary saw at once, by the way Harry moved, that he had trouble with his back.

"Now, Harry," she said, "you go and lie down on the couch straight away, and I'll bring you some aspirins and a cup of tea. Tomorrow, you'll not be going to work."

"Don't fuss so, Mary, I'll be all right by then, you'll see."

Judging by the way he eased himself down on the couch, he was still in considerable pain.

Just as Mary had expected, the next morning Harry was no better, so I made my own way down to the farm. Harry had told me to ask for the gaffer, whose name was Glyn. I asked a man who was cleaning out a stable where I might find the gaffer.

"Mornin', lad, he'll be in the dairy."

I found Glyn standing beside a cow, brushing down its coat.

"Good morning," I said, "I'm Derrick, Harry said I should see you when I got here."

"Mornin', where's Harry then?"

I told him that lifting twenty tons of coal had half-killed him, and that he wouldn't be coming in until he was better.

"I suppose I should have sent another man with you yesterday?"

"Yes, you should have," I said.

"Tell him I hope he soon gets well. Now your first job every day is to muck out the stables and the dairy. If you go and see Tom, the man working in the stables, he'll tell you what to do."

"I've already met him, I think he was the one who told me where I'd find you."

"Well, lad, if you stay with him for the rest of the day, he'll show you how we do things around here."

"Thank you," I said.

I retraced my steps back to the stables and found Tom. He was pitchforking soiled hay up from the floor and throwing it out onto a concrete path.

"Glyn told me to come and work with today," I said.

"You're the young man that Harry brought into the Village Hall on Sunday evening, aren't you? Grab a fork and copy what I do, but be careful with the horses, give them time to get to know you. Even then, they can give you a good kick up the arse and send you head first into a pile of shit."

It was refreshing to hear someone swear after all those weeks working with a man who thought that it was perfectly all right to abuse his wife but to utter a swear word was a mortal sin.

I had the feeling that Tom and I were going to get on together. He showed me how to move a horse from one side of the stall to the other when you wanted to clean out the part it was standing on. In a very short time, any fear I had of these beautiful animals vanished, and from then on we were friends.

Tom and I went on mucking out the stables and the dairy until nine o'clock, when it was time to go off and have breakfast.

Harry wasn't up when I got back, so I went upstairs to see him.

"How did you make out, Derrick?"

"Fine, I'm working with a man called Tom. He says he'll come and see you when he's finished work. How are you feeling, Harry, are you still in pain?"

"A bit, I'll be right in a couple of days."

"Don't you think that a doctor should come and have a look at you?"

"No, he can't help, and our local doctor charges ten shillings, no less."

"Bloody hell, Harry, so perhaps you're right, lying in bed and taking aspirins may be the best cure for you."

"It's a lot cheaper, lad, that's for sure."

"Stubborn old fool, he is," said Mary, when I went downstairs for breakfast, "he won't let me call for the doctor, thinks he can't help him."

"Will they dock his pay while he's off sick?" I asked.

"Oh no, I don't think so, not if he's off sick for only a few days."

"Good, because it was their fault. They shouldn't have sent him out on that heavy coalmoving job, that's what did his back in."

"He should have been retired by now, you see, but because of the war, they asked him to stay on and help out."

"Then they must put him only on light work."

For the rest of the day, I worked with Tom in the market garden, lifting carrots and plucking Brussels sprouts off their long stems. Digging up the carrots here was nothing like the hard work it was to fork up the potatoes in Napier's clay-bedevilled fields. Pulling the carrots out of this well-drained, rich and pampered soil was as easy as it would be to uproot them from fine sand. No sticky clay stuck to them. If you gave them a small tap on your hand, you could have eaten them straight from the earth that had nurtured them. I had never seen vegetables looking in such good condition before.

In the afternoon and until dusk we did 'double digging'. This was done by cutting a trench two feet wide and the depth of a spade, the whole length of the vegetable plot. We then put a good helping of well-matured manure into it and by working backwards, we dug out another trench, throwing the earth from that into the first one. Now I knew why the soil was so light when you stuck a fork into it. There was something very satisfying about feeding the earth and helping it to breathe.

Tom liked to chat while we dug away. He seemed very interested to hear about the ups and downs of my life so far. Apart from being in France in the First World War, the furthest he had strayed from the village was to Stratford. He was married just after the war to a girl he had made pregnant the one and only time he went with her.

"I bet a good-looking lad like you gets lots of girls, eh Derrick?"

"Yes, Tom, they all queue up to romp in the hay with me," I teased.

"Well, there's none you'll fancy around here, except for one, and she's already spoken for, she's Harry's son's fiancée."

"I've seen a picture of her, she does look pretty, I must say."

"Have you got a girl, Derrick?"

"Yes, in London."

"Do you er-er go with her?"

"Go where?" I asked.

"You know, do you do it with her?"

"Oh, you mean do we fuck, yes, we do most of the time. In fact, we do precious little else."

"Take my advice, do it as much as you can, for as long as you can, because once you're married all you'll get is fed and your socks washed."

"Maybe it's because you're not doing it right, Tom?"

"I know where to put it and how to ram away. What more can I do?"

If he didn't know at his age, I wasn't going to tell him.

The next day, Harry seemed to be a little better. As for me, it was the same routine as the previous day, mucking out until breakfast. For the rest of the day, Tom and I went out muckspreading. He drove a tractor up and down a field while I stood in the dray and liberally sprinkled pig and horse manure. By mid-morning Tom noticed I was flagging a bit, so he asked me if I could drive a car. I said I could.

"Well, lad, then you can drive a tractor. It's a piece of cake compared to that."

After giving me a few instructions, he took my place in the dray. By mistake, I put the tractor into reverse and went backwards with quite a jerk, making Tom fall flat on his face into the steaming shit.

"Hey, lad, steady on, gently does it."

"Sorry," I said, as I let out the clutch more gently.

For the rest of the day we took it in turns - one hour on the tractor, one hour in the dray. By evening I had pretty well mastered the art of tractor driving, and decided that if this was a farm labourer's life, I would like to be one.

Two days later, Harry got up and declared that he was going to work.

"You'll do no such thing," said Mary firmly, "you can go back on Monday and not a day before."

"I don't want to mope about the house for the rest of the week."

"You can give Mary a hand, or do light work in your garden," I said.

"Suppose you're right."

I knew why he wanted to go - it was the company of his mates that he missed.

My day began with a task I didn't relish - cleaning out the pigsties. I had just finished doing it, and was on my way with a wheelbarrow full of purple-coloured foul-smelling pig manure, when I first caught sight of Ferdinand the bull. Tom was coming round the corner leading it on a piece of rope, attached by a ring to the bull's nose. Ferdinand was so huge and so long that it took a half-minute before he rounded the corner. As for me, I had never seen such a large animal.

"Derrick, meet Ferdinand," said Tom, "the major's just bought him. He looks a bit frightening but he's quite docile really. I'm putting him in one of the stables yonder until a permanent home can be found for him."

When the whole length of the beast had passed by, I watched in awe those magnificent balls, that, with every step taken, swung from side to side with the regularity of the pendulum in a grandfather clock. Tom called me over to help him clean out a stall, holding on to the bull while I did it. We closed the lower half of the split door and bolted it from the outside.

"Cleaning out Ferdinand will be your first job every morning."

"All by myself?" I said, a little dismayed at the thought of it.

"Have no fear, lad, you'll soon become the best of friends."

"I hope so," I said.

Tom left, and I emptied the foul-smelling load I had in the wheelbarrow into a square tub, which, unfortunately for the bull, was opposite his temporary home.

"Sorry about the stink, Ferdinand, but you'll soon get used to it."

The bull poked his massive black and white head out of the open top half of the door and surveyed his new domain. 'Not a fucking cow in sight' is, I suspect, what he said to himself as he looked around. Little did he know that his harem wasn't very far away, and housed some of the most beautiful and cosseted cows in the whole of England. I felt sure all of them were looking forward to meeting him, and when he eventually did put in an appearance, their big eyes and long, fluttering eyelashes would drive him wild with desire. How cows could bear to have a couple of tons of bull climbing on their backs was beyond me - perhaps that's how the expression 'poor cow' came about.

The next morning, when I turned up to clean up Ferdinand's lodgings, he seemed pleased to have a bit of company; after all, the poor chap had been shut up all by himself for the night. It was not possible to clean out his stall with him in it, so I put a rope through the ring on his nose, led him outside and tied him to a railing. I knew, but I hoped he didn't, that if he took it into his head to move off, half the balustrade would come crashing down, but good chap that he was, he stayed put while I cleaned out his apartment.

As soon as I got him back in, I went off to fetch his breakfast. To my surprise, he didn't seem to want any. He just stood there, looking at me and nodding his head. He's asking me to do something, I thought. It was some time before it dawned on me what he wanted - to rub his forehead, so I did. Because he started to push harder against the palm of my hand, it occurred to me that what he would really like was a good scratch. So I scratched away as hard as I could, but even this didn't seem to satisfy him. Then I had a brainwave.

"I know, Ferdy, I've got just the thing for you, I'll only be away for a minute."

I went down the path to where I knew there was a pile of bricks and brought one back. When I returned, I placed the widest part of the brick on his broad head and rubbed away, and to show how much he was enjoying it, he pressed his head ever nearer to the movement of the brick. Eventually I was pushed back to the bottom half of the split door. To get even closer, all two tons of him took a small step towards me. The hand that held the brick was suddenly pushed against my chest, and because I had stopped scraping away, Ferdinand pressed even harder. I became panic-stricken, I thought that I could almost hear my ribcage beginning to crack under the tremendous pressure. I felt the blood rushing up to my head and almost stopped breathing. Somehow, just before I passed out, I managed to put my free hand to the outside of the door and release the bolt. When it sprung open, the bull took another step towards me, which sent me reeling backwards across the narrow path, and straight into the square tub of liquid pig manure. Although I was up to my neck in shit, to me it was as good as a bath full of the very best champagne, I was just so happy to be able to breathe freely again. When I climbed out of the tub, Ferdy had a puzzled look on his stupid face. I bet he thought, why on earth did he do that? Tom, who had seen me catapulting out of the stall, burst out into uncontrollable laughter, but Mary didn't, when she opened the front door to me. She looked horrified when she saw the state I was in, and distanced herself from the smell of me by taking a few steps backwards. I stripped down to my pants and bundled up the offending clothes. Then I dumped the lot as far away from the house as was possible.

Mary, meanwhile, had put the tin bath in front of the kitchen fire and filled it to the brim with hot water. After I had dried myself, I went up to the bedroom and put on the only other clothes I had. I couldn't even bear to think how I would deal with the lot that were all mucked up. Maybe I should dig a hole and bury the problem, then buy new clothes in Stratford on Saturday afternoon. But when I got back from work in the evening, Mary had washed and ironed the whole revolting lot. Thanks to her, I didn't have to do that. Instead I took advantage of the complimentary seat Mrs Gascoyne had given me for the theatre.

This was a great occasion, as it was going to be the first time I'd ever set foot in one. I gave the letter I'd brought with me to a lady in the box office, and she wrote out a ticket. An usherette showed me to a centre seat in the front row of the stalls, plumb in the middle of a whole battery of fearsome-looking old ladies, all of them wearing long strings of pearls. I think they felt a little uneasy about this weatherbeaten and dishevelled youth in their midst I only say this, because periodically they ran their fingers up and down their pearls, just to make sure that they were still there.

The play I was going to see was called *Othello*, and according to the programme was written in 1604 by a local man and the theatre was named after him. I think the name Shakespeare did crop up once or twice when I was at school, but I wouldn't like to swear to it. I must admit, I found it a bit hard to understand the plot and the language, but I liked the sound of it.

A very sad tale, I thought, when the curtain came down on the last act. I, personally, would have preferred a happy ending, in contrast to the current real events in Europe, where it didn't look like there was going to be one for a long time to come.

Outside the theatre, a line of chauffeur-driven cars pulled up to take the fine ladies and their pearls back to their grand homes. As for me, I jumped onto the bike that Harry had lent me, and cycled back through the blacked-out countryside to the cottage. I went three more times to the theatre during my stay on the estate. I saw two more Shakespeare plays and *The Cherry Orchard*, which I liked and understood most of all.

By Monday morning, Harry was well enough to go back to work. As we walked up the path leading to the farm, he said: "See, Derrick, I'm well, and I've got ten shillings in my pocket that wouldn't be there if I had let Mary call the doctor."

"You could buy Mary a little present with that, couldn't you?"

"I could, and I will."

I introduced Harry to Ferdy and demonstrated to him how much the bull enjoyed having his head scratched with a brick, only this time I made sure that the stable door was wide open.

Most of the next three weeks was spent working with Tom and Harry in the market garden or out in the fields spreading manure on the land. One day was devoted to making trenches around large clumps of asparagus.

"Have you ever eaten any?" I asked Harry.

"No, I haven't, nor do I intend to. Eating anything that has hardly seen the light of day doesn't seem right to me."

"As it takes such a lot of work to grow them, I suppose they're expensive to buy?"

"Oh that they are, lad, but this crop isn't for sale, it all goes up to the big house."

My God, I thought, the Gascoynes were well insulated from all the shortages that most people had to put up with in this war. They were already stocked up with a wagon-load of coal, which would keep them nice and warm throughout the winter, and the dairy gave them all the cream, butter, eggs and milk they could possibly want. Fresh vegetables were there just for the asking, and apples, pears, and cherries, were available from their well-cared-for orchards. The only thing they had in common with ordinary folk was the absence of bananas, oranges and figs in their diet, but it wouldn't surprise me one bit if they found a way around that somehow.

A week or so before Christmas, winter arrived with a vengeance, and the whole county was covered knee-deep in frozen snow. Outside work came to an abrupt halt. This meant that, apart from my regular pre-breakfast task of cleaning out the stables and pigsties, the rest of the day was spent inside the unheated farm buildings, maintaining and repairing all different types of agricultural machinery, so that when spring came, they would be in pristine condition. As I was completely hopeless at anything mechanical, I said to myself, Derrick, my boy, it's time you made tracks and returned to London to see Gloria, or with a bit of luck, Stella.

I went and found the foreman and gave him a week's notice. As an excuse I told him that my old uncle was very ill and needed me to look after him.

"Hasn't he got another member of his family who could do that?" he asked.

"Afraid not," I lied, "you see, I'm his only surviving relative."

He was clearly pissed off that he was going to be deprived of the only young farmhand he had. When I told Mary and Harry that I'd be leaving a few days before Christmas, I think they were a little relieved, as now their son's room would be vacant for him when he came home on leave.

I went over to the manor to tell the Gascoynes I was going. I refrained from telling them the lie that I had told their foreman, for fear that they might phone up Uncle to enquire how he was. So I concocted another story for them. I said I was pining for my fiancée and wanted to go back to London to marry her before being called back into the Army. Why one complicates life by making up these ridiculous stories instead of just telling the truth, God only knows. Perhaps it stems from some sort of youthful arrogance, that you imagine your employer will be devastated when you hand in your notice. The reality is, of course, that a few days afterwards he's forgotten all about you.

On my way back to the cottage, I went by the stables to see Ferdinand to give him one last scratch.

"You must understand, Ferdy," I said, "I'm not like you, there's no girls for me here."

He looked at me and I think he was saying 'what about me, I've been here all this time and haven't clapped eyes on a single cow'.

"Don't fret, Ferdy, I promise you, your time will come. Soon spring will be here, and then you'll be out in the meadow with more cows that perhaps even you can manage."

I stroked his ears and then gave him a good scratch with a brick. It saddened me to leave my mighty friend, but I knew that Tom would take good care of him.

Back at the cottage, I went up to my room and packed my suitcase. Harry offered to run me to the station in the truck, and I gladly accepted. I found Mary in the kitchen, putting some rock cakes into the oven for tomorrow's tea. I thanked her for the way she had taken care of me and said goodbye.

"Goodbye, Derrick, mind how you go now, write to us soon and let us know how you are getting on."

"Thank God we haven't come here to pick up coal, eh, Harry?" I said when he dropped me off at the station.

"Yes, lad, that was hard going, wasn't it? Still, it got done, didn't it?"

"Only by half crippling you," I said.

Harry walked with me to my carriage and stayed until the train pulled away. I am going to miss this kind and gentle man, I thought, and I waved to him out of the carriage window as the train moved slowly off.

CHAPTER TWENTY-FOUR

It was mid-afternoon when I arrived in London, too early to see Gloria, as she would still be at work. So I took a cab to St John's Wood. It was four o'clock, just the time Uncle would be having his afternoon nap. Not wanting to disturb him, I sat on my suitcase downstairs in the hall for half an hour before venturing up. Although I had a key, I rang the doorbell. He opened it with his afternoon glass of whisky and soda in his hand.

"Hayden, how nice to see you, have you been given Christmas leave?"

I told him that as the land was frozen hard and covered in deep snow, there wasn't much I could do that would be of any use until spring.

"How are you keeping?" I asked.

"Oh, quite well, really, all things considered. The raids are becoming a bit wearisome, especially now the long nights are upon us, the sirens go most evenings at six and the all-clear doesn't sound until seven the next morning, you can almost set your watch by them. "

"Did a woman called Meg ring up?"

"No, only that film extras agency. I think getting hold of young men is proving to be a bit difficult for them at present."

"Thanks for inviting me, but I'd sort of promised myself to spend my first night back in London with Gloria, and I'll be leaving shortly."

I think he was disappointed that I was going off so soon after arriving, but all he said was: "Oh well, there'll be other nights we can dine together, won't there?"

"Yes, lots. Would it be OK if I had a bath, Uncle?"

"Of course, dear boy."

I told him the last one I had was in a tinbath in the kitchen of the cottage where I had lodgings.

I had two baths before feeling really clean again. It took a long time to untangle my matted hair before I could comb and brush it. I put on a clean shirt that Mrs Blaber had washed and ironed for me, and my double-breasted suit that had been cleaned and pressed while I was away, and polished my shoes. I thought Gloria would find me irresistible, turned out the way I was.

"I'll be off now," I said.

He peered at me from above *The Times*.

"My, how smart you look."

"I hope my girl thinks the same. Tomorrow being Sunday, I may spend the day and another night with her, in which case I'll see you again about ten on Monday morning."

"Have you enough money to entertain the young lady?"

"Yes, thanks, I've plenty."

"Good, so all being well, I'll see you on Monday, enjoy yourself, Hayden."

I didn't bother to wait for the lift, but bounded down the six flights of stairs like a bird on the wing. A little before closing time, I waited in the dark outside the back entrance. I could see by the dim light that shone when the staff door opened, who was coming out. Normally, Gloria was one of the first, but girl after girl emerged, and there was no sign of her. Finally I approached one I knew, and asked her if Gloria would soon be out.

"Hallo, Derrick, fancy seeing you, what have you been up to?"

"That's a long story, but could you please tell me if you've seen Gloria?"

"She left here some weeks ago. Try her at her digs. Say Jean sends her love, will you?"

"I'll do that, goodbye."

I hurried off down Camden High Street to where Gloria lived. I struck a match so that I could see where her bell was. She didn't come down, so after a while I rang it again. Still, she didn't appear. Oh dear, I thought, maybe she's gone out for the evening. I waited a little longer, then I picked at random another bell. A middle-aged man opened the door.

"Sorry to bother you, but would you know when Gloria might be back?"

"She won't be, she left here some time ago."

"Did she say where she was going?"

"No, she left without saying a word, and what's more, if you ever catch up with her, tell her that her last landlord is still wanting his back rent."

With that, he slammed the door on me.

I was crestfallen. It soon dawned on me that I had lost her for ever. If only I knew where Stella lived, that would have cheered me up a bit, but I didn't. All dressed up and with nowhere to go, I stood there feeling very fed up and frustrated. It was now too late to go back and dine with Uncle. So I retraced my steps back down Camden High Street to the Corner House in Tottenham Court Road.

On returning to the flat, Uncle was surprised to see me. I told him that Gloria had disappeared into thin air, and that the probability of ever seeing her again was slight.

"Oh dear, I am sorry, Hayden, it won't be too long before you find another girl."

So on that hopeful note, and despite the din of the ack-ack guns, I went to bed.

At breakfast, Uncle confessed that although he had vowed never again to go at Christmas and be with his difficult and quarrelsome sister, once again he just could not bear to think of her sitting all by herself in the Old People's Home, with nobody there to be at the other end of her fucking Christmas cracker.

"I'm hoping that this time will be the last."

"Don't worry about leaving me, Uncle, I won't be alone, I'll ring my friend Vic and arrange to spend Christmas with him."

"Good. I really don't like the idea of you being all on your own at Christmas."

"Uncle, I thought I'd go on and let the film extra agency know I'm back in circulation and ready for work as soon as possible. Are you leaving for your sister's tomorrow, Christmas Eve?"

"Yes, I am - I'd much prefer to travel there on Christmas Day, but unfortunately no passenger trains are running."

On Monday, I left the old boy to his copy of *The Times*, got dressed and set off - not to the agency as I had intended, but to go first to call on my friend Jack. I was hoping that with a bit of luck he was back home on leave. I had another reason for wanting to see him, for there was just a chance he might know Stella's address. His mother opened the door.

"Hallo, Derrick. I suppose you're hoping Jack is here, but he's like all the men in the Air Force, none got any Christmas leave this year."

"You must be very disappointed, Mrs Harrison, it doesn't seem fair. All the soldiers are on leave."

"Well, they ain't fighting the bloody war just now, are they?"

"That's true, but their turn will come, I assure you. When next you write to Jack, please tell him I called, and when he does come on leave, ask him to ring me, he's got my number."

"I will, Derrick."

"Can't very well wish you a happy Christmas, Mrs Harrison, but I'm sure that when spring comes and the nights get shorter, Jack will be given leave. Keep well, goodbye."

After I left her, I made my way to the film agency. At first I couldn't find the entrance to the place, but then I remembered that it was the shabbiest door in the small street. I climbed the still uncarpeted flight of stairs and entered the dilapidated room that was their office.

Archie Wolf looked up from his untidy desk and saw me standing there.

"Hallo, duckie, I can't tell you how glad I am to see you. There's lots of work for young men at the moment. All my regulars are off fighting for King and country. Are you likely to be called up soon?"

"No, not for a year or so, Mr Wolf."

"That's good news, dear."

I didn't like being called 'duckie' or 'dear', so I reminded him of my name.

"Well, Derrick, duckie, you're needed at Ealing Studios the day after Boxing Day, you'll be put into a sailor boy's uniform, and I bet you'll look gorgeous in your bell-bottom trousers, with your tight little arse sticking out beneath a sailor's jacket."

Will this old queen ever give up? I thought.

"There's three days on it, that's not bad for a start, is it, duckie?"

His assistant told me how to get to Ealing, and checked that she still had my phone number:

"When you're not working, dear, phone in every evening between five and six to see if we have anything for you."

"I will." Then I added, "Have a good Christmas!"

"You too, dear," she said, as I went out of the door.

I felt like some exercise, so I walked down Piccadilly and into Hyde Park. I stood for a while by the boathouse and watched hardy men seated in feather-light sculling boats ploughing their way through the freezing water of the Serpentine. Toffs, in riding-habits, galloped along over the sandy soil of Rotten Row, looking and behaving like there wasn't a war on.

Back at the flat, I found Vic's phone number. I caught him just as he was about to leave for his local and we arranged to meet at his place on Christmas morning. I was glad I wasn't going to be alone this Christmas and I think he felt the same way.

Shortly after I had phoned Vic, Uncle and I left for the Strand Palace Hotel. It was packed with Army officers on home leave. The place looked more like the Officers' Mess of the Grenadier Guards than a civilian restaurant. There were colonels and generals sitting at the same table as lieutenants, presumably their sons, as well as a whole host of other commissioned officers with their girlfriends or wives. I saw a sprinkling of naval officers but they, like the pilots of the RAF, were mostly on duty over Christmas. It was only because Uncle had known the headwaiter for many years, that a table was found for us. Uncle obviously enjoyed seeing and hearing all the hubbub and chatter of a busy restaurant again. I think it reminded him of the carefree days before the war.

"You've no idea, how depressing it is when you dine alone in a large restaurant with lots of tables laid out for just a few customers."

Uncle told me that it was the first time in weeks that the sirens hadn't gone off in the middle of the meal. For once, everyone could wine and dine in peace.

"Who knows," he said, "perhaps Field-Marshall Göring has decided to give his pilots a few days off for Christmas."

I knew that Uncle had enjoyed our meal out together, because when we left the hotel, he didn't want to spoil the evening by returning to the flat by public transport, but instead he hailed a cab.

After breakfast on Christmas Eve, Uncle made himself ready to leave. I watched him pack into his small suitcase a leather-bound hip-flask, which he had filled to the brim with whisky.

"A life-raft, Hayden, when things get a bit rough," he said, looking very fed up as he wrapped the flask into the safe-keeping of his spare woollen long-johns.

"Cheer up, Uncle," I said, "you're only going to be away for two days and nights."

"That, dear boy, if you knew my sister, could feel like an eternity."

At eleven, the taxi arrived, and he reluctantly left for Waterloo Station. A little later, Mrs Blaber departed, and I was alone in the flat wondering what I should do with myself for the rest of the day. Then I remembered that I had seen, in Uncle's small bookcase, a book entitled *Psychopathia Sexualis* by Krafft-Ebing. I couldn't make out what it was all about, but the first three letters of the second word gave me enough of a clue to entice me to pick it up. The book was full of case histories, recorded in detail, of the sexual antics of some highly respectable middle- and upper-class ladies and gentlemen of Strassbourg and Vienna, before and just after the turn of the century.

While the rest of the Christian world was preparing to celebrate a believe-it-or-not yarn about a virgin giving birth to a baby boy in a stable, I spent the day with my nose stuck into either a dictionary or the book's glossary, attempting to decipher words like 'cunnilingus', 'fellatio', 'sado-masochism', and 'coitus interruptus'.

One of the cases concerned a Professor W. of Vienna, who only got sexual gratification by defecating on the abdomen of some unfortunate prostitute. When I found out what 'defecating' meant, I was shocked to the core. How in hell the Professor worked out the timing for his particular aberration, defeated me. The relief when he finally knocked on the brothel door must have been considerable. It seemed to me his little lark was a very risky business. Still, he must have got away with it, otherwise he wouldn't have got a mention in Krafft-Ebing's book.

I don't remember coming across one case history of any ordinary men or women. I was so fascinated with the book that I'd completely forgotten to have any lunch, and it wasn't till quite late in the evening that hunger pains drove me into the kitchen.

In that one long day, I had learnt more about reading and studying than I'd done in my entire time at school. Perhaps it might be a good idea, I thought, if books like this were put into every classroom for pupils of fourteen and over to study. You never know, it might well stimulate slow learners like myself to forge ahead.

For supper that Christmas Eve of 1940, I had a large bowl of cornflakes and two slices of buttered toast and marmalade, then had yet another little read before turning out the light and getting into bed. On Christmas morning, I resisted the temptation to pick up the book again, in case I got so involved in it that I'd end up being late for my date with Vic.

I had a problem I couldn't imagine how to solve - what to do about a present for my friend. I'd never given one to anybody before, so I couldn't think of what to do. In the end I had the bright idea of taking one of Uncle's boxes of fifty Abdullah Turkish cigarettes. They had the advantage of looking very special with their oval shape and gold-painted tips. The disadvantage was that their aroma filled the room with a smell like camel shit on a slow burner.

Anyhow I decided they'd do. I knew they were special and expensive, because Uncle only smoked one occasionally. Having no wrapping paper, I plonked the small box into the front page of the previous day's Times, and made as neat a parcel of it as possible. The paper I held in place with an elastic band. I scribbled 'Merry Christmas, Vic' on a scrap of paper and pinned it to the parcel. Jesus, I thought, what a fucking palaver this whole Christmas business is.

Vic told me he'd be working the late shift on Christmas Eve, and didn't expect to tumble out of bed much before midday. He was still in his pyjamas when he opened the door to me.

"Hallo Derrick, I'm glad you got me up. If you hadn't, there wouldn't have been long to go before the pubs close."

I gave him the present and apologised for the wrapping.

"Don't apologise, it was very nice of you to give me anything at all. I'm afraid I haven't got you anything, so my present will be to pay for our meal. Do you happen to know if any restaurant is open?"

I told him that the previous year I had a very good lunch at the Marble Arch Corner House.

"Wonderful, and convenient too, it's only fifteen minutes' walk from here, that's where we'll make for after I've downed a few pints."

He put on his overcoat and we walked at some speed to his local.

There Vic literally fought his way through the crowd to the bar and got his first pint. This went down in seconds, then with the froth still visible on his lips, he ordered a refill.

"Do you have to go into work today?" I asked, as he drank his second pint at a more leisurely pace.

"They expect me to clock in at four, but I fucking well won't, because I intend to be well and truly pissed by then. Even if I were stupid enough to turn up, any spot-welding I did on a plane would have it end up looking more like a work of art by a painter called Picasso."

"Does he specialise in pictures of planes then?" I asked.

"No, but he has his own particular way of distorting things."

"Is that because he's not a very good painter?"

"No, dear boy, it's the way he sees things."

"Do you mean he's too poor to buy glasses?"

"Oh, let's skip it, shall we, I'm not in the mood for a long discourse about modern art."

Vic managed to get his third pint just before the call of 'Time, gentlemen, please'. The pub started to empty out and we were the last to leave.

"What a bloody country it is. You can't have a drink when you want one, and to crown it all, they expect you to fight, and perhaps even die, for it!"

We arrived at the restaurant half an hour later.

"Bloody hell," said Vic when he saw the place had only poor old dears sitting by themselves at tables laid for four. "It looks like we've ended up in the dining room of an old ladies' home."

"It's not their fault that they have no one to be with on Christmas Day, Vic. Probably their sons or daughters are all stationed miles away and can't be with them."

"If they had a spark of esprit or joie de vivre, they would all sit together and get pissed."

"That isn't the English way. We just don't inflict ourselves on strangers."

When the Nippy arrived, Vic placed an order for two bottles of red Beaujolais.

"Haven't you forgotten I don't drink?" I said.

"No, Derrick, I haven't."

What with the three pints he had already consumed, and his intention of now drinking two bottles of wine, I could foresee having to take him back legless to his digs - only today, unlike the last time we dined, there would be no cab to bundle him into.

Vic ordered the set menu, I did the same as I had done the year before, and persuaded the waitress to give me lots of gravy in place of the turkey.

"My God, Derrick, what an odd chap you are. Don't drink, don't eat meat, beats me what there is left to make life worth living."

"If you'd added girls to your list, Vic, I might have agreed with you."

Vic soon polished off his first bottle and started on his second. By now he was getting more and more drunk. Suddenly he stood up and looked around the half-empty restaurant.

"Derrick, I just cannot bear seeing all these old ladies sitting on their own any longer. I intend to do something about it."

Staggering slightly, he made his way over to a woman sitting by herself. I could see that she felt a little uneasy about the intoxicated young man standing in front of her. Vic chatted to her for a while, then went and spoke to another lady who was sitting all by herself. This lady stood up and followed him to where the first lady was, and after a few words between the two, she sat down with a complete stranger. Vic repeated this performance a few times, and before very long, a number of the single ladies were sitting with people they had never met before. Eventually, thirst drove him back to his bottle.

"What on earth did you say to them?"

"It was quite simple really, I said to the first lady. 'Good afternoon, madam, my name is Victor Blake, and I would like to wish you a very merry Christmas, and express the hope that next year you will be enjoying the company of those near and dear to you.' Then I asked her her name, and armed with that knowledge I went to the next one and said to her that the lady on the next table, whose name is Eileen Webb, would be delighted if you would join her. It worked like a charm, old boy."

"Well, Vic, you've done your good deed for this Christmas, haven't you?"

"Not really, Derrick, you see, I did it for purely selfish reasons. I just can't abide being in an eating house where you can hear a pin drop, no hubbub, dear chap, one might as well dine in a morgue."

He caught the eye of a passing waitress and ordered yet another bottle. Oh dear, oh dear, I thought, now I will almost certainly have to carry him back from Marble Arch to Maida Vale. I did get him to eat up his food, in the vain hope that some of the wine might get soaked up.

"Derrick," he said, in that affected upper-class voice which sounded even more ridiculous when he was drunk, "I have something important to tell you. I'm going to leave my fucking boring job. Just can't face it any more."

"But surely, Vic, if you do that, they'll have you back in the army pretty smartish, won't they?"

"Oh, it'll take them months before they find out I've scarpered."

"My advice is to hang on until the spring, then chuck your job in. You'll be able to enjoy the whole summer before they catch up with you."

"Damn good advice, and I'll take it, but how in hell I'll be able to stick it out until then, I can't imagine."

By now the restaurant had nearly emptied and the waitresses were obviously wanting the customers to leave so that they could go home and celebrate what was left of Christmas Day. Vic, who was totally oblivious to this, tried to get another bottle, but thankfully failed.

"Looks like the party's over, eh Derrick?"

"Yes, it's time to go," I said, hoping that he'd be able to make it. After three attempts, he finally managed to stand upright, and by leaning heavily on me, we just made the one flight of stairs down to the exit.

When the freezing air hit him, he collapsed into a heap on to the pavement, and promptly passed out. Oh shit, I thought, what the fuck do I do now? There was only one thing for it, I'd have to give him a fireman's lift, and hoist him over my shoulder. I hoped I had the strength to carry him back the mile and a half to Maida Vale.

But no matter how many times I tried to prop him up against the wall long enough to get a grip on him, he just slipped through my hands ending up back on the pavement. I toyed with the idea of letting him lie there until he sobered up, but because of the biting cold wind, I thought I'd better not, in case he died from exposure.

I was about to go and find a phone box and call for an ambulance, but fortunately a police car with two officers pulled up right by me.

"Having trouble, are we, son?" said one of them.

Now, I had learnt very early on in my short life that it is prudent to be over-polite to those in authority, especially if you want their help. So in the best English accent I could muster, I answered:

"I am indeed, sir, and I'd be most grateful if you could advise me as to how I could get my friend back to his home."

"There won't be any cabs today, lad. By rights I ought to run him in for being drunk and disorderly, but seeing him there motionless, perhaps the charge should be 'drunk and incapable'."

"Oh dear, I do hope you don't, sir. He does highly specialised work in an aircraft factory, and the whole place comes to a halt if he's not there to supervise things. We both know, don't we, sir, how important it is to produce as many fighter planes as possible at the moment."

I think the officer must have thought that the young man lying drunk at his feet was some sort of aeronautical genius.

'Well, if he is that essential to the war effort, we'd best try and get him back to his home. Where does he live?"

"Maida Vale."

"And you hoped to carry him all that way. Who do you think you are, Tarzan?"

"No, but I'm quite strong."

"Well, strong or not, I think you've bitten off more than you can chew."

Together we got Vic into the back of the police car, and a few minutes later arrived at Maida Vale. The two officers helped me carry him into the room and lay him out on his bed.

"I just can't thank you enough."

"That's all right, son, your chum will soon sleep it off."

After they left, I looked down at Vic. I left him a note saying I'd be in touch again soon and reminded him not to give in his notice until the spring. After covering him up with blankets, I walked back to Adelaide Court and spent the rest of the evening with Krafft-Ebing and his merry band of perverts.

When Uncle returned the next morning, I confessed to him that I had taken one of his cartons of Abdullah cigarettes and given it to Vic for Christmas. I wanted to pay for them, but he wouldn't hear of it. He drank in quick succession two large whiskies in order, as he put it 'to regain my equilibrium, after having endured two days of absolute hell'. That evening we dined at Frascati's. I was in bed by ten, because I had to be up before dawn, so as to be at Ealing Studios by seven-thirty a.m.

CHAPTER TWENTY-FIVE

When I entered St John's Wood Underground at six-thirty, the foul air coming up from below hit me in the face. Once down the escalator, the stench was almost unbearable. The ventilating system was never designed to cope with the awful conditions I found there. Some hundreds of men, women and children lay huddled together packed like sardines on the hard concrete floor of the platforms, and the passages leading to them. So crowded was it, that many people slept precariously near to the electrified track. If they had turned in their sleep, they might well have fallen onto it. I saw little children lying on thin mattresses, peacefully sleeping, their heads peeping out from under grubby blankets. Because they had to breathe in the evil-smelling air all night, their small faces were very pale, and dark rings showed beneath their closed eyes. Buckets placed at intervals for them to use had mostly overflowed onto the platform by the morning.

Slowly some of the grown-ups began to stir. Like their children, they looked pale and worn as they bent down to pick up their pitiful bundles of bedding. These they made into a roll secured only by a piece of string. How people could tolerate sleeping night after night in these appalling conditions, was impossible for me to understand.

When a train finally arrived, the air in the carriage was stale, but compared to the foul stuff I had breathed in on the platform, it was mountain-fresh. I got into the street at Ealing Broadway, and I didn't begin to come alive until I had taken in several deep gulps of fresh air.

As I had already worked a few days at Ealing Studios, I more or less knew what to do when I arrived. The wardrobe department had a number of people in it, being measured up, and then given different service uniforms - I was decked out as an ordinary sailor.

The set was a London pub, and we were its customers. As far as I could make out, the scene was that of a young naval officer, having a drink and chatting away with fellow officers, when in comes his sweetheart. He has to tell her that in a couple of hours, he must leave to join his ship. She gets all emotional, but being a good, middle-class English rose, succeeds in keeping her eyes dry. He, of course, keeps a stiff upper lip and says to her all the crummy things that go with that sort of scene.

Our job as extras was to make the sort of noise you would expect to hear in a crowded pub, while we drank make-believe beer. I think the froth was produced by whisking up soapflakes. During the lunch-break, the regular extras, or 'crowd artistes' as they preferred to be called, complained that no rhubarb money was on their pay chit.

"Rhubarb money, what's that?" I enquired.

"You get five shillings a day more when they ask you to make crowd noises," said one of them.

"I'm new at this game, why is it called rhubarb money?" I asked.

"Because rhubarb, rhubarb, rhubarb, is what we say to each other to make a sound like lots of people talking."

"Why not pineapple, pineapple, pineapple?" I asked.

"Because when you say rhubarb, you have to purse your lips and it looks on camera more like you're really talking."

"Why not invent a conversation?" I said.

"It's because they're not paying us to be fucking scriptwriters, that's why," was his answer.

"I suppose we'll have to tell them that they've forgotten to add it to our pay."

"Oh no, they haven't forgotten, lad, they're just hoping they can get away with it."

"So what do we do about it?" I asked.

"Tonight, when they tell us to come back in the morning, we'll say we won't unless we are paid rhubarb money."

He asked all the others if they agreed, and they all nodded their heads in approval.

"What about you, lad?"

"I'm with you," I replied.

"Now," said the man, "who is going to be our spokesman?"

Nobody volunteered, and as I, in my time, had spoken with colonels and majors, and because of Uncle, even lords, a mere mortal like an assistant director didn't worry me one bit. So I told him that I would.

At the end of the day, when the bright lights of the set were switched off, the assistant-director told us extras to line up as he had something to say.

"Gentlemen, I would like you back here at seven-thirty tomorrow morning."

"Excuse me, Mr assistant director, we all want to be paid the five shillings crowd noise money for today and any future day," I said in a loud and clear voice.

"This film is being made on a very small budget, and there simply isn't the money available to pay for anything other than the basic daily rate. So bearing this in mind, I want all those who don't agree with these terms, to take one step forward."

I took one long step forward and more or less stood to attention. When I looked to my left, and then right, I realised I was standing there in total isolation. I turned round and said to the others: "What's going on? For fuck's sake, come and join me."

Nobody stirred, not even the man who had thought up the idea.

"Right then," said the assistant director, "everyone's back tomorrow morning, with the exception of you," pointing a finger at me. "And what's more, I'll see to it that you never work in this studio again."

"You bastards, you fucking load of bastards," I shouted at the others as they slunk off the set. God, I was angry, I didn't even know about the fucking five shillings and now I was the only one being victimised.

A man who worked as an electrician on the set, and had witnessed my little performance, came over to me.

"Well, comrade, now you've found out early in life never to rely on working-class solidarity."

I didn't then understand what he was talking about, but one thing was for sure, I had taken one step that changed my whole way of looking at things for ever.

"What lot do you belong to?" he asked.

"Lot?" I said.

"Are you a communist or socialist or an anarchist, which of those are you?"

"I'm afraid I haven't any idea what you're talking about."

"Look, lad, you have (maybe unwittingly) just committed a political act and if you really don't understand what I'm saying to you, may I suggest we walk together to the station, and I'll explain to you what I mean. My name is Frederick Lohr. I'll meet you at the Studio gates in fifteen minutes. Don't worry if it takes you a little longer to hand in your gear and get paid, I'll wait for you."

I immediately liked the look and sound of this man. He was probably about forty, very tall and slim built. His well-trimmed beard nearly covered his lean face and intelligent eyes looked down on you as he spoke. His brown, wavy hair was beginning to recede and exposed a high forehead.

As we started to walk slowly towards the station, Frederick explained to me in the simplest way possible the difference between the capitalist system and a socialist one, where the workers own the means of production, and man did not exploit man. He told me that I had got off lightly with my expulsion from the studios compared to the Tolpuddle Martyrs, six Dorset farm-labourers in 1833 who were transported to Australia and enslaved there, just because they tried to improve the appalling conditions of those who worked on the land. Many of the things he spoke about (particularly those concerning injustices) matched up with my experiences.

So the seeds he sowed into my mind fell on fertile soil. By the time we got out of the train back in London, he had made a convert. Before we parted, Frederick told me that every Sunday afternoon he spoke at Speakers' Corner in Hyde Park on the anarchist platform. He thought it might be an idea if we met there the following Sunday. I told him I'd never heard of it.

"Speakers' Corner is a sort of open-air university. You'll get a whole range of diverse opinions, so when you've been going there for a few times, you will be able to decide which particular creed appeals to you most."

The next day, I went to the agency to pay in the commission for my day's work. Archie looked up from his desk and saw me standing there.

"Back so soon, are we, duckie? I didn't expect to see you for at least three days."

I told him I'd been barred for ever from Ealing Studios, all because the other extras asked me to demand our rhubarb money, and then didn't stand by me.

"Who barred you?" he asked.

"The assistant director," I replied.

"Oh duckie, you don't have to worry your pretty head about that trumped-up little peacock. He's only on this one production, and when it's finished, he'll slink back into the obscurity from whence he came. As it happens, I'm glad you're here, because you're needed at Pinewood tomorrow. You're to be a young soldier in a pub, you know all about that, don't you, duckie?"

"Thanks a lot," I said.

I ran down the stairs feeling quite good about the way things had turned out. I worked at Pinewood Studios for the rest of the week, and on Sunday met up with my anarchist friend as arranged. Frederick was holding a collapsible platform. I helped him carry it across the wide road into Hyde Park.

As I didn't want to be the only one standing in front of him before he had a crowd I went over to where a number of people were putting in position an assortment of different things that would enable them to see above the heads of the spectators. Some had soapboxes, others stepladders, one just stood on a kitchen chair. The majority had the same as my friend.

The speakers started by addressing the passing crowd in a variety of ways, as 'comrades', 'brothers', 'my friends' or 'fellow workers I heard only one whose opening words were
'ladies and gentlemen'.

There was one immaculately dressed speaker who caught my attention,

"Gather round, you cloth-capped morons, and I'll tell you how you can improve your wretched lives." He pointed a manicured finger at his audience.

"I employ five hundred men like you in my factory in the Midlands, and I exploit them mercilessly. I intend to go on doing it until they tell me they've had enough of me living on their backs, and fire me. If that day ever comes, I'll make you this solemn promise: I'll step down without a fight. Now, if all of you would only do that, the country would belong to you in a matter of days. It's as simple as that. You just have to decide not to put up with your pitiful conditions. Doesn't it bother you that I stand here before you, well-dressed, well-fed and well-off? I have a chauffeur-driven Rolls-Royce parked outside the gates, and it will wait there for as long as I want. I don't even pay my chauffeur overtime for working on Sundays. If he were foolish enough to complain, I'd sack him. Now, how long are you going to let people like me sit on you?"

No one in the crowd uttered a word.

"There you have it, your silence has answered my question, you're going to allow me, and those like me, to exploit you for ever, aren't you?"

One man did pluck up enough courage to open his mouth.

"If you were a proper boss, you wouldn't be talking to us like this, would you?"

"You're bright, aren't you, my man. You can bet your sweet life I wouldn't. The reason I speak to you this way is that I can only tolerate my feelings of guilt, by saying that it's time you got rid of those who exploit you. If you choose to do nothing about it, well then, I can go back to my factory tomorrow morning with a clear conscience."

The speaker stepped down from the platform and waved to his uniformed chauffeur, who was standing by the park gates. He came over at the double, and, without any help from his employer, lifted up the heavy stand and together they made their way out of the park.

Whether or not his performance was a sham, I really don't know.

I moved over to a little bald man that nobody stopped to listen to. He told the empty space in front of him that the wages of sin were eternal damnation, and our only salvation was to

get down on our knees and ask the Lord to forgive us for living such wicked lives.

This man's voice was almost drowned by the speaker next to him, who had set himself the task of de-christianising his audience:

"Marx was wrong when he said religion is the opium of the people – it's not, it's the chains that hold you down. Opium at least gives you temporary relief from your wretchedness while you're alive. Religion only offers you eternal life after you're dead. My friends, that's the big prize offered by Christianity, and it would be sheer unadulterated hell. It means that you would go on existing for ever and ever. After millions of celestial years, you might finally decide you've had enough, but you wouldn't be able to end it all .

"What you should be demanding is a little bit of heaven, right now, while you're alive. Tell those who offer you pie in the sky' to stick it up their collective ecclesiastical arses. And while I'm on the subject of priests, particularly the Catholic ones who maintain they are celibate, I have to tell you that they are lying. They are all secret masturbators, and some of them molest innocent choirboys.

"You, of course, may believe that in the improbable hereafter you'll be able to meet and talk with all the great men and women whot have made their mark through history --philosophers, artists, composers, soldiers and saints, emperors and kings. But most of them will be foreigners, and I'll bet all my earthly possessions that despite all the years they've been dead, they won't have bothered to learn the King's English. That, my friends, is the stark reality of heavenly life. The only guaranteed afterlife is the memories and impressions we've made on our friends and loved ones while we lived, and our genes passed on to our offspring. Why does anybody want more than that? "So I implore you to say to the archbishops, the priests, the monks and nuns that you want no more of their wares, and tell them that from this day on, you will make your own plans to create a heaven on earth for yourself.

"My friends ...."

At this point, two men in plain clothes approached the speaker and told him to step down from the platform. He was under arrest for using foul language in a public place. They grabbed him by the arms and marched him off towards the police station.

So much for freedom of speech, I thought, for as far as I was concerned, what I had heard the man say was like a breath of fresh air. He'd put into clear words all the confused thoughts and feelings I had.

By the time I got to where Frederick was speaking, he had gathered a large crowd around him. He was explaining to his audience the real meaning of the word Anarchy.

"It comes from the Greek," he said, "and strictly speaking means 'without government', but that's not what the ruling classes would have you believe. They will tell you that Anarchy equals disorder, chaos and confusion. They say that to live in a world without police, armies and priests, would be inconceivable. The fact that these people are used largely for repressive purposes and for the protection of the ill-gotten gains of the rich goes, they hope, unnoticed by the majority of the working class."

"How do you deal with those who commit crimes, if you have no police and no prisons to send them to?" asked a man in the crowd.

"Most crimes occur because of the desire of those who have very little, to get for themselves some of the possessions of those who have more than their fair share. Men who don't bear a grudge or feel envious towards their fellows are unlikely to rob them. If, however, someone persisted in this unsocial behaviour, his workmates and neighbours would do their best to make him understand the folly and unfairness of his ways. This way, the chances of him continuing with a life of crime are far less than by sending him to prison, where he is exposed to and influenced by other anti-social elements."

"I find that hard to swallow, Mr Speaker, but tell me - what do you do in your society when a man says 'I'm work shy, so I'm just going to sit back and live off the labour of others'? What will you do about him, eh?"

"He'd be taken to see for himself how miners have to crawl on their bellies to provide him and his family with coal. Farm labourers would show him what hard work needs to be done to grow the food he consumes. Textile workers would demonstrate to him what a slog it is just to put a shirt on his back. In the end, he would be shamed into pulling his weight."

The more I listened to Frederick, the more I liked what I was hearing. He was, of course, talking about an ideal world, but as I wasn't yet eighteen, I couldn't see why this wasn't possible. Sixty years later, deep down inside, I still can't.

Frederick went on to explain how the anarchist system would work.

"Imagine five hundred men walking towards the factory gates at six-thirty in the morning, each of them carrying four heavy weights on his back. The first weight is the armed forces. The second is the law and all the people who apply it – police, prison warders, judges, barristers, solicitors, court officials. The third weight is the government – ministers, civil servants, foreign office personnel, secret service operators. And the fourth is the money people – bankers, stocks and shares pushers, mortgage and insurance brokers, investors and money lenders. Add to all this the huge costs of premises. Comrades, not one of the people in these four categories produces anything as useful as a pair of bootlaces. If they all died in their sleep on the same night, the only thing you would notice the next day is that the world would be a much nicer and less expensive place to live in. So, comrades, if these weights were removed from the men's backs, by the time they entered the factory gates, they could for the first time in their lives stand erect, with their heads held high. The only restraint placed upon any citizen would be a unanimously agreed moral code."

Some of the crowd applauded as Frederick stepped down from his platform and came over to see me.

"Tell me, Derrick, did you get the drift of what I was saying?"

"I understood some of it, but not all, I'm afraid."

He recommended that I buy a small book called *The ABC of Anarchism* by Alexander Berkman, and told me where I could get it.

Afterwards I went with Frederick to have a cup of tea with him and his friends at Lyons. The way his friends dressed appeared strange to me. None had suits on, and most wore worn-out looking jackets over their vests, and threadbare brown corduroy trousers held up by pieces of string. None of them had their hair cut in the fashion of the day, which was short back and sides with a parting to one side. It was so long that it nearly reached down to their shoulders.

Frederick told them about my little lark at the studios a few days earlier.

"Well, comrade," said one of them, "that was a good start, now you can only move forward!"

Move forward to what and where, I wondered. The man who spoke said his name was Alan. He told me that he and his friends spent most of their time during the week at a grubby little caff in Charlotte Street called Tony's.

"It's run as a front by a couple of Cypriot gangsters to cover up their black-marketeering activities. One good thing is, you can sit there, out of the cold, for hours, just for the price of a lousy cup of tea, and if you're flush, you can buy an almost uneatable Spam or cheese sandwich. Most of the people who frequent the place are war-dodgers or pseudo-artists and intellectuals. There's a sprinkling of political misfits like me. Come and join us when you're not working. One word of advice, Derrick - dress less conventionally in case they mistake you for a young cop in plain clothes and make a stampede for the exit. The caff is opposite the Scala Theatre, you can't miss it."

I told Alan I'd be there some time soon, suitably dressed. I thought it best to leave Frederick in the company of his friends, so I said goodbye.

I told Uncle where I'd been that afternoon, and gave him a muddled version of what I had heard.

"Oh, if I were you, dear boy, I wouldn't spend too much time with those rabble-rousers."

"If you've never seen or listened to what they have to say, how do you know they're rabble-rousers?" I asked.

"You're quite right, I don't - but from the little I've heard, I can say with some certainty that they need their heads examined."

I knew then that it would be pointless to discuss with Uncle any new views I might acquire.

CHAPTER TWENTY-SIX

As I was doing film-extra work, I couldn't go to Tony's Café until Thursday, and when I did I got the distinct feeling that I wasn't welcome. All the same, I decided to sit it out for half an hour in the hope that Alan would turn up. I remembered him saying that the café was a pretty grubby place. It looked as if the bare, wooden floor, and the filthy tables hadn't been swept or scrubbed since the war began.

After half an hour, I got up to go, just as Alan appeared.

"Hey, Derrick, so you found it all right, eh?"

He came over to where I was standing and sat down.

"I'm glad you've come. I've been feeling a cool draught blowing my way."

"That won't happen again, Derrick, I promise you."

He turned round and faced the others.

"Lads, this is Derrick, he's not a bum and he's not on the run. Frederick told me how he got chucked out of a film studio because he led a strike. I reckon that makes him a suitable candidate to join our exclusive club. Anyone object? Right then, Derrick, you're now a member."

I found out soon enough why I was so readily accepted. A lot of them had sniffed out, correctly - just by the look of me - that I had money in my pocket. Before long, a few of them (including Alan) had 'borrowed' sixpence. Some of them even got me to pay for the tea and sandwiches that they had already eaten. I very quickly worked out that at the alarming rate my money was disappearing, this 'exclusive' club of theirs would cost me more than Uncle paid for the combined annual subscription fees of the RAC and the Naval & Military Club.

I found out later that I needn't have worried too much, because one of the unwritten rules of Tony's Café was that you were sponged on if you had money, and when you were penniless, it was your turn to 'borrow' or cadge from anybody who was temporarily in funds. I suppose it worked out even-stevens in the end.

Alan began to fill me in on who was who, sitting around the tables.

"That's Bert," he said, pointing, "If any copper stopped him and asked to see his papers, he'd show him his merchant seaman's card. If the cop took a closer look, he'd see that his papers were out-of-date by a long way. The fact is, the only strip of water Bert has clapped his eyes on since before the war is the Thames. Mind you, he did risk his life during the Spanish Civil War, running supplies in unseaworthy cargo-boats through Franco's blockade to the ports held by the beleaguered International Brigaders. He lives with a girl called Josie, who's England's strongest woman. She performs every day, standing on the pavement by Tower Bridge. She's so strong that she can put a two-inch iron bar across her shoulders and bend it without even going red in the face. One of her acts is tearing telephone directories in half. Her father was a strong man in the circus, and he trained her from childhood to be part of his act. Josie is so slim that a man's hands can meet around her waist, but she has biceps that a lumberjack would be proud of."

"Her boyfriend must feel well protected when she's around," I said, as I took another look at skinny Bert.

"He does, but although she's obviously by far the stronger of the two, she's terrified of him."

"I don't understand it."

"Nor do I, but that's women for you, Derrick. The man Bert's talking to is Johnny Bligh. He's on the run from the military, so he has to look to his left and right every time he goes into the street. Even then, when he's walking along, he has to look over his shoulder to make sure there are no uniformed or plainclothes cops following him."

"How can he tell it's a policeman when they're in civvies?" I enquired.

"Oh, that's easy, Most flat-foots wear big coppers' boots and shabby, fawn macs."

"That's not very clever of them," I remarked.

"Thank God most of them are pretty stupid, otherwise we'd have all been nicked long ago."

Alan pointed to a little man at the next table, who was reading the sports-page of the *Evening Standard*.

"He's Paddy. The lucky bastard doesn't have to worry about cop-dodging, as he's from Southern Ireland and his country isn't in this fucking war. Paddy spends the best part of his day studying the form of the gee-gees and dogs, trying to pick winners, I don't think he's much good at it as he's nearly always skint. The pimply-faced bloke sitting with him, we call Frustie because in all his twenty-five years he's never had a fuck and is for ever telling everyone how frustrated he is. We all got so fed up with his moaning that last Christmas we clubbed together and paid one of the prostitutes who come in here to take the poor sod on. Frustie's such a weed that he didn't pass his medical, so, like Paddy, he isn't on the run either.

That effeminate-looking man with the long eyelashes is Peter. He claims to be a ballet dancer, though no one has ever seen him perform. I think he survives because he's got a sugar daddy who keeps him."

"I doubt if he'd ever be accepted by the army anyway. Alan, who is that funny-looking middle-aged man over there, with a big floppy trilby and a cloak?" I asked. "He looks like some of the artists I saw in Montmartre."

"That's exactly what he wants you to think. He's Redvers Gray, otherwise known as the scrounger because he's always on the take. Never lend him anything - you're kissing your money goodbye. You'll see, he'll get round to you before you leave. He's a caricature of a real artist, with that ridiculous monocle and flamboyant cravat. I don't think he's ever held a paintbrush in his life. Rumour has it that he's a disbarred barrister. He was arrested last month trying to climb over the railings of Buckingham Palace in broad daylight. He's fucking lucky one of the guards didn't put a bullet in his back. He said it was because he wanted to see the King and tell him about his invention which would bring down German bombers without a shot being fired. He'd taken his idea to the RAF but they bundled him out of the building and told him not to come back."

Alan briefed me on how all the bums and misfits whiled away their days at Tony's. When the pubs opened, they all went across the road to the Fitzroy Tavern or, if they felt particularly energetic, they would walk the few yards to Rathbone Place, and go to the Wheatsheaf. When all the pubs had closed, the whole tribe went to a dive called the Coffee Ann in St Giles' Circus. Alan said, if I would like to, I could spent the day and evening with him, doing the rounds.

At six that evening, we entered the Fitzroy Tavern. It was packed. I soon realised that the people in here were totally different. Here were genuine painters, writers and intellectuals, some in civvies, others in uniform, the latter obviously on leave for a few days, looking as though they had been starved of convivial and intelligent conversation for weeks. They behaved like men who had finally got to an oasis after spending weeks in the desert. How they must have hated returning to the intellectual desert of your average officers' mess.

Alan pointed to a man who was leaning on the bar, surrounded by a bevy of friends who were hanging upon his every word. Every now and then, they would burst out into loud laughter.

"He's a Welshman called Dylan Thomas, he writes poetry, God only knows when, for whenever I see him, he's always pissed. He's only standing up because his chums are crowding him. He'd fall flat on his face if they suddenly stepped back. He gets all the drink he wants, as a reward for his conversation. When he finally passes out, a couple of his friends bundle him into a cab to take him home."

"Perhaps he writes his poetry during the day when he's sober."

"If that was true, he'd have to do it fairly quickly. He's back in the pub when the doors open at eleven-thirty am.

That smartly dressed man at the other end of the bar, the one with a fag pushed into the long cigarette holder, is a writer of short stories. His name is Julian Maclaren Ross - like Dylan he's very witty and amusing. He writes articles for *Lilliput*. I know he looks and talks like an affected twit, but he's not really. Those two lads in kilts talking to Maclaren are a couple of painters, Colquhoun and MacBryde. They're more or less married to each other, they go everywhere together. The chap standing next to them is also a painter. His name is Lucian Freud."

"Who's that woman talking to a sailor? The one sitting at the corner table with bright red hair, plucked eyebrows and long painted fingernails."

"Oh, that's Quentin Crisp - he's a scream. Quentin can make you laugh, no matter how down in the dumps you feel."

"Are you telling me that person over there is a bloke?" I asked incredulously.

"He's so queer and eccentric, that he makes all the other homos look normal. He earns his living by modelling at art schools. Come on over, and I'll introduce you to him."

"Not right now, thanks, I've had enough of his sort during my childhood."

"I promise you, he's not at all like some of them, he's not an aggressive homosexual. He's just very good company, that's all."

"Maybe, but I don't feel like meeting him just at the moment."

I did meet Quentin a few days later, and Alan was right, he was very amusing to be with. I covered for him once (perhaps 'covered' is the wrong word to use when you're sitting stark naked for hours), on one of his modelling days because, as he put it, he was feeling rather fragile, and hoped I'd be a 'sweetie' by going to the School of Art in his place.

Alan and I stayed on at the Fitzroy until closing time, then moved off down the road to the Coffee Ann. The café was triangular in shape, and you entered it at the narrow end. Against the left wall were a line of dilapidated settees, with springs poking through the faded upholstery. In front of them were rough old tables on wobbly legs. Where the floor area widened, square tables and cheap-looking wooden chairs filled all the available space. A long, rickety counter spanned the entire length of the right wall. The place was so dimly lit that you could hardly see what you ate or drank. This was just as well, since both were unbelievably awful.

The café was run by a man called Jim, who was as camp as they come. Jimmy had a boyfriend, a big beefy police sergeant. Very conveniently he was stationed locally so he was in a position to warn Jimmy when the café would be raided.

When Jimmy got the tip-off, he'd shout, "the boys in blue will be arriving in ten minutes". This gave ample time for those on the run to finish the food on their plates, before disappearing outside into the blacked-out streets of Soho. The lesbian and male homosexuals who were sprawled all over the settees kissing and fondling one another also had time to disengage and adjust their dress, so that by the time the cops burst in they had nothing more offensive in their hands than cutlery. The only time the police ever managed to catch anyone was when the sergeant had his day off and no warning could be given.

In the basement below the Coffee Ann was another dingy dive. This place was run by a Turk, and here you could get a cup of excellent Turkish coffee. The disadvantage of being in the basement was that no warning could be made of an impending raid. I was so fascinated by all the different types of people that were in there that it was well after midnight before I left. As most of the money I had on me that day had been 'borrowed' or used up on endless teas and sandwiches, I hadn't enough to buy a ticket for the tube ride back, so I had to walk all the way back to St John's Wood.

It was after two when I finally entered the flat. Uncle had put a note on the hall-stand to tell me that the agency had phoned to say that it was imperative (underlined) that I reported at Pinewood Studios no later than seven-thirty a.m. Oh shit, I thought, if only I'd known.

Somehow I did manage to get to Pinewood on time. The film was *Pimpernel*

Smith starring Leslie Howard. The scene was set in a lecture room at a university, and Mr Howard played the part of a professor who was trying to find out which, if any, of his students could speak French. When a few said they could, the professor unveiled a plan for a special undercover operation. This would involve them and him being parachuted deep into occupied France and rescuing as many Frenchmen and women of noble birth as they could, then bring them across France to the Normandy coast, where a fishing boat would be waiting. In the dead of night, under the noses of the Germans, these noblemen would be brought back to the safe haven of dear old England. This film, of course, was a modern version of *The Scarlet Pimpernel* made not long before the war, in which Leslie Howard played the role of an English dandy who went over to the revolutionary France of 1789.

My role in this epic tale was to sit at a desk in the lecture room and try and look as if I was interested in what the professor had to say. I failed miserably, because sitting at the desk next to me was a very beautiful girl, and I spent most of my time gazing at her.

The way things were set up, it looked like there would be two days' work, which meant I could take my time to get acquainted with the girl. It took me the best part of the day to think up my opening line. Finally I took a deep breath, and asked her if she had been doing film extra work for very long.

She turned her pretty head sideways and looked at me. Although I'd been sitting a few inches away from her for most of the day, I think she saw me for the first time.

"No, today is my first time on a film set and I absolutely love it, I mean, to be only a few feet away from Leslie Howard. It's the most wonderful thing that's happened to me in my entire life."

Jesus, she must have led a very dull one up to now, I thought. She turned her head away from me and continued to look adoringly at her screen idol. By the intense way she gazed at him, I knew I didn't exist.

An hour or so later the bright lights of the set were switched off, and Mr Howard vanished. Now, I thought, at last, I stand a chance, but all I managed to get from her that day was her name, Lola. Tomorrow is another day, I thought, and with a bit of luck, Mr Howard might fall down some stairs and fail to turn up, leaving the lovely Lola to focus on me.

The way it turned out, luck was on my side. The star wasn't needed for any shots that day, and the only filming to be done was close-ups of the small-part actors, the professor's students.

When Lola saw that her idol hadn't been called, she very nearly burst into tears. I tried to console her: "You never know in this business. We may all be asked to come back tomorrow."

This seemed to cheer her up, and from then on I think I existed. She told me a little about herself. She was twenty-one, and lived in Balham with her father who adored her. Her mother had died from pneumonia when Lola was eight. For as long as she could remember, she'd wanted to be a film star.

"Have you ever been to a school for acting?" I asked.

"Oh no, Daddy couldn't afford to send me to one."

"What does your father do?" I asked, fully expecting her to say he was an underpaid schoolteacher or something of the kind. 'He's in the milk-distribution business," murmured Lola, almost in a whisper.

I just managed to stop myself saying 'you mean he's a milkman?' and asked how she knew she could act, if she'd never even done it.

"I just know I can, and what's more, Daddy thinks I can as well. You'll see, one day I'll be picked out of the crowd by a talent scout, and become a star. Lots of girls in Hollywood have had that happen to them, you know."

Right, boy, I said to myself, this is the cue you've been waiting for. I leaned towards her and took her hand in mine, looked straight into her large brown eyes and said to her (trying to imitate Ronald Colman):

"You're such a very beautiful girl that anyone not noticing you would have to be nearly blind."

"Do you think I'm beautiful then?"

"Oh yes, I do, indeed I do - you're the loveliest girl I've ever seen."

Now, at last I was on track. From now on, it was full speed ahead. It was at this point that for the first time she really saw the young man who had been sitting so close to her all this time, and if the look in her eyes was anything to go by, I think she liked what she saw.

Fortunately we were hardly needed that day, as most of the filming being done, was close-ups of the small-part actors. This meant Lola and I could spend most of our time away from the bright lights of the set, and could withdraw to the semi-darkness at the back of the huge stage. A couch was conveniently placed there, so that Mr Howard could rest between takes. I guided her towards it. The thought that her beloved idol had sat on it must have acted like an aphrodisiac, because before long, she was lying on it, and I was down on my knees by her side, frantically exploring all the parts of her wonderful body that I could get at without actually tearing her dress.

Thus engaged, it occurred to me that perhaps I was being used as a Leslie Howard stand-in, but that would have required a huge leap of imagination. For one thing, the film star was much shorter than me, and of slight build. He was old enough to be her father. Not that I cared who she imagined I was, because I was having a whale of a time. However, any notion I might be a case of mistaken identity was soon dispelled, when, as my hand was sliding around within the confines of her camiknickers, she gasped, "Oh no, oh no, Derrick!"

Except for the brief intervals when we were required to be on the set, Lola and I spent most of our day kissing and petting on Mr Howard's couch, and as a bonus, we were being paid by the film company while doing it.

We weren't needed the next day. I didn't feel like parting from the girl I'd been so close to all that day, so I asked her if she'd come and have a meal with me.

During it I told her a whole heap of untruths about my past and present-day self, even pretending that because of my Uncle I had a foothold on the ladder leading to the upper classes. This seemed to impress her. By the time the meal was over, a very heavy air-raid was in progress, so I offered to escort her back to her home in Balham. I had an ulterior motive.

"Oh, Derrick, that would be wonderful. I get so frightened walking all by myself through the streets once I've left the protection of the Underground. And you can spend the night at our place if you don't mind sleeping on the couch downstairs in the front room."

Whoopee, my chivalry had paid off. Of course, I said that I didn't mind.

"Won't your father object if you bring me back?"

"He won't even see you. By the time we get in, he'll be in his bed fast asleep. He goes to bed early as he has to get up at five in the morning to go to work."

Whoopee again. Now that I knew her father would be asleep, my chances of getting under the sheets with her were looking good.

When we left the restaurant, the cloudy sky was bright red reflecting the glow of the fires burning in the East End. Anti-aircraft guns were blasting away and many searchlights raked the night sky in an attempt to pinpoint a German bomber within their powerful beams. With small fragments of iron raining down from the exploding ack-ack shells, we made a dash to Leicester Square Tube station. The platforms below were already full of people laying claim to the bunk that would be their bed for the night. When we surfaced, just before midnight, in Balham, the air-raid was still in full swing, but thankfully we were now further away from the target area. Lola lived some distance from the station, and as we walked through the dingy, blacked-out streets, I realised why she preferred to have the companionship of someone she knew.

Lola's home was in the centre of a short row of terraced houses. Even in the dark I could see that it was a very modest dwelling. The front door was only a step away from the pavement.

Lola opened it without making a sound.

"Shush," she said, as we crept into the tiny front hall. "We don't want to wake him up, do we?"

She put on the dim hall-light and I followed her into the kitchen.

"Would you like a cup of tea?"

I nodded. As she filled the kettle, I put my arms around her waist and started to kiss the nape of her slender neck.

"Wait a moment, Derrick, let me take off my coat first."

Then, like a pair of boxers in the ring when the bell goes, we were frantically at each other, only to stop when the kettle boiled over. Lola made the tea and poured out two cups. We sat at the table and slowly sipped away without saying a word, just gazing into each other's eyes. Then Lola took me by the hand and led me into the front room, to the couch that was to be my bed for the night. Now at last the moment I'd been hoping for had come. I took off my shirt and vest and was just about to undo my trouser buttons when Lola jumped up.

"You mustn't get undressed!"

"Why not?"

"Because my dad could come down at any time, to see if I got safely back home."

"Can't we go up to your bedroom then? I so want to be lying next to you."

"We will, I promise you, but not while he's in the house. We'll have to wait until five in the morning."

I got dressed and we continued to kiss and cuddle for a little while longer. Lola gave me one last long kiss, then said she was tired after such a long day and had to go to bed. She left a note for her father, explaining who was sleeping on the couch. As she crept upstairs, she whispered:

"I'll come down and bring you up when Dad's gone."

As it turned out, Lola didn't have to come down to fetch me, as I caught a fleeting glimpse of her father on his way out. I made my way up the short flight of stairs and entered Lola's room, making as little noise as possible. The room was lit by a low-voltage bulb in a shaded lamp. I wondered why a twenty-one yearold girl was afraid to sleep in the dark.

I crept over to her bed. She was lying on her side and fast asleep. The long tresses of her reddish-brown hair were spread out across the white pillowcase. Not wanting to disturb her, I slid very carefully under the sheets, put my arm around her waist, and buried my face between her shoulderblades. Within a short time, I too, was sound asleep.

It was daylight when I awoke to the feel of Lola kissing my back. I turned round to face her. Naked, she climbed on top of me and raised her head.

"Good morning, Derrick," she said with a smile.

"What time is it?" I asked.

"It's nine."

"What time does your father come back?"

"About two, so we have plenty of time to ourselves. Would you like some breakfast?"

"No, thanks, Lola."

I slid my hands down her curved back until they came to rest on the cheeks of her bottom. She lifted herself higher by extending her arms, revealing to me for the first time her firm and rounded breasts. I was about to sink my face into the hollow between them, when Lola asked:

"Why is it that in the middle of winter you're so brown?"

"It's what's left of the tan I got last summer."

Lola began to slowly kiss her way down to my chest. She nestled her face in my hair and said: "You're like the brown teddy I lost when I was a little girl."

She stayed with her face buried in the hair of my chest for quite a while. To move things along a bit, I flipped her over onto her back, and lay on top of her. Going by my past experiences I expected her legs to part, but they didn't. She just crossed them so tightly that to prise them open, nothing less than a crowbar would have sufficed. To my surprise, she didn't seem to want me to get off her. This I perceived because her kisses and embrace became even more passionate than before. I was confused. After all, she had allowed me to lead her along this road for a day and most of a night, only now to find out it was a dead end.

"You don't want to make love, is that it, Lola?"

"No, Derrick, it's just that I want to stay a virgin until I'm married and the possibility of becoming pregnant worries me a lot."

Not yet eighteen, it wasn't one of my top priorities to get married. I was about to ask 'so where do we go from here?' when she turned on her side with her back towards me.

"Darling, hold my breasts," she said in almost a whisper. Never one not to respond to a reasonable request, I carried out her wish. Cupping her breasts into my hands, I gently squeezed them. Lola pressed the firm and soft-skinned cheeks of her bottom into my groin. I felt her hand travel down to between her thighs, then she started to stroke herself, first slowly, then gaining momentum. By now, my penis was getting so charged up that it could have glowed in the dark. Something had to be done about it, and quickly, so I slid it up and down between the cheeks of her sensuous buttocks, and judging by the duet of our oh's and ah's, I think we climaxed simultaneously. Being the innocent I was, I had previously believed that only men masturbated.

Lola turned round and faced me.

Without speaking, we lay there, entwined in each other's arms, for some time, the silence only broken by me asking her what the chances were of getting a cup of tea and slice of toast.

We went downstairs and Lola made breakfast. After we had washed up, she put her arm around my shoulder and kept on kissing me as I carried her up the short flight of stairs to her bedroom. There we repeated the whole performance we had done earlier, only this time there was a difference - she didn't insist that a sheet had to cover her beautiful body. Like the first time, when all the ooh-ing and aah-ing was over, we lay clasped in each other's arms. Suddenly, Lola freed herself from my embrace and jumped out of bed.

"What's up?" I asked, puzzled by her abrupt departure.

"My dad will be back any moment now."

"Jesus, Lola, I left all my clothes in the front room."

"I'll go and get them."

Panic-stricken, she put on her dressing-gown and rushed downstairs. We hurriedly got dressed and two minutes later, when her father came through the front door, we were sitting on the couch in the front room, looking as though butter wouldn't melt in our mouths.

"Hello, Daddy," said Lola. I saw that he had on his milkman's jacket, with 'UNITED DAIRIES' embossed in large letters on the lapels. By fixing my gaze onto the photographs on the mantelpiece, I pretended I hadn't noticed the insignia. By the time I turned my head, Lola had removed her father's jacket, and put it out of sight.

"Daddy, this is Derrick, my new friend. He's an actor I met at the film studios."

Why she deemed it necessary to promote everybody, I couldn't understand. She had told me her Dad was in the milk-distribution business, and now she was telling him that I was an actor. He shook me by the hand and held it in a strong grip.

Lola's father was a handsome man of about fifty with the same chestnut-coloured curly hair as his daughter. His kind, strong-looking face was slightly weatherbeaten. When he looked at Lola, a light came into his grey-blue eyes.

"Did you manage to sleep all right on the couch?" he asked.

"Like a new-born baby," I said.

Lola disappeared into the kitchen to make her father a meal.

'Thanks for bringing Lola home last night."

"It was a pleasure, Mr ...?"

"Grant."

"Mr Grant."

"Since you're already an actor, what do you think the chances are for Lola getting into films?"

"I don't know. Perhaps she will be picked out of the crowd one day."

"I do hope so. Her heart is set on it."

He pointed to a photograph that took pride of place in the centre of the mantelpiece.

"That's my late wife. Lola is the image of her, don't you think?"

"Yes, she is," I agreed, "you can hardly tell one from the other. I suppose you have to keep reminding yourself that Lola is your daughter ?" I said with about as much tact as making a loud fart at the vicar's tea party.

"No, lad, I don't, my late wife and Lola are both very different people."

I glanced at the clock on the sideboard.

"My goodness, it's after three, I really must be on my way. So I'll leave you in peace to have your meal."

"You're welcome to stay if you want to, lad."

"Thanks all the same, Mr Grant, but I promised my uncle I'd see him later on this afternoon. I'll just pop into the kitchen and say goodbye to Lola."

She looked up from the stove when I came in.

"I'm off now, darling. How about Saturday, at the Corner House, say about seven-thirty?"

"I'll be there," she said with a smile.

I gave her Uncle's phone number, just in case she couldn't make it, and a quick kiss and hug.

I saw Lola a few more times during the following weeks, but I finally stopped because it was such a sweat making the long journey to her place, ending up with half the night sleeping on a couch that was too small for me, and the other half lying mostly awake in her bed waiting for her to open her eyes. Even when she did, all that could happen was mutual masturbation. To end our relationship, I told her I couldn't see her any more because of an experience I had with a man. I said that to my surprise, I had found out that I was a homosexual. How she swallowed that story I just don't know, because only a few hours before, I had been worshipping all the very female parts of her body.

The fact is, it was a lot less bother for me to lie in the comfort and solitude of my own bed and indulge in a do-it-yourself orgasm while I flicked through the erotic images of her that I had in my mind. It was after one such session that I thought up the idea that it would be only fair if, when a woman was used in this way (especially so if she was a famous film actress), the wanker (because it was the correct thing to do) would feel honour-bound to send a two-bob postal order as a sort of royalty, just as you would to an author or a composer if you used anything they had created. Film stars like Hedy Lamarr, Merle Oberon, Jean Harlow, Alice Faye, and of course, Mae West, could look forward to sackfuls of postal orders dropping through their letter boxes.

The only childhood picture circa 1924

*With Uncle in front of Maida Vale
Underground Station, London, 1937*

Me in France, 1938

Uncle near Arles, 1938

*Me in drill uniform, first time in the army,
1939*

*On the left, me examining the bullet that
missed me, with Dr. Gadd and his friends*

Mrs. Blaber with gasmask, 1940

Me in 1941

Advertising photo promoting Craven 'A' cigarettes,
1944

Bobbi, photograph by John Collingwood,
London 1945

CHAPTER TWENTY-SEVEN

The next few weeks were taken up with two or three days doing film-extra work, and the rest sitting at Tony's most of the day, and at the Coffee Ann until two in the morning. Every Sunday I was at Speaker's Corner trying to improve my grasp of politics.

One Saturday, Frederick took me to an anti-war meeting at the Aeolian Hall in the West End. Among those on the platform was a well-known writer and anarchist by the name of Ethel Mannin, a pacifist Labour MP called Fenner Brockway, and Donald Soper, a Methodist priest. Seeing him up there wearing a clerical collar and long black cassock, nearly made me get up and go, but I'm glad I didn't. This priest was very different from the bastards I'd had to put up with as a child.

He was a fine-looking, robust man, approaching forty, and had thick black hair combed straight back from his broad forehead. Frederick told me he was as dedicated to socialism and pacifism as he was to Christianity, and if he was approached on one subject he didn't try to ram the other down your throat. He was, he said, anti-communist, not because communists had rejected the teaching of Christ but because he believed that under communism, man still exploited man. Besides running a large church and youth centre in Kingsway, he spoke every day, in all weathers, standing on a soapbox at Tower Hill. On Sunday afternoons he was at Hyde Park, telling his audience that Christ was a pacifist and a socialist, and if he were alive today, it would be telling the multitudes to stop killing each other. According to Frederick, Soper's oratory was amongst the best at Speaker's Corner.

Ethel Mannin was a marvellous-looking woman in her early forties. She wore a billowing red dress which let you know that it covered a sensuous body, and she delivered her speech with vigour and conviction. She hated the dictatorships of Hitler and Stalin, Stalin because of the way he had massacred anarchists and others who protested against his rule, and Hitler's fascist regime because, like Stalin's, it had crushed without mercy any opposition, and was planning to put the working classes of all Europe into serfdom for a thousand years. The only way to defeat the dictators was to have an anarchist uprising backed up by passive resistance, the type that Gandhi was using with such good results against British imperialism in India. She maintained that a revolt would become contagious, and very rapidly spread throughout Continental Europe including Russia and Germany. Her final remark was in her opinion the only weapon a young man should learn to handle well was the one buttoned-up inside his trousers.

Frederick filled me in a bit about this impressive looking woman. He said that she had three children, and while she banged away on her typewriter doing the manuscript for her next book, the children played at her feet on the floor. As far as he knew, she had no husband, but did have a string of men friends. He said that if she took a fancy to you, there were two choices open: one was to escape - the other was to surrender and let her strong personality and insatiable sexual appetite gradually swallow you up.

"I suppose you opted for the first, eh, Frederick?"

"No, I never had to make any decision, I'm not her type, too old, you see, she prefers virile young men, so don't say I haven't warned you."

"I don't need to be, as I once got involved with a woman of her age who was married to a mad farmer, and it very nearly cost me my life."

"Are you one of those rare people who learn by their mistakes?"

"Sometimes," I said.

The next person to speak was Fenner Brockway. He looked to be older than the others. In the last war, he had been a conscientious objector and was imprisoned for refusing to join it, and twenty-one years later, he was still an unrepentant pacifist. He didn't agree with the other speakers' opinions on the Soviet Union; it was, he thought, a great experiment that might one day bring about tremendous changes worldwide. He was convinced that before long (despite the pact they had signed with Germany to respect each other's sovereignty) German armies and panzer divisions would soon cross the frontier into Russia. He said the only hope for the millions who lived there was to resist the invader by adopting a policy of passive resistance and non-cooperation. These tactics would make it impossible for that vast land, with its harsh winters, to be effectively occupied. The alternative was too horrendous to contemplate. Millions of young men in both the Russian and German armed forces would be slaughtered.

"Comrades, I am a pacifist because I want to do my best to prevent this happening. I cannot find any justification, under any circumstances, to shoot a metal missile into the flesh of another human being, whether he be Russian, German or Italian. If those countries now occupied by Germany did what I earnestly hope the Russians will do if they are invaded, Hitler's dream of a thousand-year Reich would remain but a dream, and thousands of lives would be saved."

After hearing his speech, I became a pacifist. When the meeting was over, Frederick took me to the front of the hall and introduced me to Donald Soper. When he shook me by the hand, I knew that I liked this man, despite his chosen vocation.

"You should come to the centre one day," he said. "We have table tennis, billiards, darts, and netball."

"I'll come one day soon, Vicar."

"Call me Donald, everyone does. I'll look forward to seeing you at the centre shortly."

Even though the playing of games wasn't exactly my forte, I nevertheless made up my mind to go there one day and help out if I could.

I was so impressed with what all the speakers had said that when I got back to the flat, I wrote a short poem. I can't remember it very well, but it went something like this:

'It wasn't many years ago a man called Jesus lived
His philosophy was based on love and human kindredship
But the Christian of today in bombers he will fly
High up in God's blue sky
And drop bombs on human beings who are just like you and I.'

As this was the first time in my life that I had ever written anything, I was a little proud of what I had done. Gathering up a bit of courage, I read it to Uncle.

"Very good, Hayden," he said, but as he believed that the best song ever to be set to music was 'Teddy Bears' Picnic', I thought it unwise to give too much credence to his critical faculties. The only ditty he knew was what a little boy says when he's asked what his family did:

My pretty sister Lily
is a whore in Piccadilly
Me muvver earns her living
in the Strand
Me bruvver hawks his arsehole
round the Elephant & Castle
And I toss Gents off gently with me 'and.

A few days later I made the mistake of showing my poem to Frederick. His comment was that the idea expressed was all right, but he thought it would be best if I left the writing of poetry to the poets.

Later that week I went to the youth centre in Kingsway. It was a hive of activity, full of teenagers of both sexes. In one corner of the large basement hall was a counter where tea and cakes could be bought for a few pence. I went over to the man who was serving there.

"My name is Derrick. When I met Donald Soper the other day, he suggested that I might be able to make myself useful. Can I?"

"You certainly can. I'm Robert, the general factotum around here - any help is welcome."

"How long do you stay open?"

"Basically until the last kid has gone home, which is generally about ten. If they haven't gone by then, I give them a couple of blankets and they can kip down here on the floor. It's not too comfortable, but if it were too cosy, they would be here every night, half of them with their girlfriends, not that Donald would mind, but I think their parents might."

Robert was twenty-one, but looked younger. He wasn't exactly handsome, pretty would be a better way to describe him. I should think he appealed to the maternal side of most women, and was probably bothered by homosexuals quite a lot. I did wonder for a moment if he was queer, but quickly dismissed this idea when he mentioned his girlfriends. He said that he had worked at the centre for some months, mainly because he wanted Donald Soper to speak on his behalf when, in a couple of weeks' time, he had to appear before the tribunal.

"Tribunal for what?" I enquired.

"For conchies. Conscientious Objectors."

"Is that all you have to do, to dodge being called up, get a priest to speak for you?"

"No, but it doesn't half help. Donald will say he's known me since my early teens and that I've always been a pacifist. My father will testify that he brought me up from childhood to be a pacifist."

"Will they, between them, manage to get you off the hook?"

"Not necessarily. Hardly anyone gets let off. They imply you're a coward and are prepared to let other, braver, men do the fighting for you. They cite passages from the Old and New Testament, justifying the use of the sword, and 'an eye for an eye', and any others that suit them, all of which are in direct opposition to Christ's words. You'll be asked what you would do if had found a German raping your mother while you had a loaded pistol in your hand. This is one of their favourite trick questions. If you said you would do nothing, they'd know you were a liar, and your case would be dismissed."

"So how do you answer them?"

"By telling the truth, which is, that if anyone from any country, including England, tried to harm my mother, I would do whatever was in my power to stop them."

"If you're turned down by the tribunal, what happens to you then?"

"The next day, at six am, a copper arrives on your doorstep with your call-up papers in his hand. If you refuse to accept them, he carts you off to the police station. Next morning in court, the magistrate will ask you if you still refuse, and if you do, he sentences you to nine months' hard labour."

"When you're released, are you left in peace for the rest of the war?"

"Not bloody likely. The moment you poke your shaven head outside the prison gates, you'll find a copper standing there with your call-up papers clutched in his hand, and if you refuse them yet again, you're taken to a judge who sends you back to clink for another nine months."

"Do you have to do anything if you're made exempt from military service?"

"Yes, one of two things - you can join up as a non-combatant in the Pioneers or the Army Medical Corps, or work on the land. I suppose it would have to be the land for me, although I don't relish the idea, I'm just not cut out for hard physical work."

"Working on the land isn't so bad, you know, I did it for half of last year, and quite enjoyed it. I'd keep you company, if you do have to go. Having a sympathetic person with you can make all the difference. Some farm labourers are a bit on the dull side and the only females about are village girls, who aren't much to write home about. For that matter nor are the pimply-faced, wide-hipped ladies in the Women's Land Army."

"I'm not too bothered about that, one or other of my girlfriends would come and visit me occasionally."

"Jesus, you're lucky, one or other of your girls. I haven't even got one at the moment."

"Well, you're not going to the places where it's easy to pick them up. Where I go is to the concerts given at the Albert or Wigmore Hall, it's there that the girls worth meeting are. You should come with me one evening."

"But what do I say if I'm asked my opinion about Bach or Beethoven?"

"Oh, that's easy. Just say you haven't yet quite made up your mind and then ask the girl which she prefers, and try and look as if you're interested in her answer. Then say that on reflection, you tend to agree with her, and change the subject. I'll give you a good opening line: you look her straight in the eyes and say, 'what's a beautiful looking girl like you doing here all on her own?' and if she says she has come to hear wonderful music, say, so have I, but meeting you is a bonus I didn't expect. And if after that she doesn't take off, well, you'll know you've backed a winner. I think now it's time we stopped chatting and started to work."

He gave me a tray and sent me to collect all the cups and plates that were scattered about. When I had washed them up, Robert handed me a broom and dustpan and brush, and asked me to sweep up the hall and the adjoining rooms. By the time all that was done, it was nearly ten and many of the youngsters had left for their homes. To those who wanted to stay on, Robert gave blankets so that they would be warm when they slept on the cold concrete basement floor. It was the safest place to be during the air-raids.

When all of them had settled down for the night, we could go outside, and I suggested we went to a café called Coffee Ann.

I think Robert was at first a little shocked by what he saw there, but after I had introduced him to some of the crowd, he began to relax. By the time we left in the early hours of the morning to go our separate ways, the café had gained a regular customer and I a friend. Whenever possible during the following weeks, Robert and I went everywhere together, with the exception of Speakers' Corner, for although he was a pacifist, he wasn't the least bit interested in politics.

Spring was nearly upon us, and I hadn't been in touch with Vic since I left him paralytically drunk on Christmas Day. I thought it was about time to see how he was faring and to introduce him to my new life, in the cafés and lively pubs in and around Charlotte Street. I remembered he'd told me that come the spring, he was going to chuck in his job and then spend his time frittering away his money until he was called up again.

I phoned him and we arranged to meet the following Sunday morning at his digs, but not too early because Saturday was his last day at the factory, and to celebrate the end of months of hard labour, he was going to get blind drunk. My hope was that by the time I got to him he would have slept off the drink, so that I could take him to Speakers' Corner, where perhaps a whole new world of ideas and politics would open up for him.

I got to his place about midday and the landlady let me in.

"I haven't seen him today, I think he's still sleeping."

"He's expecting me, so he won't mind if I wake him up."

I entered the darkened room and immediately knocked a chair over. The noise woke Vic up. He sat up and held his head in the palms of his hands.

"Sorry, I didn't see it."

"Turn on the light, old boy, the switch is by the side of the door. Jesus, Derrick, have I got one hell of a hangover!"

"Shall I make you some coffee?"

"No, thanks, old chap, the only thing that will return me to the land of the living is a couple of pints."

On the way to Vic's local, I told him the real purpose of my visit. He agreed to come with me on condition that he had at least two pints first Within a minute of standing by the bar he had the first glass in his hand. It went down his throat as quickly as water goes down a plughole. I managed to persuade him to eat two sandwiches before virtually bundling him out of the pub.

The walk in the fresh air from Maida Vale up the Edgware Road to Marble Arch and then to Speakers' Corner seemed to clear his head. Vic was immediately intrigued by the motley collection of orators. I let him flit from one speaker to the other for a bit before nudging him towards Donald Soper. He got so absorbed in what the priest was saying that some time elapsed before I could steer him over to my friend Frederick. I think both Soper and Frederick gave Vic plenty of food for thought, just as they had done to me some weeks earlier.

We stayed on until the speakers stepped down from their soapboxes. I suggested to Vic that he came to Lyons Café where I could introduce him to Frederick and his friends.

"Good idea, I'll be able to ask your anarchist chum some pertinent questions that are floating around my mind."

We followed Frederick and his friends out of the park and into the café. I introduced Vic to them, but I could see that when they got a sniff of his phony upper-class mannerisms and affected way of speaking they didn't like him very much. Frederick saw through his façade and was more tolerant than the others. To my surprise, Vic, who was normally very talkative and who liked to be the centre of attention, just sat at the table, hardly saying a word. I couldn't make up my mind whether this was out of utter disdain for those present, or because he was overawed by Frederick. I came to the conclusion that he was a little out of tune with everybody, so under the pretext that we had to be somewhere else, I extricated him from their company.

"Derrick, with the exception of Frederick, I didn't think too much of them. Why do they all wear such shabby clothes and let their hair grow so long? "

"Maybe it's because they think differently from most people that they look different."

"Their frayed corduroys and worn-out jackets are a sort of uniform really, aren't they?"

"If you think that, you haven't understood a single word of anything you heard this afternoon."

"That reminds me, despite of what your anarchist-pacifist friend said, I think anarchism could only come about by the use of violence."

"Do you mean using the sort of violence that governments resort to when they use the Army and the police to keep themselves in power ?"

"They, dear boy, only use force to restore law and order, and to maintain the status quo."

"Like Hitler, Franco and Mussolini do, is that what you mean ?"

"No, of course not, I'm talking about governments of democracies."

"England, Vic, is a democracy, but the violence we do in the name of British Imperialism, is legendary. If you don't believe me, ask an Indian, or anyone who lives under British colonial rule."

"Despite what you're saying, I still can't imagine living in a country without a government running things."

"Tell me, do you need to be told by Parliament not to jump off the top of St Paul's, or not to step in front of an oncoming car? Do you have to be told to go to a place of work of your choosing? What do governments do for you? Do they feed or clothe you, or give you a roof over your head? They only do that for you when you are in one of their jails."

"People mainly get sent to prison when they steal things that don't belong to them. Tell me, who in your Utopian society is going to protect the citizen from the criminal. Answer me that, if you can?"

"Crime has its roots in poverty and unemployment. When these are eliminated, people will stop turning to theft as a way to augment their basic needs. Just as the middle classes and the well-off wouldn't dream of breaking into someone's house to take something that wasn't theirs, nor would those who are no longer poor."

"Are you trying to tell me that under anarchism, everyone would have the moral standards of professional people?"

"Yes, I am, and why the fuck shouldn't they?"

"Because, dear boy, they haven't been bred that way."

"You talk as if they were racehorses or something. Humans from whatever stratum they happen to be born into can feel responsible for the well-being of others. Look at me, Vic, I wasn't exactly born with a silver spoon in my mouth, but I don't go around robbing people, do I?"

"There's good'uns and bad'uns born every day since man inhabited this imperfect world of ours, what determines the way we turn out is as haphazard as throwing a coin into the air. By sheer luck, dear boy, in your case the penny landed the right side up."

"So according to you, to be good or bad is purely a matter of chance. That being so, why aren't there as many middle- and upper-class people in our prisons as there are poor and unemployed ones? The simple reason is, Vic, the tossed coin is weighted in their favour. The penny can be weighted in favour of everyone, then the disadvantaged would turn out to be just as decent and honest as those citizens who by sheer luck land on more fertile soil. I think we shouldn't pursue this discussion any further until you've read a book I'll lend you called *The ABC of Anarchism.*"

"What I want to pursue at the moment, dear boy, is a pub."

"Well, if we pop onto the next bus going down Oxford Street, I'll take you to one that will make all the others you've ever been in seem like they were run by the Salvation Army."

The Fitzroy Tavern was packed when we arrived. I could see Vic's eyes widen as he watched the flamboyant customers pushing their way to the bar, eager to get hold of the first of the many drinks they would consume during the course of the evening.

As usual, Dylan Thomas was holding court at one end of the bar, while Quentin at the other end had the small group around him in fits of laughter. Vic gazed for a long time at him and just couldn't accept that with his plucked, black-pencilled-in eyebrows, painted long fingernails and lipstick, he was male.

When the pub closed, I took him on to the Coffee Ann. He took to it like a duck to water. As he watched in awe the carryings-on of male and female homosexuals, I could almost see the chains of suppression of his own latent homosexuality slip away from him. I introduced him to Robert and before the evening was out they became friends. From then on, the three of us, like the musketeers, went, whenever possible, everywhere together.

The next day I took Vic to Tony's Caff. I warned him he'd be immediately set upon by all the scroungers wanting to 'borrow' sixpence. All the regulars were there, Alan, Bert, Johnny, Paddy, Frustie and the mad pseudo-artist, Redvers. He managed to cadge two bob off Vic by telling him that he needed to buy some paint to finish the masterpiece he was currently working on. It was, however, Peter, the beautiful and effeminate self-styled ballet dancer that Vic most wanted to meet. They were obviously attracted to each other from the word go. One could almost hear Peter purring as the slim, fair-haired, apparently straight young man sat down beside him. Somehow he sensed that Vic was a homosexual.

Not wanting to intrude on the couple, I moved over to where Alan and Bert were sitting. Bert was describing to Alan how he'd spent most of yesterday going round the nightclubs trying to persuade them to audition Josie, his girlfriend, do her strong lady act. The fact was, he said, she didn't earn enough to keep herself, let alone him, when she did her stuff, standing on the kerbside in front of Tower Bridge.

"Any luck?" asked Alan.

"No, they all turned down the idea because they thought men wouldn't like to watch a young woman performing feats of strength that they couldn't do themselves. Men, they told me, like to think of women as the weaker sex."

"What a lot of rubbish," said Alan, "haven't the stupid bastards ever heard of

Boadicea, Joan of Arc, or more recently Amy Johnson, to mention but a few?"

"I think they were meaning physically weaker than men, Alan."

"Physical my arse, most women live longer than we more fragile men do, and as for me, Bert, I'd much prefer women to be stronger, then I wouldn't have to spend half my time protecting them, would I?"

"You don't spend half your time protecting any fucking thing, most of your day is spent with your arse glued to one of Tony's lousy chairs."

"That's how it might appear to you. In fact, when I'm sitting here, I'm not just staring into my cup of tea, I'm planning how to bring about an anarchist revolution."

"Luckily for our Russian comrades, Lenin wasn't like you. He got off his arse and brought about the revolution."

And that concluded the banter between them.

At five, Peter had to leave Vic to hurry back to the home of his sugar daddy (a well-known barrister) before he got back from chambers. But I could see that Vic's life had changed for ever.

CHAPTER TWENTY-EIGHT

Now that Vic had Peter, and Robert had numerous girlfriends, I was left out on a limb. Robert decided that something should be done about it, so the next Saturday afternoon he more or less frogmarched me to a concert at the Albert Hall.

"Now, Derrick," he said, as we entered the oval auditorium, "what we do first is cruise up and down the aisles until we spot a girl who hasn't got a bloke's arm draped around her. That won't be difficult because most of their boyfriends are away doing their bit for King and Country."

"I do wish you hadn't said that, Robert, I feel a real heel taking advantage of them when their chaps are away."

"Don't worry about it, I assure you if they don't like being approached, they'll soon let you know."

Within seconds, Robert's roving eyes caught sight of a girl he fancied. Moments later, I spotted a very attractive looking one, a few rows nearer to the platform. There was no one sitting on either side of her. I was about to make my way down the aisle when Robert took me by the arm.

"Have you remembered the best way to start up a conversation?"

"No, remind me," I said eagerly.

"You wait until the first piece is over, then ask her whether she liked the conductor's interpretation. Whatever her answer is, say you haven't yet made up your mind. Then try and look as if you are contemplating, then, after a short pause, say that upon reflection, you tend to agree with her. After that, it is absolutely vital that you steer off the subject that you know fuck-all about. Change tack by asking her, what a beautiful girl like her is doing here all on her own. If she answers in a friendly way, from then on the conversation should flow quite naturally."

"You make it sound so easy, Robert."

I squeezed my way past a line of people and sat down next to the girl.

I resisted the temptation to take a sly sideways glance at her, and contented myself by looking down on her lap which was partly obscured by sheets of music. Just my bad luck, I thought, for this girl obviously knew her musical onions and was going to read the score as the orchestra played. I decided to abandon Robert's suggested opening line, and tell her the truth, that this was my first time ever at a concert. I passed the time waiting for the orchestra to appear by observing the interior of the building and looking down at the girl's knees. If I had been the architect, I mused, I would have placed the orchestra on a fixed platform in the centre of the auditorium, with a piece of machinery underneath that would silently rotate the rows of seats. It would complete one cycle every five minutes. This would allow everyone to see the conductor and musicians from many different angles. I decided that the girl might be more impressed with my novel idea than by me pretending to know anything about music.

Eventually the members of the orchestra, all dressed in evening suits, took up their places. When they had finished tuning up their instruments, the conductor appeared. He got loud applause. I didn't understand why, because he hadn't done anything yet. He bowed to the audience, then turned and faced the orchestra. With his baton in his right hand, he raised both his arms. The vast hall went silent, and the orchestra started to play. I didn't know what piece it was that I was listening to, I only knew that it pleased me - so much so, that I completely forgot about the girl in the next seat.

Twenty minutes into the piece, the music gained tempo and got louder and louder. The trumpeters blared, the violinists scraped away for all they were worth, the pianist's hands glided dextrously up and down the ivory keys. The cymbalist clashed his brass plates together, and the kettle-drummer banged his sticks with such a speed that human eyes couldn't follow their movement. The music ended in a tremendous crescendo of sound. When all went quiet, the silence seemed hard to bear. Full of admiration, I started to applaud vigorously. Some seconds went by before, to my horror, I realised I was the only one in the packed hall doing so. People in the row in front turned round and scowled. The beautiful girl next to me, in order to disassociate herself from this musical moron, pointedly stood up and sat down in the vacant seat to her right. I think at that moment I was about as popular with her as a skunk at a garden party. I thought it was unfair that I should get all this disapproval just because of my untimely clapping. How was I to know that it was only a pause in the composition? I dearly wished I could have made myself small enough to crawl under my seat and stay there until the hall was empty. So I sat very still until the performance was over, and only got up to leave when most of the audience had departed. Since that day, I've never started to clap until everyone else has for at least three seconds.

I looked for Robert, but couldn't find him and caught up with him later at the Coffee Ann. He said he had only left the concert without me because he wanted to get the girl he picked up back to his place before she changed her mind.

"How did you make out with yours?" he asked.

"Robert, how the fuck can you ask such a question after I'd made such an ass of myself?"

"I don't know what you're talking about."

"Didn't you hear me clap like mad when I shouldn't have?"

"No."

"Then you must have been the only one in the hall that didn't. Anyway, it sure put the girl off me."

"Never mind, Derrick, there's plenty more fish in the sea. Betty, that's the one for you, I don't know why I didn't think of her before. I've known her since she was a child. She's grown up to be quite a beauty. My guess is, you two are made for one another."

"Why?"

"Because I know she likes well-built blokes."

"Then why isn't she one of your girls?"

"I'm not her type, I just told you, she likes the brawny ones and you can hardly describe me as that. Tomorrow we'll call on her."

The next morning, Robert and I were going up the outside concrete steps leading to the second floor of a small working-class block of flats off Baker Street. Robert gave two taps on the unpolished brass knocker.

"Hope she's in," I said.

"I'm sure she'll be in, on Sunday she probably has a lie-in, the poor girl has to get up at the crack of dawn all week to go off to work."

He tapped again, and this time the door was opened almost immediately. When I caught sight of the girl standing in the doorway, I could hardly believe my eyes. She had long, silky, auburn hair that reached down to below her shoulders, a neatly trimmed fringe framed her big grey-blue eyes. She had high cheek bones, and small but full lips. Her lovely body was visible through the flimsy flowered dress she wore and she was barefoot.

"Hallo Robert, this is a nice surprise, come in."

"My friend Derrick and I were just on our way to go for a row on the Serpentine, and I remembered I hadn't seen you for a very long time. So how are you?"

"Much better now that spring is here. Come and sit in the drawing room."

I knew it was time to stop gazing at this vision and say something. I don't know what possessed me, but I asked her why a lovely girl like her was wearing such a terrible dress. She would have looked adorable in a paper bag! "Don't you like it? In that case I'll go and put another one on. Make yourself comfortable, I'll only be a minute."

"Derrick, whatever made you say such a thing?" asked Robert.

"I don't know, must have been some skew-whiffy idea that I'd make some sort of an impression."

"Perhaps you should try slapping her on the face - I'm sure that'll make a lasting impression!"

When she came back into the room, wearing a similar looking dress, I told her that this one suited her so much more.

"I'm glad you like it," she said without a trace of sarcasm.

"As it's such a nice day, would you like to come boating with us?"

"I'd love to."

Out in the street, Robert tactfully 'remembered' that he'd promised his parents he'd have lunch with them.

"It looks like it'll just be the two of us, if that's all right with you," I said.

"Yes, provided you don't mind doing all the rowing."

"All you have to do is lie back and relax."

When we arrived at the lake, there was a long queue of people waiting to hire a boat.

"Sorry about this," I said.

"I really don't mind. As it's such a nice sunny day, we can sit on the grass and watch the boats go by."

I removed my shirt so as to bask in the first sun of the year, and I sat down on the grassy bank close to her. Betty turned and looked at me:

"You're very muscular, aren't you?"

"I do a lot of exercises to keep myself fit and for half of last year, I did very hard physical work on the land."

"I like men who keep themselves in shape," she said, looking approvingly at me.

"How old are you, Betty?" I asked.

"I was eighteen last week."

"That makes me two months older than you."

"I prefer older men," she teased.

Her answer gave me the green light. Very timidly at first, I stroked her long, soft silky hair. She put both her hands round the back of my head and pulled me gently towards her. Our lips touched and before long, we were kissing passionately. Slowly her back went down onto the grass. I followed her until my chest came to rest on her breasts. As we kissed, Betty's hands glided up and down my bare back. After a while, she slipped them under the waistband of my trousers, and squeezed my buttocks. I responded by gingerly putting one hand under her dress and edging it up the velvety skin of her thighs, coming to a momentary halt before lifting the elastic of her knickers.

So engrossed were we in exploring one another's bodies that the outside world didn't exist for us. In the end, what brought us back to earth with a bang, was a woman's voice shouting from a distance: "It's disgusting, behaving like this in public, absolutely disgusting!"

Leaving my hand where it was, I raised my head to see where the shrill voice was coming from. A few yards away, sitting on a neatly laid out rug, were a prim and proper middle-aged couple, all decked out in their Sunday best. When the woman saw she had got my attention, she started shouting again:

"I'm addressing you, young man, you should be thoroughly ashamed of yourself, behaving in this disgusting manner."

"Madam," I said, "it's all a matter of how you interpret the meaning of the word 'disgusting'. For me, this war with its killing and maiming people is disgusting. Did you ever protest about that? I'm sure you didn't. What my girlfriend and I are doing is good, clean, wholesome stuff, compared to anything that's going on in this bloody war."

"I'm going off to report your indecent behaviour and your impudence to the police. They'll know how to deal with the likes of you!" she screamed back at me.

"Before you go, madam, may I recommend that you and your husband try out what we are doing? You never know, you might find it pleasurable - but on second thoughts, looking at the man by your side, perhaps you shouldn't."

"How dare you talk to me this way, how dare you!"

Whenever I'm confronted with a pious, interfering person like this lady, an irresistible urge comes over me to be quite vulgar, so I shouted back:

"Why don't you fuck off, you silly old cow, and take your weed of a husband with you!"

She stood up and with her crumpled rug under her arm, said: "Come along, Henry," in a commanding voice, as she stumped off in the direction of the Park police station.

Betty, who had been giggling away throughout this little scene, pulled my head down to between her breasts.

"Let's go back to where we were before the old cow interrupted us."

"I think we should go to the other side of the park where the grass hasn't been cut since before the war there, we can do what we like without being bothered. Are you hungry? If so, we could stop off at the Serpentine Café for a bite."

"I'm starving. When I opened the door to you and Robert, I'd only just got out of bed, and hadn't had my breakfast."

"You should have told me, we could have gone to a cafe before making for the park."

"I wanted to have a nibble at you first, Derrick boy," she said coquettishly.

It was a long wait to get served at the café. Behind the food counter were two old dears, moving at snail's pace, trying their level best to cope with the ever-lengthening queue. I sent Betty off to reserve a place for us at a table while I got in line. A half hour passed by before it was my turn to be served.

"Yes, dear," said the serving lady.

"Four cheese sandwiches and two cups of tea, please," I said.

"Sorry dear, but I'm afraid everyone is rationed to one sandwich per person."

"I'm asking for four cups of tea and four sandwiches because my girlfriend has brought her parents along with her."

Luckily the old dear believed me.

We left the café hand-in-hand and strolled under the cloudless sky towards the Round Pond, stopping there for a while to watch the model sailing boats being pushed along by a gentle breeze. It was a pleasing sound, hearing the children scream with delight as they watched their little yachts plough their way through the still, shallow water of the pond. This happy scene transported you for a moment out of the war into a peaceful England.

We walked on a little further to the edge of the park in Kensington Gardens, where the grass had now shot up to above our waists.

"This is perfect," I said, trampling a small area underfoot.

I removed my shirt and swung it into the air, then like Sir Walter Raleigh, laid it down onto the flattened grass.

"For you to lie on, my lady," I said reverently as I bowed my head.

"Oh thank you, kind sir, your chivalry won't go unrewarded, I promise you."

Betty raised her arms to the back of the neck and undid the buttons that held her dress in place. I slipped off my trousers and twirled them rapidly above my head before letting them go. They disappeared into the long grass some distance away. My pants followed. One by one, Betty took off her bra, then her knickers, and dropped them on top of her discarded dress.

Naked and motionless, we just looked at each other. She's a goddess put on this earth to be worshipped, I thought. Never before had I seen such perfection. Two steps later, our bodies touched from head to toe. We became irrevocably entwined. Betty's hands came to rest around my neck, then she wrapped her shapely legs in a tight grip round my waist. The palms of my hands became her seat. I twirled her round and round to a Strauss waltz playing in my head until I lost my balance and we both ended up on the grass. There wasn't a part of her body or beautiful face that wasn't caressed and kissed, before I seduced her. I refrain from saying 'made love', because the passion between us was undisguised lust. Between fucks, we puffed away at a cigarette as we lay outstretched on our backs, soaking up the warm and comforting rays of the spring sun.

Towards evening, the sun set and the air cooled. I would have liked to have stayed where I was until the war ended, but alas, the time had come for us to get dressed. It became a matter of urgency to find the trousers and pants that I'd thrown into the high grass. Betty got dressed and helped me search for them. It was getting darker by the minute. Thank God Betty, who searched more methodically than I, found them just before it became pitch black. Relieved, we left the park and made for the Corner House in Marble Arch.

Over the meal, Betty told me something about her background. When she was four, her father had deserted her and her mother, and hadn't been seen or heard of since. Her mother tried as best she could to support them both, it hadn't been easy. For most of her childhood, they'd lived on public assistance and hand-outs from charities. She couldn't remember ever having anything to wear that wasn't second-hand. Her mother's brother helped out a bit as he had a job, but Betty had to pay a price for his help. She told me that her uncle had sexually abused her from the age of eight, and continued to do so right up until she was fourteen. It was only then that she could pluck up enough courage to tell him to stop it. The only pocket money she ever got, was the sixpence her uncle gave her after abusing her.

"How on earth did he get away with molesting you right under your mother's nose?" I asked.

"It was easy. To 'give her a break' (that's the way he put it), he offered to take me to his place most weekends."

"Why didn't you tell your mother what he was doing to you?"

"She wouldn't have believed me. And I wouldn't have got the sixpence he gave me."

Betty went on to say that two years before the war, her mother finally got a job as a shop assistant in Selfridges, and since then, things had improved. Even more so now, because she herself was earning two pounds ten shillings a week working at a factory.

"Considering," I said, "that you were so deprived, I'm amazed that you've grown up to be such a bonny girl. It just goes to show, doesn't it, that the poor can give birth to a baby that can grow up to be as beautiful as a princess."

"I do like the way you put things, Derrick. It's what makes you different from the other boys I've gone out with."

"Nicer as well, eh?"

"You're much nicer to touch, that's for sure. The others mostly had pimply faces and, unlike you, they looked better with their clothes on."

"I suppose a stunning-looking girl like you has had lots of boyfriends?"

"Quite a few, but I only necked with them. Apart from my uncle, you are the first boy I've gone the whole way with."

"Do you mean your uncle f... had intercourse with you?"

"Only when I was thirteen. Before that he only asked me to play with what he called his 'dolly'."

"Jesus Christ, the bastard. You're lucky he didn't make you pregnant."

"He used a thing-uma-bob."

"I suppose I should have used one when we were doing it. But the problem is, you can only get them at the barber's, and as I'm letting my hair grow I don't go to them anymore."

"I wouldn't mind having your baby. If I did, I wouldn't have to do war work in a lousy factory anymore."

"War work, Betty, is only for the duration, a baby is for life."

"Our life, Derrick."

Oh Jesus, what a thought, I could feel my stomach tighten at the very idea of becoming a father, but I relaxed when I remembered that I hadn't taken any precautions with either Gloria or Stella, and as far as I knew neither of them became pregnant. Who knows, with a bit of luck, I was sterile. Comforting myself with this false optimism, I returned to my devil-may-care ways.

After our meal, I suggested going to the pictures, but she said she couldn't, as she had to be up at the crack of dawn to be on time for work the next day. She worked at a factory in the Mile End Road, packing up the uniforms and putting them into boxes ready for dispatch.

"Are the people you work with nice?" I asked.

"They're not bad, but they're mostly old fogies. I'm the only young one. I'll change my job soon, and go somewhere that has a bit of life."

I walked Betty back to her home. We were standing by the entrance of her block kissing and cuddling when the sirens sounded. Shortly after, the anti-aircraft guns started to blaze away.

"I'd better go in," said Betty. "Mum gets very frightened when she's on her own in an air-raid."

"Can I come and see you again tomorrow night?"

"No, Derrick, I don't get back from work until after six and as I have to get up so early, I only go out at weekends."

"Does that mean we can't see each other until next Saturday then?"

"Yes, it does, because I'm really tired by the time I get home."

"I suppose you are, it's just that next Saturday seems such a long way away."

We kissed and embraced a while, and then she turned to go.

CHAPTER TWENTY-NINE

As I set off to walk to the Coffee Ann in what was rapidly becoming one of the heavier air-raids in recent times, I made up my mind that the time had come when I must move out of Uncle's flat and get a place of my own, somewhere I could take Betty to. I knew I couldn't rely on the long grass of Hyde Park. What's more, although Uncle never complained, I think he must have been a bit put out by me arriving back at all hours of the night, and then sleeping in until midday. As an ex-military man, he must have found it difficult to come to terms with my long hair, and the shabby clothes I now wore to be in tune with my anarchist comrades. As I was very fond of the old man, I decided I'd have a meal with him at least once a week. If my long hair embarrassed him, I'd tell him to say to the other club members, I had to let it grow for a part in a film. As my suit was always kept at his place, I would at least be suitably dressed. Vic had told me that the room he rented cost him fifteen shillings a week, and as I was getting two or three days' extra work most weeks, I thought I could well afford to pay up to a pound.

Vic and Robert were sitting together when I entered the Coffee Ann.

"How did you make out with Betty?" enquired Robert.

"Didn't you notice that I was floating on air? Jesus, Robert, what a girl, what an absolutely wonderful girl you introduced me to."

"I had an idea that you were made for each other. But don't expect to have serious conversations with her. She might not understand what you're talking about."

"I don't want serious conversations with her. All I'm wanting to do is hug her so close that you couldn't put a cigarette paper between us."

"Is that why you didn't turn up at Speakers' Corner, where, I might remind you, we'd arranged to meet? It seems you preferred to indulge in the pleasures of the flesh, rather than promoting the cause," said Vic.

"They say that suppressing the urges of the flesh warps the mind."

"My God, Robert, we've got a right little Freud in our midst."

"The need to have sex has got nothing to do with Freud, whoever he is, it's a basic human activity. If your parents hadn't had a fuck at least once, you wouldn't be in this world."

"Quite so, and that's another thing I hold against them."

"What were your poor parents supposed to do, ask your permission?"

"If only they could, the world would have a quarter of its present population. I don't think it's an unreasonable request to want to view the place you might spend over eighty years in, before being propelled into it. For God's sake, man, you wouldn't dream of purchasing a house, or for that matter a motor car, without first having a good look at it, would you? But on an important issue like this, you're not even consulted."

"You can always opt to leave this world if you find it a bore. You could jump off a cliff, for instance."

"That's the snag, dear boy, you can't because built into the human psyche is a strong instinct for self-preservation. You are, in effect, a prisoner in a high-security jail, serving a life sentence with absolutely no hope of parole."

"Given the choice, would you have decided that this world was not for you?"

"I would have, up until I met Peter. Now I'm not so sure."

"That's the wonderful thing about this life of ours, you never know what's in store for you."

"That's another thing I don't like about it."

Vic prodded Robert in the ribs and said: "Would you have chosen to come down to earth?"

"If I knew there were no beautiful girls on it, I'd cling to the inside lining of my dad's balls every time the alarm bells rang."

"How about you, Derrick, what would you opt for?" asked Vic.

"I'd have stayed all snug in my mother's womb until she'd found me a father and a home to be brought up in."

"Oh, of course, I'd forgotten that you're an orphan. It's really quite amazing that you've shaped out as well as you have, when one thinks about it."

"I never think about it, I just get on with my life on a day by day basis, and don't worry about the future. I recommend that you do the same."

"Sound advice, dear fellow."

Then, as if to underline what I'd just said, a bomb exploded a bit too close for comfort, and sent some of the crockery flying.

"Shit," exclaimed Vic when his cup of coffee ended up on the floor.

Jimmy, who was serving at the counter at the time, got the screaming hab-dabs when he saw what a shambles his café was in. Not only were a number of cups and saucers smashed, but the blast had blown in the entrance door, and a huge cloud of fine dust came in from the street and settled everywhere.

One of the regulars went over to him and put a comforting arm around his shoulders.

"There, there, Jimmy, calm down. We'll put everything back to normal. All you need to do is give us a broom, a bucket and a few floorcloths."

It was all hands on deck for those that were sober enough to get down on their hands and knees and wield a floorcloth.

"This is the second fucking time today I've had to come to someone's aid," complained Vic.

"What was the first?" I asked.

"Frederick got into a sticky situation when he was speaking in the park. Half-a-dozen boys in khaki tried to pull him off his platform to beat him up. I and a couple of Frederick's weight-lifting chums rescued him."

"Good for you, helping out a comrade. Now you've really joined the class struggle, haven't you?"

"Not quite, I came to his assistance because I've not been in a good scrap since leaving the army, so it was an opportunity for me to brush up my prowess as a pugilist."

"Why do you always use such high-faluting words? Couldn't you have just said you felt like a punch-up?"

"I like to make use of my vocabulary. It sets me apart from the hoi-polloi."

"If you decide to become a socialist or an anarchist, you really will have to ditch that snobbishness of yours."

"Are you saying I'd have to restrict myself to the eight hundred or so words of basic English?"

"It would help, especially when you're communicating with me and ordinary people."

"I endeavour to avoid ordinary people whenever possible, dear boy."

"All this chat isn't getting the floor cleaned up, is it?" I said, as I dipped the floorcloth into the murky water of the bucket.

"I'm not wiping the floor with my mouth, am I?"

"No, but you stop working every time you open it."

"I reckon we ought to get a coffee and a bite of food on the house, after all that sweat," remarked Robert.

"It wasn't Jimmy's fault that the bomb dropped, was it?" I said.

When Jimmy came back and saw the place all shipshape, he was thrilled.

"You darlings, you absolute sweeties!" he exclaimed. "I'm going to give you all a hug and a kiss."

What we actually got was a free cup of coffee and a sandwich. While Vic ate his Spam sandwich, I asked him if he could advise me on how to find a furnished room.

"Certainly, old boy. First go to the area you want to live in, and look at the boards outside any newsagents. Landladies put little cards on them. You'll not have the slightest problem finding one, what with half of London empty."

"I'd thought of taking a place near you in Maida Vale. It would also be handy when I visit my uncle."

"Finally chucked you out, has he?"

"On the contrary, I'm not looking forward to telling him I'm leaving."

By now it was getting on for two in the morning, so I started to walk back to St John's Wood. The air-raid had intensified. Every few minutes, bombs exploded close by and in the distance. The Germans were obviously wanting to bomb the shit out of us before the nights became shorter. The flashes from our anti-aircraft guns lit up the sky, and the streets were illuminated by the fiercely burning fires that engulfed many buildings.

The light was so bright, I could have easily read the small print of a newspaper by it. The ack-ack guns situated on that famous pitch of Lord's Cricket Ground were pounding away. I needed to go down Circus Road but couldn't, because it had a rope slung across it with a board reading 'Danger, keep out, unexploded bomb'. I went further up the road to first one, and then another, of the turnings

I could have taken, but they too were sealed off. As my day had already been fairly hectic, I was by now beginning to feel a bit weak in the knees. So rather than face the wearisome diversion, I retraced my steps back to Circus Road and ducked under the rope. I dared fate by deliberately walking slowly down the road that could have brought about my instant death.

At breakfast, I told Uncle I was going to move out. He was unhappy about having to face the prospect of living alone again, but cheered up when I told him we could still meet and dine out together. I went into my room and packed my few belongings. When I closed the door behind me, I somehow knew that I would never spend another night in the flat that had been a home to me since leaving Miss Minter's.

Today for the first time in my life, I would have a place and a space I could call my own. I made my way to the newsagents in Maida Vale. Looking on the board, I saw at once that there were plenty of rooms to let. The card that caught my eye read 'A spacious room in well-kept house, one pound a week'. I decided to go and see it, mainly because it was only a few doors away from where Vic lived.

A woman in a dressing-gown opened the door. She had curlers sticking out of her mousy hair, and a cigarette drooped down from her closed, unevenly rouged lips. I should have said I had rung the wrong bell, but for some reason I didn't. Instead I heard myself saying: "Good morning, I've come about the room."

"You're quick dear, I only put the card up yesterday afternoon."

She opened the door a little wider and beckoned me into a gloomy front hall.

"Follow me, young man, and I'll take you up and show it to you."

The room was on the second floor, up a staircase with worn and threadbare carpet. The advert was grossly inaccurate: it should have read 'Large dump to let.' I summoned up enough courage to say, "It's not in a very good state, is it?"

"No dear, it isn't, but what with the war and the shortage of labour and materials, I haven't been able to get it done up."

By the look of the place, I think she must have been referring to the war of 1914. Dirty brown strips of wallpaper hung from all the walls and the ceiling. There was a cracked leather armchair with its horsehair stuffing and springs protruding through the seat, in the centre of the room, next to a table scarred with cigarette burns. The lino floor was so disgusting that to walk on it barefooted would have put your health at risk. The room however, did have one very important asset, as far as I was concerned - a large double bed. Since the main reason for moving out of Uncle's was to have somewhere private I could bring Betty, this persuaded me to rent the room. As I'd been a bit hesitant in saying I'd have it, the landlady offered to reduce the rent by four shillings a week.

"OK, I'll take it."

She looked visibly relieved at my reply.

"That's settled then, dear, I need a week in advance though, and for an extra shilling, I'm prepared to wash the sheets once a fortnight."

"That's fine," I agreed.

I gave her a pound, which she tucked into the pocket of her worn-out dressing-gown. She handed me back three shillings change.

She pointed to a single gas ring and a gasfire that had half its elements missing.

"The meter for those is over there, below the corner cupboard. In the cupboard are two cups, two plates, one knife and a teaspoon. I'll bring up a kettle later. The toasting fork is by the side of the gasfire. You've got everything you could possibly need. Now, I'm not one of those landladies who make a fuss when a tenant brings a girlfriend back, all I ask is, whatever you do, do it quietly. Come with me and I'll show you where the bathroom and toilet are."

I followed her down one flight to a combined bathroom and toilet. The bath had a long rusty stain the length of its base and a chainless plug. Large chunks of enamel had come away and exposed the metal beneath. The geyser was covered with verdigris and the flue was full of holes where the rust had eaten away at it. I'm sure that if you were foolish enough to ignite it, you would have been blown to bits or asphyxiated by carbon monoxide. I made up my mind never to use it.

"Tuppence will give you enough hot water to have a bath," the landlady informed me. Going by the state it was in, I think the last two pennies fed into the meter had Edward VII's face embossed on them.

"Well, dear, now you know where everything is, come down with me and I'll give you a front door key."

When she handed it to me, she told me to make sure that I remembered to pull the curtains at night before putting the light on.

"We don't want Jerry to drop a bomb on us, do we, dear?"

Why she should worry about that, when up one flight was a geyser almost as lethal as an unexploded bomb, I don't know.

After we had exchanged names, I went back up to my room. There I contemplated on what on earth I could do to make this shithouse of a place more palatable by the time Betty saw it. I knew I'd have to give the revolting lino a good clean, and do something about the bare light bulb that hung down from the centre of the ceiling. My only hope of improving things was to do what I'd seen on film sets - create an illusion. The unshaded light could easily be dealt with by turning it off. The subdued glow of a few candles dotted about the room would, like magic, make most of the shabbiness disappear. Throwing a blanket over the dilapidated armchair would make it look passable. If I bought a few spring flowers, and plonked them into milk bottles - well, hey presto, the room would look a lot better. Of course, the illusion would be shattered come the dawn, but provided I didn't pull the curtains before bundling Betty out of the house to have breakfast, I might just get away with it.

Now, I thought, was as good a time as any to start on the conversion. I borrowed a bucket and mop from the landlady and she gave me a large slab of Sunlight household soap without charging for it. I spent the whole afternoon on my hands and knees, beavering away. On my third attempt at removing all the trodden-in grime, I noticed that a flowered pattern on the lino was beginning to emerge through the dirt. This egged me on to scrub even harder, and eventually I brought the decorative design out into daylight. When I'd finished, I looked down admiringly at my handiwork. I may not have been given a formal education, but I certainly was taught how to scrub a floor well.

I had promised to go to Uncle's that evening and before dining out I had a bath at his flat. The bathroom here was so different, it was hard to imagine that they could both be used for the same purpose.

All the roads near the flat were roped off because of the unexploded bomb. I thought a walk to the Underground would prove too much for the old man, so I suggested we went by taxi to the RAC.

"This infernal war is getting damned expensive, what with the increased taxation to pay for it, and now having to use cabs when one dines out. If we don't throw in the sponge soon, I'll end up a pauper."

"Surely your dividends are still paying you something, aren't they?"

"Extraordinarily, the shares I have in industry seem to be paying out a bit more."

"Well, Uncle, you can use the extra you get to go towards paying for the cab, can't you?"

"I suppose you're right, Hayden, if you look at it that way."

The knowledge that he was earning even more out of factories churning out weapons of destruction almost put me off my meal.

After dinner, I went back with him to the flat and got out of my smart suit before going on to my new abode. Lying in the huge bed, all I could think about was Saturday, when the lovely Betty would be in it with me. It's really awful how long a week can seem when you're so looking forward to something at the end of it.

Next day, as soon as I was back from Denham, I headed straight for the Fitzroy Tavern. Vic saw me as I entered.

"Hallo, Derrick, where were you last night?"

"I went to bed early, I had to be at the studios at the crack of dawn."

I told him about my room and what a shocking state it was in, and said the one good thing about it was that the landlady didn't mind if I brought back my girlfriend.

"You're very lucky, dear boy, most of them think they are there to supervise the morals of the nation. If mine knew what capers Peter and I got up to, she'd turf us out into the street."

"What has it got to do with her, provided you don't damage her property?"

"Absolutely nothing, old boy. Shall we move to Ann's? Robert will be there by now."

Robert looked very down in the mouth when we met him.

"What's up with you?" I asked.

"The fucking tribunal turned me down. Luckily Donald Soper managed to wangle an appeal which I'll have to attend in the autumn."

"Why are you looking so depressed? The autumn is months away."

"I know, but they very rarely reverse the decision of the tribunal."

"Cheer up, Robert, old boy, by then they'll have caught up with me, so we can go and play soldiers together."

"Vic, I'm a pacifist, I won't be fighting alongside you or anyone else. Why the fuck can't you understand that? I don't think the Germans will take too kindly to pacifists, we'll be among the first on their list for the firing squad."

"If you think the Germans are that bad, why don't you join up and fight the bastards?"

"Get it into your head, Vic, I am a pacifist."

"All the way to the firing squad, eh?"

"Yes, if need be."

To calm things down between them, I intervened.

"Robert, I'm sure that the judges at your appeal will be more sympathetic than the Colonel Blimps you had today. Look on the bright side and enjoy the next few months ahead of you. Go and spend the night with your girlfriend, she'll cheer you up."

"I can't."

"Why not?"

"Because I don't bloody well feel like it, I'm too depressed. Sorry, Derrick, I'll be all right by tomorrow, it was the possibility of having to spend the rest of the war in jail, that has depressed me. I think I'll fuck off and relieve you two of my unsociable company."

"Don't go on our account, you never know, we might snap you of out of it. Did I ever tell you the funny story about me and the bull?"

"No, not now, Derrick, I'm not in the mood."

When Robert was out of earshot, Vic said:

"I don't know what he's making such a fuss about. We both know the army isn't that bad, don't we?"

"How you can ask me a question like that, when you know how much I hated it? Have you forgotten how overjoyed you were when you got released?"

"That's the trouble with memory, old boy, one tends to remember the few days that were fun, but for some obscure reason the mind erases the sheer boredom and misery that one has to endure for ninety per cent of the time. If I had designed the human brain, it would recall things the other way round. All the same, dear boy, thank you for reminding me how fucking awful army life was. Are you doing anything tomorrow evening?"

"No, why?"

"Well, last Sunday, when you were romping around in the long grass with your amour ..."

"My what?"

"...your lady friend, and I was at Frederick's meeting in Hyde Park, I met a young doctor friend of his who is also a dedicated anarchist. The doctor told me he has this idea of launching a fortnightly paper on behalf of the movement. He's holding a meeting to discuss his plans tomorrow at seven-thirty. He invited me to come along and bring anyone else who might be interested. I know Frederick will be there, so I thought I'd go, provided you came with me."

"Yes, I'll come, but I don't think I'll be much use, I'm incapable of putting together a few sentences to fill up the back of a postcard, let alone contributing anything worth reading in a newspaper."

"I doubt if the doctor has you or me in mind you as writers for the paper. More likely he'd be thinking of us in terms of helping with its distribution and sales."

"Correct me if I'm wrong, Vic, but I remember you saying that you were more persuaded by the arguments of the Communist and Socialist parties than us Anarchists."

"I was, until I read Marx's *Das Kapital*. His thesis on economics didn't convince me, bearing in mind man's nature to look after Number One first. For Marx to assume that a Communist state would have the best interests of the proletariat at heart is frankly naive. His premise that the state would eventually allow itself to wither away, is ridiculous. Whenever have those in power voluntarily handed over their privileged positions without shedding blood? Can you envisage turning up at the Kremlin and saying to Stalin 'Joe, lad, thank you for all you've done but the time has come for you to fuck off?' Stalin would do one of two things - he'd either shoot you on the spot, or, if you were lucky and caught him in a good mood, he'd have you banished to Siberia, and make sure you never saw the light of European Russia again.

"I've come to the conclusion, dear boy, that no man or group of men should have the power to be in charge of the well-being of a nation's population. It's not true that power corrupts - it doesn't. All it does is enable those that have it to act according to human nature. In other words, it's the 'Fuck you, Jack, as long as I'm all right' philosophy that will always prevail."

"Christ, Vic, you have thought it all out, haven't you? Frederick once lent me his copy of *Das Kapital*. I found it such hard going that I never managed to get further than the first paragraph. It must have taken you weeks to get through it."

"Not at all, old boy, I read it over a weekend."

"A weekend! My God, you must be a fast reader. How on earth did you digest all those complex theories in just two days?"

"Unlike you, I'm an intellectual. I have the ability to pick the raisins out of the cake very quickly."

"Geniuses like you shouldn't be let loose on us ordinary mortals."

"Sarcasm, dear boy, is what people resort to when they can't think of anything constructive to say."

"Get off your high horse for a moment and tell me where and at what time do we meet up tomorrow."

"The doctor lives in Southwark, so if we want to be there at seven-thirty, I think we ought to meet in Tony's about six."

"OK, I'll see you then."

I left Vic and for once, was in time to catch the last Tube back.

The next day I went to the Youth Centre to give Robert a hand. He'd got over his depression, largely because Soper had assured him that the judges who would hear his appeal were in the legal profession, and wouldn't be as bigoted as those who were at the tribunal. I suggested that, as summer was almost here, he and I went and worked on a farm somewhere within easy reach of London. It would, I told him, rid him of his fear of doing manual work, and if, after his appeal, he was directed to do it, maybe he wouldn't mind it so much.

"Nothing, Derrick, but absolutely nothing, would persuade me to volunteer for that drudgery. I'll go only as an alternative to going to prison."

"It was only an idea, Robert. As for me, I'm more than happy to spend the summer in London, especially now that you've introduced me to the Betty."

I carried on helping at the centre until it was time to meet Vic at Tony's.

When we entered the doctor's house in Southwark, I was surprised how many people had turned up. Some had travelled from as far away as Birmingham to be there. Frederick took me across the large room and introduced me to the doctor.

He was slim and of medium height. I guessed that he was in his mid-thirties. He had an intelligent face and spoke softly. A lock of his hair fell across his forehead, concealing his right eye.

"What's the doctor's name?" I asked Frederick.

"Hewetson, John Hewetson. He's a really good man, a lot of his patients are the dockers that work on the local wharves. Their bosses hate him because he gives out sick-leave certificates, particularly to the older men, who are mainly suffering from fatigue. I've heard he is also very good and understanding with his working-class women patients."

"I wish we had one like him in North London," I said.

"Don't worry, Derrick, under anarchism, they'll all be like John."

After everyone had been given a cup of tea, Frederick asked us all to sit down so that the meeting could begin.

He thanked everybody for coming, then outlined John's plan to start up a fortnightly paper. The discussion was mainly about who the regular contributors would be. John said he'd already approached Herbert Read, who had agreed immediately to write for the paper. Frederick said he would sound out the writer Ethel Mannin, and knowing how enthusiastic she was about the cause, he felt pretty certain we could count on her. Frederick asked if any of us had any ideas. One person thought that our neutral American comrades should be asked to write about their views on the capitalist war going on in Europe. Another said that London had many refugees, who were prominent members of the Spanish anarchists. Their experiences in the fight against fascism would be an invaluable contribution to the paper. I suggested that Donald Soper should be approached.

It took up a lot of time to decide on a name for the paper, but finally the consensus was that it should go under the name of War Commentary. Hewetson offered to finance the first issue, on condition that thereafter, the paper would pay for itself from the revenue it received from sales. It was decided that Freedom Press should print it, and that five hundred copies would be ordered for the first edition.

Vic and I said we'd man a pitch on weekends outside the park gates at Speakers' Corner. Others offered to sell the paper at any venue publicised for a political rally or meeting. It was unanimously agreed that the aim should be to get the first copy on the streets by the end of June.

We all left the meeting feeling that something of significance had been achieved.

"Fuck me," said Vic as we left, "we must have gone mad, committing ourselves to be somewhere every weekend."

"Don't worry, Vic, I'll make sure that you do."

CHAPTER THIRTY

In the spring and summer of 1941, when the Germans were busy grabbing for themselves Yugoslavia and Greece, and in June following up those successes by invading Russia along the entire length of its 2000 miles frontier - what, you may ask, was I, Hayden Derrick Cartlidge, aged eighteen, doing? Well, I'll tell you: I was living a life almost as predictable as that of a bank clerk. My days between the months of May to September hardly ever varied. Except when I was on film-extra work, Mondays to Fridays I spent either on Hampstead Heath or at the Serpentine, swimming, sunbathing and doing my daily exercises. In bad weather you'd find me in Tony's Caff with Vic and all the other regulars, only to leave there when the Fitzroy pub opened its doors. I'd remain in the pub until closing time, then go on with the mob to Ann's, where I'd lounge about until well after midnight. Most Wednesdays I'd dine with Uncle.

Saturday and Sunday afternoons, Vic and I sold *War Commentary* outside the gates of Hyde Park. The evenings of those two days were totally devoted to being in my digs with Betty. In there, the same performance went on every weekend: have sex, then relax, repeat this two or three times, then break for a meal out. This routine was the ignominious way I spent my weeks throughout the summer, while the Germans were conquering most of Europe and the Russian Army was retreating on all fronts.

I took Betty along with me a couple of times to the Coffee Ann and Tony's, but it didn't work out too well. For one thing, Vic, who had by now declared he was a homosexual, wasn't in the least impressed by her sexual charm. He found her extremely dull, and let her know it. Most of the others did as well, except for Robert. In her company, serious conversation with anyone else was not possible. The poor girl had virtually nothing to contribute to any discussion; all she really wanted to do was sit in a corner and kiss. In a vain attempt to try and make her more acceptable to my friends, I taught her a few swearwords. I got her to repeat them until they rolled off her tongue without a trace of inhibition. By the end of the summer, she no longer said when she felt sexy 'Let's do it', but came out with the more explicit 'Let's fuck, Derrick'. In the end, she was using the word even when asking where the toothpaste was.

In the middle of August, Betty chucked in her job, and except for spending a couple of nights a week with her mother, moved in with me. Now this was all very nice, but I needed to be free to spend some of my time with my friends. Man cannot live by sex alone, so to make it possible for me to go to my usual haunts unaccompanied by her, I came up with the idea that she should do what Robert's girl did, work in a nightclub. I told her I was sure they'd jump at the chance to have a stunning-looking girl like her. What's more, I told her, in all probability she'd earn in one evening more than she got for a whole week in her last job.

Betty's eyes lit up at my suggestion, then immediately faded.

"Derrick, I don't think the Labour Exchange will let me work anywhere that's not doing war work."

"You don't go and ask them for their permission. Persuade your mum to tell any Labour Exchange official that calls, that you've left home and she has no idea where you are. It'll be months before they catch up with you, and maybe never."

"Mum's no good at lying."

"Give her a fake address, then she'll be telling the truth, won't she?"

"What sort of work would I have to do in a nightclub?"

"Probably you'd be doing what Robert's girl does, sell cigarettes from a tray slung around your lovely neck. You never know, some rich toff might take a fancy to you and ask you to marry him."

"Don't people of that kind mostly marry their own sort?"

"Some of them don't."

"How would you feel, if I married one of them?"

"I wouldn't care provided your husband didn't mind if his wife spent her nights with me."

"So all you want from me is sex, is it?"

"Isn't that all you want me for?"

"Maybe," she said.

Betty found a job in Soho at the Cabaret Club. My manipulating had got her off my hands, and I was free (in the evenings, at least) to be with my friends. As the nightclub was only a short distance from the Coffee Ann, I went to meet her when she'd finished work. She emerged from the back door along with three other girls, looking very pleased with herself.

"You've no idea how easy this job is," she told me. "I spend most of my time sitting in an armchair in the back room. Every half hour, I go round the tables selling cigarettes. One gentleman bought a packet of Abdullahs, which, would you believe, cost three shillings. He handed me a pound note and I was just going to give him his seventeen shillings change when he put his arm behind me and squeezed my bottom. I was about to tick him off, but he told me to keep the change. None of the others behaved like that, but they all tipped me. I would never have thought it possible to earn so much money for doing so little work."

"Jesus, Betty, if that man gave you seventeen shillings when all he did was pinch your bum, imagine what he'd give you to pop under the sheets with you."

"A lot, I shouldn't wonder." She paused for a moment, then continued: "When you think about it, my uncle only gave me sixpence when he abused me. The old man tonight didn't bother me that much and gave me a lot more!"

It occurred to me that Betty had realised she could offer for sale something more than a mere packet of cigarettes.

"As you're in the money, how about us taking a cab back?"

"Of course, we will, I think whenever the tips are good, I'll always take a taxi home."

It was nice to hear Betty describe the dump we lived in as 'home'.

On the last Saturday of June, Vic and I went to Hyde Park with copies of *War Commentary*. We took up our pitches at either end of the wide park gates. Some minutes had gone by before I could pluck up enough courage to open my mouth. At first I spoke so quietly that only those passing close by would have heard what I was saying. Finally I managed to shout: "Read how we anarchists would halt the war!"

Then, when an obviously working-class man went by, I'd call out: "Living without bosses, read *War Commentary*, the anarchist paper, and find out how this can be achieved."

When my voice began to fail me, all I could manage was a subdued "*War Commentary*, tuppence!"

After an hour, I made my first sale. Four hours later, I'd sold five. I was a bit disheartened, having sold so few out of the thirty I'd been given. To cheer myself up, I strolled over to see how Vic had fared. I saw a glance that he'd done a damn sight better than me. Only a few papers were still tucked under his arm.

"You've done well, I've hardly got rid of any - why do you think that is?"

"It's all a matter of presentation, dear boy. I've done what the vendors of the evening papers do, shout out a headline that has absolutely nothing to do with the paper's contents."

Just then, two men passed by and Vic called out: "Read all about what the randy girls in the WAAFS get up to with the boys in khaki!"

Immediately the men forked out their tuppences and surreptitiously slid the paper into the inside pockets of their jackets.

"What the fuck is the point of calling out that sort of rubbish? It's got nothing to do with our paper."

"No, Derrick, it hasn't, but it does sell them like hot cakes. The fools think they're getting the sort of salacious news items that are printed in rags like *Reveille* and *Titbits*."

"So, the poor sods who bought a paper from you, when they open it, locked in a lavatory and out of sight of their wives, will realise that they've been cheated."

"They can always use it to wipe their arses on, after all they've paid tuppence for the privilege, haven't they? You never know, one or two might actually read it."

During the course of the summer, Vic and I got more serious about politics. We spent many hours discussing the pro's and con's of political concepts with Frederick and others. As we mostly met in cafés around Marble Arch, we decided to rent a small room in Noel Street, where we could all gather without being disturbed by all the hustle and bustle of café life. A basement room was found in an almost derelict building behind Oxford Street. The rent was five shillings a week, which was far less than it cost for all of us to sit around in cafés.

Vic was becoming quite a character around Soho. He walked about everywhere barefoot, rain or shine. His hair had grown down almost to his shoulders, and his untrimmed beard covered most of his face. His threadbare corduroy trousers were permanently rolled halfway up his calves. Around his neck hung a large ebony crucifix, crudely attached to a lavatory chain. Now that he was having an affair with Peter and no longer needed to suppress his homosexuality, he didn't get so incapably drunk. The money he'd saved when working, had evaporated by the end of summer, so he had to rely on what Peter could squeeze out of his barrister sugar daddy to pay his rent.

I, too, was relying on my girl to pay the rent. I couldn't face being shut up all day in a film studio when the sun was shining, and that summer, it shone most days. Most nights Betty, who by now had got bottom-waggling down to a fine art, brought back oodles of money given to her as tips by the half-pissed customers. It never entered either Vic's or my head, that we had, in effect, become pimps.

One night I took Betty to the cinema. The film was '*Waterloo Bridge*, with Vivien Leigh and Robert Taylor. When the lights went up, nearly all the women were wiping away tears. To console the almost inconsolable Betty, I said softly to her: "Would you like to go back home?"

"Yes," she mumbled between sobs.

When we arrived, she was still upset, so I sat her on the bed and gently stroked her hair. I couldn't understand what all the fuss was about. It wasn't as if her screen idol had really died.

"Shall I make you some toast and a cup of tea?"

"Yes, please, but only one toast. I'm not feeling very hungry."

That was just as well, because we'd nearly come to the end of our margarine ration.

After she had had her tea and toast, she cheered up and became her normal very self.

"Come on, Derrick, fuck me."

I didn't need to be asked twice, and in a matter of seconds I was stripped naked and from where I stood took a flying leap and landed bang on target. Every time we had sex that night, we had a smoke. In the morning, there were six butts in the ashtray. As Betty was nearest to the clock, I woke her up and asked her to tell me the time. She raised herself up a little and I slipped my arm around her waist and kissed her beautiful back. "Quarter past eleven," she said sleepily.

"Jesus Christ, I promised Vic I'd be at a meeting at eleven." She lay back on the bed and pulled the covers over her.

"Well, you'd better get your skates on, you can't keep M'Lud Victor waiting, can you?" She didn't like Vic, as she thought he took up too much of my time.

I got dressed, and gave her a kiss on the cheek:

"See you at Tony's this afternoon," as I hurriedly left for Noel Street. When I got there, Vic looked up: "Oh you've arrived at last, we were just talking about you."

"What about me?" I enquired.

"We've decided that you would be the best one to sus out the possibility of us sitting out the rest of the war with our American comrades."

"Why me?" I asked.

"Because you are the only one of us who's not on the run from the military or the Labour Exchange."

"Anybody got any bright ideas how I get there?" I asked.

"Join the Merchant Navy."

"But comrades,"I protested, "the U-boats are knocking down our merchant ships in the Atlantic like ninepins. I might get killed."

"It's for the good of us all, old boy," said Vic.

Well, I supposed I couldn't argue with that.

So off I went along to Tony's, where I knew I would find Bert. Who, I remembered, had done a few trips to Spain before the war. There he was, sitting at his usual table, flogging his clothing coupons at half-a-crown each. I waited until the deal was done, then sat down next to him.

"Bert," I said, "I want to get on a boat going to America. Can you tell me how I set about it?"

"You must be fucking mad," he said, "but if you're hell-bent on a watery grave, the Norwegian Shipping Office in Tavistock Square is your best bet."

"Thanks a lot, Bert."

"You won't thank me if you're nuts enough to do it," he said.

I set off straight away to the Shipping Office.

I was expecting to find a big office, but all it consisted of was one small room, sparsely furnished, with a couple of men sitting down behind a trestle table.

"I've come to enquire if you have a job for me on one of your ships," then quickly added, "to America, just for one trip."

"Have you been to sea before?"

"No," I said.

"There's a job going as assistant steward on one of our tankers. It's not too well paid but when you add the danger bonus, it's not too bad."

"Sounds good," I heard myself say.

"OK," he said, "the ship is the *Mosli*, she's lying alongside Pier 3 in Plymouth Dock Yard, she's bound for New York and leaves Plymouth early tomorrow morning." He handed me five pounds in ones. "That will more than cover your expenses."

Instinctively my hand shot forward and grabbed it. He looked at his watch.

"The train for Plymouth leaves at two p.m. today from Paddington, that'll give you just enough time to sat goodbye and pick up your belongings."

"That's all there is to it?" I asked.

"No, I still need your name and address, so that I can inform the captain you're on the way."

I gave him Uncle's address.

Later I found out why the interview had been so quick. It wasn't so easy to find people to go to sea at that time. All I possessed was on me, and there was no reason to fetch anything from my digs, so I went straight to Tony's.

"I'm leaving for New York in one hour," I said, interrupting the conversation.

"You're doing what?" they said in unison.

"I'm off to New York, today. You still want me to go, don't you?"

"Yes, we do, but none of us thought you'd really do it," said Alan.

"I only went to enquire, but I was offered a job on the spot, it was a case of now or never, so I accepted it."

"We'll miss you, dear boy. How long will you be away?" asked Vic.

"Probably about three weeks, provided the tanker doesn't get hit by a torpedo."

"Oh God," said Vic, "perhaps we should call the whole thing off."

"No, we won't, it's probably the only chance I'll ever have to go and see New York."

"When you get there, make contact with our comrades, I'll give you their address in a minute. Find out if they'd like us to come over and help them bring about a revolution," said Alan.

"Ask them how we can survive by just bumming around," added Vic.

"OK. Vic, Betty will be here later on. Tell her why I had to leave without saying goodbye. You can cheer her up by saying I'll bring her back lots of nylon stockings, and that I'll send her a postcard from New York. And Vic, be nice to her!"

"I will, I promise."

After a lot of handshakes and slaps on the back, I left Tony's and phoned Uncle.

"You'll send me a postcard from New York, won't you, Hayden?"

I promised I would. I'm sure he felt sorry I wouldn't be around for a while, but I think he was pleased that I was returning to a world inhabited by what he would consider to be normal people!

CHAPTER THIRTY-ONE

I got to Plymouth and jumped into a waiting cab. I still had plenty of money left from the five pounds I'd been given.

"To the docks, Pier 3, please."

As the cab turned onto the pier, I could see at once all the activity of an old naval country at war. There were warships of all sizes - boats being refitted and repaired - the din of rivets being hammered into iron - acetylene welders throwing out huge sparks and cutting their way into metal like a knife through butter. The men were working their guts out, the same men, no doubt, who were two years earlier idle and rotting away on the dole.

At the far end of the pier was my tanker. She was smaller than I had anticipated, but looked well cared for. A coat of matt grey paint had been recently applied. I climbed up a small gangway which was slung casually from the middle of the boat to the quayside. I walked across the iron-clad deck to the end of the boat, then up a short flight of iron stairs onto a well-scrubbed wooden deck in the shape of a horseshoe. As I turned round the bend, I saw a crew member standing there, looking aimlessly over the side. I hoped he spoke English.

"Excuse me," I said, "I've been sent here to work as a steward. Who should I report to?"

He answered in very good English: "A steward? I did not know we needed one. Come with me, I will take you to the skipper. He is in his cabin on the bridge."

I followed him.

We went along a narrow raised iron gangway, strung about four or five feet high, across the middle of the deck (I found out later it was called 'the catwalk'), then up a few steps to the bridge. Going down a narrow passage, he stopped by a well polished brown wooden door and knocked gently. A voice from the inside said something in Norwegian, so we entered.

The captain's cabin was quite large considering the ship wasn't. It had dark wooden panelled walls. The blacked-out portholes were draped with gingham curtains. The built-in bench was generously covered with large navy-blue cushions. A dog was sleeping peacefully on one of them, and in the middle of the floor stood a large mahogany desk. The captain was standing by it. He was a small, thick-set man with short, grey, curly hair, blue eyes and thin tight lips. I knew immediately that here was a man you didn't fuck about with.

"Ah, boy, head office radioed they were sending me a mess boy."

I interrupted him. "I was told I would be an assistant steward, sir," I mumbled.

He raised his eyebrows and his voice.

"A steward? Have you ever been a steward?" then, without waiting for an answer, "you have to be a mess boy for some years before you could become that."

"I see," I said, then plucked up enough courage to continue, "I was also told that the trip was to New York and back, is that correct, sir?"

"Yes, but you can't be sure of anything in war."

I assumed he meant you could be torpedoed.

"How long before we are back in England?" I asked.

"Oh, six or seven weeks."

"Seven weeks," I repeated, "I thought it would be quicker than that."

"This isn't the *Queen Mary*, and even if it was, once we're in convoy, we have to go the speed of the slowest ship, and that can be the pace of a tortoise with only three legs!" He gave a loud laugh. I couldn't even manage a faint smile.

"Go aft and - "

"Aft, sir?" I enquired.

"Back end of the boat. There you will find the galley. Ask the galley boy where your cabin is. He'll know because it's where he bunks. Off you go. Just a word of advice, boy. You do your job well. It's everybody pulling their full weight on this ship. If you do that, you'll have a smooth ride."

"I'll do my best, sir," I said. I hoped I wouldn't have to see too much of him.

There was no one to be seen in the galley, so I turned to leave. Just then a voice said something I didn't understand. My eyes focused on where I thought the sound came from. There, sitting on a stool almost out of view at the end of a huge kitchen range, was a young man who I guessed to be about my own age, eighteen or so. He was smaller than me, had short-cropped hair, a rounded baby face and a mischievous twinkle in his eyes. He was plopping peeled potatoes into a bucket of water.

"Can you speak English?" I asked.

"Yes," said the young man.

"The captain told me you would show me where my cabin is." I said. "He said I would be sharing it with you."

"Yeah, that's right. Come, I take you, what's your name?"

I told him.

"Eric, easy - Eric."

"No, no," I corrected him, "Derrick."

"Ah, Derrick, mine's Olaf."

I followed him down a flight of stairs to the crews' quarters below deck. Our cabin was tiny, one bunk either side of it, with enough space between them for a person to stand. You wouldn't be able to pass each other unless one of you went outside the cabin. It had one blacked-out porthole and two little cupboards fixed to the wall above the bunks. Olaf pointed to one of them.

"You put your things in there."

"I've nothing, only this," I said, taking a small paper bag out of my jacket pocket.

"That's all? Oh well, you can buy anything you want in New York."

"Have you been working on this boat long?"

"I was on this fucking tanker on the way back from the West Indies, with tanks full of oil, when the Germans invaded my country. The captain was told by the British to make for England, but the head office in Oslo instructed him to return to Norway at once. We were all called on deck, and the captain said: 'I will do what most of you want. So put up your hands, all of you who want to go home.' Everyone did, except the cook and the chief engineer, and that was because they had no family. The captain told us in that case, he would make for home. Not to see our families again for the rest of the bloody war was no good."

"But here you are, in England, so what happened?" I said.

"Well, after a lot of radioing back and forth, the captain had us all back on deck again. He looked very angry. He said that if we didn't make for England, a British warship would force us to stop, board us, and take us there anyway. Once there, we would be put in a prisoner-of-war camp. Also, if we didn't stop, they would sink the ship. Now you know why I'm here."

Olaf stared at the floor and remained silent.

I thought to myself, here I am making a fuss about being away for eight weeks, when he might not see his mother, father or girl, for as long as this bloody war lasts. Olaf looked up from the floor. His eyes were a little moist, then with a complete change of expression, he gave me a smile:

"Tonight we go together into Plymouth and have lots of drinks and look for girls, OK?"

"Good idea," I said.

A small, thin, balding man, wearing a white jacket, poked his head into the cabin and looked at me.

"You are the new mess boy?" he said.

"Yes, I am. My name's Derrick."

"Don't worry about your name – you'll be called 'Mess'. And as I am the Chief Steward, you will call me Chief. Come with me and I will show you your duties."

We passed through what I assumed was the crew's dining room, to the other side of the ship, then into a narrow passageway with six doors. Three on one side, three on the other. He walked up and down and knocked on all of them. There was no response from any.

"They must be all ashore." He opened the doors. Turning to me, he pointed to each cabin in turn: "First Mate, Second Mate, Third Mate, Radio Operator, First Engineer, Second Engineer. Every morning, you tidy their cabins, make the bunks up, and polish the floors and all the brass."

"Including Sunday?" I asked.

"The ship doesn't stop just because it's Sunday," he snapped, "anyway you get paid for a seven-day week."

I followed him up to the deck to the officers' mess.

"This is where your officers eat - you keep it clean, OK?" I nodded. "Work starts at six a.m., when you wash up all the plates left by the night-shift, then lay the table for breakfast, which is at seven a.m., serve it, then wash up. Polish the floor and all the brass. After that, go and do all the cabins I showed you. At eleven o'clock you take coffee down to the Engine Room for the Chief Engineer and two men working with him. At noon there's dinner, so before that, you lay and set the table, and make sure that the glasses have a nice shine on them." (I thought to myself you'd think I was working at the Savoy, not on a fucking tanker.) "Then wash up. At two o'clock, take coffee down again to the engine room. You can rest then until six- thirty p.m., when you serve supper, wash everything up and leave it nice and tidy for the night-shift. And that's your day, Mess. Now come with me, and I will give you some jackets that must be worn when you are serving the meals."

We went to his quarters on the bridge, and he handed me a spotless white jacket and black trousers.

"Try that on."

I did, and it was a perfect fit. He gave me another two.

"Wear a clean one of these every day, got it? Lots of trouble from me if you don't. You can be off now until six tomorrow morning."

I left this horrible little man and took myself and the jackets back to my cabin. Olaf was lying on his bunk.

"How did you get on with him?" he asked.

"Not well, didn't like him."

"Don't worry, nobody likes him except the boss."

Then he looked at his watch.

"It's four o'clock, time for coffee."

In the Dining Room, seated at a long dining table, were eight members of the crew. They were all tall, broad-shouldered, and handsome men, most of whom any Hollywood producer would be lucky to have under contract. They were talking Norwegian. At the far end of the table, seated separated from the others, were three men in British Army battle dress. Olaf put his arm on my shoulder and announced to all in English :

"This is Derrick, our new Mess boy."

"Hello, mate," they said in chorus, and then went on drinking their tea out of tin mugs.

One of the soldiers beckoned me over.

"Thank God, you're not another Norgie," one of them said in a low voice. "I'm Alfred, my mates are Ken and Jim, and you're Derrick, is that right?"

These three looked like they were from another planet from the Norwegian sailors. They were small, skinny, and pimply-faced. Looking at them, I couldn't help wondering how they managed to get through the army medical. At a glance I knew they were not my type, and that my friend on this voyage would be Olaf. Alfred handed me a mug of tea, while Ken leant across and whispered in my ear:

"These Norgies hate us, you know!"

"Oh, why?" I said.

"Because they reckon we forced them to leave their country and come over to our side."

"Really?" I remarked. "None of you had anything to do with it, did you?"

"Maybe not," said Ken, "but they hate us just the same."

"They get well paid for their work, the lucky bastards," Jim now chimed in. "All we get is lousy army pay."

"What do you do on board?" I asked. "You're army, not navy."

"We man the pom-poms on the bridge to scare off Jerry planes, and the anti-submarine gun on the aft deck."

"Is this your first trip?" Jim asked. "Dodging the call-up, are you?"

"No, I'm not. I'm not due to be conscripted until I'm nineteen. Have you done many trips before?" I asked.

"No, none of us have, this is our first run."

Alfred wanted to know if I had met the skipper yet. I had I said, but I didn't like him very much.

"Yeah, he's a right bastard, but he's got a nice dog though, and it's real clever, it understands Norwegian."

I thought he was joking, but he wasn't.

"Well," I said, "I'll go and join my cabin mate. See you all tomorrow."

Olaf was back in the cabin. He'd taken off his singlet and shorts, and was wearing a smart suit.

"When you're ready, Derrick, we'll go off to the pubs in Plymouth."

"I'm ready, let's go."

By the time we got there, all the pubs were closed and wouldn't open until five-thirty, so we had an hour to kill. Rubbing his hands together and smiling, Olaf said: "Right, we go and look for girls."

"Where do we start?" I said.

"We just walk about, you'll see."

We did, but didn't see any, as I had expected.

As soon as the pubs opened, Olaf made for the nearest bar.

"What do you drink, Derrick?"

"I don't," I had to admit.

"You don't drink?" he said in a shocked voice. He was obviously unhappy that he couldn't treat me to a pint, so I told him I really would like a lemonade. He ordered himself a pint, then asked for mine. Two or three pints went down his throat in quick succession.

"We aren't allowed to have drink at sea, not a fucking drop. So if you don't have it on land, when the fuck can you? The bloody captain is like you, he doesn't drink, nor does the Chief Engineer. You three should get on really well together. No, on second thoughts, you won't get on with the Chief Engineer because he's an old man, fifty at least, and he can't speak one word of English."

"I don't like people because they drink or don't drink," I said, "I like them or I don't like them."

He nodded slowly, then turned to the bar and ordered yet another pint. By now the pub was crowded, mainly with sailors, all of whom it seemed were intent on getting themselves pissed as quickly as possible. Olaf by now was well under wraps, and whenever I talked to him, he replied in his native tongue. Time for me to leave, I thought.

It was dark outside and what with the blackout, it wasn't easy to see where I was going. Finally I saw a glimmer of light inside two large swing doors. It was the The Playhouse. The show was about to start in a few minutes. 'Variety at its very best' the billboard claimed. So I paid my one shilling and ninepence, and got a ticket.

If today I'd seen performances like I did on that night, I would leave within the first five minutes. However, as it was my last night on England, and could well be my last, I sat through one appalling act after another. The show did, however, distract me from thinking about the lunatic thing I was about to embark on. I could no longer conceal from myself that I was beginning to feel a bit nervous.

The show ended to tremendous applause from a packed house. I left as quickly as possible to avoid the playing of the National Anthem. I found I had two shillings left in my pocket, so I took a cab back to the ship. I was glad I did, for I would never have found my own way to the docks through the blacked-out city.

Once on board, I made my way down to my cabin. Olaf was fast asleep, spread-eagled out fully clothed on his bunk. I carefully removed his shoes and put a blanket over him. Then I got into my bunk and was soon fast asleep, never giving a thought as to how I would wake up in time to start work at six in the morning.

The next thing I felt was a hand on my shoulder. Opening one eye, I saw Olaf bending over me.

"Derrick, you start work in a quarter of an hour!"

I shot out of my bunk and hurriedly dressed.

"What woke you?" I said.

"My alarm clock."

Thank God for that, I thought. As I was leaving the cabin, Olaf reminded me to put on the white jacket before I stepped out onto the deck.

First light was just showing through the grey skies, and the ship was already moving. The coastline had disappeared in the distance. I could have stayed on deck for a long time, looking out to sea and watching the waves curl up along the hull of the moving ship, but my work had to start.

The Officers' Mess looked a shambles. Dirty plates, cups, cutlery, bits of uneaten food, full ashtrays, had been left by the night-shift. All this had to washed up and tidied away, and the table laid for breakfast, before the officers arrived.

On the stroke of seven, they did. They walked through my little space and sat down at the table in the dining room. None of them said good morning nor introduced themselves to me.

I went off next door to the galley to bring in a jug of hot, black coffee.

"Come back and pick up the toast and eggs when you've served that," Olaf said.

When I got back, they were all talking to each other. One of them looked up at me and said: "Mess, the sugar, where's the sugar?"

"Oh, sorry!" I said.

"Sorry, sir," came the snapped reply, "you call all of us officers SIR, understand?"

"Yes, SIR," I said loudly.

I quickly put square little cubes of sugar into a bowl and plonked it in the middle of the table. I don't know why they were in such a rush, because they never put these into the coffee. They would clench one cube between their teeth, and the hot coffee was drunk through the dissolving lump.

I went back to the galley to pick up the six plates of eggs on toast. These I placed on the table in front of each of them, and they started eating, which they did in silence. After another cup of coffee all round, they got up and left without saying a word to me. Unfriendly bastards, I thought. I found out later that unlike their British or American equivalents, there was no fraternising between the officers and the crew. They behaved like little tin gods, going around bawling out orders and expecting to be obeyed immediately. To me, they were all fascists - no wonder they wanted to go home and join the Germans.

After clearing up, I went down below to get some breakfast for myself. Everyone was there, chatting and eating away, including the three soldiers. I sat down opposite Olaf.

"Everything work out all right?" he asked.

"I don't know," I said, "they never said a word to me."

"Oh that's good," he remarked, "if they say anything at all, it's only to complain, so you did all right."

Suddenly, there was the shrill sound of a siren making short blasts. It was deafening. The soldiers jumped up and rushed out making for the deck.

"What's happening, Olaf?"

"Probably an air attack," he said, then added, "it's best if we stay down here, it's safer."

I heeded his advice. I heard the drone of a plane's engine coming nearer and nearer, then the rattle of fire from its guns. Shit, I thought, we've only been at sea for a couple of hours and all this drama is going on. Then our guns on the bridge started up. After a while, all went quiet. Olaf and I continued our breakfast and were joined by the soldiers a few minutes later.

"Chased the bastards off?" I enquired.

"No, we never got anywhere near him. Luckily, two of our planes from the RAF Coastal Command arrived and sent him packing. The bridge took a bit of a bashing though, but no one was hurt. The damage is not too serious, just a few holes in the wheelhouse. It can easily be patched up."

"I bet the skipper's proud of you," I said.

"No, he wasn't, our fire never hit the plane."

"Oh, well, next time you'll get 'em," I said, hoping there wasn't going to be another time. I had a distinct feeling that these soldiers weren't much cop as gunners.

Leaving them to their breakfast, I set off to do all the six cabins in my charge. All of them were very untidy. I think they were making sure I had plenty to do. Olaf had told me that officers in the Norwegian Merchant Navy seldom came up from the crew. They all left their cosy homes at the age of fifteen or sixteen to become cadets in the Mercantile Marine College. There they were taught how to be arrogant ship's officers and, as I later had to admit, good sailors.

To clean up one cabin is tedious, to clean up six is six times more tedious. Their bunkbeds were covered with a kind of fluffy eiderdown, the like of which I had never seen before so I started to look in all the cupboards for the top sheet and blankets. In the end I just threw the eiderdown thing on top of the bed. I found later that it was the right thing to do and these fluffy things were called duvets.

At eleven o'clock, it was time to take the coffee down to men in the engine room. When I opened the door, the noise that met me was deafening, and once inside, it took me some time before my eyes got used to the dim electric lights. I found I was standing on a little platform from where three long flights of steep, oily metal steps led into the bowels of the ship. Going down these for the first time was very unnerving.

Huge oily pistons, many feet high, were going up and down continuously. Holding a tray in one hand, and gripping the safety rail tightly with the other, I slowly descended. Those giant rods exuded some inexplicable magnetism, which made me feel I was being pulled towards them. It was the sort of feeling you have when standing on a high flat roof, and it seems something is drawing you nearer and nearer to the edge. Very relieved, I got to the bottom where an engineer was sitting at a grimy little desk looking up at a panel of big and small gauges, and writing down their readings in a logbook.

"Thank you, Mess," he said shouting above the din, "put the tray down there." He pointed at a stool. I did and then made my way up those terrifying stairs. Back in the daylight and the peace of the deck, I looked across at the bridge and saw the damage done by the German plane. It was already being patched up. The sea was very calm and we seemed to be going at full speed, probably to leave the English Channel and German dive-bombers well behind us as quickly as possible. It was eleven forty-five, time to go and get lunch ready.

On the stroke of twelve, they all filed in and sat down at the table. The first course was a soup made out of dried fruits. At first I thought I had been given this in the galley by mistake; surely this was meant to be the dessert. But Olaf assured me it was OK. Weird lot, these Norwegians, I thought. As at breakfast, they didn't talk while eating, only between courses or at the end of the meal. Once again, I didn't exist except as a robot. With lunch over, and everything washed up and put away, my time was my own until three p.m., when it would be time again to do that terrible run with the coffee down to the engine room.

I sat on the deck, and looked out to sea. The sky was overcast, a gentle wind was blowing and for the first time I understood why sailors got so attached to their way of life. At sea you have the feeling you've left the world behind and you're in a little world of your own. One big snag - no girls. Living with just men can, I found out, get unbelievably boring.

Olaf came and sat beside me.

"The captain told me we were going to cross the Atlantic in convoy with other ships. Do you know where we meet up with them?" I asked him.

"In Scotland, where the Clyde meets the sea. We will be there early tomorrow."

Well, at last I now knew where we were making for.

"When does the convoy leaves?"

"Straight away, they are waiting for us to arrive."

"No time for us to go ashore then?"

"No, no. Next time you put foot on land will be New York. We will be there for a few days, because we are going into dry dock to have the hull scraped, then we load up with crude oil to bring back to Glasgow." He gave a yawn, "I'm going down for a sleep."

"See you later," I said.

Three o'clock, time again for the dreaded coffee run. I learned something useful on my second trip down, by watching one of the 'grease monkeys' (the name for the men in the engine room) as he ran easily up and down those slippery steps carrying an oil can. You don't face forward, but go up and down sideways. I tried this, and it was much better. It also took some of my fear away.

I had nothing to do now until supper, so I thought I would do the same as Olaf, and go to the cabin for a little lie-down. Olaf was lying on his bunk facing the cabin wall. He was crying very quietly.

I sat on the edge of his bunk and put my hand on his shoulder.

"Olaf, what's the matter?"

He turned on his back, tears rolling slowly down his cheeks, and said:

"I miss my parents and Toni."

"Is Toni your brother?"

"No, she's my girl and ..." he buried his watery eyes in my arm.

"Cheer up, Olaf, I'm sure the war will be over soon and you'll be able to go back home. When we're in New York, we'll go and get ourselves a whole lot of beautiful girls. I mean, a couple of good-looking lads like us can't fail, can we?"

This seemed to do the trick, as he sat up and dried his eyes on his vest.

"Yeah, we will do that, Derrick!"

He pulled a photograph out of his wallet, "That's my girl, Toni."

"She's lovely, Olaf. How old is she?" I asked.

"Same as me, eighteen."

He took the photo out of my hand and returned it carefully to the wallet. He laid down on his bunk and was soon asleep. I did the same.

Waking up a couple of hours later and feeling refreshed, I saw that I was alone. Olaf, I assumed, must have gone off to the galley to help the cook prepare supper, which reminded me that I had better go and do the same.

At six -thirty on the dot, in they came, gobbled silently away, then left. I did my chores and by seven-thirty my working day was over. Pausing on the deck for a moment and looking into the total blackness of the night, I decided that I'd go down to the crew's mess and see how the rest of the evening was passed away.

Some were playing darts, while others played cards or dominoes. One man was darning his sock. The English trio were sitting as usual apart from the rest, reading some old magazines, so I joined them.

"Apart from the little drama this morning," I asked Alfred, "how was your day?"

"Our day?" he repeated. "Like every day is spent, doing absolutely nothing."

"Cosy number," I said, then thinking, no wonder I get paid more than they do.

"Yeah, that's why we volunteered for it," said Jim. I knew that my first impression of these three was correct - they were boring. I noticed that Alfred had one stripe on his sleeve, and pointing to it, I remarked: "So you're the boss."

"No one's the boss," Ken piped up, speaking to me for the first time, "not even the captain. Our bosses are on land and far away, thank God!"

I asked them what they had been doing in civvy street before the war. Alfred, it seemed, had been a bank clerk. Jim had worked in a men's wear shop and Ken was an unemployed labourer.

"What were you doing before you came on this lark?" asked Jim.

"Oh, bumming around," I mumbled. I just couldn't be bothered to tell them everything that had happened to me in the last two years. I left them with their heads buried back into the magazines and joined Olaf who had finished playing cards, and we had a game of dominoes until it was time to hit our bunks.

I lay on mine hearing only the hum of the ship's engines as I dropped off to sleep. I was awakened by the sound of Olaf's alarm clock. He and I had a tacit agreement that there was to be no talking until we had breakfast.

At dawn on deck, I saw for the first time what this convoy business was all about. Ships of all sizes and shapes, about thirty or so, were spaced some yards apart, stationary. Flanking the convoy on either side were three cruisers, with two corvettes at the rear, all of them painted in light battleship grey. A lot of signals were being flashed from one boat to another. I think they were being told by the captains of the cruisers what position they were to take up when the convoy moved off. Although a pacifist with no liking for the activities of war, I had to admit to myself that I was witnessing an impressive sight.

The Morse code between the ships stopped. Standing by the open door of the engine room, I could hear the bell that was the signal for the ship's engines to start up. I now realised what the captain meant about going the pace of the slowest ship: we were moving at less than half the speeds of the two previous days. The next few hours were taken up with the manoeuvres needed to get every boat in the position it was to hold for the crossing of the Atlantic. At daylight I could see the coastline of Northern Ireland, and when that faded, there was nothing to look at but the vast grey ocean, stretching out as far as one could see before merging with the clouds. You were never quite sure where one ended and the other began.

The daily routine never varied. However, after a few days at sea, I tried to get the snooty lot I looked after to call me by my name instead of just "Mess". I borrowed a dictionary from Alfred, and showed it to the Second Engineer. The dictionary explanation for 'Mess' was 'a dish of soft, pulpy or liquid stuff; pulpy or smeary dirt; a mixture disagreeable to the sight or taste; to befoul'. There was more, but I felt I'd made my point.

"So you see, sir, that's why I'd rather be called by my name - Derrick."

"I've understood everything you're saying, the dictionary is right, it describes what you are perfectly. So now you can fuck off, Mess, and get on with the washing up."

That's it, you bastard, I thought, and from then on I only did what was absolutely necessary, and moved and behaved as much like a robot as possible.

Another little incident occurred to break up the monotony after about ten days into the crossing. It was my afternoon break period, and I was sitting on my bunk, when all of a sudden, there was a God-Almighty bang, and something whizzed past my right ear and embedded itself in the cabin floor. I looked up at the ceiling and saw that a sizeable hole had appeared. Christ, I thought, it's another air attack, then realised it couldn't be: we were too far out in the Atlantic for German planes to attack us. Moments later, Ken came rushing in.

"You all right, Derrick?" he panted.

"Yeah, what's going on?" I asked.

"I don't know how it happened, I was cleaning one of the pom-pom guns when it suddenly went off. A shell must have been left in the breech."

"It very nearly blew my head off, Ken!"

"Jesus, Derrick, I'm really sorry," he said apologetically.

At that point, the First Mate appeared at the cabin door.

"What the fuck's happened?" he asked.

Almost inaudibly, Ken told him.

"You idiot!" he shouted, "Come with me to the captain."

Even though Ken had nearly killed me, I couldn't help but feel a bit sorry for him.

When he returned, he looked pale. The captain, it seems, had nearly blown his head off without the use of a bullet. He was going to put the incident into his log and Ken would be reported to his regiment when the ship got back to England.

"I'll probably be court-martialled," he reflected.

"Oh well, Ken, there are some weeks to go before we're back, and by then the whole thing may have been forgotten."

"Not much likelihood of that," he sighed.

CHAPTER THIRTY-TWO

Day followed day without any more dramas, and time started to drag. Cruisers escorting us sometimes went ahead and sometimes dropped behind in search of U-boats. The sea remained calm, and the clouds stayed grey. I was told by one of the sailors that we were now somewhere near Iceland, which was a huge detour but he said that by doing that we were almost out of range of subs. From Iceland we would make our way to the Canadian coastline, and hugging it from Newfoundland down to Halifax, Nova Scotia, and from then on we'd take the most direct route to New York.

When we got near to Canada, some cargo ships left us to make their way to other ports. Our Royal Naval escort made for Halifax to bring another convoy back to England. You really had to admire those chaps going back and forth across the dangerous Atlantic, month after month, and as it turned out, year after year.

When they had gone, we were left to fend for ourselves. There was, however, one compensation: no more need for blackout. Now we could leave our portholes open at night, and light a cigarette on deck.

The grey clouds that had been our canopy since leaving England rolled back. At last, we could bask in the sun and see blue skies reflected in the sea below. One morning on deck, on what was by now my twentieth day at sea, the coastline of Long Island became visible as the dawn broke. I was so excited that I nearly forgot to serve the officers their breakfast. When I had served it, I was back on deck taking in all the sights as they came into view. I ran from one side of the ship to the other, always looking and looking. Suddenly, this whole trip seemed worthwhile.

At the mouth of the Hudson, we stopped to let a small launch come alongside. A rope ladder was thrown down to a man standing in it. It turned out, he was to pilot our ship up river to the New York docks. I crossed the deck to get a good look at the first American I'd ever seen. At close quarters, he was a bit of a disappointment, he looked nothing like Gary Cooper or Cary Grant.

Fortunately the rest of the journey was in my afternoon break, so I was able to see everything. All the landmarks I had only seen at the pictures, became a reality: the Statue of Liberty, and the skyscrapers that were themselves dwarfed by the Empire State building. After going under Brooklyn Bridge, our engines were shut down and the ship stood still. Three tugs came out, one took us in tow, the other two nudging us from the stern.

We finally docked at Pier 5 in Bethlehem docks. Our ropes were thrown to the stevedores on the quayside, and they secured us to the pier. Two huge iron gates closed behind us, and the water we were floating on gradually drained away, leaving us literally high and dry. Work on scraping our hull was due to begin the next day.

When the gangplank was lowered, three men came aboard. Two of them were in smart uniforms, they were the immigration officers; the other man, who was short and tubby, was in a suit. He turned out to be the port's medical officer. Orders came through that all the crew were to assemble in the ship's Officers Lounge. We were told to bring all our documents with us. The only piece of paper that I had was my wartime Identity Card. As I had left in such a hurry, there had been no time to get seamen's papers. I joined the queue outside the lounge, we were allowed in one by one. After a long wait it was my turn. The immigration officers sat at a table, and with them the captain. One of them looked up at me:

"Papers," he said.

I handed him my Identity Card.

"What's this?" he asked.

"It's all I have, sir," I told him.

"It's no good, sailor, can't let you ashore with that."

I was crestfallen. Thank God the captain intervened and explained the hurried circumstances under which I had signed up.

"OK," said the other officer (who turned out to be an official from the British Consulate), "I'll give him a temporary seaman's Identity Certificate."

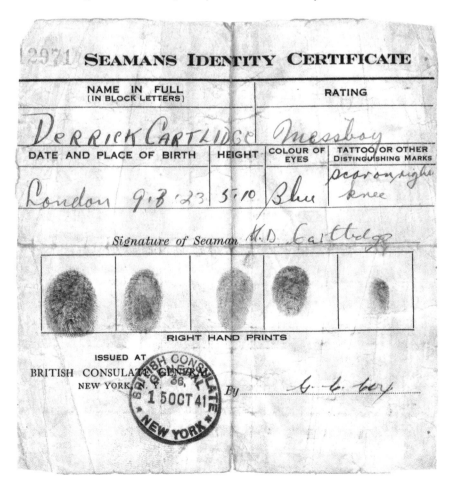

He filled in my name, then asked for my right hand. Finger by finger he pressed them onto a pad and then onto the paper.

"Have that with you whenever you're ashore."

He pointed to the other side of the Lounge:

"Go and see the doctor."

He was slouched in a chair, his arms folded across his fat belly. When I was about three feet away from him, he snapped: "Stop there! Pull it out!"

I didn't understand what he was asking me to do.

Then, with some irritation: "Your cock, boy."

So I did.

"Foreskin."

I looked blankly at him.

"Pull your foreskin back."

I obliged.

"OK, boy, you can go," and he waved me away.

To this day I don't really know what he was looking for.

As I stepped out of the room, Olaf was waiting to go in.

"All right, Derrick?"

"Only just," I said.

"Now comes the good bit," said Olaf. "Wait for me and we'll go to the radio officer to get paid. One thing, Derrick, when you're asked how much sub you want, say a hundred dollars."

"That on top of the pay I'm due?"

"Yeah, always owe them, not they owe you, so if you're blown sky high on the way back, they won't owe you anything, get it?"

We made our way to the radio officer's room. He peeled off three one-hundred dollar bills and three single dollars from a stack neatly piled on his desk.

"These two are the wages, and this one is the sub, sign here please."

I didn't have a clue how much I had been given, not having seen a dollar before. I didn't have the slightest idea of their value, nevertheless I felt rich. I had to wait until I had served supper before I could go ashore. On the way down to my cabin, I bumped into the English gunners.

"Going ashore, Derrick?"

"Yes," I replied, then thought, I don't want to spend the evening with you lot. They were forever moaning about how much I was being paid compared to them. I suspected their idea was to sponge on me for the five days or so that we would be in New York.

"Olaf and I are going to visit some of his Norwegian relatives," I lied.

"OK, see you about then," they shouted as they made their way to the gangplank.

Olaf was sprucing himself up to go ashore. He looked very smart in his light brown suit, clean white shirt and brown tie. For the last three weeks, he had only worn a blue singlet and shorts, and walked about barefoot.

"Shall we go looking for girls, Olaf?"

"I can't, Derrick, I promised I'd go with a mate to visit one of his relatives."

My lie to get rid of the soldiers turned out to be true after all. It seemed all the crew had relatives or friends in New York, as more Norwegians lived there than in the whole of Oslo.

"We go out together tomorrow, OK?"

"Yeah, tomorrow," I said, a little disappointed.

I shaved, then brushed and combed my hair. No need to put on any fine clothes like Olaf; I hadn't got any. In seconds I was down the gangplank and stepped onto American soil for the first time. The huge arc-lights illuminating Bethlehem docks turned night into day. The whole area, as far as the eye could see, was a hive of activity. Men working round the clock were hurriedly knocking together the Liberty ships, so urgently needed by Britain to replace those sunk by the U-boats. The sheer scale of this enormous undertaking made Plymouth docks look like a sideshow. I walked around a while, marvelling at it all, before making my way to the dock gates. A few yellow cabs waiting outside.

"Where to, bud?" said the driver.

"Times Square, please."

Driving through the brightly lit streets of New York was like fairyland compared to blacked-out London.

After a twenty minute journey, the driver said: "Times Square, Bud."

I looked at the meter. it read '75'. Fuck me, I thought, that's already goodbye to one of my 100-dollar notes. I handed him a 100-dollar bill and was just about to say "keep the change", when he asked:

"Haven't you got anything smaller?"

I remembered the three one-dollar bills I'd been given.

"Only ones."

"OK, Bud, that's fine."

I held out all three, but he only took one, then to my surprise, he offered me some change.

"Oh no, please keep that," I spluttered.

I now knew one dollar equalled a hundred cents and the meter read seventy-five cents, of course. Christ, was I relieved to find that out. I stepped out of the cab into the square, fortified by the knowledge that as far as money went, I was still rich. I walked around this exciting city for a couple of hours, ending up in a huge bar called Dempseys, owned by the famous ex-world champion boxer. Large pictures of him in various pugilistic poses were plastered all over the walls. A massive mahogany bar in the shape of a horseshoe was packed with people sitting on high stools, talking loudly. After a long search, I managed to find a seat at one of the tables. Eventually, a waitress arrived, chewing gum, just stared at me without saying a word. Finally it dawned on me I should tell her what I wanted.

"A cup of tea, please."

"No tea, only drinks."

"Lemonade?" I said hopefully.

Very quickly, she was back with my drink and immediately held out her hand, wanting instant payment.

I sat there sipping away and soaking up the unfamiliar atmosphere of the place, when the houselights dimmed and a spotlight beamed onto a small stage. A man in tails sat ready to accompany her on a miniature grand piano. A sleek blonde in evening dress, resembling Veronica Lake, sang a popular song of that time 'I don't want to set the world on fire', accompanied by a man at a grand piano. She got a rapturous applause from the audience. It went through my mind, that she should be sent to Berlin and sing that song to Hitler. Who knows, the lyrics just might persuade him to have second thoughts about setting all Europe alight.

When the applause stopped, a big man who looked like a gorilla in an evening dress, came over to me: "Want another drink, Bud?"

"No, thanks," I said.

"Then, fella, it's time to beat it."

I had the distinct feeling, that if I didn't go at once he'd have picked me up by my arse and slung me head first out of the door.

The shops in New York were all open until past midnight. I took the opportunity to buy some white shirts, vests, underpants, and three pairs of blue slacks, clothes were rationed at home. For my Betty, I got six pairs of nylon stockings and a selection of pretty underwear.

After that, I was getting really hungry, and for the first time in my life ventured into a Chinese restaurant. I had not the slightest idea what to order, the only Chinese dish I'd ever heard of was chop suey. It came slopped all on one plate, and looked like something the dog had brought up. I didn't eat it, just paid and left. Still very hungry I found a café called a drugstore, where I stuffed myself with cheese sandwiches, followed by the best ice cream I'd ever eaten.

By now it was midnight, and I was still not far from Times Square. I was thinking it was time for me to return to the ship, when I saw a neon sign flashing away 'GIRLS, GIRLS, GIRLS, a continuous performance. That's for me, I thought. Once in, a very pretty usherette showed me to a seat, and I sank into it, glad at last to sit down. I had by then been on the move since six o'clock in the morning.

In the orchestra pit was a small but very loud band and when the curtain rose, a bevy of scantily dressed chorus girls appeared, all about six foot tall, with very long legs which they kicked high into the air. They were all big-busted and endowed with amply upholstered bottoms which they waggled at the audience, who responded by shouts of appreciation.

The more comfortable I got in my seat, the harder I found it to keep my eyes open. Very shortly, I was sound asleep, only to be occasionally woken up when the crowd screamed their approval. With half open eyes, I peered through narrow slits at bouncing bosoms, waggling bottoms and high-kicking legs. Then I'd drop off again. This happened a few times. It was a sort of pleasant nightmare.

The next thing I was aware of was a hand shaking my shoulder.

"Come on, bud, the show's over."

He was the doorman. With the lights on, I saw that the theatre had emptied out and I was the only one there.

"Sorry," I said sleepily.

"That's OK. Goodnight."

I stumbled out through the foyer into the street. A clock on a building read 3.00 a.m. Jesus, I thought, at this hour I'll never get a cab. But this was New York, not London, and one picked me up in seconds. It was nearly four when I climbed on board. Having had such a short night, I got through the next day like a zombie. Nobody seemed to notice. Perhaps like me, they were sleepwalking.

The next few nights out on the town, I had Olaf's company. I think we visited most of the bars between Brooklyn and New York, always ending up in some nightclub that specialised in taxi-dancing. The drill was, you ordered a drink at the bar, then went over to the dance floor and picked a girl you fancied. At a pay desk, you bought a ticket for one dance. Olaf was a good dancer, and I think the girls didn't mind being with him. But I had never danced before, so after treading on my partner's toes a few times, she took my hand and led me off the floor, put me on a chair, then sat on my lap and put her arms around me. We cuddled and kissed until the music stopped. I reckoned I had a better deal than Olaf. These taxi-girls were the nearest I or any of the crew ever got to a woman.

One evening, New York had an air-raid rehearsal. Everything was blacked out. The only difference from the real thing in London was that all the traffic came to a halt and even car lights were switched off. Who, I wondered, did they think would attack them from the air? German planes could hardly bomb the north of Scotland, yet alone cross the Atlantic, drop their load and return to base. While this nonsense was going on, I stood in a doorway, pulled out a cigarette and struck a match. Two men wearing armbands rushed over to me and screamed: "Put that light out, put that fucking light out!"

In my very best English accent, I told them that if I could smoke in the streets of London, that had real air-raids and was having the shit bombed out of it night after night, there was no reason I couldn't do it in this mock one. They seemed to get my message, because they disappeared without another word.

One day, while working on board, an American (who I guessed to be three or four years older than me) started to talk to me. He told me he was training to be a docks manager, and this was the first job he'd had since leaving college. After a little chat, he invited me to a party at his parents' home that evening. I accepted. He wrote out the address of his home in Brooklyn.

"It's only a short way from the docks. Still, it's best to take a taxi. See you about eight then."

I put on a new shirt, a new pair of slacks, and gave my shoes a shine, all in honour of a visit to an American home. The cab pulled up in a long avenue of quite large wooden houses. Unlike England, the front gardens had no hedges.

I walked up the garden path and knocked on the front door. My host opened it and I entered into a large hall. By the noise I could hear, the party was in full swing.

"Have you left your jacket in the taxi?" he enquired.

"No, I haven't got one."

"Oh, oh well, well err…. Derrick, at a party, a jacket and a tie is what people wear."

I realised I had made a mistake coming here and was about to say that I'd better leave when he guided me into a small side room and started to fumble around inside a big wardrobe. He took out a jacket and tie.

"Try this for size. I'm about your build."

The jacket fitted. It had a herringbone pattern, the sort of thing I wouldn't normally be seen dead in. The tie didn't match anything else I had on, but that seemed of no consequence. Dressed like this and feeling completely out of place, I followed him into a big room full of people in little groups, chatting away. My host introduced me to some of them.

"This is Derrick. He is from London, England."

Their response was nearly always the same. 'Hi' or 'Oh England', then they would turn their backs on me and carry on talking to their friends. I thought that I'd be bombarded with questions like 'How are you Londoners bearing up to the air-raids?' 'When do you think you will open up the second front?'. A woman did ask me: "How are your King and Queen managing? It must be terrible for them."

I assured her that they somehow coped, living as they did in Buckingham Palace and looked after by a depleted complement of butlers and servants. I told her, that they did occasionally visit the very poor and bombed-out people of the East End. It was very comforting for them, when they crawled out from under the rubble that was once their pitiful home, to find their King and Queen giving them a royal wave from their Rolls-Royce as they drove by.

"I have the feeling you don't approve of them very much," she said.

"I couldn't tell you whether I approve or disapprove. I've never met them, and I'm never likely to."

An Englishman who talked like that about his monarchy was too much for her, so she turned her back on me as well. My host, who, I think, was beginning to regret having invited me, walked me over to a couch where an officer of the American Merchant Navy was sitting. I was introduced as the Second Engineer on a tanker. Having given me this rapid promotion, he left to join his other guests.

"What tonnage is she?" asked the man.

I had absolutely no idea about anything technical to do with the boat, I hadn't even worked out yet which was 'port' or 'starboard'. So I said the first number that came into my head.

"17,000 tons," I said, hoping that would impress him.

"Oh, she's small. Diesel or coal?"

Well, I knew it wasn't coal, because I had seen no sign of it down in the engine room. so I said: "Diesel." Then, to change the subject, I asked:

"Do you think your country will enter the war soon?"

"Oh no, I don't think we will, not our fight really."

I was reassured by his answer. After all that was why I was here, to find out the possibilities of staying in a neutral America.

"It's ten o'clock," I said, "I must be off, got an early start in the morning," and with that I sneaked out of the room, remembering to leave the jacket and tie in the cloakroom.

No taxi came down the road, so I ended up having to walk two miles back to the docks. On my arrival there, lying flat out on the pavement by the iron railing surrounding the docks, were Olaf and the cook, paralytically drunk. I found out later they had been dumped there by a taxi-driver, who by way of a reward for his efforts had relieved them of all their money. As the cook was quite an old man, I picked him up first, put him over my shoulder and carried him up the gangway to his cabin where I laid him out on his bunk. Then I did the same for Olaf.

Judging by the bruises on Olaf's swollen face, and the bloodstains all over his white shirt, I guessed they had been in a brawl in some bar. But, as we were moving to the refinery up river in the morning, to fill our tanks with oil for England, I knew that they would have plenty of time to recover.

At dawn, water came gushing into our dry dock, and we were soon afloat again. The pilot came aboard and tugs nosed us away from the pier out into midstream. When our engines took over, we made our way to the refinery unaided. Huge tubes were swung across the deck and screwed into inlets. Pumping in the oil took all the rest of that day and well into the night.

When I woke in the morning, we had left the refinery and were once again moving along the coastline of Long Island, stopping only for a short while to let the pilot off. Now it was full speed ahead for the open sea. Our destination was Norfolk, Virginia, where a convoy was to assemble.

On arrival there, we weighed anchor about a mile offshore, and waited for the rest of the cargo ships to arrive. It became apparent that we were going to be a small convoy, about fifteen boats in all, escorted by only one destroyer. This didn't bother me, because all I cared about was that we were soon setting off for England. I was now beginning to feel homesick and wanted to see Betty, Uncle and my friends again. I had, after all, done what I set out to do: find out if New York was a suitable place to sit out the war. With its mixture of people from all over the world, I was sure that a few of us Soho bums could be easily lost in that hustle and bustle.

In a few hours we moved off, leaving the safety of the American waters behind. The first day or two at sea was always the same: the crew getting over hangovers and licking the wounds they had received in punch-ups. When they all felt better, the normal daily routine was once again established.

We were only nine days away from England when Olaf gave me some very bad news. He said we'd been ordered to leave the convoy and make for Iceland, where we would join another convoy going to Archangel.

"Christ, NO!" I bellowed.

"By the time we're in the Barents Sea, it will be late December, and the ice-breakers will have to cut a way through for us," said Olaf, "Well, at least there won't be any U-boats to worry about!"

"I don't give a fuck about U-boats, I only signed on to go to New York and back, that's all."

Olaf reminded me that he undertook to go to the West Indies and back, and should have been away for about six weeks. Now - eighteen months later - he still wasn't home yet.

Then, rather thoughtlessly, I remarked: "Your fucking country is occupied by the Germans, mine isn't."

"The way the war's going at the moment, it may well be occupied by the time we've been to Russia and get back to England."

Saying that, he got his own back on me for being so insensitive.

"Sorry, Olaf, it's just that I'm so pissed off."

"It's all right, Derrick, I know how you're feeling."

It was in the first days of December 1941, that we dropped anchor in a bay about forty miles from Reykjavik.

A few hours later a mantle of snow covered the ship. The bay was a bleak-looking place, surrounded on three sides by now extinct volcanoes. Their lava had turned into smooth slopes leading straight down to the icy sea. There was not a tree to be seen in this barren, snow-covered landscape.

The day after we had arrived in this God-forsaken place, an American cruiser came alongside and tied up to our seaward side. A plank was put between us so that it became possible to visit each others' quarters. They lived like kings compared with us. They had better and more varied food, nicer cabins, larger rooms for recreation and even a small cinema. At night, the cruiser was all lit up, even the masts. It looked like a giant floating Christmas tree. We, on the other hand, being at war, maintained our total blackout.

I was standing on deck one evening (it was 7 December, to be exact), when all the lights on the cruiser suddenly went out. I could just make out the silhouette of a sailor standing on deck.

"Excuse me," I shouted, "blown a fuse, have you?"

"It's no fucking fuse, Limey. We've joined your fucking war. The Japs have bombed our fleet in Pearl Harbour and sunk a lot of our Pacific Fleet."

"But surely, the Japs won't have any of their warships or aircraft anywhere near here, so why are you blacked-out?"

"Because it looks like we're about to declare war on Germany as well!"

"Now you're in, I don't suppose it will last long. You know, like the last war."

"Fucking hope so," he said, as he left the deck. I hadn't a clue where Pearl Harbour was, nor did I care. But what did become painfully obvious was that now

America had entered the war, all our plans and hopes had become a pipe-dream - my trip was a total fuck-up.

By the morning, the cruiser had gone, no doubt to do battle with their new-found enemy. We were once again all by ourselves in this dreary place.

Christmas came and went, with still no sign of movement. By mid-January, I began to feel like a caged animal. Although land was less than a quarter of a mile away, there was no way of getting to it. In any case, those bleak and cold mountains didn't look at all inviting. To add to the frustration and boredom of being stuck in limbo, food rationing was introduced. In America we had taken on enough supplies to get us to England. The Icelanders needed their own food and couldn't spare us any.

I wrote in a letter to Uncle that one night for supper, there was only tinned meat and mustard. As I never ate meat, I had mustard.

One day, the Chief Steward told me that the captain wanted me to take his dog ashore to give it some exercise.

"Christ, we'll both freeze to death," I complained.

"Well," he said, "you go and tell him that you won't do it."

Preferring to face death by exposure rather than face the captain, I said grudgingly: "OK, I'll do it."

Olaf lent me a heavy winter coat and some fur-lined shoes. Fully equipped, I presented myself on the bridge. The dog didn't know me at all, but unfortunately took an instant liking to me.

"Give him a good walk for an hour," said the captain.

Why doesn't he take his own bloody dog for 'walkies'? I thought.

A sailor lowered a small boat into the near-freezing water, and with the dog under my arm, I climbed down a rope-ladder into it. I was dropped off at a little jetty. As the sailor sped away, he told me he'd pick us up in about an hour.

Christ, one hour in this icy wind! I was sure it would end up with both of us frozen to death. As the dog had spent most of his life curled up nice and snug on cushions in the skipper's cabin, I think it was even more uncomfortable for him than me. He hated the snow and wind which seemed to be blowing right through both of us. Walking was the only way of staying alive, so up the snow-covered hills we went. I was amazed that he followed me, but I suppose he'd worked out that I was his only hope of ever getting back to the comfort of the ship. We'd not gone far when I noticed in a dip a battery of anti-aircraft guns, next to three huts. I called out to a British soldier carrying a bucketful of snow: "I say, could I come with you, mate?"

"Sure," he said, and then waited for me to catch up with him.

"What the hell are you doing in this dump?" he asked as we entered the nice, warm Nissen hut.

"I was just about to ask you the same!"

I told him how I came to be there.

Six of them manned the guns. They had to do a four-month duty before being relieved.

"Four months here? Bloody hell, do you ever go into Reykjavik?" I enquired.

"It's forty miles away," said one of them, "and there's no roads to get you there. Even if we could, it would be a waste of time, the Icelanders hate us, they reckon we 'occupied' them."

"What do you mean?"

"It was going to have to be either us or Jerry, and there was no way that we would let Jerry. If they had, the Atlantic would have been theirs and no convoys would have got through with supplies."

"Surely they prefer us to the Germans!" I remarked.

"No, as far as they are concerned, we are a foreign army who took their island by force."

"It's a pity you can't go into town sometimes, you know, drinking, dancing and girls."

"Even if we could, there'd be no girls," he complained.

"There must be girls in a town as large as Reykjavik."

"Oh, there are, but if they're seen going out with an Englishman they are treated like collaborators, and have their hair shorn off."

"Jesus Christ!" I exclaimed.

I was given a big mug of tea, so I stayed on and chatted with them for a bit.

I left this unhappy band of men to be on time to meet the boat. The volcanic ash made the ground very springy beneath the snow; it felt like walking on rubber foam. The dog and I could take huge leaps into the air, and land softly many feet down the mountainside. After a few jumps, we were back down by the jetty where the boat was waiting for us.

I gave the dog back to the Captain.

"Did my dog like his little outing?"

"I think he felt the cold more than I did, sir," I said in the hope that he'd never put his dog through the ordeal again.

On returning to my cabin, Olaf said he had some good news.

"We're not going to Archangel after all."

"Whoopee, Olaf, now we'll be back in England in a few days. That's wonderful news!"

"No, not England."

"Why the fuck not?" I cried.

"Because tomorrow a Russian tanker is coming alongside to take the oil off us, and they will take it up to Archangel themselves. No point in going back to England empty, is there?"

"Are we going to New York?"

"No, to Curaçao."

"Where the fuck is that?"

"The Dutch West Indies, stupid."

"But that's miles away." I complained. "It will take for ever to get there!"

"Yep, but compared with this place, it's paradise, I know, because I've been there."

Paradise or not, I was very unhappy now, knowing that I would be stuck on the boat for many more weeks.

The next day, the Russian tanker arrived and we immediately started to pump our oil into their tanks. Up to now, I had thought that our ship was pretty old and should be soon due for the scrap heap, but compared with this rusty old Russian boat, ours looked brand new. Olaf had told me the Russians had women working on board, and in fact there were more women than men in the Russian crew. Lucky sailors, I thought, but I changed my mind when I saw them. Mostly they were as broad as they were tall, and had weatherbeaten faces. The hard skin on their hands, and the callouses caused by the tough work they did, made one lose all sight of their gender. One had to admire these women. How they would ever get that old crate of a ship to the North of Russia I couldn't imagine, I wouldn't have trusted it to go up the Thames Estuary without breaking down.

After the Russians left, we had to wait another week before it was our turn to go. We were to meet up with a convoy crossing the Atlantic. Having been stationary in this awful bay for some seven weeks, it was good to hear the hum of engines again.

CHAPTER THIRTY-THREE

Out in the open sea, I got my first taste of what it was like to be in rough weather. By the time we met up with the convoy, the storm that was brewing, worsened. The next day, we faced winds that peaked at one hundred miles per hour. It became impossible for the ships to hold their positions in the convoy. I was glad that both the crew and officers were professional sailors, for it was certainly no place for amateurs.

One minute the waves took you up as high as a four-storey house, then down you'd go and a wall of water towered above your head. Most of the time the ship was at a frightening angle, rolling from side to side and front to back. When you were high up on the crest of a wave, you could see for miles in all directions. Although it was terrifying, it was magnificent to feel the power of nature tossing the vessel about like a ping-pong ball. It was awe-inspiring. When you wanted to cross the deck, you had to wait until it was tilted upwards - because if you didn't, one small step could easily turn into a run and send you headlong over the side into the sea, with no hope of getting rescued.

Whenever you had to walk anywhere, you'd end up banging against something or other and after a few days there was no part of your body that wasn't bruised. To lie down on your bunk was only possible provided you were well strapped in, and even then it was hard for your rocking body to get to sleep. Hot meals were abandoned, because the pots and pans wouldn't stay still on the stove long enough. With the exception of coffee, all food was out of a tin and no bread was baked, so all we had were dry, tasteless biscuits.

Under these conditions, the convoy broke up completely. All any of the ships could do was to try and face the hurricane-force winds. One huge cargo ship got perilously near. When it was up on the curl of a wave, it looked like the knife-edge of its bow would come crashing down on our stern as we passed each other, going up and down. I'm sure it would have been possible to touch the other ship with your hand. Finally, after what seemed a very long time, we managed to get ahead of it and breathe again. That cargo boat was the last we saw of any ship, including the Royal Navy, in what had once been a large convoy.

I found out much later on from an old copy of a magazine that the storm was the worst that had hit the Atlantic for a century. It reported that nearly half the vessels of our ill-fated convoy went down, their backs broken in half by the gigantic waves, as easily as dry twigs are snapped between strong hands. None of the crews were saved. Many of those boats were the hurriedly made Liberty ships; the rest were so old that they shouldn't have been at sea at all.

In the bitter cold, the spray from the huge waves froze before landing on the boat. Yet, in those appalling conditions, the crew had to spend most of their time going around breaking up the ice, to stop the ship becoming topheavy. Two crew members were actually washed overboard while hacking the compacted ice off a mast.

Even I had to carry on working as best I could, though by the fifth day I was tempted to give up and retire to my bunk, strap myself in, and sit, or rather lie, out the storm. However, the example set by the rest of the crew kept me going.

The task I dreaded most was the twice-daily journey down to the men in the engine room with their coffee. Going down the three flights on those oily steps while the relentless waves were throwing me about took all my strength. The mighty piston rods, which in normal waters had a consistent rhythm, now went berserk whenever the propellers came out of the water, which happened every fifteen seconds or so as the bow nose-dived into another oncoming wave. Whenever the ship tilted sideways, I was pushed helplessly to within inches of those huge pistons going up and down, seemingly out of control. One had to thank God that somehow those engines did keep going. For as sure as night follows day, if they had stopped we would have capsized within minutes.

One evening, a call came to the galley from the First Mate doing his watch on the bridge. He wanted some hot coffee. Up to then, the furthest I had travelled on deck during the storm was the forty yards from the galley to the Mess. Going to the bridge meant using the long and exposed catwalk half the length of the ship.

"Why doesn't the Chief Steward do it? It's his job, not mine," I said to the cook, forgetting that he didn't speak English. Olaf answered for him:

"He's seasick, Derrick."

"Fuck me, he's been at sea for years, why is he seasick?"

"Not in seas like this, he hasn't."

With Olaf's coat on, I made a pot of coffee and set out on the fearful journey to the bridge. With a one hundred-miles per hour gale blowing, I felt as helpless as a feather in a light wind. The only way to negotiate the catwalk and to stop yourself getting blown overboard was to hook yourself over the rail with the crick of your right arm, gripping your wrist tightly with your left hand. With both my hands used in this manner to secure myself, I had to carry the coffee-pot by its handle clenched between my teeth. Inch by inch I made my way along the catwalk, with the frozen spray thrown up by the sea hitting my face like splinters of glass. Finally I made it to the ice-covered steps leading up to the bridge. One at a time, I pulled myself up on them and entered the wheelhouse. I felt very pleased with myself, having made it, and grateful I hadn't been washed overboard. Rather than face that terrible ordeal again, I thought I would ask if I could stay up there for the night. I poured the coffee into a cup and handed it to the First Mate. He took one mouthful, then spat it out all over the floor.

"Shit, this is SHIT, as weak as piss - take it back and make it strong next time!"

The fucking bastard, I thought! I had risked my life to bring it to him. Inch by inch, I plodded my perilous way back. The return was a little easier as the wind was blowing from behind. Finally I made it back to the galley. Olaf and the cook had gone, so I made another pot - only this time, as requested, very strong. To give it a little extra kick, I took a few cockroaches from the wall and squeezed them one by one into the coffee. Hope it kills the bastard, I thought. Once more, back I went, poured the drink out and handed it to the First Mate. He took a large gulp, then put the mug down.

"Ah, that's better, Mess, you're learning, aren't you?"

"Oh yes, sir, I'm learning all right."

Then, feeling a little happier, I made my weary way back to my cabin and told Olaf what I had done.

"Perhaps, Derrick, you have invented another kind of coffee!" said Olaf.

Upon waking the next day, I took off the straps that had secured me in my bunk for the last seven nights, and stepped onto the cabin floor. To my delight, everything was steady. At last we were in calm waters again.

To stand on deck was a joy. The tremendous winds had subsided, and the sea looked so innocent you would never have believed it was capable of behaving so badly. All there was to worry about now were U-boats - this was perfect weather for them. We were an easy target now, as we didn't have the protection of the Royal Navy.

From now on, it was full speed ahead for Curaçao, with one stop in Norfolk, Virginia, where stores would be taken on again. Food by now was getting pitifully short, and the daily rations, with the exception of coffee, were worse than in England. The routine on board returned to normal and after about ten days we dropped anchor offshore in Norfolk. After the stores were hoisted aboard we set off for the West Indies, where we were due to arrive in about seven days.

With winter hundreds of miles away, it was getting warmer by the day. I spent all my spare time on deck basking in the sunshine. The sea remained like a still lake, only disturbed by the bow of our boat or flying fish when they leapt over its surface. The transparency and blueness of the water was so perfect, you could easily believe the journey to heaven was this way.

In these ideal conditions, the captain decided that the English gunners should have target practice with the anti-submarine gun mounted on the stern. Olaf and I and some of the crew went on deck to watch.

The gunners in their army-issue white shorts that reached down to below their knees were standing by the gun. The captain was by their side. Ken opened a large box that was bolted to the deck, and took out a big shell. He handed it to Jim, who loaded it into the breech. Alfred sat on an iron swivel chair and by turning a small wheel, he lined up the gun sight with the target. Ken attached the lanyard to the firing mechanism, and told the captain that they were ready.

An empty oil barrel was thrown over the side as a target. When it was a few yards away from the boat, the captain shouted:

"GET READY - AIM - FIRE!"

We put our hands over our ears. Ken pulled the lanyard, which promptly snapped in two, leaving a piece in his hand dangling impotently in midair. All of us burst out laughing except the captain, who went red in the face. He got down on all fours and banged his fists so hard on the deck, that it's a wonder he didn't damage it. Then he raised his head and shouted: "You fucking, lazy bastards, for over three months you've been on my ship, doing fuck-all, and in all that time, you haven't even managed to keep your bloody gun in working order. When we get to Canada, I'm going to have you incompetent bastards taken off and put behind bars!"

With that off his chest, he stood up and stumped off. All three looked very downcast. "It wasn't our fault, it was the storms," Ken managed to say. "The seawater must have got into the box and rotted the lanyard." He'd forgotten that they'd had four days in calm water to check the gun and its equipment.

None of us answered him, and with good reason. After all, if a submarine had surfaced, it could have captured our ship and taken us all back to Germany to spend the remainder of the war in a prison camp. This could easily have happened without a shot being fired. Or they could have blown us sky-high. For the rest of the time they were on board, apart from me, no one spoke to them.

In a few days it got so hot that sunbathing became impossible. Whenever I was on deck, I kept well in the shade. At night I took my mattress up and slept under the brilliant stars. Now out of range of any U-boats, we were able to dispense with blackout precautions. At last, we could leave the doors and portholes wide open.

Two days after the incident with the gun, we arrived in Curaçao and docked at the oil refinery, which was three miles from the capital Willemstad. As soon as we had been paid, there was a mad scramble for the gangway. Apart from me when I took the dog ashore in Iceland, no one had set foot on dry land for over three months. That's a long time for young, virile men to go without women or alcohol. I almost pitied the poor people of Willemstad, that this lot was going to be let loose on them.

I walked while the others ran to the perimeter gates of the refinery. Two taxis were waiting there, and as I was the last person needing one, an argument between the drivers broke out about who was to take me. So to settle it, I just got into one of them.

Apart from Paul Robeson films, I'd almost never seen black people before. This lot were as black as coal. It took me a while to get used to them. The countryside I passed through was very hilly and, with the exception of cacti, the scorched earth was barren. Small, obviously hand-built, wooden huts were dotted about the hillsides. They were the size of an average English garden shed. One of them had a door open and I could see inside. It was sparsely furnished, but nevertheless looked clean and tidy.

Paying the driver off in Willemstad ended up with an argument about what the fare. After he'd told me his wife and children would starve to death if I didn't pay up, I yielded to his emotional blackmail.

Willemstad was a busy and bustling small town, cut in two by a river, three hundred yards wide. Connecting one half of the town to the other was a bridge made of flat-bottomed wooden boats, which could be towed to the opposite bank when any ship needed to go upstream. The main street, which faced the river, was full of shops in buildings only one storey high selling souvenirs, native art and hand-made rugs. Along the river banks, junks were moored, tied together. They came up from the centre of the island to sell their produce - bananas and many other kinds of delicious tropical fruits. At the end of the town was a big market place. Lines of low wooden platforms in neat rows displayed a variety of fresh fish. Even the beautiful flying fish that I watched with such joy only the day before, were on offer. The people, I guessed, were for the most part very poor; all the same, they had a happy-go-lucky way of moving about, and always seemed to be smiling or laughing. The men were mostly dressed in spotless white shirts and slacks, while the women wore very colourful dresses. I marvelled at how these women carried heavy parcels and baskets on their heads with such poise and balance.

I went into a very posh-looking restaurant for lunch and was seated at a table placed on a balcony, one floor above street level. A large canopy kept you cool and shaded. The menu was incomprehensible, as it was all in Dutch. A smart-looking waiter, who luckily could speak a bit of English, came to take my order. What I really wanted, was fish and chips. He seemed to understand me.

"And to start, sir?"

I looked blankly at him. So he suggested soup.

"Yes, that's fine," I agreed.

This arrived in a soup plate, with nothing in it but a small bowl, turned upside down in the centre. He lifted it and out poured a brown-coloured liquid, with thin leaves of gold floating on top. I tasted the soup and it was stone-cold, so I beckoned the waiter.

"It's cold!" I complained.

"Yes, sir, it's meant to be."

"...and this gold?"

"Oh sir, very very good for you."

He answered in such a confidence-inspiring way that I ate it. Perhaps in such a hot climate it was usual to serve cold soup. The fish came, not with chips, but fried, sliced potatoes, and was very good.

In the afternoon, I walked around this wonderful town and spent a lot of time watching the swing bridge open and close as boats went through.

When night fell, I decided to go and look for Olaf. He wasn't very difficult to find as the main street had only four cafés, all with their chairs and tables on the pavement. I found Olaf in one of them, sitting at a table with three of the crew and knocking back the local drink, which was named after the country. Curaçao was a strong drink, as potent as vodka, if not more so. He waved at me as I passed and asked me to join him. Although he'd had more than enough to drink, he was still capable of standing upright.

"Come on, Derrick, have a drink!" he said, pouring me one from the half-empty bottle on the table.

I reminded him that I didn't drink alcohol, and ordered a glass of fruit juice from a passing waiter.

"Come on, Derrick, drink it, it will put hairs on your chest!"

I opened my shirt and exposed my hairy chest "See, Olaf, if I drank that stuff, my hair would soon reach down to my knees. Anyway, it can't be true because you haven't any on yours, or for that matter, on your face."

I found out that he had been drinking all day and hadn't eaten anything, so to sober him up enough to last out the evening, I ordered him some sandwiches and persuaded him to eat them. This seemed to work.

"Well, Derrick, it's time to get a girl."

He said it as casually as one might when buying a shirt in a men's wear shop.

"Where do you find one that's not carrying a basket on her head?" I asked.

Olaf pointed down the street.

"Not the next café, but the one after that. They're all there, and you don't have to find one, they find you, and then you go on the mat."

"On the mat? What's that?"

"You go with the girl by taxi to the beach. All taxis carry a straw mat behind the back seat, and the girl lays it out on the sand - and away you go."

"Very easy," I said.

"Yes, it is, and the girls have the rubbers too. It's a good idea to use them!"

"I'll take your advice, Olaf," even though I'd never used one before. We left the café and made for the one down the street. We hadn't gone but two paces when the waiter came running after us.

"You no pay," he shouted. As I'd only had a fruit juice, I let Olaf settle the bill.

"Sometimes it works," he laughed.

The next café was a West Indian version of the Moulin Rouge. Girls in brightly coloured frocks were sitting at the bar and tables, and excepting the officers, the whole crew of our ship were there. A band playing oil drums cut in half banged away on a small stage. Olaf ordered more drinks from the bar, and we sat down at a table.

Two girls, who were sitting on bar stools, started to look over our way.

"Do they know you?" I asked Olaf.

"Don't be silly, of course they don't. They're just working out if we're good for a few dollars."

They must have decided we were, because they got down from their stools making sure that as much of their legs showed through a split in their skirts as was possible. They walked slowly towards our table, swaying their hips as they did.

The next moment they were on our laps. My girl turned to me and ran her hand through my long hair.

"Fuckee fuck," she said.

I found out later, those two words were the only ones in English the girls knew. I turned to Olaf for help.

"What do they charge?"

"Ten dollars for a quick one, and thirty for the night."

I quickly worked out that as it had been so long since I'd been with Betty, it might be cheaper for me to pay for the whole night.

I put my arm round her slim waist.

"Me like to fuckee fuck."

Closing my eyes, I laid my head against my folded hands to let her know it was to be for the night. She, in response to my mime, flicked out both her hands three times. "Yes, thirty dollars," I nodded.

Olaf told me he was on the same ticket.

We stayed on in the café for a little longer as Olaf wanted to have some more drinks. Then we left with the girls, Olaf carrying a nearly full bottle of Curaçao in one hand, and his other on the girl's shoulder to steady himself. I thought, he's never going to last the night without falling asleep, and I reckon his girl had worked that out as well.

The taxi took all four of us the two-mile journey to the beach. The driver spoke some English, so I told him to pick us up at six a.m., as I knew we had to be back on board before our boat left at eight.

The beach had off-white, soft sand. The light breeze blowing was warm, a full moon shone its yellow light onto a calm sea. You couldn't have wished for a more ideal setting. Our girls laid out the straw matting a few yards apart on the sand. I took off my shirt and shorts, and knelt naked on the mat. My girl was facing the sea as she pulled her flimsy flowered cotton dress over her head and dropped it. She wore nothing underneath it, so there she was, standing naked in the moonlight.

I saw her now for the first time. She was about eighteen, five foot tall, with black wavy hair that reached down to her shoulders, and skin the colour of ebony. She turned round and came to kneel down beside me. Her face was small, with big black beautiful eyes, and when she parted her lips, they revealed gleaming white teeth.

She lay down on her back and smiled at me. I lay beside her and buried my head between her firm small breasts. I kissed every inch of her body two or three times. I need not have worried what to do with a rubber, because she took one out of a little packet and put it on for me.

The poor girl had hardly any sleep that night, I just couldn't stop.

When I woke up at dawn, Olaf was standing by the water's edge, with an upturned bottle in his mouth. His girl was still fast asleep on her mat. He told me he had slept all night, and that he was now going to down the rest of the bottle before returning to the boat.

My girl was on her side, also fast asleep, and as I knew the taxi would soon arrive, I gently kissed her out from her slumbers. I'd have given anything to stay on in this small island, with its friendly people and this wonderful girl, for the rest of the war, but real life being what it is, I knew that when my money ran out, the local police would have bundled me onto the next ship leaving the island.

I gave my girl all the money I had (apart from the taxi fare), and it was more than the thirty dollars she had asked for - I'd have given her the shirt off my back if she'd wanted.

When the taxi turned up I went down to the water to fetch Olaf. He was by now lying flat on his back with an empty bottle by his side. I got the driver to help me put him over my shoulder so I could carry him to the taxi. I sat next to my legless friend in the back, the two girls, one on the lap of the other, sat next to the driver. We stopped to let them off in town. After I gave my girl a last kiss and hug, the cab took us to our ship. A lot of cabs arrived at the same time as we did, all carrying members of the crew in the same state as Olaf. I helped the drivers unload their legless cargoes as each cab pulled up. I had them laid out in rows at the bottom of the gangway, then, one by one, carried them fireman's lift-fashion up to the deck and plonked them down wherever I could.

With our tanks now full of crude oil, our boat was ready to leave - in fact, we had to leave as another tanker was waiting to come in.

The problem was, there were now only three sober able-bodied men left to take the ship out - the Captain, the Chief Engineer, and me - the Mess Boy. The Captain took the wheel (which I'm sure he hadn't touched in years), the Chief Engineer started the engines up, while I hopped about the deck throwing off the mooring ropes. Somehow, we made it out to sea.

If an aerial photograph had been taken, it would have shown a tanker going flat out with its crew lying motionless in various positions on deck. As the day progressed, one by one, they came slowly back to life, with only the sea breeze to blow away their horrendous hangovers.

CHAPTER THIRTY-FOUR

All the crew had been cleaned out of any money they had taken ashore. But to the credit of those unaggressive people of Curaçao, none had been beaten up in bar brawls. Olaf's girl had helped herself to all the money he had on him. Still, the same thing had happened to me, the difference being - I had volunteered.

We were now on our way to Halifax, Nova Scotia, to join a convoy that would take us back to England. It took ten days to get there. By now it was late February, and we were back again in deep winter, with temperatures down to well below zero. Our engines needed a major overhaul. I knew we would be stuck in Canada for two or three weeks. Still, I couldn't complain, those engines had kept us going in that terrible storm and thereby saved all our lives.

We were moored about half a mile away offshore. To get to Halifax, we had to go by a small boat that called at all the many ships every evening to pick up any crew wanting to go ashore. The same boat left at eleven p.m. to take you back to your ship. This service was laid on free by the town, but well worth their while, considering all the money we spent there. As I didn't possess an overcoat, I could only go ashore in these freezing temperatures when I could borrow someone else's. Days passed before I set foot in the town.

If a prize were given for the most ugly town in the Western world, Halifax would win it hands down. Apart from the surrounding countryside, with its tall pine trees, there was nothing memorable about the place. At night, the town was like a huge barracks. Aimless packs of army, navy and merchant seamen walked around looking for some sort of entertainment, but they were wasting their time. Apart from the YMCA, and a few sleazy bars that closed at ten p.m., there was only one sizeable café, the Green Lantern, known locally as the Green Latrine, which stayed open till eleven. It had one saving grace - it served the most delicious waffles. But you couldn't spend the whole evening eating those. Girls were thin on the ground, and I suspect that most of them stayed in the safety of their homes, rather than face the drunken morons who staggered about the streets.

Every night without fail, fights broke out between all the different groups. Canadian soldiers laid into the sailors of English Royal Navy and merchant seamen, especially foreign ones like Norwegians or Yanks, and when all of them were drunk enough, they fought amongst themselves. Things got so bad that a rota was worked with the naval captains and the commanding officers of the local barracks, whereby their men were only allowed to go into town on alternate nights.

I disliked the town so much that by eleven o'clock, I was quite happy to take the ferry back to the ship. The ferryman asked each one of us, which ship we wanted to be dropped off at. Mine being the furthest out was the last call. As we got near the *Mosli* he asked if the gangway was port or starboard, and although I had been at sea for many months, I still hadn't worked out which was which. Taking a fifty-fifty gamble, I said "Port". Well, it wasn't. This didn't amuse the boatman one bit.

"Must have changed it," I said limply, as he chugged his way round to the other side. One thing is for certain, I thought, as I climbed back on board, I won't often want to borrow anyone's coat to go to that dump of a town! Olaf and the rest of the crew went ashore most nights, as no drink was allowed on board; their thirst drove them there. Night after night they went through the same routine: shave, groom their hair, and put on their Sunday-best suits. Inevitably they came back with blood all over their clean shirts, and a black eye or a broken front tooth.

After nearly two weeks on board, I needed to stretch my legs, so one Sunday I took the six o'clock boat. On Sunday everything was closed in Halifax except the YMCA. That, of course, served no alcoholic drinks, which made walking about the streets reasonably safe. Large posters all over the town advertised in big letters 'COME AND SEE MARTHA, at the YMCA 7.30p.m. on Sunday, 4 October' and then in very small print 'performed by the Halifax Amateur Operatic Society'. As today was the 4th, and it was now seven, I made my way there. To get out of the cold and be in a warm building for a couple of hours, was very appealing - also, by now, I was craving to hear some good music.

To my surprise, a motley crowd of men had formed a large queue, waiting in the freezing cold outside. When the doors opened a mad scramble ensued to get inside. Most of the men pushing and shoving were twice my size. I was the last in, by which time there was only standing room left. I couldn't believe that this lot were such enthusiastic opera fans.

The lights dimmed, the noisy audience went quiet, and the curtain rose. Everything was fine for the first two or three minutes. Then a big, fat lady came on stage - 'Martha' - the one they had all come to see. Well, when they saw her, pandemonium broke out. A stampede for the only exit started, chairs went flying in the scramble. At this point, the stage director jumped up onto the stage.

"Stop!" he shouted, "These people have worked hard to entertain you tonight!"

"Fuck off, you cunt!" was amongst the more polite retorts he got back from the fleeing audience.

If there had been a raging fire, the auditorium couldn't have been emptied quicker. In the end, the only ones left, apart from myself, were half-a-dozen officers and a few friends of the cast. When the final curtain came down, we few that remained clapped as loud as we could.

Back on the boat, I teased Olaf about what he had missed.

"Martha," I said, "was a gorgeous girl doing a wonderful, sexy dance, driving the audience mad waggling her hips as she pranced about, dressed in a grass skirt."

"I wish I'd come with you, Derrick. I'll go and see her tomorrow."

"You can't, I'm afraid, this evening was the only performance."

The engineers were making good progress overhauling the motors, so it seemed likely that we would be able to go with the next convoy due to leave in a few days. Two days before we were to move off, I went ashore for the last time to have a waffle at the Green Lantern, but couldn't get in as it was packed with customers all waffling away. Instead, I made for the only other café I knew of. This was a small, one-room affair up a rickety flight of stairs. With all its faults, it was a lot better than freezing to death in the street. The place was almost full, but I managed to find a seat at a table where a small Royal Navy sailor was sitting. I asked him if the other seat was free.

"Och aye, sit ye down, mate."

He told me he was on a cruiser on convoy duty, and he would be leaving for home in a couple of days.

"I'll be sailing with you, I'm on a Norwegian tanker, the *Mosli*."

"The Navy will see that you get home safely, have no fear," he assured me.

Just then, a huge American sailor walked over to our table. He was well over six feet.

"Fucking limeys, are you?"

My little Scottish acquaintance stood up to his full height (which was five foot nothing):

"I'm Scottish and proud of it, you lanky Yankee pisspot." And he pulled back his arm and with all his strength banged his fist as high as he could reach straight into the American's balls. The American doubled up and reeled backwards, obviously in great pain. When he recovered, he picked up the Scotsman with as much effort as needed to pick up a rag doll, and threw him across the small room. The flying Scotsman landed plump in the middle of table, where four tough-looking men were sitting. Immediately the whole café was in uproar. It seemed to me that nobody was taking sides, it was just a case of thumping anybody you didn't know. Derrick boy, I said to myself, it's time to leave. I started to crawl on all fours across the floor towards the exit.

Suddenly I was flipped over with a whole load of fighting men on top of me. I was as helpless as an overturned tortoise and could hardly breathe. Out of my left eye, I could see a sailor standing by the entrance. He rubbed his hands together, then took a flying leap from where he stood and landed on the pile on top of me. Looking down, he saw my unprotected face sticking out from underneath. With a nasty grin, he raised his arm, then, with the speed of a pneumatic drill, he pummelled his fist into it. I felt nothing, I only saw stars.

When the police arrived, thankfully the weight on me began to lighten, as one by one the savages were taken off and dragged into a Black Maria. I was in no fit state to walk, so they carried me down the flight of stairs and laid me out on the floor of a waiting van, then they drove us all to the local police station. I should have been taken to hospital, but instead, I was locked up with the rest and put in a cell on my own for the night. My head throbbed all night and felt like the size of an over-ripe pumpkin.

In the morning, a policeman brought me a cup of tea, but my lips were so swollen I had to give up trying to drink it. I couldn't talk properly either, so with slurred speech I tried to ask him when I could expect to be let out. With difficulty, I managed to convey to him how unjust it was to hold me, the victim, and not one of the hooligans, so after talking to his sergeant, he came back and set me free. I limped out of the police station and took a cab to the jetty. It cost me quite a bit to hire a launch to get back to the ship, but I didn't care. All I wanted to do was to get back and lie on my bunk.

In considerable pain, I made it up the gangway and crossed the deck to my cabin. Olaf was shocked when he saw the state I was in and went to fetch the chief steward. I looked in the mirror and hardly recognised myself. No wonder Olaf was horrified. My swollen lips were curled up and reached the tip of my bruised nose. Both eyes were bloodshot, blackened and almost closed. Huge bumps close together lined my forehead. One of my upper front teeth had a big chunk missing, leaving an exposed nerve. Compared to me, Charles Laughton as the Hunchback of Notre Dame looked like Rudolph Valentino.

The steward took one look at me and went off to fetch the captain. He came straight away.

"Jesus Christ, what the hell's happened to you?"

Olaf told him.

"You must be taken to hospital at once." He told Olaf that one of the crew would take us both ashore in the tender, and that he, Olaf, was to go with me to the hospital. To me the captain said:

"We're leaving in the morning. I'm afraid you're not fit enough to come with us, so you'll have to be paid off."

"Captain, I'll be all right in a couple of days," I mumbled through my swollen lips.

"No, no, boy, you must go to hospital. Don't worry - when you're better, the Merchant Navy Manning Pool will find you a ship back to England very quickly. I'll tell the radio operator to come and pay you up. Good luck, boy!" he said and shook my hand.

"Fuck, fuck, fuck, Olaf, I don't want to be stuck in that bloody town," I said, almost weeping.

'It's best to see the doctor and make sure that you're OK."

He was right, of course, but I was really pissed off.

The radio operator came and paid me what I was due. It wasn't much, after deducting subs. Olaf collected all my things and put them into his kitbag.

"You can keep the kitbag, Derrick, it's a goodbye present from me. Don't worry, I've got another one. Come along now, the tender has been lowered."

Feeling miserable, I left the Mosli which had been my home for all these past months, and with Olaf in a borrowed coat, and me in his, we crossed the bay to Halifax, a place I had hoped I would never see again.

At the hospital Olaf handed over the captain's letter, and before long a doctor arrived. Olaf knew it was his cue to leave. He was about to hug me when he realised he shouldn't, as every part of my body was bruised. I took his hand and reminded him that he had my address in England.

"I'll see you again, and we will go out in London, and have a good time, find some girls, eh?" said Olaf. He turned to go.

"Olaf - your coat, you mustn't forget this is your grandfather's coat!"

"What will you do without one?" said Olaf.

"Don't worry, I have enough money to buy a windjammer. I've really liked being your friend, Olaf, take care of yourself, and keep out of fights."

It saddened me to see him go.

"Come with me," said the doctor, "we're going to have you X-rayed." A nurse gently stripped me down to the waist and laid me down on a couch. She put my sore head into a padded vice, so that it couldn't move, and lined up the X-ray machine above it. A lady radiologist arrived and took X-rays from every angle around my head, then did the same to my ribcage, back and front. I was told to go and stay in the waiting room for the doctor. I sat there for over an hour before he arrived.

"Well, young man, you're very lucky," he said, holding the X-rays up to the light. "You don't seem to have any bones broken in your face or your chest. Why you people think it's fun to smash up our town and yourselves completely baffles me."

I couldn't be bothered to tell him that it was no fault of mine, but thought that if his town wasn't the most boring place on earth, there would probably be less brawling in the streets.

Now that the doctor had got his complaint about us hooligans off his chest, he applied his mind to what was to happen to me.

"That broken tooth of yours must be attended to straight away. Nurse will take you to see our dentist. I'll want to see you again in a week, she will give you an appointment."

He'll be fucking lucky, I thought, I'll be gone by then.

As the dentist pulled up my upper lip, I screamed out in pain.

"I can't do anything with you in this state except put a temporary plug over the exposed nerve."

Somehow he managed to do this. He too told me to come back in a week, when he would screw in a false tooth. I was given a bottle of painkillers and was told I could go. I left the hospital and went into the freezing street, wearing only a shirt and carrying Olaf's kitbag. Fortunately a taxi was standing there. I asked the driver to take me to the manning pool but stop off en route at the nearest shop that sold warm weatherproof jackets.

The manning pool was on the outskirts of the town. When the taxi dropped me off, I felt like I was back in the army. The place reminded me of Mill Hill barracks; the only difference was the absence of any military paraphernalia. There were a dozen or so large wooden huts, built on small stilts, with no pathway connecting them. Wherever you walked, you were ankle-deep in snow. A large wooden structure housed the dining area and the kitchens, and attached to it was a small shed that was the office. It was here that I checked in. I showed my temporary seaman's papers to a man sitting at a desk. He took down all my particulars.

"Mess Boy, eh? Not much call for them, they generally only need one or two on each boat. Now if you were an able-bodied seaman, it would be easier. They are needed all the time."

I explained why I had ended up at his place, and told him how long I had been away. He sympathised with me, and said he would do all he could to place me as soon as possible. He said I would be housed in hut No. 8, and suggested I went there and claimed a bunk. I left the office feeling very disheartened. It sounded like I might be stuck in this God-forsaken place for some time.

The hut had a line of five double bunks on each side. I found a lower bunk that was free and put my kitbag in a locker. As it was noon, I went to the dining room to have lunch. I could see that most of the men at the tables were Canadians, waiting like me to get jobs on merchant ships.

The dining room was self-service, with a few motherly-looking women behind the counter doing their bit for the war effort while a young woman went round clearing the tables. I picked up a tray and asked for food that could be easily mashed up. I felt a little better after that, but drinking tea still proved to be a bit of a problem.

I decided that the best treatment for me, until the bumps and bruises had subsided, was to stay in the centrally heated hut for a few days, and rest as much as possible. In the end, I hung about the place until it was time to keep my appointments at the hospital. The doctor examined my face and chest, and told me that, considering the bashing I had taken, I had made a good recovery. The dentist gave me an injection, then filed my broken tooth down to the gum, and spiked a false one into the root.

After a few days, I began to look and feel my old self again. By now I had very little money left, only enough to visit the Green Lantern a few more times. Two weeks later I was penniless, so from then on I was forced to stay at the manning pool. With nothing to do in the day or evening, I thought I would go out of my mind with boredom. I couldn't even write letters, because stamps cost money. The only entertainment was playing darts, which I hated, or cards, and that wasn't possible as whoever you played with, only wanted to for money. I never found a kindred soul amongst any of the people there. I was desperately lonely. Oh God, I thought, if only they would find me a boat out of here soon. Facing the German U-boats, and maybe another storm in the Atlantic would be a welcome relief compared to this.

Something happened just when I was at my lowest ebb. The young woman who picked up the plates in the dining room started to flirt with me. She hadn't noticed me, of course, when I looked like a gargoyle. She was four or five years older than me, a tall, fat, plain-looking girl - in England I wouldn't have given her a thought. But in this dump, she had one important thing in her favour: she was female.

As the days went by, she paid more and more attention to me. I was obviously expected to respond. So I said I would love to date her, but couldn't, because I had run out of money. I asked her what her name was.

" Sally," she said, then added: "I've got money, so we could go out for a meal, or maybe the pictures, if you'd like."

"Oh I would," I assured her, "but I don't really like a hard-working girl like you to pay for me."

She smiled. "Please don't worry about it. I don't know your name?"

"It's Derrick," I said.

"Well, Derrick, how about tonight? I'll meet you at the gate at say, six o'clock. How's that?"

"That would be wonderful, Sally, see you at six then."

To get out of this open prison for the evening cheered me up a lot. We went first to the Green Lantern and had a meal, then to the pictures. The film hadn't run for long, when Sally put her arm around me. She turned her head and started to kiss me, first gently, then passionately. While she did this, her hand moved up and down my body. Because her face was smack in front of mine, I hardly saw the screen at all. Still, it was warm in the cinema, and with a good meal inside me, not seeing the film didn't bother me a lot. When it was over, I walked Sally to her digs. She couldn't invite me in because she lived as a paying guest with a family. So, after a long kissing session outside her front door, I thanked her for a lovely evening and caught the last bus back to the pool.

Although Sally wasn't very attractive, I amused myself for the next few days by flirting with her unashamedly. One day I'd be Cary Grant, imitating the charming and cheeky way he wooed his leading ladies. Another I'd be Charles Boyer (with a phony French accent) as he made love to the Countess in *Mayerling*. And with these hammy performances, Sally became like putty in my hands. For my final number, I was Laurence Olivier as Heathcliff in *Wuthering Heights*, telling Cathy, his childhood sweetheart, of his lifelong love for her. Olivier was my best performance, because after all, he was an English film star. I overplayed my hand something awful. Poor Sally became absolutely besotted with me. Every free moment she had, she sought me out, sometimes taking tremendous risks. One afternoon, I was lying asleep on my bunk in my underpants, when I was woken up by Sally kissing my bare back, and her hand inside my pants. Luckily, there was no one in the hut at the time.

"Sally, darling," I said, "stop it, Jesus, twenty men could come in at any moment."

"I don't care," she said.

"Maybe you don't, but I do."

The only way to stop her was to promise to go out with her that evening. Derrick, I thought, you have gone too far with this girl. My only hope was to get a boat out of here soon.

Sally treated me to a meal, then suggested, as it was a nice moonlit night, we should go for a walk in the pine forest. Although I would have preferred to stay in the warm, I agreed. It was the Enchanted Forest all right. Tall snow-covered pine trees glistened in the moonlight, with a carpet of virgin-white snow on the ground. Even the sub-zero temperature couldn't take away the beauty of this wonderful place.

When we had walked for a little, Sally stopped and put her fur-covered hands around my neck. I slipped my bare hands inside her open ski-jacket around her ample waist. She guided my hands under the elastic of her slacks. They were warmed by the cheeks of her buttocks. Soon my hands and fingers were all over her.

What the hell am I doing, I thought. If things went the way they looked, we would both suffer frostbite in unexplainable parts of our bodies. But this didn't seem to deter Sally, nor, in the end, me. She pulled down the front of her slacks, I opened my flies, and the moment I was inside her, there was no need to worry about frostbite. No wonder, I mused, the human race had survived, if they could fuck under these conditions.

I took her back to her digs, then walked the mile back through the frozen streets to the civilian barracks that had become my home. For the next few days, Sally and I fucked in places she decided were safe, sometimes in the broom cupboard. The safest time to do it was when she was supposed to be clearing the tables. We would pop off singly and meet outside the ladies' lavatory because it could be locked. I would sit on the seat and she would be on my lap. Sally just couldn't have enough of it.

One Friday, she declared she wanted her parents to meet her 'lovely English boy'.

"OK," I said, "where do they live?"

"In Montreal."

"Montreal? That's miles away."

"About fourteen hours on the train. You'll like them, they are nice people."

"I'm sure I will, but how are you going to get time off, and what about the cost?"

"I get this weekend off anyway, and I'll just take off Monday as well without asking. Don't worry about the cost, I have plenty saved."

"I'll have to check with the office and make sure that they haven't got a boat for me."

This I did, and was told that no convoy was leaving for at least three days.

So early on Saturday morning, Sally and I set off for Montreal. We didn't arrive at her home until after ten o'clock that night.

Her parents were very nice and kindly people. Even at this late hour Sally's mother had prepared a meal for us. The house was a modest one, made of wood, two up and two down, with a little kitchen area attached to the back room. Her father told me he worked as a stevedore in the docks, and if I came back to Canada at the end of the war he could easily find me a job working alongside him. This was a hint, I suppose, that I should return and marry his daughter. Sally thought her father's suggestion was a wonderful idea, but I certainly didn't. Her parents soon went to bed, and as she left the room, her mother asked Sally if she was coming up.

"In a little while, Mum."

Sally took me into the front room and showed me the couch that had been made up for me.

"When they're asleep, I'll be back."

She gave me a kiss and went up to her room. I settled down on the couch and prepared myself for what was obviously going to be a disturbed night. Three times during the night I woke up, with Sally's not inconsiderable weight on top of me. All I had to do was lie on my back and let it all happen. I felt a bit like a cow must feel when being milked.

Thank God, breakfast wasn't early so I had a bit of a lie-in after a heavy night. Then Sally took me out to see her town, but I didn't see much of it, as there was a freezing, damp mist hanging over it. As in Halifax, nothing was open except the churches on the Lord's Day. After a while, the cold dampness got to us, so we hurried back to the warmth of her home. The rest of the day was spent chatting or playing cards. By evening, I had eaten three huge meals. I'd never had so much food in one day in all my life. I knew now why Sally was such a big girl.

We all went to bed fairly early, as Sally's father had to be at the docks at seven, and we had to catch our train not long after. I had more sleep that night as Sally only came down twice. I got up in time to say goodbye to her father. He reminded me about coming back after the war. I lied, and told him I probably would. I wished I could have given his wife a bunch of flowers in gratitude for the generous way she had looked after me, but without a penny to my name, that wasn't possible.

By the time I left Montreal I was feeling a bit ashamed of myself, the way I was deceiving these kind people, and that included Sally. Most of the way back, she talked about the life we would have together after the war. I just hadn't the heart to disillusion her. She was a sweet-natured girl and I hoped that one day she would find a man who would give her all the love she craved for, and deserved.

I finally got back to the pool about two a.m. I had a hard job finding my hut as there were no exterior lights. Most of the twenty men sleeping were either snoring or farting, some doing both. As I lay down, I said almost audibly "Dear God, please, please, get me out of this place soon."

The first thing I did in the morning, was to check in at the office and let them know that I was back.

"Glad you came," said the man behind the desk. "I was just about to call you over the loudspeakers. I've found a place for you as a mess boy on a British tanker. It leaves tomorrow morning."

"Whoopee!" I shouted.

"Her name is the *Augusta*, she is carrying aviation spirit. It's a bit like going to sea in a powder keg, but you can refuse if you like..."

"No, no, I won't refuse," I interrupted.

"OK, here's a letter for the Chief Steward, get the eleven o'clock ferry out tonight, and good luck!"

"Thank you, thanks a lot!"

I was so happy to be on my way back to England that I forgot to ask what the pay was. Not that it mattered - I'd have done it for nothing, if that had been the only way to leave Halifax. Now all I had to do was to wipe the smile off my face, and go and tell Sally. I didn't look forward to doing that. I found her in the dining room and motioned her to come outside for a moment.

"See you in the broom cupboard in about five minutes, Derrick."

I knew what she thought I wanted, but what could I do - I wasn't going to tell her while she was clearing the tables. When Sally came running down the passage, I took her by the hand.

"Come into the cupboard, I'm afraid I have a bit of bad news."

When I told her, she burst into tears.

"Sally, please stop crying, we both knew this would happen one day."

"I know," she said between sobs, "but I hoped it wouldn't be so soon."

I laid her head on my chest and stroked her hair and thought up all the soothing phrases I could. I told her we would spend any free time she had that day together. After I had kissed and embraced her for a little while, she stopped crying.

"We'll spend our last evening together, won't we, Derrick?"

"Of course we will, and you can come to the jetty and see me off, if you want."

"I want to be with my lovely English boy right up to the last moment."

When I left the manning pool with her that evening, there was no one else I needed to say goodbye to, even though I had been there for seven weeks. I just hadn't made any contact with anyone there.

We had one last meal at the Green Lantern, and I ended it with a double portion of waffles, laced with maple syrup. Sally's appetite seemed to have deserted her; she hardly ate anything. After the meal, we had a couple of hours to kill with nowhere to go, so we went to a cinema and sat in the back row, kissing and cuddling until it was time to leave for the ferry.

I thought the part to play for my goodbye scene should be Robert Taylor in *Waterloo Bridge* - the bit where he's saying his farewell to Vivien Leigh, before leaving her to go off and fight in the war. I remembered that when I saw the film with Betty, most of the women had their handkerchief out, wiping away their tears.

A damp mist enveloped the jetty on which we stood, and visibility was so poor that you couldn't even see the lights of the boats anchored a short distance offshore. As tears started to roll down Sally's cheeks I pulled her close to me and held her face between my hands.

"Sally, Sally, no tears, please, I'll be back, perhaps sooner than you think. This bloody war can't last much longer!"

"You know that's not true. The Germans are winning everywhere. You're going to cross the Atlantic, when it's so dangerous. I'm frightened I might never see you again, so so frightened, my darling."

I mopped up the tears still streaming down her face with my lips.

"Really, Sally, there's little to worry about, it's nowhere near as dangerous for the convoys nowadays as it was when the war started. The navy gives massive protection to the boats at sea. So please, please, don't worry. I'll be all right."

I hoped I had reassured her, but this was difficult to do. All the Canadian newspapers were reporting huge losses in the Atlantic, and were more or less saying that the battle for it was almost lost.

"You will write to me, won't you, darling?"

"Yes, I will, I'll write to you every day while I'm at sea, and post them all from London, so you'll get a whole big bundle, all at once."

"I'll write to you, my darling, every day, and think about you all the time," said Sally. "And when I'm in bed at night, I'll pretend your body is close to mine."

The men on the jetty jumped into the waiting boat and I knew it was time to say goodbye. I gave Sally a last kiss and embrace.

"I'll be back, I promise you, darling, you'll see."

She didn't answer but just stood there, crying, as I jumped into the end of the boat. I waved to her for as long as I could, but the darkness and the sea mist soon blotted her from view. I felt unhappy about leaving her so upset, standing all alone on the jetty. There and then, I made a vow never to be so dishonest with a girl again.

CHAPTER THIRTY-FIVE

My daily duties on the *Augusta* were almost a repeat of what I had done before. Once again, I shared my small cabin with the galley boy. He was a Canadian, about a year older than me. He had joined the ship in New York where it had tanked up with aviation spirit, before coming to Halifax to join the convoy. I introduced myself and he told me his name was Frank.

"Have you been across the Atlantic before?" I asked.

"No, I've only done one trip, and that was to Lisbon, and back."

"But," I said, "I thought you just told me that you hadn't crossed the Atlantic, you must have crossed it twice if you've been to Lisbon."

"I never know where the fuck I'm going anyway."

"You do know this boat is going to England, don't you?"

"Yeah, I know that."

How anyone could cross the Atlantic twice in wartime, and not know it, was beyond me. I knew straight away that he wasn't going to be a laugh a minute - still, I didn't care because it would only be for three weeks at the most.

In daylight I could see that this convoy was by far the largest one I'd been in. It looked like half the British Navy was there to protect us. This was comforting, because I did want to get back alive if possible.

The *Augusta* was about the same size as the Mosli, but there the comparison ended. She was probably about fifteen years old, but looked twice her age. I don't think a coat of paint had been applied to the hull or the living quarters since before the war. Rust flaked off anything that was iron, and paint peeled away from wood if you so much as scratched it with your fingernails. All the crew except for Frank were much older men, and a very rough lot. If they'd been French, one could have easily believed that all of them were deserters from the Foreign Legion. Both Frank and I were more afraid of them than we were of the U-boats.

By the look of the men on this ship, it seemed to me that in Norway, the cream of the country went into the Merchant Navy, while in pre-war England it was only the scum. On the other hand, the officers were quite different from the Fascist lot on the *Mosli*. They were much more friendly, and nowhere near as fussy about the service I gave them. They called me straight away by my name, and they were also more polite to the crew. This might have been for the same reason that I was afraid that if you fell foul of any of them, you'd have your throat cut before being slung overboard. Only the captain had any authority over them, and I suspect that was because he had the power to dock their pay. And if that didn't work, he could have got a cruiser of the convoy to take the man off, and have him put behind bars.

By the end of April 1942, we were in calm waters, and everything on board was working well, when, halfway across the Atlantic, disaster struck. The engines failed and we came to a dead halt. The engineers thought they could get us going again in twenty-four hours. That information was relayed to the nearest cruiser and its captain offered to stand by us, provided we got going within the estimated time. After that, he would have to leave us, and catch up with the convoy.

Our men worked frantically all day and through the night to get the clapped-out engines working - but to no avail. The cruiser could stand by no longer and had to leave us to our fate. Jesus Christ, I thought, here we were, unprotected in a calm sea, bang in the middle of the Atlantic - loaded to capacity with aviation spirit, one of the most volatile cargoes imaginable. We were a sitting target for any German sub on the prowl. A lit match put in the right place could have blown us sky high, let alone a torpedo. We were to all intents and purposes sitting on a powder keg. From now on, every breath you took, every step you made, could be your last. When you went to sleep, you never knew whether you would wake up again.

However, something did surprise me. The big, tough villains who made up most of the crew rapidly began to lose their nerve. These men, who forty-eight hours ago would have cut your throat without feeling a moment's remorse, could be seen in their cabins, on their knees, praying to the Almighty to save them. They all wore life-jackets, and kept them on even at night in their bunks. God only knows why, as there was absolutely no chance of ending up in the water and eventually getting picked up. You could only get blown to bits - that was a certainty.

For five days and nights we remained motionless on the still sea. Even the officers were beginning to crack up. I, for some unexplained reason, stayed as cool as a cucumber. I think it was because I was convinced that you didn't leave this earth until your number was up, and I didn't feel that mine was going to be called just then. The officers put my apparent lack of fear down to my youth. After all, I had not seen, as they had, a tanker like ours go up in a ball of fire that could be seen for miles around.

On the afternoon of day six into the breakdown, the engines started up. A big cheer went up the length of the boat. At last we were moving again. But after a few minutes, they stopped. My heart sank. Fortunately they soon started up again, and this time they kept going for the rest of the voyage. We had about ten more days at sea on our own, before we'd get to Scotland. Everyone was still very nervous. The closer we got to home waters, the more we were in danger of a U-boat attack.

It was a sunny day in the first week of June when the *Augusta* made it into the mouth of the Clyde, and finally docked in Greenock. The crew, like Richard III, when waking up after suffering terrible nightmares, became their villainous selves again. Gone was their pious behaviour, and off came their life-jackets.

As our cargo had yet to be discharged, no one was going to be paid off until the next day. We were, however, allowed to go ashore for the evening. I borrowed three pounds from Frank, as I thought it would be a good idea to put my heavy kitbag in the safekeeping of the Left Luggage at the Glasgow station.

Even by the light of the setting sun, Glasgow looked dark and grey. Nevertheless, I infinitely preferred its drabness to the lifeless desert of Halifax.

In the morning, all the crew were hanging about on deck, waiting to be paid off. Frank and I had already been told we wouldn't be free to go until we'd served the ship's officers lunch. I was killing time, standing on deck watching stevedores unloading a cargo boat lying in the next berth, when I noticed three men in civvies and two policemen coming up our gangplank. They went straight to the captain's room.

I crossed over to the other side of the ship to have my last look at the sea. Looking down on the water, I saw tins of butter, huge slabs of cheese, even a whole side of bacon, being thrown out of the portholes from the crew's quarters. All went plop into the water, and drifted down the Clyde. I couldn't imagine why this was happening. It seemed to me that half the ship's stores were being thrown overboard. What a shocking waste, I thought.

It wasn't long before the captain came aft, accompanied by two of the ship's officers and the three men, plus the two policemen, who had come aboard earlier. "Everybody stand by their bunks," he shouted, "and take all your luggage with you." He told us that the cold storage room had been broken into, and most of the stores had been stolen.

The men in civvies were from the CID. They went into every cabin and made a thorough search. Everyone had to empty all their luggage on the floor. They found nothing - naturally they didn't - because all the stolen goods were by now under the sea. When they came to my cabin, I had to tell them, that my kitbag was already in Glasgow, and to prove it, I showed them the ticket. Well, as the robbery had taken place that morning, it put me in the clear. Nevertheless, one of the detectives decided to look under my bunk. There, to my horror, was a whole crate of Canadian apples.

"What's this?"

"I don't know, I don't know anything about it, some bastard must have put it there, when they saw you coming aboard."

One of the officers intervened.

"I assure you, inspector, this boy and his cabin mate are the only two of the crew that wouldn't be involved in this sort of thing."

"OK, lads, you're off the hook," said one of the detectives.

The captain told everyone to go up on deck, as he wished to speak to us.

"You thieving bastards have stolen and dumped most of the rations needed for the voyage out, which means that the next crew are going to have to manage on half the rations until we can restock. When they complain, as I am sure, they will, I will tell them about you bastards. Now go and get paid, and get the hell off my ship."

I served the officers their lunch, and thanked the one who had spoken up for me to the detective. All that was left to do now was to go and get paid.

The Radio Officer was pleased to see me, as I was the last one to be paid off.

"Now let's see, you've been on board four weeks - at five pounds per week, I owe you twenty pounds, is that right?"

"Five pounds a week, is that all I get? What about my danger money? With the Norwegians, I got ten pounds a week plus five pounds danger money."

The radio operator pushed twenty one-pound notes across the table towards me.

"Look, lad, you're not on a fancy Norwegian boat now. This is an English one, and we don't pay danger money. We are at war, and war, lad, is dangerous. Do you think our boys in North Africa are being paid danger money? You should have asked what the pay was, before taking on the job!"

I picked up my money, signed for it, and left the room. All I had got was twenty pounds for four weeks' work, including seven nerve-racking days sitting on a time-bomb. Still, all that really mattered was that I was alive, and back at last. I went back to the cabin to pick up my jacket. Frank was waiting for me.

"Here's the three pounds you lent me."

"Are you coming to London?" I asked.

"No, I'll stay in Glasgow. There'll be more chance of getting another boat out from here."

"Well, in that case, I'll say goodbye and good luck. Remember now, you have crossed the Atlantic to get here."

"All right, all right, Derrick, anyway, good luck to you too."

I walked down the gangway, and after a few steps, stopped - then turned round to have a last look at the old crate that in the end had somehow got me back. I'm not sorry to be leaving you, old lady, it's time you went to the scrap-yard, I thought. I made my way to Greenock Station and got on the local train to Glasgow.

Glasgow Station was packed with men from all the three services. I stood in a queue at the ticket office.

"One single to London, please."

"Seven pounds, mate."

"When does it leave?" I asked.

"In one hour from Platform 3. With luck you'll just about squeeze onto it."

I went over to the Left Luggage office.

"I've come to pick up my kitbag," I said to the man sitting on a chair looking as though he was half asleep.

"Your ticket, mate."

"Yes, of course, my ticket," I reached to the inside of my jacket pocket, where I remembered I had put it after I had shown it to the detective. It wasn't there, nor was it in any of my other pockets.

"I'm sorry, I seem to have lost it."

"Oh dear, oh dear," said the man, "maybe I can find it. Tell me what colour your case was?"

"It's not a case, its a kitbag, a light blue kitbag."

"Oh I remember, it was a heavy one, wasn't it?"

"Yes," I nodded, "that's mine."

"Well, mate, a friend of yours picked it up for you, it was about lunch time."

"I haven't got a friend."

"Well, I don't know, mate, all I know is, he handed me the ticket and I gave it to him."

"Those thieving bastards - I'll kill 'em, I'll fucking kill 'em."

"Sorry, mate," he said, "I just handed over the item that matched the ticket. That's what I do all day long."

"I'm not blaming you, it's just that I'm fucking pissed off, that's all."

I left the luggage office and found a bench to sit on. I had to fight back the tears. I wasn't so upset about the loss of my own things; what made me feel so miserable was I'd no longer be able to give Betty the nylon stockings and the pretty underwear I'd bought her in New York. Uncle would be bitterly disappointed not to get the two bottles of Haig's Whisky I'd mentioned in a letter, not to forget a big bottle of Curaçao I got for Vic. I'd so looked forward to giving them all these things that were now gone. How on earth could they do it to their own mates, these shits?

The loudspeakers announced that the train for King's Cross was leaving in five minutes. I boarded it. The train was crammed full with standing room only in the corridors and we were wedged in tight like sardines in a tin. It took me over half an hour to get to the toilet, when I urgently needed to go.

After over seven hours, squeezed like a sardine in a tin, the train arrived at King's Cross. I stumbled out onto the platform and at last could fill my squashed lungs with air.

The station clock read eleven-thirty pm. London was having one of its nightly air- raids. The anti-aircraft guns were banging away, and search lights criss-crossed one another in the black sky. Looking up at the exploding ack-ack shells, reality hit me - after nine months away, I was back at last. I'd returned more or less as I'd left, with only the clothes I stood up in, and after paying my train fare, just a few pounds in my pocket. Now that America was in the war, the whole journey had been completely futile. During the months that I had been away, nearly all the major countries were now at war. The only safe place for me would be the nearest Air Raid Shelter, but I had no intention of going there. I was going to make for the only place I knew would be open at this late hour and where I'd be welcomed. I got into the only taxi that had a driver brave enough to stand in the rank while all hell was going on above his head.

"To the Coffee Ann, please."

"Where's that, mate?" he said.

"Near St Giles' Circus."

I sank back into the blue leather seat, crossed my legs, and lit a cigarette. Despite all that had happened to me, I couldn't prevent a little smile appearing on my face.

CHAPTER THIRTY-SIX

Nothing had changed at the Coffee Ann during my absence. Nearly all the regulars were there, some still sitting at the same tables they'd occupied when last I saw them, as if they were trapped in a time-warp. This thought soon vanished when Vic's voice rose above the hubbub of the crowded café.

"Good heavens, it's Derrick," he shouted as he manoeuvred himself deftly through the tightly packed tables, "You're back, dear boy, I'd almost given you up for lost. The news about the convoys crossing the Atlantic made me wonder whether I'd ever see you again. I phoned the major some weeks back, but all he could tell me was that the last he'd heard of you, you were marooned in some ghastly place in Nova Scotia. How long have you been back?"

"Less than an hour."

"Dear boy, I can't begin to tell you what a relief it is to see that you're still in the land of the living. Come and join Peter and me, you can tell us what kept you away for so long."

"Peter! What's he doing here at this time of night? I thought he had to be with his barrister friend in the evenings."

"Oh, he gave him the push a while back. Peter and I shack up together now, in Berwick Street to be precise. Our digs are a tip, but convenient when you want to get here or Tony's."

"What does Peter do for money, now that he no longer has a sugar daddy?"

"He relies on me, God help the poor boy."

When I sat at the table, Peter just managed a faint smile. I think he worried that I was going to lure Vic away from him, even though I had introduced them in the first place.

"Now Derrick," said Vic, "let's hear all about your travels."

I gave them a condensed account of my sea journeys and told Vic why I no longer had the bottle I'd brought back from Curaçao as a present for him.

"Jesus, what fucking thieving bastards, robbing one of their own mates like that."

"Are you still selling *War Commentary* at Hyde Park and is Frederick still at Speakers' Corner?"

"Frederick's always there, and I am mostly on Sundays. It's got a bit rougher since you were last there. The boys in khaki and the police aren't (to put it mildly) quite so tolerant as they were in the past."

"Tell me, how did Robert make out when he appealed to the tribunal for Conscientious Objectors?"

"Oh, he got sentenced to hard labour on the land for the duration. The poor chap's been slogging away at it since autumn. He hates every moment of it, so much so, that he nearly slung it in and joined up. But he manages to get back to civilisation most Saturday evenings. With a bit of luck, you'll see him here tomorrow night."

"How is it that you're still floating around? Hasn't the Army called you back in yet?"

"They tried, dear boy, but thanks to Peter's inspired choreography and Quentin's flamboyant dress sense, I got turned down. My papers say, I'm psychologically unsuited for service in the armed forces."

"How the fuck did you work that one?"

Vic was about to reply when Peter stood up and announced he was tired and was going home to bed.

"I think he's a bit piqued because we're not including him in our conversation. No matter, I'll smooth his ruffled feathers when I get back. Now, Derrick, to answer your question: on the day of my medical examination, I arrived dressed in my old corduroys and the canvas shirt Peter made for me. Quentin lent me a wide-brimmed, floppy hat and I had my large ebony crucifix, attached to a lavatory chain. Peter rouged my lips, varnished my finger- and toenails, and stuck on a pair of long eyelashes. With the rouge visible through my bushy beard, by the time I made my entrance at the medical centre, I looked like Rasputin in drag.

"What the fuck have we got 'ere ?" said the three-striper when I presented myself to him.

"Mind your language, if you please, sergeant," I said, brandishing my crucifix at him.

"Follow me, sir or madam," the sergeant said in a pitiful attempt to be sarcastic.

He took me into a drill-hall, where a long line of half-naked men were waiting for the MO's arrival. When they saw me, they just fell about laughing. Some even wolf-whistled. With my skills as a pugilist, I could have easily laid them out one by one, but I refrained because that would have given my little charade away. As the MO went along the line of men, and then came face to face with me, he didn't even try to disguise a look of horror. A full two seconds passed before he opened his mouth.

"Are you one of those homosexuals?" he said.

"'m only sexually attracted to my own gender, if that's what you mean," I replied.

"I think his Majesty's Army can do without your sort," said the MO looking disdainfully down his nose at me. 'The war may be going badly, but we're not that desperate yet, thank God!' "Are you implying that you're not going to take me in, doctor? I can't tell you how disappointed I'll be, I was so looking forward to being in a dorm with other men."

"I bet you were, you bloody pervert. In the army, we don't have dormitories, we have barrack rooms," he snapped. That is how I worked my ticket, Derrick."

"Brilliant, Vic, absolutely fucking brilliant."

"Not as clever as all that, old boy, after all, I am a homosexual."

"Have you been barred from having to do war-work as well?"

"Oh no, the Labour Exchange did send a note inviting me to come for an interview. I replied promptly, of course, and told them how much I appreciated their kind invitation, which I would most certainly take up one day when I felt up to it. Meanwhile, I wrote, do please continue your correspondence, as nowadays I get so few letters, and be sure to let me know if you should ever change your address."

"They must have decided you were a complete loony. I wouldn't mind betting that you never heard from them again."

"I don't know whether they did or not, old boy. Now that I've moved they haven't the faintest notion as to my whereabouts."

By now it was well after one, and it had been a long day since I got out of my bunk at the crack of dawn in Greenock. Flaked out, I desperately needed some sleep. I was too tired even to go and see if Betty was still working at the Cabaret Club. Vic saw that I was wilting fast and suggested that I went back with him and sleep on the floor.

"Won't Peter mind?" I asked.

"He'll be dead to the world by now. I doubt if he'll even realise that you're there until his cock crows."

"Surely you mean the cock crows?"

"No I don't," he said.

In daylight I saw that the room I'd slept in was disgusting. I decided it would be wise to get out before the lice realised they had another host to feed on.

Leaving Vic and Peter to sleep on, I crept out and made for the Corner House to have breakfast. As I waded into a plate of piping hot porridge, laced with black treacle, I decided two things had to be done as soon as I'd eaten. One was to find Betty and the other was to get fixed up with a room.

Locating Betty took priority. I headed for my old digs, in the hope that she might still be living there, but alas, the landlady said she'd left shortly after I had. I called at her mother's and got no answer. I only had one more card to play: the Cabaret Club when she finished work at two in the morning. With no trouble at all, I found a cheap room near King's Cross.

After lunch I called on Uncle. He had aged quite a lot, and his movements and speech were slower, but he was delighted to see me and wanted to know every detail of my adventures. I ended my tale by telling him what had happened to the bottles of whisky I'd bought him. He was clearly disappointed, but all he said was that the important thing was that I was back safe and sound.

I arranged to have dinner with him and then, while he had his afternoon nap, wallowed in the luxury of a bath. Jesus, I mused, as I lay submerged in the hot soapy water. I shaved, combed my hair and put on the clean suit and white shirt that I kept at the flat. Thus transformed, I looked into the mirror. Thank God my Soho friends couldn't see me now, looking more like a member of the Young Conservatives than an ardent anarchist. I had to admit that it was nice for once to feel clean all over and wear clothes that had been washed and ironed.

As we talked over dinner, Uncle told me that his cantankerous sister had died, so he wouldn't have to travel all the way to the New Forest to pull her blasted Christmas cracker. But he complained that nearly all his friends were out of London, so that on most days he had to put up with his own company. I suspected that he was hoping I would move back into the flat, but although I was very fond of the old man, his lifestyle was wholly incompatible with mine. All I could do was assure him that I'd be visiting him frequently once I'd sorted myself out.

We went back to the flat and listened to the nine o'clock news. For me, it was the first complete news I'd heard for nine months. Sitting here in London with Uncle fingering his moustache as he listened to all the bad news coming in from nearly all the theatres of war, I had the uncanny feeling that for these last months I'd been out of it. God knows why, since the very opposite was the case.

After the news, I got out of my fancy clothes, said goodbye to Uncle and made for the Coffee Ann in the hope of meeting Robert there. He was, but I hardly recognised him. He looked a lot healthier than when I'd last seen him. His face was tanned and weatherbeaten, and his body had broadened out. The first thing I said to him was how well he looked.

"Maybe I do, Derrick, but at what a fucking price."

He told me he'd spent the winter up to his knees in mud and freezing water, digging ditches in the company of a host of conscientious objectors. Now he had to clear the bushes, shrubs, weeds and anthills that had grown over the land during the years of the depression.

"Surely it's not that bad now that the winter is behind you," I said.

"Well, at least I'm no longer up to my knees in shit and freezing water, but I just long for the day I'm no longer compelled to work on the land like a slave."

"Still, look on the bright side, Robert, I bet your girlfriends like you muscular and healthy-looking instead of the puny chap you were before."

"I don't think they even thought of me as puny. I never had any problem attracting girls. So piling on the brawn hasn't done a thing for me except make me suffer."

"Betty said she was attracted to me because of my muscular body, but being on board ship for months, doing nothing more strenuous than washing up and cleaning out cabins, has made my poor muscles almost disappear. When I meet her later on at the nightclub, she may well send me packing."

"She's not working there any more, Derrick."

"Not there? Where is she then?"

"Some rich man has set her up in a very expensive flat just off Park Lane. He's bought her up lock, stock and barrel, tits, bum and fanny."

"I suppose this means that my chances of ever seeing her again are pretty slim?"

"No, you'll find her on fine days sunbathing at the Serpentine, doing her best to get a golden tan so that she can make herself even more attractive to her sugar daddy. The more sexually desirable she becomes, the more hard cash she can expect. From what she's told me, her bloke is a bit of a bore. By now, she may well be pleased to see you again."

"If I can't persuade her to come and live with me, I'll join you on the land. I feel the need to be out in the open air, doing hard physical work."

"I'd like that, I can't begin to tell you how fucking boring the conchies are. You being there would make a world of difference."

"Are you working near London?"

"About forty miles away in Aylesbury. I live in a hostel with those non-fucking Bible punchers. We're employed by the Buckinghamshire War Agricultural Committee. They send us out in small groups to clear the land anywhere within a ten-mile radius of the town. They're short of labour, so there'll be no problem getting them to take you on. If you turn up with me on a Monday morning, you'll be hired on the spot."

"OK, if things don't work out with Betty, I'll join you. How's that?"

"Fine!"

The next day, the sun was shining so brightly that its rays penetrated the blackout screens in front of the windows. The sunlight was the 'reveille' for me to jump out of bed and get to the Serpentine to see if Betty was there. I dressed hastily and it was only when I grabbed a towel that I remembered that my swimming trunks had been stolen along with everything else. It was Sunday, my only hope was to see if Vic had some I could borrow.

I arrived as, he and Peter were arguing about whose turn it was to make breakfast. Seeing me, they stopped their bickering, but by the way they glowered at each other I knew the truce would be broken the moment I left. Pretending that I hadn't noticed their petty quarrel, I asked Vic if he could lend me some trunks.

"Certainly, Derrick, but really they're more suited for a swim in the Vatican's pool than the Serpentine."

"Why?"

"They're a bit on the holy side, dear boy!"

"The fucking moths have been nibbling away at them, old boy."

It was too early in the day for me to be amused by silly jokes, so rather abruptly I said: "They'll have to do, holes and all."

I was the first person that Sunday morning to go through the turnstile at the swimming pool. Quickly I put on my motheaten trunks and mounted the few steps that led up to the grassy bank of the sunbathing area. I lay on my towel facing the sun and hoped that I would have the foundation of a tan by the time Betty turned up.

Most of the morning passed before I caught sight of her. She was coming out of the changing rooms and was wearing the briefest two-piece costume I had ever seen. Wanting to surprise her, I turned over and lay on my stomach and hid my face in my hands. Through my fingers I watched her, as indeed did all the other males around, make her way up to the bank. I am sure Betty knew that she was being ogled by a whole load of lecherous men, but she behaved as if she was oblivious to their very existence. I waited patiently for her to settle down. Then, as she lay on her back, eyes closed, I got up and stood in front of her, casting a shadow over her face. She opened her eyes.

"Derrick, darling, it's you, I can't believe it."

A second later, a frown creased her forehead.

"You bastard, you never once bothered to write to me in all the time you were away."

"I did, Betty, honestly I did, I wrote you no less than five times. I sent them to where we used to live. The reason you didn't get them, was that you never gave the landlady a forwarding address."

"How do you know I didn't?"

"She told me so when I called there yesterday."

"It was because I wanted to avoid the Labour Exchange catching up with me. I suppose I should have called there from time to time, to see if she had any mail. Anyway, darling, you're here now and that's all I care about. Sit next to me and tell me what you've been up to."

I sat beside her and before I could utter one word, Betty pushed me onto my back and started to shower me with kisses. I slid my arms around the firm flesh of her bare waist, and for some time not a word passed between us. When our lips did finally part, I told her how much I'd thought about her while I was at sea.

No sooner had I said it than I remembered what Robert had said about her now living with a wealthy man in Mayfair. I told her I knew about her affair and asked if that meant we would not be able to see each other.

"We can't during the week, but most Sunday mornings about nine his chauffeur collects him and whisks him off to spend the weekend with his wife and children. They live near Cheltenham."

"How does he manage to have a car and such a huge petrol ration?"

"Because he's a very high up minister in the War Cabinet, that's why."

"What's his name?" My imagination ran wild thinking up the possible candidates. Perhaps it was Beaverbrook, Eden, or even the Prime Minister. No, no, I thought, not Churchill. Surely she couldn't bring herself to get under the sheets with him.

"I'll never be able to tell you his name, Derrick, he made me swear on my mother's life that I'd never divulge it to anyone. He said that if I did the Secret Service would have to get rid of me. I'd meet with an accident, or they would fake my suicide by throwing me off the bridge that spans the Archway Road."

"Jesus Christ, your bloke is a real gentleman, isn't he?"

"As a matter of fact, he is. It's just that in his position, he can't afford to have any scandal. He told me he'd be sacked for laying himself open to blackmail by enemy agents."

"I know what I would do if I were you, I'd get the fuck out of it."

"That's easier said than done. You see, he's absolutely crazy about me. I sometimes think he'd have me done away with if I upped and left him. Mind you, he need have no fear of that – I like this lavish way of life. Not in your wildest dreams could you imagine how luxurious it is. I'm in a circle of privileged people where rationing simply doesn't exist, and money is as easy to come by as water from a running tap. I never want to return to the poverty of my childhood if I can help it."

"I know what you mean, being very poor is only tolerable if there's a ray of hope that one day a magic carpet will fly you out of it. It looks as though one came for you, Betty."

"It sure fucking well did. So far, we've only been talking about me. I want to hear all about the wonderful places you went to."

I gave her a short account of my travels, but she was only interested in the more glamorous things I'd done.

"Oh, Derrick, you were in New York - that's one city I'd sell my soul to see."

A mean thought entered my head: as she'd already sold her body, was there a soul left to sell?

"When the war is over, I'll go there, see if I don't."

"All you need to do, girl, is stash away some of the money that your chap showers on you, and hey presto, it'll be New York here I come."

"I'm quite rich already, you know, I have more than three hundred pounds hidden away in a cocoa tin."

"Christ, Betty, that's a huge amount."

"You're damn right it is. My poor mum, bless her, works fucking hard for almost two years to earn that sort of money, and she doesn't have a penny saved by the end of it. I've hoarded my nest egg in just a few months, and lived like a princess in the meantime."

I couldn't comment on the rights and wrongs of this, so I changed the subject.

"I take it that your lover boy is with his family today. Does that mean we can be together until he returns?"

"You bet your sweet life it does. This evening I'll treat you to any restaurant you care to name, and then we can go back to my place and fuck ourselves stupid all night long. How does that appeal to you?"

"A lot," I said.

The rest of the day we spent lying flat on our backs soaking up the sun. When I ran my hands up and down Betty's velvety, sun-tanned skin, it made me feel so sexy that now and then, with my hands camouflaging the front of my swimming trunks, I had to make a mad dash for the water to cool my ardour.

When it was time to leave the pool and I came out of the changing room, Betty was waiting for me in the shade of a big chestnut tree, lit up from behind by the low rays of the evening sun. The sheer beauty of the girl almost took my breath away. The dress she wore clung to her magnificent figure, even the outline of her nipples showed through the flimsy material. I'd only ever seen such a revealing garment on film stars like Marlene Dietrich or Greta Garbo.

"Betty darling," I said finally, "we can't go to a Corner House with you looking like you've just left the set of a Hollywood movie."

"We're not going to a Corner House. I thought you said your favourite restaurant was the Strand Palace?"

"I did, but they wouldn't let me in dressed the way I am. I only go there with my uncle when I've got my suit on."

"Don't worry, I've got it all worked out. We'll hop into a taxi and go to my place, then you can put on one of my bloke's. You're about the same height. It'll be a bit baggy on you because he's got quite a tum, but if you leave the jacket open, no one will notice."

"Has he got a shirt and a tie I could borrow?"

"Yes," she said as she waved down a passing cab with the authority of a person who uses them regularly.

We sped through the Park and stopped outside a grand house in Half Moon Street. Comparing this residence with the dump of a place that she and I shared before I went to sea, I realised to what extent Betty had moved up in the world. My heart missed a beat, when after paying off the cab, she ran to the front door and rang the bell. The door was opened by the butler.

"Hello Jackson, this is my friend Derrick," said Betty.

The butler nodded his head in my direction, and asked me if he could get me a drink.

"No, thanks," I said in the hope that he'd soon go away. He turned his eyes away from me and spoke to Betty.

"My wife and I will be retiring for the night shortly, madam. Is there anything you require?"

"Nothing, thank you, Jackson, we'll be off out again shortly."

"What time would you and your friend like breakfast?"

"Nine o'clock please, and goodnight, Jackson."

Wondering how it was that the butler assumed I'd be staying for the night, I followed Betty upstairs.

"Shit, Betty," I said when we entered the bedroom. "That's fucked it. Why didn't you tell me that the bloody servants live in?"

"Because it doesn't matter, that's why!"

"Surely the lackey will tell his boss what you've been up to during his absence?"

"No he won't, and even if he did, it wouldn't matter one teeny-weeny bit."

"What do you mean it wouldn't matter?"

"Because, Derrick my darling, he doesn't fucking well mind, as a matter of fact he'll be rather pleased about it."

"Are you telling me, he likes to hear that some other bloke has fucked his girl?"

"Yes, as long as I describe exactly what goes on. It gets him all worked up and feeling randy, you see."

A look of utter disbelief showed on my face. "Jesus Christ, I learn something new every bloody day!"

` "And so you should. Anyway who cares a damn as long as it makes him happy."

"I don't, but for heaven's sake, don't tell me what you get up to with him, will you?"

"Come on, Derrick, let me show you round."

To please her, I allowed myself to be led by the hand, even though all I wanted to do was get her onto the huge bed. Betty showed me the paintings that hung on the panelled walls all the way up the curved mahogany staircase. All the rooms were furnished with antiques that left the onlooker in no doubt that the owner was extremely rich and had excellent taste. There wasn't one single piece that was plain or ordinary. I couldn't have lived with all this opulence for more than a day.

At last we got back to the bedroom. Within seconds she was lying naked on top of the blankets that covered the big bed. As I stood looking down at her, I couldn't for the life of me comprehend why her man needed more stimuli than just the sight of her.

After we'd been at each other's flesh like hungry wolves devouring the carcass of a sheep and our hands and mouths began to tire, Betty pushed me onto my back and sat astride of me. Looking up, I saw that we were reflected in a huge mirror that was fixed to the ceiling above the bed.

"That's an odd place to have a mirror," I said. "It would be useless for shaving or if you wanted to see yourself full length."

"Derrick, darling, you sweet innocent boy, tell me what you do see in it."

"You crouched on top of me and your beautiful arse going up and down as we fuck."

"Well, now you know why it's up there, don't you?"

"Oh, I see," I replied, but I was still baffled.

Betty pushed me off her and sat upright on the edge of the bed. I held her there with my arms gripped tightly round her slender waist.

"Let me go, Derrick, so I can go and find you something to wear."

When I let go, she crossed the room and opened the double doors of a huge wardrobe, packed with immaculately kept suits. She picked one out and handed it to me.

"What do you think?"

"I wouldn't be seen dead in it, but if it gets me past the doorman of the Strand Palace, it's worth it."

When I had put on the ill-fitting suit, Betty asked me to call for a cab. I went over to a desk that had two telephones on it, and was just about to pick up one of them when she screamed out: "For Christ's sake, Derrick, don't use that phone. It's a direct line to Number Ten."

"Fuck me, might God-Almighty Churchill in person have answered it?"

"For all I know he might have."

"Oh dear, now I'm really tempted, I'd be able to tell the old bastard exactly what I thought about his bloody imperialist war."

"If you did we'd soon be dead."

"Bumped off by the Secret Service boys, I presume? In that case, I'll use the other one," I said, feigning fear.

As I dialled, I noticed on top of the leather-covered desk a folded card. Written on it in large letters were the words 'Betty's Menu'.

"I never knew you could cook, Betty."

"I can't, what makes you think I can?"

"This card says 'Betty's Menu'."

"Oh shit, I should have put that back in the drawer, the servants might have opened it."

"Mustn't they know that you pick the menu sometimes then?"

"No, it's not that, it has nothing to do with that all. It's a list of the sexy games my bloke likes to play when he gets back in the evening from Downing Street. You can look at it, if you want."

I opened the card and read it.

"Jesus Christ, Betty, the things you're expected to get up to, I can't imagine what half of them are about."

"I knew you wouldn't understand."

"OK, what's this? Item No. 5, 'saucy schoolgirl in gym slip'. No. 6, 'Nanny spanks the naughty boy'. And what in fuck's name is No. 7, 'Betty mounts and whips her stubborn donkey'?"

"If you can't imagine, there's no point in telling you."

"All right, don't. But why has everything got a different price?"

"Derrick, like all menus, what you pay for is what you get. Beans on toast cost less than fish and chips, don't they?"

"I see you charge a fiver for a straight fuck, that seems to be the cheapest thing on offer. After that the prices go rocketing up to an unbelievable fifteen pounds."

"That's right, it gets more expensive when I'm asked to do things I'd prefer not to."

"Doesn't your allowance cover all his sexual peculiarities?"

"Not fucking likely, it doesn't. That only pays for me to live with him. Any extra I earn goes straight away into my cocoa tin."

"When does he tell you what he wants for his sexual supper? Does he poke his nose over the top of The Times at breakfast and say 'Betty my pet, tonight I fancy having No. 7'?"

"How do you know he reads *The Times*?"

"Well, I'm pretty damn sure he doesn't read the *Daily Worker*. I suppose he has to give you some advance notice so that you can get all togged up. I'm amazed, with all this occupying his mind, that he has any time left to help run the bloody war."

"He told me that his ministerial duties take up a totally different compartment in his head."

"Just as well, otherwise we might have all the girls in the army running around with their hair in pigtails and dressed in saucy little gymslips."

"Don't be so silly, Derrick. Come on, our cab has arrived."

On the way to the Strand Palace, Betty handed me a five-pound note to cover the expenses of our night out. The price of a straight fuck, I thought, as I put the note into the inside pocket of my double-breasted jacket.

It was quite late by the time we reached the restaurant and we were almost the last to be given a table. It felt strange having Betty sitting opposite me. Up to now I'd only been there with Uncle.

"Aren't you worried that a chum of your bloke's might recognise you?" I asked.

"Not a bit, they would never dine at a place like this. They go to the Savoy or the Ritz."

"Where did you meet your minister friend?"

"It was partly due to you that I met him. It was you who suggested I should get a job in the Cabaret Club and it was there that he first saw me. He came every night for a fortnight before persuading me to chuck in my job and go and live with him."

"Then I suppose it's me you should blame for your downfall."

"Downfall, Derrick! I've haven't gone down, I'm riding high, thanks to you."

"That's put me in the clear, then, has it?"

"It's put me forever in your debt."

Betty leant across the table and kissed me as if to underline what she had just said. As for me, all I wanted was to be near at hand if she ever fell down from the high and dodgy horse she had chosen to mount.

In her new and extravagant life, Betty had acquired a taste for very expensive wines. She downed a whole bottle during the course of the meal, and got more and more affectionate as the bottle emptied. As people were beginning to look at us, I had to tell her to behave, or risk the possibility of us being asked to leave before we'd finished eating. I ended the meal with my favourite sweet, trifle, which despite rationing, the restaurant still somehow managed to make almost as delicious I'd remembered it before the war.

I awoke in the morning to find myself flat on my back with Betty astride me, helping herself to one last fuck before it was time to get up and go down to breakfast.

"Do you prefer your eggs boiled, scrambled, or fried, sir?" the butler asked.

Did he say eggs, meaning that there was more than one on offer, considering the ration was one a month? I could hardly believe my ears.

"Scrambled please, on buttered toast if possible."

"Well, of course, on toast, sir. Tea or coffee?"

"Tea please, with sugar."

"The sugar is in the silver bowl that is on the table in front of your plate."

Why did the servants in upper-class houses always find a way to put me down? Probably it's because they instinctively knew I thought they were a load of arse-licking lackeys.

"When does your chap get back from the country?" I asked when Jackson had left the room.

"He mostly goes straight to Downing Street, but sometimes he pops in here for a change of clothes. He never arrives before eleven, though."

"Good, so I don't have to bolt down my scrambled eggs then."

"No, take all the time you want."

I kept Jackson on the go throughout breakfast filling up the stupid little teacups that could have been put to better use as an eye-bath. When we'd finished our breakfast, Betty and I arranged how best we could meet during the coming week. The plan was that when the sun shone, we'd meet up at the Serpentine, on dull days I'd be in Tony's. Soon it was time for me to go, so I picked up my towel and Vic's swimming trunks and left for Charlotte Street.

It was Wednesday before we saw each other again. I was lying on the grass sunbathing under a clear blue sky when Betty came and lay down beside me.

"So you couldn't make it to Tony's yesterday, eh? I was there for most of the day hoping you'd turn up."

"I didn't come because I felt I had to go and visit my mum. She's having her annual one week's holiday. I hadn't seen her in ages."

"How is she?"

"Oh, she's fine now she's moved in with her brother. She's not lonely any more and he's happy because he has someone to look after him."

"Isn't he the bastard who molested you when you were a child?"

"Yes, but my mum, bless her, knows nothing about that. Listen, Derrick, how would you like to get ten pounds for doing something you like? It would take you less than half an hour."

I had just been thinking that soon I'd have to do something to earn some money.

"What a silly question. Who in hell wouldn't like to get that much for half an hour's work? Jesus, it's more than two weeks' wages in a good job. What do I have to do?"

"It's to do with my bloke. He's happy to pay just to watch while I'm being fucked by a young man. How about it, will you do it?"

"Does that mean he stands over us wanking away while we're at it? Because if it does, I think I'd rather not."

"I promise you, you'll not even see him."

"What does he do, peep through the keyhole?"

"Honestly, you won't be aware of him."

"Three weeks ago, Betty, for five long days and nights, I was sitting motionless in a calm sea in the middle of the Atlantic. The old tanker I was on had broken down. She was loaded up to the brim with tons of highly explosive aviation fuel. A U-boat in the area could have blown the ship and me to kingdom come at any moment. You'll never believe what I got paid to be in those dangerous waters - a measly five pounds! So I'd have to have my head examined if I turned this offer down."

"So you'll do it. Then be at my place tonight, at ten o'clock. I'll open the door to you myself."

"Oh, not the snooty-nosed butler? I'd have loved to tell him that I'd come to co-star in a sex show to be performed for the benefit of his lord and master!"

"Jackson is very nice when you get to know him. There is just one little problem, Derrick. We do have to try and make our performance last for a while, and you know what you're like on your first fuck, don't you?"

"No, tell me."

"It's just that sometimes you tend to spill the beans prematurely. So I thought it might be a good idea if you had a wee wank before setting off."

"So, what you're saying is that your bloke would feel cheated if what he'd paid to see came to an end a few minutes after the curtain rose. You know, Betty, the last time I had to take the edge of my appetite before leaving to go somewhere was when I was a small child at boarding school. I was invited to a birthday party for one of the day children, and the headmistress made me gobble down four thick slices of bread and marge before I set off. The idea was that if she stuffed me enough I wouldn't give her school a bad name by making a pig of myself."

"That's really terrible. But what I'm suggesting isn't quite the same thing, is it?"

"No, of course, it isn't. Your idea just reminded me of it, that's all."

Betty glanced at her expensive-looking gold wrist-watch.

"Jesus Christ, I should have left here by now."

"So I'll be standing outside your front door at ten then. Don't worry, I'll remember to do what you asked before leaving. Hey, could you lend me half-a-crown as an advance? I haven't even got the price of a bus ticket or enough to get a bite to eat."

"It's not a loan," she said, and she pressed a pound note into my hand before kissing me goodbye.

Dead on time, I stood outside the imposing front door of the minister's London house. I felt a bit guilty, not because of what I was about to do, but because I hadn't got round to doing what I'd promised Betty I would. Jesus, I thought, it would be awful if I let her down. Just as I decided it might be best for all concerned if I bunked off, Betty opened the door.

"Derrick, I've a plan on how best to do our little show. When we're in the bedroom, you try and kiss me, I'll push you away, then you grab hold of me and say 'Come on, give us a kiss'. 'Piss off,' I'll say. Then you get a grip on my shoulder straps and rip them apart. I've already cut into the material so the dress will tear easily. Don't worry about ruining it, it's only a cheap one. When I'm naked, you push me backwards onto the bed, I'll struggle like mad and keep shouting 'Stop it, stop it, you're hurting me'. Eventually, I give up the struggle. You can leave the rest up to me."

"When should I undress?"

"As soon as I've stopped resisting and behave as if I'm beginning to enjoy it."

"Bloody hell, Betty, if I'd known I'd have to do all this acting I'd have taken a crash course at drama school."

"Stop being silly and come upstairs, he's up there waiting for us."

"Oh my God, we mustn't keep His Majesty's minister waiting, must we? You never know, he might have us thrown into the Tower or something."

Except for the light of a standard lamp that shone down onto the snow-white and creaseless sheet that covered the bed, the room was in darkness. I could just make out the silhouette of a man sitting in an alcove cut into the wall opposite the bed. Our little drama was played out more or less along the lines that Betty had worked out, until, that is, a minor disaster occurred. Being very aware of the creep who was peering at us through the darkness put me right off my stride. The more I tried to rise to the occasion, the harder it became for me to perform. Just when I'd decided that I had better beat a hasty retreat, Betty saved the show. Expertly she coaxed my reluctant member into life. In the end she had us both turning and twirling in so many different positions that I began to feel like a chicken on a spit.

When the climax had passed and I was lying exhausted on top of her, she whispered into my ear: "Thank God you finally made it, eh? Your money's under the vase on the mantelpiece."

"Do you think I ought to give a bow?" I whispered back.

"Oh fuck off, Derrick," she said as she gently eased me off her.

I got dressed quickly, then went over to the mantelpiece and picked up the cash from under the vase. Before I left, I glanced back at Betty. She was still lying on her back with her legs in the same position they were in when I got off her. With outstretched arms pointing towards the alcove, she beckoned to her man to come over and take up the space that I'd only just vacated.

Derrick boy, I said to myself, as I stepped into the cool and clean night air, what you've just done isn't politically the correct thing for a socialist and anarchist to be doing. So, there and then, I made up my mind that I wouldn't cater again to the sexual quirks of a Tory minister. As far as I was concerned he could go and fuck himself. Mind you, I did have to admit that to hold in my hand two crisp new five pound notes was very comforting. Flush with all this money, I treated myself to a taxi instead of walking to the Coffee Ann.

CHAPTER THIRTY-SEVEN

Vic was biting into a spam sandwich when I sat down next to him.

"You look as though you've been in the sun all day, Derrick. You should watch it, old boy, one can very easily get burnt this time of the year."

I told him I had been with Betty at the Serpentine, and then stupidly mentioned what I'd been up to. I was even mad enough to tell him how much I'd been paid.

"Good God, my dear fellow, Peter and I would have given the man an unforgettable show for half that amount."

"The man isn't queer, so he wouldn't part with a brass farthing to watch you and Peter at it, would he?"

"Derrick, you do tend to put things in the crudest manner. You could have said that as the chap is heterosexual, watching me and Peter having sex wouldn't exactly be his cup of tea."

Then, just to spite me, he stood up and in a loud voice announced to all the bums and scroungers lolling about that I was in funds. By the time the café closed in the early hours, a sizeable chunk of my ill-gotten gains had been wheedled out of me.

The next morning, I decided to join Robert on the land. I felt a compelling urge to do some hard, physical work, so that I could become fit and strong again. When I met up with Betty at the Serpentine later in the day, I told her what I planned to do.

"That means you won't be my partner any more, I suppose. It's a pity - I'd rather it was you than any of the others I use."

"I'm sorry, Betty, but I've been cooped up in a boat for the last nine months and I feel the need to be working out in the open air. I'll always be in London on Sundays, so we could spend the day together."

I gave her Uncle's telephone number, and told her she could always leave a message with him.

"You're my one and only girl, you know, Betty, and I'd be very unhappy if we couldn't see each other at weekends."

"We will, Derrick, I promise you."

Towards evening I walked back with her through the Park to the exit at Hyde Park Corner. I stood by the gates and watched her provocative hips sway from side to side as she made her way along Piccadilly before turning into Half Moon Street. It was sad that she wouldn't leave her rich bloke and come and live with me, I thought, even though all I possessed was the shirt on my back and my youth. I still couldn't really understand why she preferred him to me.

The next day when Robert came into Tony's, I asked him if I could return to Aylesbury with him.

"Derrick, that would be wonderful. You've no idea how fed up I am; you being there will make life much more tolerable."

"What about the people who run the hostel? Won't they object to me just turning up without notice?"

"No, all the warden gives a fuck about is that on Friday nights he gets his thirty shillings."

"What's the pay?"

"Two bob an hour. With overtime, it works out somewhere between four and five pounds a week. The thirty shillings the hostel charges includes breakfast and a hot meal at night. We're also given a couple of sandwiches to eat when we're working out in the fields."

"Blimey, that sounds cheap, Robert!"

"It's not all that fucking cheap when you consider that the bulk of what we get for our main meal consists of unpeeled potatoes."

"I was more or less brought up on spuds, and look what a bonny boy I've turned out to be!"

"Who knows, Derrick, you might have turned out bonnier if you'd been given a more varied diet."

"How do we get to the place where we work?"

"We all have bikes. They're old crocks – you'll find out that it's sometimes quicker to push the bloody thing. You'll be given one by Steve, our foreman. You'll meet him on Monday when we turn up at his little office in the town centre. Steve puts us into groups and tells us where we'll be working. He's a good chap. He'll be very relieved when I tell him you're not a Bible-thumper."

Robert finished his sandwich and said he had to go. He'd promised to see his girl before she left to go and work in the nightclub.

"Be at the Coffee Ann tomorrow night at nine, and we'll get the train to Aylesbury together."

No sooner had Robert gone than Johnny Bligh came in and sat down at my table. He looked awful.

"What on earth's the matter?" I asked.

"Derrick, I can't tell you how lucky I am to be sitting here next to you right now."

"Do you mean that the law has finally caught up with you?"

"They almost did, but not because of any effort on their part. It was all my own fault, I just got fed up with always having to look furtively to my left and right. That's what I've been doing these last eighteen months every time I venture out into the street. It began to wear me down.

I spent the whole of last night pacing up and down my room, debating with myself whether or not to give myself up. By seven I'd had enough of being indecisive, so to stop myself changing my mind again, I walked up the street to the police station in Tottenham Court Road. There was a big beefy sergeant standing behind the counter filling in a pile of forms. He ignored me, so I coughed a couple of times. Without even glancing up, he asked me what I wanted. 'I've come to give myself up,' I said, thinking that he'd jump with joy at the thought of having someone to lock up, but I was wrong. All he did was to look up at the clock and say: 'Would you mind coming back in half an hour, when my relief will be on duty? I'm already behind with doing the reports from the night's activities. If I start on all the paperwork involved in booking you in, I'll get even more behind.'

Well, I can't tell you how quickly I agreed. Once outside in the fresh air, I came to my senses. Johnny, I said to myself, this must be a sign from your guardian angel. He's telling you that this isn't the time to throw away your freedom. I feel like a condemned man who is reprieved moments before he climbs the steps leading up to the gallows. From now on I'll stay on the run."

To fill in my last day of idleness before joining Robert on the land, I had breakfast with Uncle and told him of my plan.

"Does that mean I won't see you?"

"No, I'll cycle down from Aylesbury every Sunday, and if it's OK with you I'd like to join you for breakfast and be with you for most of the morning."

"But Hayden, dear boy, Aylesbury is forty miles away. Unless you have a strong tail wind, I doubt if you will arrive here much before lunch."

"No, really, Uncle, if I leave at six, I'll be here before nine."

"How do you propose getting back in the evening?"

"I'll go back the way I came. If I leave at eight, I'll be back at the hostel by eleven."

"Where will you find the energy to do all this after working so hard all week long?"

"I really don't know. Perhaps the desire to see you and Betty will help power the bike along."

I stayed with the old man until he left to lunch at his club, then made my way to Speakers' Corner. Having spent the last nine months only in the company of merchant seamen, I had a real need to be amongst men like Frederick Lohr and Donald Soper. I desperately wanted to hear these two magnificent orators again in the hope that they could revive in me the enthusiasm I had for pacifism and anarchism before I'd been to sea. I listened to them the whole afternoon and then talked to them.

When I left the park, I saw Vic standing by the huge double gates. He was selling the fortnightly anarchist paper. I took a stack of my own and made a pitch by the kerb at the other end of the gates.

"*War Commentary*," I shouted at the top of my voice. "Read what we anarchists think about this Imperialist war and find out how we'd bring it to a speedy end."

No passer-by came anywhere near me, until, that is, two hefty-looking guardsmen crossed the wide pavement and came over to where I was standing.

"*War Commentary*, tuppence."

"Piss off, you fucking quisling and friend of Jerry's, and take that shit with you."

I didn't like their tone one bit, so I pulled myself to my full height, which still made them a good five inches taller than me, and said: "Not that it's any concern of yours, but I have to tell you that I'm not a collaborator or friend of either German or British Imperialism. I stand for the liberation of all the working-class from the chains of capitalism." Then I added, unwisely, "I'd even like to see the likes of you two idiots liberated."

Before I could do anything about it I was caught in a pincer movement. One guardsman went behind me and held me in a tight headlock, rendering me as helpless as a trussed-up chicken. This left his mate free to pound away at will into my unprotected body.

"Vic," I screamed, using the last bit of breath that remained in my pummelled lungs. Thankfully he heard me.

"Hold on, Derrick, the cavalry's on the way," he shouted as he ran to my aid.

The guardsman who was using me like a human punch ball paused to see who was coming to my assistance. He shouted to Vic: "If a bearded cunt like you is the cavalry, that makes me and my chum 'ere a fucking armoured division."

He then made the near fatal mistake of attempting to land a blow onto Vic's chin. Vic parried it with ease, then rained a flurry of blows onto the face and body of my assailant sending him reeling backwards. He ended up spreadeagled in the road, where an oncoming bus narrowly missed him. The soldier who was holding me let go and wisely decided not to tangle with Vic, but to assist his blood-spattered friend to his feet.

"If you lads want another chat with my comrade or me, you'll find us here on Sunday afternoons. In the meantime I suggest you trot along back to your barracks and have a little weep on your sergeant's shoulders," taunted Vic as the men slunk off down the Bayswater Road.

"I think it's more than likely that they'll come back next week with half their regiment."

"Precisely, that's why for the next two Sundays I won't be here, old boy."

"Thanks for coming to my aid. I dread to think of the state I'd be in if you hadn't."

"I do recommend, Derrick, that you learn how to defend yourself. I won't be on hand every time you get into a scrape, you know."

"If you weren't around, I'd be less inclined to provoke a couple of gormless six-foot-four guardsmen. My trouble is that I seem to lack the aggression that you can summon up at a moment's notice."

"Being aggressive does help, but my expertise in the art of pugilism is what really counts."

"The art?"

"To be able to put a man who is much taller and heavier than oneself flat on his back in a matter of seconds does, I assure you, take some considerable skill. Now, dear boy, let's have a look at you and see what damage, if any, you have sustained."

Vic looked me over and announced that in his expert opinion I had only been bruised here and there.

"Come on, let's go to Tony's. A cup of their lousy tea and a cheese sandwich will soon put you right."

I spent the next couple of hours with him and our friends in the caff, then went to my digs and stuffed the few things I possessed into my rucksack before leaving to meet Robert at the Coffee Ann. I crept down the stairs in order to avoid bumping into the beady-eyed landlady, but she caught me as I was gingerly opening the front door.

"Are you vacating your room, Mr Cartlidge? If you are, there's the small matter of a week's rent in lieu of notice to be dealt with before you leave."

"Ah, yes, er Mrs Cook, I was just about to come and see you."

"Really? Did you imagine that my room was outside of the front door?"

"I was only looking out to see if the friend that I'm expecting has arrived yet. I would never have left without giving you the rent," I said, with shammed indignation. I grudgingly gave her the pound she thought she was entitled to, then left, to be in time to meet Robert and accompany him on the train to Aylesbury.

At seven the following morning I was waiting with Robert and the others from the hostel outside the foreman's office. When he emerged, he set about dividing everybody into working parties and told them the location they were to make for.

Steve was a friendly-looking chap, probably in his late forties. I could see that he had spent most of his life close to animals and the soil.

"Robert says you'd like to work here for a time, is that right? All I need to know is whether or not you're on the run. Don't worry, I wouldn't turn you in. It's just that I can't take you on if you are."

"I'm nineteen, and won't be called up before the autumn."

"Good, so you're not one of those conchies then, and as you're Robert's friend I suppose you're not a Bible-pusher either."

"I'm the opposite, I'm an atheist."

"That's your right, lad. I'm a Christian but I don't push my religion down other people's throats. Now I'll just jot down your name and then get you to sign for the bike I'll give you. Have you done any manual work before?"

"I did work on a couple of farms for six months not long ago."

"So you know what you're letting yourself in for then, eh lad?"

He handed me a battered old bike and a time sheet.

"Robert will show you how to fill it in at the end of the week. Go and join him and the others outside and he'll take you to where you start work."

It seemed that our group was to do land clearing on a derelict farm some five miles out from the town.

"How did you get on with Steve?" Robert asked as we pedalled along.

"Fine, he seems a nice chap."

"He is, but he doesn't care a lot for that mob," Robert said, tilting his head back in the direction of the Jehovah's Witnesses and their like trailing behind us. "He avoids speaking to them if he possibly can. He doesn't mind them being conscientious objectors. What gets up his nostrils is that they're vegetarians. In his eyes, a man who doesn't eat meat isn't a real man."

"You'd better not tell him that I don't."

I asked Robert if we were expected to clear the land with our bare hands. As far as I could see, no-one was carrying any tools.

"They'll be there all right, Steve will have seen to that, and talking about bare hands, I've brought a pair of my old gloves for you to wear, to prevent you getting blisters as I did when I first started."

"You're a good pal, Robert," I said, as we cycled along the weed-infested path that led up to the farmhouse.

When I saw the state of the land and the farm, I was shocked. The mad farmer I'd worked for kept his land in good condition, and on the Gascoynes' estate, all the produce, from the asparagus right down to the humble swede, was so well tended that everything could have won a prize in a horticultural show. By contrast, this was agricultural chaos.

"Jesus, how can any society let the land get into such a state? Especially when you consider that before the war so many of us were underfed."

"Apparently, during the depression twenty per cent of all arable land ended up like this."

"You'd think that anyone with an ounce of intelligence who saw this would know at once that capitalism is a lousy and wasteful system, wouldn't you?"

"You might, Derrick, but believe it or not, most of the farmers who were made bankrupt, and the hands who worked for them went on voting Conservative, even though they ended up on the dole."

"Don't tell me things like that, it depresses me."

The whole week was spent digging a four-foot deep ditch and cutting down anything growing that would get in the way of a tractor when it came to plough up the land. We even had to chop down and dig up the roots of quite big trees that had haphazardly taken root in what was once a cared-for field. Bushes, shrubs, brambles, nettles, and gigantic thistles were all dug up and thrown onto a bonfire that blazed away fiercely throughout the day. Shovelfuls of anthills were lifted and put into the raging fire. The standing order was to dig it up and burn anything that grew. I said to Robert that I felt like a surgeon, who was cutting out a cancerous growth.

'You can kid yourself all you want, Derrick, but one thing is for sure, a surgeon wouldn't be paid the miserable two bob an hour that we're getting."

"It has nothing to do with money, I just find the clearing of derelict land very worthwhile, that's all."

In the middle of the week, our foreman arrived to see how our group was progressing. He asked me how I was making out.

"I'm fine, thanks. Mind you, I never realised how the land can degenerate when it's left unattended."

"Let's hope it will never be so neglected again, eh!"

Steve pointed to the others who were working some distance away from Robert and me.

"If it was left up to those vegetarians, the whole countryside would soon be in the same state. There'd be no cattle or sheep to graze and fertilise the fields and meadows, and without the animals to keep down the weeds and bracken, the grasslands would soon vanish. At first the countryside would look quite charming with buttercups, daisies and poppies. But the next year the view would be very different. Broad-leaved docks, nettles, thistles, brambles, scrub and thickets would have almost suffocated the grass. A few years later, the hedgerows would be overrun and the land would soon revert to forest, as it was when our ancestors ran around painted in woad. The soil would no longer be drained, so for the best part of the year it would be water-logged. From the open cockpit of a biplane you would see a carpet of green - but not the green of meadows and grasslands, but of leaves of tall trees, pushing for ever upwards as they compete for the sunlight."

I was so impressed by this that I only just stopped myself from applauding.

"Steve, have you ever said all this to that lot working over there?"

"It would be a waste of time. They'd only say that it was sinful to kill God's creatures."

"But surely all they need to do is look around them to see what happens to the land when it isn't farmed, I mean what the f- (I remembered just in time that our foreman didn't swear) the hell do they imagine they're doing right now, clearing up this shambles?"

"Lad, I'm a lot older than you, and I've learnt that there's no point in trying to argue with people's faith."

"Well, Robert, he's no country bumpkin, is he," I said as Steve left us to go back to his truck.

"You're right, he's not, but all the same, I'll bet you sixpence he votes Conservative."

"Are you trying to tell me that a man who has thought things out the way he has done goes and votes for the Tories? If you're right, socialism will never become a reality."

"That is precisely the reason why I never bother my head about politics. The English working man will never overthrow those who have conditioned him into believing they are his natural masters."

"That can't be true. I was brought up to put my faith in God, King and Country, and given the chance I'd fight the bastards tomorrow."

"As with any article that is mass-produced, there is occasionally a reject, and that, Derrick, is what you are. You're a fucking human reject who doesn't fit in. But luckily for them, there's not too many of your ilk about."

"Lenin managed to free the Russian people from their bondage, didn't he?"

"On that score, I think only time will tell."

"You have absolutely no faith in the good nature of man, have you?"

"None whatsoever, I'm sorry to say."

"How about men like Donald Soper? Now there's an example of a good man if ever there was one."

"Like you, Derrick, Donald is the exception to the rule."

And he started to hack furiously away at a particularly stubborn root of a blackberry bush.

CHAPTER THIRTY-EIGHT

Compared to weekdays - which by any standards were hard enough - the task I set myself on Sundays was the difference between a slow trot and doing a marathon. It started before six, when, half asleep, I'd cock my leg over the worn-out saddle of the dilapidated BWAC bike and set off to cycle the forty miles to London so as to be in time to join Uncle for breakfast. Uncle had said that I'd never make it unless I had a tail wind to help me along. Well, what with the pedals scraping against the frame of the bike on every turn, a galeforce wind pushing me from behind would have been more helpful. However, by walking the bike up the hills at a good pace, then freewheeling down them, I did manage to arrive in St John's Wood a few minutes before nine.

When Uncle saw me unwashed, unshaven, and with Buckinghamshire earth and weeds stuck to my clothes, he offered to wait breakfast while I had a bath.

"I'm starving, so if you can bear to put up with me looking the mess I do, I'd rather clean myself up after I've eaten."

"Of course you can, Hayden."

I was into my third bowl of cornflakes before I told him about the shocking state of the land and the farm.

"I shouldn't wonder if it got like that because of the farmer's inefficiency," said Uncle predictably.

"But Uncle, I've been told that more than twenty per cent of all the arable land in England lay derelict before the war. Surely all that can't be due to the inefficiency of the farmers?"

"Then I presume that they must have produced more than was required by the market."

I knew that discussion was futile so I asked if Betty had phoned.

"She did, she asked me to tell you that on Sunday she would be at her home in Half Moon Street for most of the day. Your girlfriend does live at a smart address, doesn't she?"

"Not so much live, more like kept," I replied.

"Oh, the naughty girl has a rich man in tow, is that it?"

"A rich and powerful man. In fact, he's a minister in the government."

"I shan't ask his name, that's not cricket."

"I couldn't give it to you even if I wanted - I don't know it."

"Just as well you don't," he said.

While Uncle read the Sunday papers, including the *News of the World* (which would have been hurriedly put under a cushion if anybody had called}, I had a bath and kept him company for a while, then cycled over to Betty's place.

When the butler opened the door and saw me standing there, he made a pitiful attempt to disguise the look of horror on his face.

"Will you, sir, be leaving the bike propped up against the wall, or shall I lay some newspapers down on the floor, so that you can put it inside?"

This, of course, was his way of saying I hope you'll leave the filthy thing outside. As always when I come up against a toffee-nosed git like him, the urge to become uncouth is irresistible.

"It's all right, mate, even a gipsy wouldn't want to nick this fucking old crock."

The butler behaved as if he hadn't heard my reply.

"If you'll wait here, sir, I'll go upstairs and inform madam that her 'friend' has arrived."

"Don't bother, mate," I said, doing my best to imitate a cockney accent as I pushed my way past him, "I'll go and tell 'er meself."

Betty was sitting at her dressing table, brushing her long silky hair. She was wearing a particularly transparent negligée. Catching sight of me reflected in the mirror, she turned round.

"Hallo, Derrick, I was hoping you'd be here soon. When did your train get in?"

"I cycled here."

"You what?"

"Pushed the pedals of a crummy old bike."

"Did Robert cycle with you?"

"No, he came by train, late last night."

"Got more sense than you then, hasn't he?"

"It's all right for him, he can stay at his girl's place, I can't because your bloke is here."

"You could stay at your uncle's flat, couldn't you?"

"No, I'd arrive too late for that to be possible. Anyway, I prefer to cycle down."

Betty walked over to the bed, slipped out of her negligée and lay on top of it.

"You must be tired, take off your clothes and come and lie beside me."

Within seconds, our bodies were so entwined that nothing less than an earthquake could have parted us. With only short breaks for a smoke, and a longer one at tea-time, we were sexually engaged until nearly seven, by which time we were quite hungry.

"Derrick, would you like to go and eat at the Strand Palace? I'll pay."

There wasn't the slightest possibility that I'd be paying, because the last time we went there the bill came to more than I was getting now for a whole week's work.

"Not the Strand Palace, thanks all the same, I can't face going through all the palaver of putting on a suit again. Let's go down the road to the Coventry Street Corner House."

That night I ate such a huge meal that I reckon it cost her almost as much as the Strand Palace. I wasn't just being greedy, I needed the food to provide me with enough energy to do the forty-mile journey back to the hostel. It was midnight before I got there, with what felt like water running through my veins.

I staggered into bed completely exhausted. It was to be the same more or less every Sunday for the entire time I worked in Buckinghamshire.

In the morning, Robert had quite a job waking me.

"Come on, Derrick, if you don't get up soon you'll miss breakfast."

I sat up and put my feet on the floor. I couldn't stand.

"Jesus Christ, Robert, my fucking legs have seized up, I can't move them."

"No wonder, considering how you overdid it yesterday. The only cure for that is to get yourself moving. Sitting down all day will only make your legs worse."

Somehow I managed to get down the stairs. Robert was right: the more I moved, the freer my legs became. By the time I got to the foreman's office for the weekly briefing, I was feeling a lot better. When he'd dispatched the others, he called Robert and me into his office.

"You two will start the week working on Mr May's farm near Princes Risborough. He thinks he might need you for two or three days. Don't forget to get him to sign your time sheets when you've finished working there."

We cycled the seven miles to the farm and introduced ourselves to the farmer. He looked fearsome, but sounded quite friendly.

"I want you to clear the weeds from a couple of fields. That's something you can manage, I take it?"

"Oh yes, we can do that all right," said Robert confidently.

"Good. Some of the men I've been sent didn't know which end of a cow to milk."

The farmer handed us two long-handled tools with bent metal blades at one end. Neither Robert nor I had ever seen anything like them before, but we didn't let on, and followed him out to the fields. They were some distance away, so we got a good idea of how much acreage he farmed.

Mr May stopped by a gate.

"This is one field, and the other runs parallel on the other side of the hedge to your right. When you've hoed up the weeds, put them into heaps and burn the blighters, that will make sure they don't seed themselves again. I have to go to London on business, but I'll be back in time to sign your work-sheets. Mrs May will make you a pot of tea if you go to the house at midday. I'll leave you lads to it, and see you both in a couple of days. Goodbye."

"Blimey," exclaimed Robert, as he surveyed the neat green lines of weeds all over the field in front of us, "if the other field is the same size, we'll be here until the end of the week."

Holding in our hands what we now knew was called a hoe, we climbed over the gate and started to whack away at the weeds. As no one was about, we stripped down to our underpants so as to take full advantage of the sun.Compared to digging ditches, this was a cushy number.

Up and down the field we went in unison uprooting the almost rootless weeds. Stopping occasionally to make small heaps of them. Then, when the scorching sun had turned them into the colour of straw, we burnt them.

Towards the end of our second day we stood looking admiringly at our handiwork. There was no longer the green haze of weeds over the fields; now all that was visible was the rich brown colour of the soil. The transformation was amazing.

Suddenly, from behind, we heard someone shouting. It was the farmer, running full pelt towards us with a double-barrelled shotgun in his hand. "You lunatics, you fucking maniacs, what the fuck have you done to my crop! I'll murder you, you stupid bloody bastards."

As we had done such a good job, we couldn't understand what he was raving about. In the event, there was no time to think about it as our B.W.A.C. bikes came flying over the high hedge, narrowly missing us.

"I'll sue the incompetent fools that sent you idiots to me. Now get off my land, or I'll put a load of buckshot up your arses."

"I get the feeling he wants us to leave," I said in an attempt to make light of the nasty turn of events.

We grabbed our shorts and bikes, and beat a hasty retreat to the gate at the far end of the field.

"Ungrateful bastard," said Robert as we pedalled away, still in our underpants.

"Yeah, and he didn't even sign our time sheets, the shit," I said.

The following morning Steve told us that we had pulled up and burnt the farmer's entire crop of kale that was needed to supplement the cattle's winter feed.

"It's his own fault," said Steve, "he should have made sure that you knew the difference between a young vegetable and a weed."

I heard later that the BWAC made a substantial out-of-court settlement to the farmer, and I know for certain that never again were a couple of enthusiastic amateurs let loose on a farm without supervision.

For the rest of the week, we were put back on hard labour, digging ditches and whamming away at brambles and thickets.

"Oh God," said Robert with the fierce sun beating down on his back, "how I do hate doing hard physical work."

By the middle of July, when we were more than fed up living at the hostel, Steve came to our rescue. He told us that a pre-war horse-drawn caravan was available as free living quarters and we jumped at the offer.

Considering the caravan hadn't been lived in for over two years, it was in remarkably good shape. It had been well shuttered, so the interior was dry and dust-free. The blankets had been stored in a cupboard under the lower bunk, so they weren't damp or motheaten. A sturdy lino-covered table was fixed to the middle of the floor. At one end was a small stove which could burn wood or coal, with a flue poking through the roof. Two iron lids had to be lifted to put the pot or frying pan to the flame. Robert soon became a dab hand at using the stove. My job was to light it, and before long, I could get it going almost as quickly as putting a match to a couple of gas rings.

My only worry was how to feed ourselves, but Robert assured me he could cook. I soon found out that this wasn't strictly true. His idea of cooking was to throw as many potatoes and other vegetables into a huge pot after work on a Monday. He would add a jar of Bovril or Marmite for flavouring and shove in our week's ration of lard to give the stew body. If it tasted a bit on the thin side he would add a few more potatoes midweek. This dish had one big advantage – it required virtually no washing up. But eating the same thing day in and day out did become monotonous.

Our toilet was a roofless old barn. The combined washbasin and bath was a self-filling cattle drinking trough, conveniently placed in the middle of a field near to our caravan. As it was a very long one, we would, after a hot and sweaty day's work, take a bar of soap and bathe in it together, and stay in the cool water for a very long time, completely ignoring the cows and horses patiently waiting for a chance to quench their thirst. What the poor creatures would think of the soapy water never entered our heads.

In August we were taken off land-clearing and sent to various farms to help with the harvest. Harvesting wasn't new to me, of course, but it was to Robert. I loved it, he hated it. For me it was the rhythm of the work that I so enjoyed: bending to pick up the sheaves and stooking them, then, when they had ripened in the breeze and sun, with a twist of your body and pitchfork in your hands, you swinging up the bundles of wheat to the deck of a slow- moving, horse-drawn cart. The whole activity was a sort of ballet, choreographed by a farm labourer. And all this hard physical work was changing my general appearance. My arms and chest were expanding at a rate I wouldn't have thought possible, and because of the marathon cycle ride to London and back on Sundays, my legs were developing at the same pace. One evening, when Robert and I were sitting on the steps of our caravan, marvelling at a particularly spectacular sunset, Robert said, "Do you remember telling me that you'd read in Everybody's Weekly that if you're pursued by a wild animal like a lion or a bear you should stop dead in your tracks, turn round and start running towards it?"

"You're right, you're not wrong, I did say that, and what's more, I believe it."

"Well, now's your chance to put your theory into practice."

Robert pointed to a young bull grazing peacefully at the other end of the field.

"We'll go over to him, then you can demonstrate how it's done."

"I can't, for the simple reason he's not chasing me," I said, grateful that my answer got me off the hook.

"Oh," said Robert, "I'm sure we can do something about that. We'll goad him into action, and he'll lower his horns and start to charge."

Oh why, oh fucking why did I open my big mouth, I thought, as we walked across the field. I wondered whether to say I'd invented the whole story, but for some lunatic reason I preferred the possibility of being gored to that of losing face.

We got a few paces away from the bull, but he didn't even bother to look up at us. He just carried on grazing.

"OK," said Robert, "we'll start shouting and making aggressive movements, that'll get him going. Then I'll hop out of the way and leave you to do your stuff."

I had no alternative but to go ahead. But no matter how hard I tried to antagonise the poor animal, it wouldn't budge from where it stood. I yelled and screamed until the bull finally got pissed off. He showed his annoyance by pawing the ground with his front legs and lowering his large head. For a moment we faced each other, eyeball to eyeball, separated by only a few feet. I made one last, desperate attempt to get him moving and with my arms outstretched and screaming as loud as I could, I made a huge leap towards him. The bull hesitated for a moment. Then, to my amazement, he turned his back on me and jumped over the gate into the next field.

"There you are, Robert, now I hope you believe what I told you," I said cockily. In the end, all I'd proved was that a young bull had a deal more sense than a young man. However, in common with a lot of the stupid things I've done in my life, some good did come out of my foolhardy behaviour. After that, I'd always think twice before picking up the gauntlet.

One very hot and humid day, Robert and I brought in loads of ripened wheat from the fields into a barn, where it was to stay until a threshing machine could be brought in. When we arrived, all hot and sweaty, with a wagon-load that was stacked so high the poor horse could barely pull it, the farmer's wife gave us a jug each of her sweet, home-brewed, thirst-quenching cider. I had never touched a drop of alcohol in my life, so I was drunk by the time I'd emptied the jug, and feeling unsteady on my legs.

"Say, Robert ol' chum, how about you going to the top of the wag – er – wag – er, cart, and me keeping my feet on the ground?" I said. My words were slurring in a way they'd never done before.

"Sorry, I can't, I get dizzy if I stand on anything higher than a kitchen chair." Robert had not been affected by the brew.

"Right, right, fucking right," I mumbled to myself. I climbed the ladder and staggered perilously about, throwing the sheaves down to Robert some twenty feet below. What with the heatwave and the lack of ventilation in the barn, I'd sweated out all the alcohol in my body by the time I'd worked my way down to the cart floor, so when we set off again, back to the fields, I was completely sober. As we brought in eight loads that day, I was drunk and sober eight times during the course of a single day.

The weather was perfect for harvesting, but because the English climate is so unreliable the farmers asked us to work all the hours of daylight. That week, we couldn't knock off for the weekend until sunset on Saturday.

"Shit, fuck and blast," shouted Robert as he threw his pitchfork forcibly to the ground, "it's too bloody late for me to catch the last train to London. That's done it, I've had it. When I leave here in the morning, that'll be the last time Aylesbury will clap eyes on me. Sorry to leave you in the lurch, Derrick, but I just can't face another day on the land. It's not only the work I hate, I don't even like being in the countryside. I'd rather look at a London bus trundle down Oxford Street than a primrose in a hedgerow. I'm a city person, I love the hustle and bustle of a big town, and the variety of people who live in it. To me at the moment, the noise a German bomb makes sounds more appealing than a cock crowing at dawn in a tranquil village. The very idea of facing another bleak winter up to my knees in mud, digging fucking ditches, turns my stomach. I know I've let you down, but I just can't help it."

"You won't be letting me down, I came here because I wanted to. Really, Robert, I do sympathise with how you feel. But what will you say to the cops when they stop you and want to see your papers ?"

"I'll have to bluff it out by showing them my CO's card, and just hope they don't pull me in to check out where I'm working."

"Your hands will go soft very quickly. One look at your palms and they'll see you're not doing manual work."

"I'll tell 'em I've been off sick for a few weeks. With a bit of luck I might pull the wool over their eyes. Look at Johnny, he hasn't got any documents to show when he's stopped, yet he's still free. Will you stay on here now that I'm fucking off?"

"Yes, I think so, at least until I'm called up, which won't be very long now."

"Register as a conscientious objector. By the time the tribunal hears your plea, at least six months will have passed."

"No, I can't face all those jingoist retired colonels sitting there making a judgment on whether or not they thought I was a genuine pacifist. In any case, I'd never get away with it once they find out that the man before them has already served in the Army and the Merchant Navy. No, I'll just let myself be roped in, then, after a bit, I'll desert."

"That's fucking mad, Derrick, deserters have two lots of thugs tracking them down, the civil and the military police. Then, when the bastards grab you - as in the end they will - it'll be the glasshouse you'd be sent to, not to a civilian nick. I know from men who've been in army jails that they're the worst by far."

"I'll face that hurdle when I get to it. In the meantime, I'll stay on here and visit Betty every Sunday for as long as I can."

The foreman was none too pleased when I told him that Robert had chucked the job in. Now he was stuck with a bunch of Bible-pushers. He once told me he thought he ought to couch his Monday-morning instructions in religious terms. To demonstrate this, he bent his arms heavenwards and aped what he presumed to be the posture of Moses when he came down from Mount Sinai.

"Brethren, last night the Angel Gabriel appeared at the foot of my bed, and sayeth unto me to say unto thee, that God's work for the week will be for thee to dig up ten acres of water-logged turnips."

That way they would do the job without moaning.

Now Steve told me that with Robert gone I would have to vacate the caravan at the end of the week. He had a farm labourer and his wife desperately waiting for accommodation, I would have to go back to living in the hostel.

"In that case, Steve, I'll be finishing up on Saturday," I said. "I just can't bear being housed with that lot."

"There is an alternative I can offer. It's a small caravan that used to belong to a gipsy. He abandoned it rather than face being called up. It's a bit dilapidated and wouldn't be any use in the winter. It stands on the brow of a hill near Tring, overlooking the countryside. If you were housed there, would you change your mind about leaving?"

"Yes, I would, anything is better than being cooped up with those Jehovah freaks. As a matter of fact, Steve, a spell on my own appeals to me. I was caged up on an oil tanker for nine months recently and wasn't alone for a single minute."

"Right, come and see me after work on Saturday and I'll find a map."

CHAPTER THIRTY-NINE

When I first caught sight of what was once a traveller's home, I was struck by its fairytale beauty. Lovingly painted wild flowers adorned the outside panelling. There were blue gingham curtains, bleached by the sun, at the small windows. The horse-shaft and the spokes of the wooden wheels were yellow. The beading around the panels was painted in gold. The curved roof was blackened by tar. Some of the steps leading up to the unlocked door had rotted away, but those that remained didn't give way when I ran up them. As I entered, two loose floorboards sprang up and hit me in the chest, and I was sent crashing down to earth with an awful thump. Chaplin couldn't have thought of a better entrance than that, I mused as I lifted my bruised body back into the interior. Having no talent at carpentry, I knew that one day soon, I'd have to ask Steve to come and fix the boards for me. Meanwhile, I'd have to remember on entering to avoid the huge hole in the floor.

Unlike the caravan that I had shared with Robert, this one had no water close at hand. It could only be got, a bucketful at a time, by going to the nearest farm, which was some distance away. This was a real sweat after a hard day's work. So any idea of personal hygiene, including shaving, had to be postponed until my regular Sunday morning visit to Uncle's. The hard-gotten water I only used to make tea and cook vegetables.

Having lost my chef, I somehow had to try and recreate the weekly-made stew that Robert had done so well. In the end, I more or less mastered it.

My next fortnight was spent at various farms helping the men with the big and noisy machines that farmers hired in to thresh the corn. It was the sort of work I thoroughly enjoyed doing.

One evening when I returned to the caravan, I found a gang of young boys pelting it with stones and shouting. They must have assumed I was inside.

"Fight for your country, you yellow-belly! You're even too much of a scaredy-cat to come out and chase us!"

Then, in unison, they chanted: "He's a coward, he's a coward, come on out, coward!"

When they saw me standing only a few yards away, they scampered off down the hill.

My first instinct was to go running after the little bastards and clip their ears. Luckily for them, I remembered reading a book by A. S. Neill, the anarchist founder of Summerhill Boarding School, which specialised in new and revolutionary methods on the best way to treat maladjusted and neglected children. So, taking a leaf out of his book, instead of giving chase I called ut:

"Don't run away, I won't hurt you, come back and let me join in your game, it looks like fun."

The boys stopped running, but couldn't quite summon up enough courage to come too close to me. To encourage them further, I picked up a few pebbles and threw them one by one at the wheels of the caravan. This had the desired effect, and they slowly started to come back. To egg them on, I picked up a really big stone and threw it with all my strength at the axle of the front wheels. My missile was the only one thrown that evening which went straight through a window. The boys broke out into peals of laughter.

"Fuck, shit and to hell with Neill and his bloody theories!" I shouted as I turned on the little blighters, "run for your lives, you bastards! When I grab you, I'll give you a beating you'll never forget!"

They cunningly fanned out in all directions and pelted down the hill as fast as their little legs would carry them, hoping, no doubt, to put as much ground as they could between themselves and the madman who was chasing them. I only managed to get hold of the one with the shortest legs. I picked him up by putting my hands under his arms to the level of my face. The little chap promptly burst into tears.

"Don't hit me, mister, I promise I won't never do it no more!"

I lowered the weeping boy to the ground and released the grip I had on him.

"I'll not hurt you," I said, as I patted his curly hair. He wiped away his tears with the sleeve of his worn-out jacket, then walked off to join his friends. By the time I got back to the caravan, I felt thoroughly ashamed of myself. As I swept up the pieces of shattered glass, I gave myself a little lecture:

"So, Derrick, you profess to being a pacifist, do you? Pacifists don't frighten little boys and threaten them with physical violence. They're supposed to set an example. What you should have done was to try and win the boys over to your way of thinking by kindness and discussion. To start with, you could have explained why they were wrong to call you a coward. You could have told them you'd been in the Army and the Merchant Navy. You could even have told them how you got a bull to back down. As the kids had assumed you were a conscientious objector, you could have told them that passive resistance sometimes needs as much courage as it does to fight. You never know, some of what you said might have given the boys food for thought."

I made a solemn promise that in future, when I felt I was being attacked, I'd not react the same way again. I'm sorry to say that in the years ahead, I broke the promise I made that day, many more times than I care to remember. It seems it's in my nature to become very aggressive when I feel I've suffered an injustice or, for that matter, if I think anyone else has. I hoped the boys would return one day so I could make amends, but, alas, they never did.

With the approach of autumn, I was back digging ditches and land-clearing. I didn't mind so long as I could get to London every Sunday and see Uncle and Betty. It was on one such Sunday toward the end of October that Uncle handed me an ominous-looking, beige envelope with OHMS printed in bold type above the address. I was to present myself for a medical examination at the HQ of the King's Royal Rifle Corps, Fulford Barracks, York, before fifteen hundred hours, on 5 November 1942. If I passed my medical, I would immediately be admitted into the KRRC for the duration of the war. The fifth of November, what a date to call up an anarchist! What I should be doing on that day was to hop on a 24 bus to the Houses of Parliament, and try to succeed where Guy Fawkes in 1605 had so miserably failed.

Some time back, I'd made up my mind what I would do when the dreaded letter arrived. I knew Uncle would never understand that because of my political convictions, I would rather go on the run than be conscripted, so to avoid upsetting him, my plan was to go in and do the six weeks' basic training, then desert. That way I hoped the old man would feel at least I'd tried, and perhaps, it might be less painful for him to bear.

Betty thought it was a crazy idea.

"If you're going to bunk off in six weeks, what's the fucking point in even starting?"

"It's just that I can't bring myself to hurt my uncle more than is necessary."

"You must love him a lot then."

"I do. Until I met you, he was the only person in all my life who cared tuppence about me. I feel for him as much as you do for your mother. Now do you understand why I'm doing it?"

"Yes, but all the same, I'm unhappy about not seeing you for such a long time. Putting up with my middle-aged minister is made more bearable when I know I'll have your firm brown body close to mine on Sundays. It wipes out the soft, fleshy feel of him for a day at least. I'm wondering how you're going to manage without a fuck for six long weeks? The girls standing outside the barrack gates won't be anything like as desirable or amenable as I am, you know!"

"Girls don't hang about by barrack gates any more. Nowadays they're at the exit of the nearest American base, hoping that a Yank who looks like Robert Taylor will pick them up and whisk them off in his jeep to have a meal in a smart restaurant, then give them a pair of nylon stockings and a packet of chewing gum. Anyway, I'll not even look at the girls in York. All I'll be doing is counting the days until I've got you in my arms again. Six weeks isn't anywhere near as long as the nine months we were apart when I was at sea. In the meantime, my beauty, we've got the whole day in front of us, so off with everything and let me devour you!"

With only short breaks for lunch and tea, we were at it one way or another until it was time to go and dine at the Corner House where, as usual, I stuffed myself with enough food to give me the strength to cycle back to the caravan.

In the morning, I told Steve why I'd be leaving at the end of the week.

"First Robert, now you. That only leaves me with those pious vegetarians. At least you're going off to do your duty by fighting for your king and country."

I wasn't going to tell him the truth. However, I did manage to say that whatever else I'd be doing, that would be the last reason for me to go off and fight.

"What other reason can there be then?"

"One day, you might work it out for yourself - that's what I did, Steve. Think about how all this dereliction of the land came about, and what caused it. Think about what befell the small tenant farmers and their families, and the farm labourers, who lived and worked on those farms. When you've thought about that, you may come to the same conclusions as I have - that the last reason for working men to go and fight would be for their king and country."

"My father lost his job as a herdsman in the depression. He put it all down to the Jews."

"What in heaven's name made your father imagine that the Jews were responsible?"

"I don't know, he never said why he thought it was their fault."

"Well, I know why, it was because he couldn't."

I was about to say that the most likely cause for his father being laid off was because a bank or a landowner foreclosed on the farm where he worked. There was no time because the truck arrived to take a gang of us to the fields. As I clambered into the back of the truck, Steve called out to me, "I'll think about our talk, Derrick."

When he paid me off on my last Saturday, he said:

"I'm sorry to see you go, Derrick, look after yourself, lad. Give Jerry one in the eye from me when you catch up with him, eh?"

"Sure," I lied. "Oh Steve, I forgot to mention that one of the windows in the caravan got broken. I'm afraid I have no idea who did it."

"Don't worry, I'll have it fixed."

He's a good man, I thought, as we shook hands.

"Derrick, before you go, I just want to say I've thought about the chat we had the other day, and I've decided that my father had the wrong idea."

"Good for you. Goodbye, Steve, I've liked working for you."

I'd become very attached to the caravan and felt a little sad that I was to spend my last night in it. At dawn, I kindled a fire in the grate and put the badly chipped saucepan on it to boil up some water for tea. When I'd drunk up three mugs of the strong brew, I extinguished the fire, then descended the dodgy wooden steps for the last time. As I had neither a camera nor the talent to make a sketch of the gipsy's home, I had to make do with taking one long final look at it, hoping a picture of it would stay in my mind for a long time.

When I arrived at Betty's, she had a broad smile on her pretty face.

"Derrick, darling, he's gone away for a few days, so you can stay here with me until you have to leave for the Army. He's had to go to North Africa. Churchill has sent him to have a pow-wow with Montgomery. It seems the P.M. is worried that the General is getting too big for his boots, now that he's been so successful at getting Rommel on the run in El Alamein. My man has been sent to remind Monty who's still running the war."

"Yeah, I bet Churchill wouldn't like it if anyone became more popular with the people than he imagines he is. Mind you, I don't know why he worries. He should know that the cadets at Sandhurst are trained to obey their political masters no matter how high they climb in the Services."

"It's a pity my chap didn't consult you before going. Who knows, he might have saved himself a journey."

"I know you're teasing, but all the same, I'm glad he didn't. Otherwise we'd not have these few days together, would we?"

And my goodness, what a blissful few days they were. Reluctantly, I left her side twice - once to see Vic, as I needed his help with something before I left, and the other time to go and say goodbye to Uncle.

When I entered the Coffee Ann, I saw Vic at a table with Robert. They were chatting to Jimmy, who was behind the counter making sandwiches.

"Look what a gorgeous brown young man has just walked in," said Jimmy in his usual exaggerated, camp manner.

Vic stood up and looked at me with feigned horror.

"Cartlidge, Robert has told me of your hare-brained scheme. I have to say that up until now I had credited you with the God-given gift of natural intelligence. Obviously I was mistaken, only a congenital idiot would go into the army with the intention of deserting. Why in fuck's name don't you do what Robert or I did?"

"Robert had a pacifist father who spoke on his behalf at the tribunal along with Donald Soper. Between them, they got him off the hook. Who would do that for me? Nobody. As for doing what you did, Vic, that is totally out of the question. Not for a moment would I get away with hoodwinking the MO into believing I was queer. All he'd have to do to call my bluff would be to show me a photo of Hedy Lamarr in the nude, and my cock would pop up so quick that he'd have to take evasive action."

"Before that, old boy, he'd have to put on his spectacles to see exactly what it was that he needed to evade!"

Robert laughed, I didn't.

"And just for the record," Vic went on, "I don't like being referred to as a queer, I'm a 'homosexual', and what's more, proud to be one."

"If your lot don't like being called 'queers', they should think up a name that they would like. 'Homosexual' is such a mouthful."

"It's only one fucking word, for Christ's sake. Anyway, to come back to your problem, I concede that you can't do what Robert or I did, but why on earth go and do six weeks and then desert? Why don't you go on the run straight away and be done with it?"

"It has to do with my uncle, I won't bother to say what, because you'd never understand. But Vic, there's something I need you to help me with."

"What's that, dear boy?"

"I want you to hang onto my ration book and identity card until I return. It's important that you continue to buy my rations each week, then as far as the MOD is concerned, I'm still in circulation. Tomorrow I'll register with the little grocery shop in Rathbone Place, that'll be handy for you. Whatever you do, Vic, hold onto my identity card, I'll be sunk without it when I'm on the run. Betty will bring both to you here on Sunday night, and do please try your best to be nice to her."

"I'll heap on the charm, old boy, and don't worry, I'll guard your documents with my life. Your rations will be a great help to Peter when he does his 'slaving over the kitchen stove' performance."

Vic went off to get me a cup of tea, which gave me the opportunity to say to Robert that I would have preferred it if he'd have looked after my things. We both knew that Vic could be unreliable, especially when he'd been drinking.

"I couldn't ask you, Robert, just in case they caught up with you and put you in the nick."

"You were right, that could happen at any moment."

I told him how much I enjoyed living in the gipsy's caravan after he'd left, and how, on the whole, I was sorry to have to leave the land.

"Not me, Derrick, I'd rather go to prison than face another freezing winter digging ditches. In the nick, you are at least dry and warm."

I drank up my tea and got up to go.

"All being well, I'll see you both in six weeks' time. We could all spend Christmas Day together, eh?"

"Good idea, oh, Christ, Derrick, by then your nice wavy hair will have been shorn and styled in that frightful short back and sides cut the army insists on."

"I'm not worried, it'll grow again soon enough. Well, goodbye Vic, and good luck, Robert, keep on weaving."

The next morning I went to say farewell to Uncle.

"My goodness, Hayden," he remarked as he opened the door, "the regiment you're going to will be pleased to see such a strapping young recruit. All that hard work on the land has really built you up. I was a little worried that when the time came you might have registered as a conscientious objector."

"No, Uncle, I promised you I'd have a go, and that's what I'm going to do. If I find it goes too much against the grain, then, perhaps, I'll need to think again."

This I said so as to plant a seed of doubt in his mind that I might not stay the course.

"Once you've settled down, you'll be fine. You're nearly four years older than you were the last time you were in, and I'm sure you'll do very well."

"We'll see, Uncle. If I get Christmas leave, I'll come and see you. And I'll write and let you know how I'm making out."

The old man crossed the room and put his arm around my shoulders.

"Hayden, I'm really proud of you, my boy!"

"Goodbye, Uncle, keep well!"

Betty and I spent our last hours under the sheets with our bodies welded together. All we wanted to do was to kiss and cuddle. We both resisted any desire to sleep, so that the morning would be a long time coming.

When the moment came to kiss her goodbye, she started to weep. I tried my best to comfort her, but to no avail.

"For Christ's sake, girl, do stop crying," I said, thinking it would help if I got firm. "It's not as though I was going off to fight, we're only going to be parted for a little while."

"I know, Derrick, but I just can't help it."

"Come on, Betty love, give us a smile."

She managed a little one before I left and the sight of the tears running down her cheeks as she tried so hard to smile, lingered in my thoughts, only to fade when I was caught up in the hustle and bustle of the crowded station.

CHAPTER FORTY

It was raining hard when the train pulled into York Station. Most of the passengers who alighted were, like me, young men in their late teens, heading for the same destination as I was. Standing at intervals along the platform were a few soldiers with megaphones close to their mouths.

"All you men who are making for Fulford Barracks must go to the station forecourt where coaches are waiting for you."

I held back a bit before getting on, the last one in the line. As the coach manoeuvred its way through the narrow streets of the town, the limited vision I had of it, as I peered out of the misted-up window, didn't impress me much. I was glad I had no intention of staying in this place for long. My fellow passengers sat in silence as we drove along. No doubt they were a little apprehensive about what was in store for them. I had no such misgivings: I knew only too well what to expect.

At the barrack gates we were left standing in the downpour until a corporal turned up and told us to follow him to the reception area. This was some distance away and by the time we got to it we were all soaked to the skin. I put myself at the end of a long queue of men who were waiting to be checked in by a sergeant seated at a desk at the far end of the Assembly Hall. I had a reason for wanting to be the last. With any luck he'd be feeling a bit weary by the time I got to him and wouldn't make a fuss when I confessed that I hadn't got a ration book or an identity card to give him.

Half an hour went by before I reached him. The sergeant, whose eyes were fixed firmly on the list in front of him, said to me in a gruff voice:

"Your surname?"

"Cartlidge," I replied smartly.

"Forenames?"

"Hayden Derrick."

"Aden Derek," he spelt out.

I corrected him.

"Hand in your ration book."

"I've lost it."

"Your identity card then."

"Lost that too I'm afraid."

He looked up at me for the first time:

"Did you manage to bring your cock with you or 'ave you lost that as well?"

"I didn't need to remember to bring it, Sarge, because I don't have one."

"All right, wise guy, what's your religion?"

"None, I'm an atheist."

"The form in front of me states you have to be one of the following: C of E, RC, any other Christian denomination, Jewish or agnostic. So make your fucking

349

mind up which it's to be?"

"I'll stick on agnostic, if that makes you happy."

"What'll make me 'appy, mate, is when they've cut that long 'air of yours in a proper manner. Now you can piss off."

"Before I do, sergeant, I feel I must thank you for the friendly way you have welcomed me into the British army."

"I'll see you around, smart arse. I get the feeling you're going to be a troublemaker."

The man's a clairvoyant, I thought, as I tagged myself on to a small group that a lance-corporal was taking to the barrack room that would become our quarters for the next few weeks.

The room was lined with two-tiered bunkbeds. When we'd all piled in, the others spontaneously paired off, leaving me to take the only single bunk. They must have felt instinctively that I was the odd one out. Certainly, I was physically different. In all my life I'd never seen such an emaciated-looking lot. They must have been reared on a diet of crisps, chips and cheap sweets, these no doubt with Tizer or Coca-Cola. They were either all skin and bone, or fat and flabby. Pimples and blackheads peppered their foreheads and pale cheeks. Some of them had boils, ripe for pricking, poking through the short hairs in the nape of their necks. Jesus, I thought, how in the hell is the drill sergeant going to turn this weedy-looking lot into a fighting unit? Who knows, I thought, perhaps plain army food, coupled with gentle PT, might bring about a small miracle.

If I'd been the MO who examined them, I'd have rejected ninety per cent, but when it came to it, provided their pulse was just detectable and both arms and legs had a modicum of movement, they were declared to be A1.

The next morning we were all taken to the assessment room, where we had to fill in a questionnaire and do an intelligence test. This was the army's subtle way of weeding out the wheat from the chaff, so that the ex-university and public school chappies could be segregated from the riff-raff when their basic training was finished, and then sent on to the officers cadet training unit.

The questionnaire was mostly designed to find out what sort of education and what standard you'd reached. Not having had any education worth mentioning, I just put a line through the ample space provided. As to the question about my previous employment, to cut a long story short, I put down landworker. That one word was the sum total of my contribution to this lengthy form. The intelligence test was fun to do, so I did it as best I could.

When everyone had finished, we were called in singly to be interviewed by an officer, taking with us all our completed forms and tests.

My interview with the captain went along splendidly at first. We chatted away affably and I had the feeling he was glad that the young man standing in front of him appeared to be both robust and articulate. This one is definitely officer material, I could almost hear him thinking. We swapped a few more pleasantries before he asked me to give him the sheaf of papers I had in my hand. Watch out for the flak, I said to myself, as I handed them over. But to my surprise, he didn't utter a word, just busied himself shuffling my forms about.

"I think you must have mistakenly picked up someone else's. What I have here doesn't in any way match the impression I have of you," he said eventually.

"They are mine all right, captain, look at the top of the form, you'll see my name on it - Cartlidge."

"Oh now I understand, you imagine that by spoiling the questionnaire you can duck out of doing the hard training that's the lot of an officer cadet. I have to tell you that this little ploy won't wash."

"Captain, it's not a ploy. Suffice it to say that my education wasn't high on the agenda of the people who were responsible for my upbringing. This has resulted in my almost total inability to read or spell. However, I am able to communicate verbally reasonably well. If you doubt what I've said, just ask me to spell out almost any of the words I've just used."

"So the line you put through the space intended for details of your education was, I presume, to make me believe that you'd had none? Now you know this to be absolute nonsense, don't you. The law requires that every child has to attend some school or other."

"You're quite right, it does, but what it failed to do in my case was to check up on whether I was being educated or merely used as unpaid child labour."

"I see, so what you are really saying is that you are an ignoramus masquerading as someone who has had a good education."

"I suppose you could put it that way."

"Well, under those circumstances I'm left with no alternative but to recommend that you remain in the non-commissioned ranks indefinitely."

"I didn't really imagine I would be considered for anything other than a foot-slogger."

"I must say, this is all most unsatisfactory. You can go now."

On reflection, I think the captain was quite right, it was indeed most unsatisfactory.

My next interview was with the chaplain. This I looked forward to, because I was going to amuse myself at his expense. "Sit down, will you. It states on the form here that you describe yourself as an agnostic. Is that correct?"

"No, it isn't."

"Then why did the sergeant put it there?"

"For the simple reason there was no space for him to write down what I really am."

"Oh, and what might that be?"

"I'm an atheist."

"I suppose you think that means you'll be able to dodge church parade on Sundays? Well, my boy, you're in for a little disappointment. All those who don't attend Sunday service are put on fatigues, which means you'll spend your time either peeling potatoes or cleaning out the pots and pans in the cookhouse, or washing out the latrines. The latter is not a pleasant task, I promise you. Now I advise you to think hard before you answer me - do you still maintain you're an atheist?"

"Your blackmail will not make me change my mind. However, I feel it's only fair to warn you that I'll retaliate by applying my considerable powers of persuasion to dechristianising as many of your flock as I possibly can."

"There's no such word in the English language as dechristianising."

"Maybe not, but I assure you I'm good at it."

The chaplain thought for a moment: "If I get you excused from doing Sunday morning fatigues, will you in return promise to leave what you call my flock alone?"

"I call them your flock, because they must have brains the size of a sheep's to swallow all the fairy tales that you and your kind propagate."

"Our Lord's life cannot be equated to that of a fairy tale."

"Of course, you're right. Most fairy tales have a happy ending, don't they? Now, to get back to your proposition, I do promise to keep my opinions to myself provided you stick to your side of the bargain."

I think the chaplain was relieved when I made my departure.

This wartime army was very different from the one I'd been in before. Gone was the interminable waste of time spent on spit and polish, and on kit and barrack-room inspections. The easy-to-don battle dress had replaced the blanco-belted tunic and the knife-edged, creased, three-quarter-length trousers. In this new army they concentrated on training the recruits as quickly as possible, so that they could be dispatched to North Africa, or to the battles expected in Europe once the Second Front had opened. Only the barracks themselves were similar. The buildings here were as old as those in Mill Hill, and perhaps even older.

Square-bashing, for me, this second time round, was a piece of cake. I could do all the drill blindfolded. The sergeant, who, of course, didn't know I'd done it all before, thought I was the brightest rookie he'd ever encountered. I was his blue-eyed boy and he held me up to the rest of the squad as an example. This undeserved praise didn't stop from me from enjoying the idea that for the one and only - not to be repeated - time in my life I was top of the class. Because of the bad physical condition of those in my squad, they went easy with the drilling on the parade ground. Being used to the hard manual work on the land, I was left at the end of the day with so much unused energy that the only way I could work it off was to go on a three-mile run followed by a workout in the gym. As I was streets ahead of the others, both on the parade ground and in the gym, it didn't make me at all popular with my fellow squaddies, so to get their own back they more or less ostracised me. This didn't bother me a lot as the majority of them were very boring.

By the end of November a damp cold mist coming in from the moors hung over the barracks and the surrounding countryside. This resulted in nearly all our company going down with heavy colds and rib-shaking coughs. The MO came up with the bright idea that the best treatment for this epidemic was to have us stand before breakfast out in the freezing weather and attend a mouth-wash parade. This was done in typical army fashion, half the company at a time. A corporal went along the four long lines of coughing and sneezing men, and poured a large measure of foul-tasting disinfectant into their tin mugs. Then a Sergeant would shout the order:

"Company, attention!" followed by "Company raise mugs!"

Up went four long lines of mugs to mouth level.

"Company, take a gulpful and start gargling!"

The noise of some one hundred men breathing through the liquid in their mouths was ear-piercing. A minute later came the final order:

"Company, spit it out!"

Now this was OK for those in the back line, but the poor sods in front of them got a mouthful of spent disinfectant spewed out all over the back of their legs. This nonsense was dispensed with after a few days when it dawned on the MO that it wasn't doing any good at all.

Halfway through the basic training, our company was marched off to the assembly hall to be addressed by our commanding officer. His opening words were inaudible, since nearly everyone in the packed hall was coughing continuously. He waited patiently for a few moments in the hope that it would cease, but if anything, it got worse until, exasperated, he finally snapped.

"The next man who coughs will be put on a charge."

Now to give an order is one thing, but to demand the impossible is quite another matter. I saw red-faced men all around me holding the palms of their hands tightly over their mouths, in a futile attempt to stop themselves coughing. Within seconds, their veins stuck out from their foreheads, and they looked as if they were about to burst at any moment. Inevitably, when they could hold on no longer, the deafening roar of some two hundred men simultaneously coughing, rocked the hall. When the noise subsided, the CO bawled out:

"Sergeant major, this company is to be confined to barracks for seven days. Perhaps staying in might cure them of their damn coughs."

He strutted off the platform, never to be seen again for the duration of our training.

A few days after this fiasco, our squad had to report to the medical centre to have all the inoculations required for service overseas. We were to be given shots for typhoid, cholera, malaria, and God knows what else.

Having no immediate plans of my own to go overseas, I had to have a quick think on how to dodge the cocktail of incapacitating jabs. Fortunately, the interior design of the room helped me solve the problem. A medical orderly called us in, in batches of fifteen. As we entered, he noted on a list our names and Army numbers, then he told us to roll up both sleeves, after which we had to cross the room to where the MO was waiting to wham in the vaccines. I held back until the others had formed a queue by the doctor, and waited, unnoticed, in the background, until a few were dealt with. When they made their way across the room to a door marked Exit, I followed. On leaving, an orderly ticked us all off his list. This meant that as far as army medical records were concerned, I had been immunised. I even got rewarded for my cheek because the squad was excused duties for two days on the grounds that the next day their arms would stiffen up and scabs would form where the hypodermic needles had penetrated the skin.

While the rest of the squad was off sick, I was either out running or doing my exercise routine in the gym. I think they thought I was some sort of superman. One even asked me how it was that I seemed to be unaffected by the inoculations, and I told him it was an example of how mind over matter.

By mid-December I was looking forward to the short leave we'd be given on completion of our basic training. It was then that I planned to desert and get a free trip back to London by using my return railway warrant as a one-way ticket. Two days before this would become a reality, fate dealt me a terrible blow. I woke up in the middle of the night with the glands on both sides of my neck throbbing madly. I was feverish, and my throat felt as if it had been rubbed down with sandpaper. I tried to soothe it by taking sips of water, but swallowing was so painful that I had to give up. When reveille sounded, it was a tremendous effort to get out of my bunk and leave the barrack room. To add to my suffering, a blizzard was raging outside. Somehow, I got to my sergeant, who took one look at me and told me to report sick straight away.

The walk through the swirling snow from the sergeants' mess to the sickbay was a nightmare. To my horror, I had to wait with two other men out in the freezing cold until it was my turn to be called in. Gusts of icy wind cut through my heavy greatcoat so easily that it might just as well been made of muslin. I started to shiver uncontrollably and felt that my strength was ebbing away. In the end my legs crumpled up under me and I collapsed into a heap on the snow-covered ground. One of the men rushed inside and got hold of two orderlies. They lifted me onto a stretcher, carried me in and wrapped me in blankets in a vain attempt to stop me shivering. I lay there for the best part of an hour, until the MO arrived. When he put the flat of his hand onto my burning brow, he said sharply to one of the orderlies: "Jesus Christ, why wasn't I called to this man long ago?"

"We didn't think it right to disturb you while you were having your breakfast, sir."

"You bloody idiot, he might well have died on us. Call an ambulance immediately."

By the time the ambulance came, all I wanted to do was roll over and die. The alarm bells rang as we drove over the icy roads to the nearest civilian hospital, where a doctor was called immediately to have a look at me. He carried out a variety of tests and diagnosed glandular fever coupled with the possibility of pneumonia. He told me there was nothing he could do about my condition other than instruct the nurses to make me as comfortable as possible until the fever had subsided. After that, he said, I would need quite a long spell of convalescence.

I think he imagined I'd cheer up at the prospect, but it only made me feel worse. It had completely scotched my dream of seeing Betty, and joining Vic and Robert for Christmas. I consoled myself with the knowledge that I'd do all I could to get well as quickly as possible. Then, when I was given sick leave, I'd be off like greased lightning.

For ten awful days, all through Christmas, I lay in the ward only able to take little sips of water. It was some days into the New Year before I managed to swallow a small amount of mashed potatoes. That started me on the road to recovery and gradually my strength and weight began to return.

I was in hospital for three and a half weeks altogether before the doctor decided I was well enough to be discharged. His plan was to send me to an army convalescent home called Askham Grange. I tried hard to persuade him that as I was already feeling so much better, I didn't need to convalesce. But alas, nothing I said would make the doctor alter his mind.

CHAPTER FORTY-ONE

Askham Grange was a grand family estate, situated in the country some eight miles away from the City of York. It had been loaned to the army as a patriotic gesture by the family for the duration of the war. Prudently, they had taken the precaution of having the walls and pillars covered with plywood and putting their possessions under lock and key in the top two storeys of the house. The army had the use of the rest. What had been the ballroom was now a huge dormitory. Some fifty beds and their lockers lined its four walls. We had our meals in the magnificent banqueting hall with its frescoed ceiling. A large basement had been converted into a recreation area, equipped with billiard and ping-pong tables. One section was fitted out as a workshop for the inmates. Some made toys for their children, others lovingly and with great skill carved model war planes and ships out of balsa wood. A kiln and potters' wheel had been installed. Everything possible was done to make the time spent in this place very pleasant. The end result was, that apart from me, nobody - but absolutely nobody - wanted to leave. They would all have been quite content to sit out the war there.

As far as Major Radcliffe, the MO, was concerned, it was easier both medically and administratively to have the convalescent home mostly filled with men who were fit and healthy. If half the beds were occupied by patients needing treatment, that wouldn't have been the major's idea of leading a quiet life. When he went on his twice-weekly rounds and asked you, how you were feeling, you would say: "Slowly improving, sir," and the major would answer:
"Glad to hear it. Nevertheless, I think you should stay here until you've quite recovered."

This collusion between the MO and inmates was to the advantage of both. In reality, the place was a buckshee wartime holiday home that compared favourably with Butlins. However, it had one serious drawback. With the exception of the major's frumpish wife, all the staff were male. There wasn't a female to be seen anywhere. For this reason only did the men finally decide that the time had come to take the sick leave due to them, and go back to their wives or sweethearts.

Within days I felt almost as fit as ever. To stop myself going out of my mind with boredom, every day I got into my army blues and took long walks in the countryside. In bad weather, I did P.E. in the gym. I amused myself in the long winter evenings by spreading the gospel according to Alexander Berkman to anyone who cared to listen. An aspiring Tory politician was amongst the few who did. This chap would have been training to be an officer if only he hadn't broken his leg on an assault course. After I'd been spouting off to him, he told me that if I repeated to an Army psychiatrist my mad ideas of a world that I believed could function without government supervision, the doctor would come to the same conclusion as he had - namely, that I was as mad as a hatter. Nevertheless the same man said he'd been landed with a task which he hoped I could help him with.

"What is it?"

"I've been asked by the entertainments officer to organise a debate on Friday after supper. The motion for discussion is 'A Woman's Place is in the Home'. I'm quite prepared to propose it, but I'm finding some difficulty in getting anyone to oppose the motion. It's occurred to me that you with your revolutionary ideas would be ideal. Can I put your name on the order paper?"

"My name? You must be joking, in my whole life I've never spoken to more than four people at once. Thanks for offering, but no."

"You do realise, don't you, that you're missing out on a chance to put forward your theories to a receptive and intelligent audience whom you might even influence. I doubt too, that your political masters would be pleased to hear that you'd dodged such a golden opportunity."

"Unlike you Tories, we anarchists don't have political masters. But you do have a point. Perhaps I should take advantage of a captive audience."

"So you'll do it then?"

"Yep."

"Good, you've got three days to prepare your case, and may the speaker with the best argument win, eh!"

As he shook my hand, a nasty smirk appeared on his face. Derrick boy, I thought, you've done it again, even though you vowed you never would. Gone and picked up the fucking gauntlet, haven't you? Just like you did when Robert challenged you to fight a bull, only this time you'll most likely look like a complete twit in front of a whole lot of people.

Because of my incomprehensible handwriting and spelling, it was quite pointless to make notes about what I might say, as I'd never be able to read them back. The only way to compensate for my disabilities was to try and memorise any ideas that came to mind. For two whole days and nights, none did. Luckily through sheer panic some opening words materialised on the morning of the third and final day. I'd just have to hope that I became inspired by the cut and thrust of the debate.

On the dreaded evening, many more people turned up than I ever imagined would. The major and his wife and all the staff were there, along with a fair number of the inmates. I presumed that most had come to escape another dull evening, mooching about the place wondering how best to amuse themselves.

My opponent was applauded as he rose to speak. He started off by drawing a vivid picture of what life would be like for husbands when they got home after a hard day's work and found the little woman lying exhausted on the sofa, still in her working clothes. He felt it his duty to warn us that a working wife would soon insist on her husband doing the washing up, bathing the children and putting them to bed, and even pushing a pram in public places. As the breadwinner, the husband had the right to expect to find his evening meal ready and his slippers waiting by his favourite chair.

The speaker went on to say that women didn't want to compete with men: their one ambition was to make a home for their families, while the men gave them sustenance and protection. This was the way it had always been, and he was sure that was how women wanted it to stay.

Judging by the applause, this speech went down a treat. Then I stood up. I was greeted by a wall of silence. I took a deep breath. To my surprise, words began to emerge. I gave myself a kickstart by saying the few sentences I'd memorised.

"My friends, the very title of this debate is a good enough reason why you should vote against the motion," I began. "A woman's place is in the home. All you need to do is switch the gender and you'll see what nonsense this is. In a democratic society, a woman's place can only be where she wishes to be. My opponent referred to women as the weaker sex. This is only true physically. In every other way women are our equals, and sometimes even superior to us. Women are just as intelligent as men and can do just as well in science, medicine, commerce or any other professions or trades. Boadicea and Joan of Arc led their armies into battle just as effectively as Hannibal, Napoleon or Lord Kitchener. But the proposer of the motion would have us believe that such a woman would have served the community better by staying at home darning her husband's socks. He thinks a woman's role is to be an adornment and an unpaid cook-housekeeper-cum-nanny. This vision of his is outdated. How would he feel if his wife referred to him as 'my little man'?

"The speaker said he expected his wife to make a home for him and his offspring. His offspring indeed! Is he the one who gives birth and suckles the baby? If the children are exclusively anyone's they must be the mother's. The father's tiny contribution can in no way be compared to hers."

By now I was feeling confident enough to give my audience one of my stock-in-trade lectures on the benefits of ending capitalism. I could see by the look on the major's face that this part of my speech didn't please him at all. Undeterred, I soldiered on.

"Comrades" – addressing them thus sent a shock wave through the audience – "I look forward to the time when neither men nor women are exploited, and when the workers, not the money lenders, reap the rewards of their labour. I want to see a society where there is equality for both sexes at work and in the home."

Foolishly I ended up by saying: "There can be no real justice in the world until the idea that women are inferior to men is rooted out. Husbands should want to share the responsibility of bringing up children, and should do their fair share of housework. Only then will women be free to realise their full potential, and to stand shoulder to shoulder with men in the struggle. Thank you, comrades."

To say my speech was not appreciated would be an understatement. When I returned to my seat, the room was so silent you could hear a pin drop. The chairman broke the silence by jumping to his feet to take the vote.

"Will all those in favour of the motion please raise their right arm."

Simultaneously, a sea of rigid arms shot up, reminiscent of the salute given at a Nazi rally.

"Those opposed, please raise your arms."

For a moment, nothing stirred, until that is, timidly at first, then resolutely, the Major's wife put up her arm, and so as to make quite sure she was seen she stood up. Her husband looked as if he would have liked to pull her back down but didn't dare to as all eyes were on her. I felt like leaping off the platform and hugging her. The organiser waited until she was seated, then announced that the motion was carried unanimously.

When the audience got up to leave, my opposite number called out:

"Before you go, gentlemen, I feel you should be made aware of the awful job I had to find anyone to oppose me in this debate. Very commendably, Derrick Cartlidge volunteered. Now, although I don't agree with one word he said, I do have to admire the courage it must have taken to put his unpopular argument across. I think he deserves to be applauded."

To the sound of half-hearted clapping, he crossed the rostrum and shook me warmly by the hand.

By mid-February, I was still trapped in the convalescent home with no sign that I'd ever be discharged. Already my plan to desert had been delayed for over two months, and I was getting more and more restless. I began to feel that if I didn't soon get my arms around Betty, I might even start to fancy the major's wife.

Then with only two hours' warning, the major had a phone call informing him that the chief medical officer for the North of England would be arriving to inspect the place. As ninety per cent of the inmates were A1, panic ensued. He rushed about ordering anybody who didn't look too healthy to get into bed. The rest were to sit on their beds and only stand up if they were spoken to.

When the colonel came round accompanied by the major, he stopped and said a few words to each man. Those wishing to stay on gave an award-winning performance. Men who an hour before had been working out in the gym or playing a fast game of table tennis were now hoodwinking a senior MO that they weren't feeling well enough to be sent back to their regiments.

When the colonel got to my bed, I jumped up smartly and stood to attention.

"At ease, soldier, tell me, how do you feel?"

"Me, sir, I've never felt so well in my life."

"I presume this man is for immediate discharge?" he asked the major. The major looked as if he would like to have had me at the wrong end of a firing squad, but he pulled himself together and replied: "He's due for release tomorrow, colonel."

"I must say, major, you've done a good job with this young man. He looks fit enough to be in the Commandos. Looking forward to rejoining your company, are you, lad?"

"Can't be soon enough for me, sir," I replied enthusiastically.

"That's the spirit, my boy, can't abide malingerers who try to spin out their convalescence."

While the colonel was still within earshot, I asked the major when I should collect my rail pass.

"Ten hundred hours at my office," he snapped.

Whoopee, Derrick, you've worked it at last.

On the stroke of ten, I was knocking on the major's door.

"In."

Not 'come in please', just 'in'. The way he shouted out that one word gave me a clue to his mood.

"It's you, Cartlidge, eh? My God, man, you put on a show and a half for the colonel yesterday, didn't you?"

"A show, sir?"

"You know perfectly well what I mean. If you felt fit enough to leave, why didn't you bloody well say so? I'd have discharged you long ago."

I wanted to point out that I'd told him at least half a dozen times that I was better, but prudence prevailed.

"Sorry, sir, but the thought never really occurred to me."

"Perhaps another time, you'll remember to speak up. Here's your rail and privilege passes, you can collect your uniform and civilian clothing from the storeroom."

At the speed of light, I snatched the chitties up from his desk.

"Thank you, sir," I said. I gave the major an exaggerated salute, then made a mad dash for the door.

CHAPTER FORTY-TWO

That evening I was sitting in the Coffee Ann, explaining to Vic and Robert how I'd been held virtually captive for almost two months.

During my first week back, I could walk about freely, secure in the knowledge that if I was stopped by the law, my papers were in order. After that, I'd have to take evasive action whenever I saw a redcap or a copper.

I found a tiny room in Notting Hill for ten bob a week. It was even smaller than the cabin I'd shared with Olaf on the Norwegian tanker. It did, however, have one advantage over larger digs: on a cold night, a penny in the gas meter heated the room up in a matter of seconds.

The day after I'd moved in, I decided it would be wise to get rid of my uniform. I had it hidden under the bed, out of sight from the nosy landlady. I felt she was the sort who would inform the police if she was suspicious. I stuffed my uniform into a brown paper carrier bag and set off for Uncle's, timing my arrival to coincide with his being out lunching at his club.

Armed with a dictionary, I sat down and wrote a letter explaining why I'd decided to desert. I wrote that, as promised, I'd tried to make a go of it, but in the end my political views combined with my pacifist convictions had made serving in the Army impossible. I told him too that my socialist ideals meant that I was unable to accept the £1500 he intended to leave me and therefore wanted him to delete the bequest from his will. I said how very fond of him I was, and how much I valued his friendship. I hoped we'd meet again in happier circumstances, and in the meantime I'd keep in touch by telephone.

Then, as a postscript, I wrote that I was sorry to burden him with the problem, but I hoped he would not mind handing in my uniform at the nearby Albany Street barracks. He could tell the duty sergeant that he found the carrier bag lying in the road outside his house. This was a stupid idea, since it had my army number clearly printed on the inside of the jacket and therefore could be traced to me and also to him as his name and address was in my army pay book as the person to be informed in the event of my death. It never entered my thoughtless head that it was insensitive of me to ask a retired, aristocratic old military man to walk through the street carrying a paper bag containing the discarded uniform of a deserter.

Although I was dying to see Betty, I had to wait until the following Sunday before attempting to contact her. Even then I had to hope that her sugar daddy was away with his family. The moment the butler opened the door, I knew I'd struck lucky.

"Oh, it's you, is it?" he said contemptuously. "Wait here and I'll inform Madam."

"Don't bother, I know the way up, Jackson," I said abruptly, as I brushed him aside.

The bedroom curtains were drawn when I entered the room, but from the dim light of the open door I could see that Betty was still fast asleep. Her long auburn hair lay spread out over the pillow. Very gently I stroked its silk-like strands. She only woke up when she felt my lips brushing across her closed eyes.

She smiled at me.

"It's you, Derrick. So you've finally escaped from that terrible convalescent home, eh?"

"Yes, how did you know I was in one?"

"When you didn't appear at Christmas, I phoned your uncle, and he very sweetly read me a letter you'd sent him, that's how I know."

"Oh, I see."

"Come on, love, get your clothes off and hop in beside me."

I did, and for the best part of that day and night I spent my time discharging all the stored-up sexual energy that had accumulated over the last three months. At breakfast I asked if everything was still all right between her and the Minister.

"Yep."

"Are you still managing to stash away lots of money in your cocoa-tin?"

"I replaced that with a shoebox some time ago. It's more than half full with crisp new fivers."

"I suppose you'll soon be able to retire in comfort, then?"

"I intend to go on milking him for as long as I can get away with it."

"And so you should, the rich milk the poor for their entire working life. Do you still have to put on those sex-shows for him?"

"Yes, but they're different now. He likes to watch while I perform with another girl."

"Jesus Christ ... I bet you had a job finding one who'd agree to do it?"

"No, it was easy. A girl I worked with when I was at the Cabaret Club said she'd only be too happy to be my partner. She said she'd always fancied me anyway."

"Didn't you find it a bit ...you know, doing it with a girl?"

"Not really. Whatever happens, it's a damn sight better than having him slobbering all over me. In general, women make better sexual partners than most blokes do - for one thing it lasts a lot longer with them, and they don't go limp on you like your average man does after he's been banging away for a couple of minutes, leaving you all sexed up with nowhere to go."

"Are you saying that lesbians get more out of making love than you and I do?"

"Perhaps."

"In that case it might have been better for you if you'd spent the last day and night with your girlfriend instead of me."

"Don't be silly, Derrick, you know I'd rather be with you than anyone."

Despite her reassuring words, I couldn't help feeling a little threatened by what she had said. I didn't tell her that, of course, but replied more in jest than anything else:

"How about the next time we're together, you taught me to do whatever it is that you and your girlfriend get up to. Then, my pet, you'd have the best of both worlds, plus that little bit extra."

She reached under the tablecloth and placed her hand between my legs, and squeezed gently: "It's not such a little bit," she said.

When the time came for us to part, we arranged, that in the unlikely event of her man being in when I called, she'd instruct the butler to ask me whether I wanted to see her or the Minister. That would then be my cue to scamper off down the street.

As a deserter, I now had the problem of earning money. The jobs I'd done before were no longer possible. Without proper papers, I couldn't return to the land, and film extra work wasn't advisable as the CID frequently raided the studios in the hope of picking up amongst the crowd anyone who was on the run. The only reasonably safe job was to work as a stagehand at one of the West End theatres where no questions were asked. You got six shillings and eight pence a performance for eight shows a week including matinées, with a little under two pounds fifteen coming in. I'd just about be able to pay the rent, and have enough left over to buy a modest amount of food, and occasionally treat myself to the luxury of a bus ride. Vic, who was working as a scene-shifter at the Hippodrome Theatre, told me there was a vacancy there for someone on the electrics.

"The job is yours if you want it, Derrick."

"How in fuck's name could I do it, Vic? I know absolutely nothing about electricity except what happens when you flick a light switch."

"You don't even have to know that, dear boy. All you'll be required to do is plug a few spotlights into their sockets, when there's a scene change. A half-witted child could do it."

"You're quite certain, that's all there is to it? I mean, I don't want to be responsible for setting the place on fire."

"I give you my word, old boy, you'll be able to do the job standing on your head."

That evening I went with him along to the theatre, and was taken on there and then. When the curtain came down at the end of Act One, I watched in awe as the stagehands dismantled the set, then skilfully manoeuvred the huge flats to the rear of the stage before erecting another one. The transformation was very quick and silent. The furniture and props were put in their precise positions within the space of a minute or so. Just as Vic had said, my only contribution was to plug a few spotlights into the floor sockets.

I worked in many of the West End theatres, but I liked being at the New Theatre best of all. It was the temporary home of the Sadlers Wells Ballet Company. Ballet wasn't popular with the other stagehands, so between acts they all skived off to a near-by caff, while I - who had never seen ballet before - watched from the wings absolutely entranced by the beautiful dancing and wonderful music. After a few weeks, I'd seen their whole repertoire many times over, and never tired of it. I fell madly in love with Margot Fonteyn, and couldn't take my eyes off her when she was on the stage. Seeing her dance in Giselle literally moved me to tears. I just flirted with the other girls in the company in the vain hope that one would come out with me one day, but with Margot it was different - I wanted to marry her and spend the rest of my life watching her as she danced about our home, helping me with the housework, dressed only in a leotard. She often stood right by me as she waited in the wings to go on, but alas, she never so much as glanced my way. I wish I could say that about her partner, Robert Helpmann, who was always trying to chat me up. One man did make it with some of the girls. I never understood why, because he wasn't attractive, and mostly smelt of drink. His name was Constant Lambert, a composer, who also conducted the orchestra. Perhaps this was the reason the dancers preferred him to me.

While I worked at the theatre, there was never a vacant seat. As early as five in the morning, in all weathers, devoted balletomanes often queued up in the hope of getting a seat in the gallery. Some were ordinary soldiers on a few days leave. I reckoned I was very privileged to see all these marvellous performances and get paid to watch them.

One matinée, when the curtain came down at the end of *Swan Lake*, the audience clapped and cheered so much that only umpteen curtain calls would satisfy them. When finally the curtain came down and stayed down, the director, Ninette de Valois, strode onto the stage.

"Nobody is to leave the stage," she shouted, shaking with rage. "Never in all my career have I ever seen such disgraceful dancing. Do you think that the matinées don't matter, and therefore there is no need to give of your best? If you do, you had better think again. This company has built up a world-wide reputation, precisely because it doesn't give shoddy performances. Matinée audiences have the absolute right to expect the high standard of excellence that you would give if their Majesties were in the royal box, even more so, for they are the true lovers of ballet."

She went on to reprimand some of them individually, including my beloved Margot, and a few of the younger ones burst into tears. I marvelled at the sheer power of this tiny woman, who had the ability to make most of the company shake in their tutus. For the life of me I couldn't understand what upset her so, nor, I'm sure, would the audience, who had been so appreciative.

One evening, a new ballet was premiered in front of all the critics and a very distinguished audience. It was a patriotic piece about the victory of good over evil. The good were the brave, ill-equipped English, symbolised by St George, and danced by Robert Helpmann. The bad were the Germans, represented by a dragon. Just in case the audience hadn't caught on a wooden swastika was attached to the dragon's neck and a Jerry tin hat was perched precariously on its fire-breathing head. I can't recall who did the choreography for this awful ballet, but I'm almost certain Constant Lambert composed the music.

My job, apart from the usual positioning of all the spots and floods, was to place a single spotlight on the apron of the stage when the curtain came down on the last act. Its purpose was to throw a beam of light on St George as he walked triumphantly across the apron, all dressed up in shining armour and carrying a flag stuck on top of a long pole. When the moment came for my spot to come on, it didn't. The orchestra helped out by repeating the sound of victory bells ringing more times than the composer intended. In desperation I opened the floor trap to make sure I'd pushed the plug right home. To my relief, I had. It meant that the fault lay in the main switchboard.

"For fuck's sake, do something!" I said in a loud whisper to the electrician who was manning it.

"It must be a break in the cable, fuck all I can do about that right now."

"Jesus Christ," I muttered, with the orchestra bells still ringing in my ears. There was only one thing left to I do. Fumbling in the dark, I pulled out a number of matches, and struck them simultaneously. A flash of light streaked out over the blacked-out apron of the stage. A full couple of seconds elapsed before it dawned on St George that the light from my matches was all he was going to get.

Helpmann didn't walk across, as he was supposed to, he sprinted. By the time he reached me, the tips of my fingers were beginning to burn. I fully expected him to praise me for showing such presence of mind, but all I got was: "You fucking idiot, don't you even know how to push a bloody plug in?"

Unfairly, monstrously unfairly in fact, the next day I got the push. I suspected that Helpmann had engineered my dismissal. It was probably his way of getting his own back for giving him the brush-off. My only consolation was that the ballet got a slating from the critics, and was dropped after only a few performances.

Although the very idea of a regular nine-to-five job was absolute anathema to me, you could have set your watch by my daily routine. By ten in the morning, I was at the Porchester Baths in Bayswater, where I did half an hour's vigorous exercises before diving into the pool and doing the crawl for forty lengths. By midday I'd run through the Park to the Serpentine, where I hired a skiff with a sliding seat and - stripped to the waist, even in freezing weather - rowed at full pelt the entire length of the lake three and a half times. By two I'd walked from the boathouse to Tony's caff in Charlotte Street. My lunch never varied, omelette made from powdered eggs and greasy chips cooked in fat that was added to, but never changed. My afternoons were spent sitting in the café drinking endless cups of tea with Robert and Vic, or any other bum who drifted in. At six-thirty, except on matinée days, I'd be going through the stage door of one or other of the theatres. As soon as the final curtain came down, I'd make my way to the Coffee Ann, where I'd remain until one in the morning. Sundays I devoted to my gorgeous Betty.

This routine never altered until late spring. Then you'd have found me on Hampstead Heath, either basking in the sun or swimming in the ponds. I never kidded myself that this life would last for ever. Always lurking beneath the surface of my mind was the fear that I would be apprehended and have to come face to face with reality.

So far, when I was stopped by the law, I had got away with it by showing my old army discharge book. Using ink-eradicator, I had managed to erase the reason for my release, leaving in only the glowing testimonial. This fooled the average, uniformed copper on the beat, but wouldn't have hoodwinked the boys in plain clothes. Fortunately they were easy to spot, as they mostly went about in pairs, dressed in their regulation fawn macs, and shiny black shoes. Oddly enough, the best way to put them off the scent was to make yourself as conspicuous as possible. The more eccentric you looked, the more likely they were to assume you were some misfit the armed forces had rejected. To make sure they thought that of me, I let my hair and beard grow and wore a pullover I had mutilated by hacking off its sleeves, leaving my bare arms free to poke through the gaping holes. My corduroy trousers were permanently worn rolled up to my calves, and when spring came, I went about everywhere barefooted. Another ploy I used successfully more than once, was to walk boldly up to the mackintosh brigade and ask in a stuttering mock-public school accent if they would be so kind as to point me in the direction of Oxford Street. By the time I'd get it all out, they were relieved to see the back of me.

Looking the way I did, meeting up with Uncle was out of the question. I missed not being able to see him. I knew he worried about me, so I made a point of phoning him every week. On one such a call, he pleaded with me to give myself up.

"Hayden, if you did, I could use my influence to see that any sentence imposed was reduced considerably."

Dear Uncle never could understand - and it would have been futile to try and explain it to him - that the fact that the system allowed people in his position to pull strings was just one of the many reasons I so disliked the unfair and class-conscious society that ruled England.

That spring of 1943, the weather was so good that by the end of May I was as brown as a berry, and very fit, thanks to all the vigorous exercises I did. One perfect morning I'd just finished my breakfast and was about to leave to meet Vic and Robert at the ponds in Hampstead Heath when my landlady shouted up the stairs.

"Mr Cartlidge, there's two gentlemen down here wanting to see you."

Good, that'll be Vic and Robert, I thought, as I ran down to meet them. Alas, standing in the hall were two men in fawn macs.

"Are you Hayden Derrick Cartlidge? You're under arrest for desertion and must accompany us now to the station."

"Can I pop back up and get my toothbrush?" I asked.

"You can, but make it snappy."

On the way up, I racked my brains to think of some way to escape, but unfortunately the dormer window of my top-floor room was too high to jump from. I decided to make a bolt for it when they opened the front door. I was sure I could easily out run the pot-bellied coppers. I saw the landlady peering through her slightly opened door. Of course it was she who'd shopped me, the bitch, no doubt because I'd fallen a couple of weeks behind with the rent. My scheme to make a run for it was scotched when I was handcuffed. I asked where their car was.

"Car, mate? No need for a vehicle, the station is only two doors down the road."

As I'd always turned right when I went out, I never knew that a whole hive of flatfoots were virtually my neighbours.

After checking me in at the desk, the coppers put me in a cell and turned the key. What a place to be on such a beautiful day, I thought. An hour went by before I was taken off to the interrogation room, where two detectives were waiting to grill me. They wanted to find out how I'd made a living as a deserter. To tell them would have only made it harder for those still on the run, so to fob them off, I made up a story of how I'd been kept by a rich woman.

"Pull the other one, mate, it's got bells on. Do you really expect us to believe that with you looking the way you do, long-haired, scruffy beard and walking about barefoot, any self-respecting woman would want you as her fancy boy?"

"What you haven't taken into account, Inspector, is that my lady friend mostly saw me with nothing on."

"OK, funny boy, what's her name and address, then?"

"I'm afraid I can't possibly give you that. Her husband would be most upset if he found out how his wife was spending the very generous allowance he gave her."

"So what you're saying is, you're a fucking pimp, that's it, isn't it?"

"Not really. S ince the lady isn't a prostitute, I can't be a pimp."

"Any man who lives off a woman is a ponce as far as I am concerned."

"Prince Albert lived off Queen Victoria. Are you inferring that he was one?"

"How dare you talk about royalty in that way!"

"Don't worry, Inspector, Albert can't hear me."

That bit of heresy got me put back into the cell.

On the way, I asked the policeman who escorted me if I could make a phone call and was told I was entitled to just one. I phoned Uncle and told him about what had happened.

"Oh Hayden, my dear, dear boy, I'm so sorry. If only you had taken my advice and given yourself up, I could have helped you. Promise me one thing, you won't antagonise them, it will only make it harder for you."

"I'll be as good as gold," I lied. "Uncle, please tell Betty and Vic what's happened to me if they phone you and don't worry about me, I'm a lot tougher than you might think."

"You will write to me, won't you?"

"Of course I will."

"Time's up," said the policeman at my side.

"I have to go now, keep well, Uncle, goodbye."

I couldn't help but feel a bit guilty for all the distress I was causing the old man.

It was mid-afternoon when the redcaps came to collect me. I was put in the back of an open jeep and taken on a journey that any tourist to London would have paid to go on. I was driven through Hyde Park which was looking splendid,with all its trees unfurling their pale green leaves in the brilliant light of the spring sunshine. We passed Buckingham Palace, entered St James's Park, ablaze with the bright colours of daffodils and tulips, and drove round dear old Nelson perched on his column in Trafalgar Square. The jeep came to a halt in a side street behind the Ministry of Defence building in Whitehall. There was no proper entrance, only a wide opening in a brick wall. I was checked in, then led along a corridor to a huge lift.

"This lift is big enough to hold a pair of horses," I said to the guard as it trundled its way to below ground level.

"Funny you should say that. That's what it was used for when the war started. This was where the Life Guards kept some of their prize horses to protect them at night from the air raids which were expected but never came. Before the war, it was an ammunition dump, very handy for the soldiers who might have to defend Government buildings and the Houses of Parliament, if civil strife ever broke out."

"Do you mean a revolution?"

"Yes, something of that kind. Now those temporary stables have been converted into cells, to put deserters like you in, while they wait for their unit to send an escort."

We left the lift and walked along a cobbled passage until we came to a long row of wooden doors. The plaques above them bore the names of the horses once housed in them. I was given 'Bessie's' stable.

I don't know what Bessie thought about her living quarters, but for me it had one enormous drawback. There was no window through which to see even a chink of daylight. The only light was a bare bulb fixed into the centre of the high curved ceiling. It burned continuously day and night. It drove me mad, particularly when I wanted to sleep. If there'd been a chair, I could have reached the bloody thing and taken it out, but the only piece of furniture, apart from a bucket to piss in, was a bunk that was firmly attached to the wall. I didn't even have to slop out, because the bucket was picked up a few moments after one banged on the cell door. I was kept locked up in this dungeon without any contact with anyone but the guards. Occasionally I heard the sound of some poor sod who'd go berserk thumping on the cell door, screaming to be let out.

For six long days and nights, I was incarcerated in this awful place before an escort arrived to take me back to York.

When I stepped out into daylight, it took my eyes a while to adjust to the glare of the midday sun. In an odd way I looked upon my escort as my saviours, even though they were taking me to the barracks to face God only knows what.

"I'm afraid I've got to put the cuffs on you," said one.

"Please don't apologise, it's comforting to know that at least one person in this hostile world is attached to me," I replied, in a vain effort to be amusing.

A jeep took the three of us to King's Cross Station. We had a long wait before the train was due. I felt that I was an acute embarrassment to my guards, no doubt because of my appearance. No doubt they would have liked to disassociate themselves from this weird, long-haired, bearded man, with his sleeveless old shirt, his trousers rolled halfway up and no shoes on his feet. To add to their discomfort, I started to address the people around.

"Look, comrades, what happens to you when you refuse to obey the orders of the capitalists who govern our country," I shouted at the top of my voice. I raised my handcuffed arm above my head.

"Do you see, comrades, they cart you off in chains. If only you would all do what I'm doing - refuse to co-operate - very soon they'd not have enough handcuffs to go round your wrists."

"Belt up!" said the man I was fettered to.

"I will, but only on condition that you get your chum to buy me a couple of packets of fags."

"He's not your fucking servant."

"Indeed, he's not," I agreed before starting to shout again.

"All right, you win, give him the money."

As I hadn't had a cigarette for some days, I chainsmoked three on the trot.

When the train arrived, we followed a porter to the far end of the platform, to a reserved carriage. The three of us sat in silence as the train pulled out of the station. Observing the expressionless faces of my escort, I pondered on what fate might have in store for me when I got back to the regiment. For the first time since my arrest, my natural cockiness deserted me and a feeling of fear gripped me in the pit of my stomach. I began to wonder how I would stand by my pacifist principles when faced with the British army at war. At only just twenty, I was perhaps too young to face what was bound to be a very rough ride.

CHAPTER FORTY-THREE

"Where the fuck did you find that monkey, 'anging from a branch, was 'e?" said the guard sergeant when he clapped his eyes on me.

"The only thing I have in common with monkeys is that I'm a vegetarian. I suspect that what you've got in common with them is the size of your brain."

He looked angrily at me, then shouted to a guard: "Uncuff the cunt and lock 'im up, I can't stand the sight of the long 'aired smart arse."

To me he said: "In the morning, mate, we'll 'ave you back in uniform, then you'd better start be'aving like a soldier, 'cos if you don't, you'll soon 'ave the posh cockiness knocked out of you. Then I wouldn't want to be in your shoes."

He obviously hadn't noticed that I was shoeless.

The cell I was put in was a lot smaller than the converted stable in London. It was only a couple of feet longer than the narrow wooden bunk that was screwed to the wall, and no more than four foot wide. The white-washed brick wall and ceiling hadn't been painted for years. The small window, iron-barred and sealed, was too high up to look out of it.

"Right, private, this cosy little place will be your home for the weeks you're waiting to face a court martial. In a while, I'll bring your supper. When you need to go to the khazee, give the door a hard wham."

"Before you go, comrade."

"What did you call me?"

"Comrade, that's what I call everyone who's not a capitalist. I was about to ask you when I get a palliasse and a pillow."

"You've already got 'em, mate."

"Excuse me, comrade, all I can see is two blankets."

"That's right, one is your mattress and the other is to cover yourself when you're having a kip."

"I see, so what do I use for a pillow?"

The guard pointed to a wooden wedge.

"That's the pillow."

"You're joking, aren't you?"

"No, private, I'm not."

"It's beginning to look like I'm going to be more comfortable when I get to the glasshouse."

"You will be, mate, the idea is, that after a spell in here, you'll be looking forward to going there. Clever, don't you think?"

"Brilliant, absolutely fucking brilliant, comrade."

"A bit of advice - cut that fucking comrade shit out, 'cos if you don't, believe me, you'll be for the high jump."

With that well-meant advice, he left. Alone at last, I surveyed my bleak surroundings. Derrick boy, I said to myself, now is the time to think up a plan of action to help me cope with what was almost certainly going to be quite an ordeal. After a lot of thought, I decided that the best plan of all was to do what I'd always done, rely on the inspiration of the moment. However, there was something I could do to reduce the odds stacked against me. It was to keep in the top physical condition that I'd been in before I was arrested. Then I'd be a lot fitter and stronger than the Grade 'C' guards who would be keeping watch over me.

With nothing to do but kill time, I could do my daily exercises three times over. There and then I stripped down to my pants and did forty press-ups, followed by running on the spot for half an hour. To keep my stomach muscles hard, I lay on the floor, clasped my hands behind my head and did thirty sit-ups. Provided I did this routine three times a day, I'd very quickly build up a layer of muscle that would cushion the effect of any blows that might land on my body.

When I'd done my exercises, I stood tiptoe on the end of the bunk in the hope that I might be able to see out of the window. But alas, it was too high. Some previous occupant had etched into the concrete sill 'Do Not Lean Out Of The Window'. The man's sense of humour cheered me up, and fixed in my head that come what may, I must keep mine. I decided that to amuse myself, I'd try to turn the tables on any guard who might be tempted to push me around. I felt fairly confident that I'd be able to give to my jailers more than they bargained for.

On the dot at six-thirty my supper was brought. It consisted of two thick slices of bread, a chunk of cheese, and a mug of tea. I'd hardly taken a bite when two mice popped out from a hole in the wooden floor.

"Hallo, come to keep me company, have you?"

I thought just the sound of my voice would have sent them scurrying off. On the contrary, the cheeky little creatures climbed up onto my bunk and beady-eyed, whiskers twitching, looked longingly at the food I was eating.

"OK, OK, I've got the message," I said.

From the palm of my hand, they nibbled at the small pieces of bread and cheese I offered. So tame and unafraid were they that I could only assume that for generations the mice that lived below the floor had realised that in return for a little companionship, the lonely men incarcerated in the cell were happy to share their meagre fare. As they were nowhere to be seen between meals, it puzzled me how they knew what time to surface. Maybe the cue for them to pop out of the hole was the sound of the key turning in the lock. I named my rodent chums Darby and Joan. I knew which was which, because the unchivalrous Darby had his fill before Joan was allowed a nibble.

With nothing but the bare boards and a wedge of wood for a pillow to lie down on, it was almost impossible to get comfortable at night. Before attempting to sleep, I'd debate with myself whether I should use both blankets as mattress, thus leaving my unclad body to the chill of the Yorkshire nights, or cover myself with one and roll up the other to have something soft to lay my head on. As I lay there in my sleeveless shirt, I tried to imagine how any self-respecting firm with an iota of humanity, could carry out an order from the Ministry of Defence for wooden pillows.

The next morning, when the mice and I had eaten breakfast, a guard came into my cell with a uniform tucked under his arm.

"Put it on, Cartlidge, and make it sharpish. In fifteen minutes you're due at the barber. He'll cut that long hair of yours into shape."

He put the bundle down and made for the door.

"Before you leave, comrade," I said, "I think you should know that I shan't be putting on the uniform, so you can take it away. Nor will I be having a short back and sides."

A look of disbelief registered on his face.

"Are you telling me that you're not fucking well putting on the King's uniform?"

"Yes, I suppose one could put it that way, comrade."

"Right then, right then," he repeated in order to give himself time to think of what to say next, "we'll soon see about that. Mark my words, me and my mates will have you in your uniform in no time at all."

A minute later, he was back with the guard sergeant and one other soldier. The sergeant came over to where I was sitting and prodded me in the ribs with his stick.

"This is your last chance, put the fucking uniform on now, or face the consequences."

"Consequences, that's a big word to use, comrade," I said to the small sergeant.

My sarcastic reply set all three of them on me. I responded by going as limp as a wet blanket. For a while, they couldn't think of how to tackle my seemingly lifeless body. In the end, they solved the problem by dressing me as they would a helpless baby. They unbuttoned my shirt, then removed my trousers - that was comparatively easy. But trying to put the tunic on, with me flopping about, was a lot more difficult. When they'd finally managed it, they had the problem of how to get this legless lump to the other side of the barracks where the barber had his premises. After a lot of thought, the sergeant came up with a solution - they'd go to the sick bay and get a stretcher. By the time they returned, I was sitting bolt upright with nothing on but my underpants. This meant they had to repeat the whole laborious performance. With my arms dangling over the sides of the stretcher, they took it in turns to lug my twelve stone to the barber. He was a civilian,who had been cutting the regiment's hair for most of his life. If it hadn't been for the war, he'd have been retired. He wasn't at all happy about the way I was brought in.

"Is this young man sick?" he asked.

"No, 'e's just being fucking awkward," said the Sergeant.

No sooner was my body dumped onto the barber's reclining chair than it slid off onto the floor.

"I can't cut this man's hair without his co-operation," said the old man, somewhat distressed.

"Don't worry, we'll 'old 'im steady while you do it," said the sergeant.

One guard knelt down and gripped my ankles, the other one stood astride me and leant on my chest. The sergeant held my face between the palms of his hands. Now that I was secured, the barber picked up his scissors and started to cut. At that point, my pacifist principles flew out of the window, and I sprang into action. I pulled my legs up behind the back of the man who faced me, then with all my might I thrust them forward. This sent the man gripping my ankles flying backwards across the room. Despite the firm hold the little sergeant thought he had on my face, I could rock my head from side to side with ease. This was making it impossible for the barber to cut my hair without drawing blood.

"It's no good, I can't do it with him wriggling about like that. The only way I can cut his hair is to take it all off with my clippers. Even then you would have to hold his head still."

When he suggested that, I stopped resisting. I realised immediately that if I was completely bald, bearded and dressed in my own clothes, I'd look even less like a soldier.

"If you promise to remove all my hair, leaving only my beard intact, I'll sit still while you do it."

"Is that all right with you, sergeant?" asked the barber.

"As far as I know, there's nothing in the King's Regulations that says a man can't have a beard, so let's get on with it."

I let the barber clip away until I was totally bald, then resumed my passive posture.

"If you'd prefer me to walk back to my cell, go and get my clothes, and then you can dispense with the stretcher and save yourselves all the humping," I said to the sergeant.

"What I'd like to do is frogmarch you back with a bayonet stuck up your arse."

"How imaginative of you. I never would have thought that a twit like you could think up something so original. However, I do have to warn you that I'm a judo expert," I bluffed, "and if you attempted anything like that, it could well end up the other way round. Mind you, I doubt that an insensitive lout like you would even feel the blade up his rectum."

"Put the bastard on the stretcher and lock him up before I lose my temper and kill the cunt."

"Calm yourself, comrade, it's bad for your blood pressure," I said, as the other two lifted me onto it.

The moment I was alone in my cell, off came the uniform. Not long after, a guard peered through the spyhole in the door and saw me back in my underpants. He hurriedly unlocked the door and came in.

"You fucking cunt, you, I suppose you think this caper will get you your ticket. Well, it won't, we'll break you first, make no mistake about it."

"Please, comrade, don't talk like that, it upsets me so," I said sardonically.

"When you're taken to the CO tomorrow, he'll upset you all right. He'll let you know what happens to your sort when they play this fucking game."

"You'd better give me my gear back before we go, otherwise I'll have to be a stretcher-case again."

"You don't tell me what I should do, you cunt."

"Wouldn't dream of it, I just thought it might be less bother for all concerned if I used my legs, but whatever you decide is OK with me, comrade."

"One day soon, mate, you're going to get such a thumping, and I hope I'm around when it happens."

"Why don't you attempt to do it right now, or haven't you got the guts?"

I could see the veins of rage sticking out from his forehead, but I think he knew that if he so much as touched me, he'd get the worst of it.

To my surprise the next morning, when two guards came to march me off to see the commanding officer, they'd taken my advice and brought my own clothes with them.

"Put them on and come with us to the guard room."

When we got there, the sergeant shouted:

"Prisoner and escort, FALL IN!"

With my hands in my pockets, I stayed still while one guard placed himself in front of me and the other behind.

"QUICK MARCH, LEP, LEP, LEP, RIGHT LEP!" the sergeant bawled out.

With me just casually strolling along, the man in front was soon yards ahead, while the one behind kept banging into me. The whole thing was so ludicrous that I got a fit of the giggles.

"Push the bastard," said the irate sergeant to the man at my rear. The only effect this had was to make me go even slower. The door to the CO's room was open when we arrived, so we went straight in. With my escort marking time, I stood still taking stock of the surroundings.

"Prisoner and escort, HALT!" came the order from the RSM, who was the master of ceremonies when soldiers were brought up before their commanding officer. My escort took up their positions on either side of me. This gave the CO his first clear view of the prisoner lolling about in front of him. His jaw dropped a little and the monocle in his right eye fell out.

"Why in God's name is this man not in uniform?" he asked.

"Because, sir, when we forcibly put it on 'im, as soon as our backs are turned, 'e takes it off again."

"Why didn't you put him into it before bringing him to see me, sergeant?"

"Whenever we do, sir, 'e goes all limp, then we 'ave to carry 'im everywhere."

"I need some sort of explanation for all this shenanigan, private," said the CO.

"Well, comrade, it's - "

"Did you address your commanding officer as comrade?"

I was just about to reply when the sergeant butted in: "'e calls everyone that,

374

sir."

"Does he now - I think you should know, private, that even in civilian life I am addressed as 'sir', because I am a baronet."

"Bully for you, comrade. Everyone who does good work for the community should be given a title. The men who clean our stinking sewers, miners, who spend their lives breathing in coal dust that kills them, fishermen who go out to sea in all weathers - all these men should be awarded some title or other, because they've earned it, not just had it passed on to them by some illustrious ancestor."

"The very men you have just mentioned are now doing their duty by fighting for their king and country."

"Do you know what their reward will be if they survive this war? Most of them will be back on the dole."

"I can see that you're one of those young people who believe they have an answer for everything, so I'll not waste my time talking to you. However, army regulations require me to ask if you have any complaints."

"I do, it's my wooden pillow."

"What's the matter with your wooden pillow, boy?"

Rendered speechless for a moment by his question, I finally came up with: "I'd need a chopper to fluff it up, that's what's the matter with it, comrade."

My reply brought a faint smile to the CO 's face before he said:

"I could arrange for you to be given a soft pillow and a palliasse, but only on condition that you abandon this ridiculous charade. Put on your uniform and behave like a soldier, then I'll give you my word that you'll sleep comfortably tonight."

"Thank you for your offer, comrade, but my conscience prevents me from accepting it."

"I have to warn you that if you persist with this nonsense, you could be transferred to a field of action. Then if you still refused your uniform, you would be treated like a man who has deserted in battle, and then you could well end up facing a firing squad."

"If you want to make me into a martyr, all I can say is get on with it."

"I take that to be your final word, so on your own head be it."

Then, with a wave of his arm, he said:

"Prisoner and escort, DISMISS!"

Back in the cell, my own clothes were forcibly removed and the uniform I had no intention of wearing was left in a neat pile on the end of the bunk.

I had the feeling that one of the two guards who dealt with me rather fancied the tanned young man who was only ever dressed in his underpants. The other one hated my guts and took every opportunity to show it. One of his nasty little tricks was to 'accidentally' drop half the food he brought onto the floor.

"Sorry, mate," he'd say, with a sly grin and a supercilious expression on his face. When he left, he made a point of slamming the cell door as hard as he could.

As I'd not smoked for three days, my craving to have a cigarette became intense. My only hope of getting any was to try and persuade the guard who liked me - or to be more precise, my body - to buy me a packet. When I next saw him, I told him that if he did I'd get my rich uncle to send him a postal order for three times their value.

"I might oblige you," he said.

Less than half an hour later, he was back holding twenty Players in his hand.

"Good chap, you've got them, did you remember to buy a box of matches as well?"

"Yes, but before I give 'em to you, there's something I want you to do first."

"I told you, I'll get my uncle to pay you three times their worth."

"The snouts are yours for nothing, if you'll suck me off."

Without waiting to find out if I agreed or not, he unbuttoned his flies and pulled out his cock, erect in anticipation of things to come. As I was on the low bunk, his penis was almost level with my face. I opened my mouth wide, then leant towards the repugnant thing, whilst at the same time I drew back my right hand and with a God-Almighty wham, hit his cock as hard as I could. It wobbled a couple of times, then shrivelled up and disappeared into his flies faster than an overturned snail retreats into its shell.

"You bastard, you fucking bastard, when I report this, they'll put you in chains!"

I flung myself at him and pressed my forearm across his throat. Pinned against the wall, and barely able to breathe, his face began to redden.

"You inarticulate cretin, how will you explain to the CO why your cock was out of your trousers, eh?"

He managed a barely audible squeak: "I'll tell him you attacked me for no reason," he gasped.

"Do you for one moment imagine that the commanding officer will believe you, when I tell him what really happened? Hasn't it occurred to you, that the CO and I speak the same language? We are of the same class," I bluffed, "the class that for generations has ruled over idiots like you. If we appear in front of him, it's you who will be doing a stretch in the glasshouse long before I do."

By now he was struggling for breath, so I let him go.

"Now fuck off, and don't ever try that lark with me again."

Before letting him go, I put my hand into his tunic pocket and relieved him of the cigarettes and matches he'd bought for me.

For the next few days, not a lot happened to relieve my boredom. I amused myself by getting on the nerves of my keepers. I'd spend some days cross-legged on the floor, breathing in deeply with my hands in the praying position. On those days, I neither spoke nor responded to anybody. On others, I'd only talk gibberish. I told the guards that I was speaking Esperanto, the language of the future. I told them that one day it would be spoken universally in the Socialist world.

"What a fucking load of bollocks. How would you say that in your daft language, eh, you cunt?"

"It wouldn't need to be translated, because in an ideal society, ignorant twits like you would have become extinct."

I also kidded them that I was practising levitation, so that very soon, I'd be able to rise up off the floor and float out of the high window. One of them must have thought that I might well do it, because one night, I heard a guard coming towards my cell to spy on me through the peephole. To tease him, I stood with my back against the the door, my shoulder just under the peephole, so that when he peered in, all he could see was an empty space.

"Cartlidge, are you there, Cartlidge?"

I stayed silent.

He beetled off at speed to fetch the keys. When he got back, he quickly unlocked the door, rushed in, then saw me casually standing with my back against the wall.

"Oh, you're there!" he exclaimed.

"Where the fuck did you think I'd be, eh?"

My little ruse got me thinking, that possibly I was getting more on their nerves than they were on mine. I was mistaken. A few days later, things began to get very nasty.

As the guards who were responsible for me had been so unsuccessful in persuading me to put on and keep on my uniform, the RSM was asked to come to their aid. Early one morning he came into my cell accompanied by a couple of heavies. He stood by the door and bellowed as loud as he would on the parade ground:

"Stand to attention when I enter, private!"

I didn't move a muscle.

"I'm ordering you to put on your uniform and be sharp about it!"

The roar of his voice was ear-piercing as it reverberated off the walls. I remained seated and prepared myself for a rough ride.

"Right, Cartlidge, your little game is over. For the last time, I command you to put your fucking uniform on or face the consequences."

There was no sign of movement from me, so he shouted to his two henchmen:

"Put it on the cunt and don't be too gentle about it."

They made a dive for me, then flung me onto the floor. I went limp. One of them pinned me down while his mate pulled the trousers up over my non-resisting legs, and secured them with a belt. Then they picked up my listless body and plonked it on the bunk. Trying to get my tunic on, with me flopping about, was difficult for them. The rougher they were, the harder it became for them. Exasperated, they resorted to violence. Blows in rapid succession landed on my stomach, chest and back. I flexed my muscles to cushion their impact, but there was nothing I could do to reduce the pain when they kneed me repeatedly in the back. After they'd finally got me dressed, they banged me back on the floor, and for a parting gift, gave me a good kicking. Before he left, the sergeant major bent down and put his face close to mine.

"Now boy, if you don't want worse treatment tomorrow, have your fucking uniform on when I arrive. If it isn't, the beating you've just had will seem child's play, and that's a promise."

When they left, I lay motionless for some time before picking my bruised body up off the floor. As soon as I'd recovered a little, I took off the uniform. I knew I must think up something to stop the sadistic bastards or they'd kick me to death. To be at the wrong end of a firing squad, as the CO had threatened, had a certain dignity about it, but to die at the hands of mindless louts would be a hideous and squalid way to go. In the hope of avoiding this, I decided to emulate my hero Gandhi, who single-handed took on the might of the British Empire. I'd go on hunger strike until I was given back my own clothes.

I didn't touch the next meal, apart from drinking the tea and giving a morsel of bread and cheese to the mice.

"A little beating has put the poor boy off his food, eh?" said the guard when he came to pick up the plates. It was the one I hated.

"Not in the slightest. You can take it away and don't bring any more until I'm given my clothes back."

"I'll bring your grub every mealtime. If you don't eat it, that's you're fucking lookout. As for me, mate, I'll quite enjoy watching a cunt like you starve 'imself to death."

"Fuck off, you bastard, and leave me in peace," I snapped.

The following morning, when the sergeant major and his hatchet-men came, they made no attempt to put a uniform on me. Instead they made straight for me with clenched fists. In the vain hope of protecting myself a little, I jumped off the bunk onto the floor and knelt down. I tucked my head between my thighs and clasped my hands behind my neck. This defensive manoeuvre didn't help me, because the sergeant major tugged at my feet while the other two wrenched my locked hands apart. They flipped me over onto my back, then stretched me out and held me in a human rack. One kept a tight grip around my ankles, while another pinned my arms to the floor. This left the third man free to bang away to his heart's content at my unprotected body. He began by ramming his fist into my face. A rapid succession of blows then landed on my forehead, eyes, nose and ears, before he started to pound away at my chest and stomach. Shock waves of pain went through me from head to toe. Not wanting to give them the satisfaction of hearing me scream, I clenched my teeth so tightly that it is a wonder that they didn't crack under the strain. After what felt to be an eternity, I was turned over, like a steak under a grill, so that my back could be given a pummelling. I think the sergeant major only finally called a halt to my pitiless beating because he was concerned that if it continued for much longer I might have died on him. Because of the clobbering my ears had taken, I could only just make out what he said to me before he left.

"I'll be back tomorrow, and the day after, every fucking day, until you've put on your uniform, mark my words. By the time I've finished with you, you'll plead with me to let you put it on."

When he and his thugs departed, I never imagined that it was possible to feel so much pain and still remain conscious. A very long time passed before I could get myself up off the floor and back on the bunk. With no mirror to look in, I assessed the damage done to my face by very gently running my fingertips over it. Huge bumps covered my forehead and cheekbones. Blood still oozed out of my nose and my upper lip was swollen that it almost touched my nostrils. Because of the pounding on my chest and ribs, I could only take in shallow breaths without pain. There seemed to be no part of me that hadn't suffered some damage. I felt dreadfully abused and totally abandoned, so full of self-pity, that I cut myself off from the brutal world by covering my head and body with a blanket. Cocooned in it, I silently wept.

Some time later, a guard that I hadn't seen before brought me food. When he saw my blood-stained and distorted face, all he said was: "Jesus Christ."

"What sets me apart from 'Him' is that the bastards who came to crucify me, forgot to bring the fucking nails!" I said bitterly.

However, I don't think he understood me, because my swollen lips made my speech almost unintelligible.

"Would you like me to take you to the basin so that you can wash the blood off your face and body?" he asked, uttering the first kind words that I'd heard in a long time.

"Oh no, comrade, my blood-spattered skin can be my uniform until such time as I'm given my own clothes back."

The guard shook his head in despair, then left.

By nightfall, exhausted and aching all over, what I desperately desired was to escape into sleep, but with only unyielding wood for a bed, and nothing soft to lay my sore head on, this was impossible. I was left with no alternative but to sit on the edge of the bunk, holding the weight of my head with one hand placed under my chin. In this position, I spent the longest night of my life, with nothing to look forward to but another clobbering in the morning.

When the sergeant major and his bully boys came into my cell and closed the door behind them, I asked:

"Did you remember to bring a coffin with you? As it's most unlikely that I will survive another assault, I hope, sergeant major, for your own sake, you've thought out how you will explain my brutal death to the commanding officer."

I said this in the hope that my words might just make him think again before setting his hoodlums loose.

"Put your fucking uniform on, then there'll be no need to give you a hammering."

I continued sitting on the bunk without moving.

"For the last time, Cartlidge, I'm ordering you to put your uniform on now, right fucking now!"

He was shouting and stamping his foot on the floor. Despite the pain it caused, I stood up to my full height and steadfastly looked straight into his fearsome eyes.

"Can't you get it into your head, even if it kills me, never, never, NEVER WILL I PUT IT ON!"

The crescendo of my voice almost matched his. He stood motionless for a moment with his eyes almost popping out of their sockets. When he clenched his fists, I realised that my last seconds on earth had come, and prepared myself to be bludgeoned into oblivion. For what reason I don't know, because it was pointless to do so, I screamed out:

"Help, somebody, please help me!"

To my utter amazement, just as he would on parade, the sergeant major about-turned and marched off, and that was the last I saw of him. At first I couldn't grasp what had happened. Then it dawned on me that my passive resistance and non-cooperation had triumphed.

CHAPTER FORTY-FOUR

Four days into my fast, the pangs of hunger I'd felt began to subside. Now when food was brought, ostensibly to persuade me to break my hunger strike, it had the opposite effect. The sight of it was nauseating, so all I took by way of nourishment was mugs of sweet tea. While I was losing weight rapidly, my mouse friends were getting fatter by the day. I must stop feeding them so much, I decided, otherwise they'll soon get too big to squeeze through the hole in the floor. On the fifth day without food, when the guard I hated brought in breakfast, I saw at once that there was no mug of tea on the tray.

"You've forgotten the tea," I said, somewhat concerned.

"I ain't forgotten it," said the guard. "The sergeant 'as decided that, as you won't eat 'olesome Army grub, you can go without char as well. Now, mate, you've got a choice, you can eiver starve to death or die of thirst, it's up to you, ha ha ha." He laughed maliciously.

"If I ever get out of here alive, I'll strangle you with my bare hands, you fucking bastard."

"I'm not worried. It's 'ighly likely that you'll cop it in a few days anyway."

To be denied liquid was a problem I'd not reckoned with. I knew that even Gandhi sipped fruit juice when he fasted. I'd have to think up something fairly quickly, or things could get very serious. Thankfully an idea born out of my instinct for survival came to my aid. I said to the guard:

"For once I agree with you. I most likely will - as you so eloquently put it - 'cop it' very soon, so with that in mind, I think it might be for the best if I wash off all this unsightly, congealed blood, and clean up my body before I'm laid out."

"Yeah, even the devil 'imself won't want to take you in, looking the way you do."

"You want me to burn in hell, don't you, so it might be to your advantage to escort me to the washbasin."

"Yeah, can't be any 'arm in it, I suppose."

With him standing behind me, doing his best to rile me by ostentatiously puffing away at a Woodbine I had a quick sluice before cupping my hands and gulping down what I hoped was sufficient water to keep me alive for the next twenty-four hours.

"You look almost 'uman now," commented the guard as he ushered me back to my cell.

I'd not been locked up for very long when the need to do a pee became urgent. I was about to bang on the door to be let out to the toilet, when I realised that if I did they'd twig that I'd been drinking. I paced up and down the cell several times before I solved my problem.

"Sorry, my friends, but I'm left with no other option," I said out loud as I aimed the stream down the mousehole. When I'd finished, Darby and Joan poked out their noses, and shook their whiskers dry before they gave me a look that said without the need for words 'Why did you do that? We're your friends, aren't we?'

"You are indeed, you are at the moment the only ones I have. Please try to understand that in my present circumstances, I have no alternative. It's a matter of life or death for me. In future, to prevent you from getting soaked, I'll stamp on the floor before I start. That will give you time to take cover."

They must have heeded what I said, because my little friends never got drenched again.

By the sixth day of my hunger strike, the guard sergeant was worried that if he ignored my situation for much longer, I might die on him, so he reluctantly called in the MO. When the doctor saw me, clad only in my underpants and with my bruises at their worst, he was horrified.

"In God's name, what has happened to this man, sergeant?"

"'e's refusing food and drink, sir, till 'e gets 'is civvies back."

"How long has this been going on for?"

"Six days now, sir."

"You've let this go on for that long without letting me know before now?"

"I thought 'e'd pack it up after a couple of days, sir."

"Two days are not six. Tell me, how do you explain all those lacerations and the massive bruises all over his body?"

While the sergeant racked his brain for an answer, I intervened.

"I can tell you, doctor, better than he can."

"I want the truth, please."

"Three thugs came into my cell in the small hours one morning, and savagely attacked me. I was unable to call for help because they bound and gagged me first."

"Are you quite certain that you have no idea who did this to you?"

"None, I'm afraid, I'd not ever seen any of them before."

"What night did you get attacked?"

"I don't know. Its not that easy to keep track of the days and nights when you're in solitary confinement."

"I'm beginning to suspect that you're too frightened to tell me for fear of reprisals."

"Really, I'm not, I assure you."

"What do you know about all this, sergeant?"

Obviously relieved that my version of events had got him off the hook, he replied: "I 'aven't seen the prisoner for the last week, sir, and once I did and saw the state 'e was in, I called you, sir."

His pack of lies didn't bother me one bit. The one thing I did not want was an inquiry to distract from what my stand was all about.

"Well, I'm going to do something about the poor chap right now. You, sergeant, will go immediately and fetch his own clothes. At the same time, send a guard to the officers' mess and ask the cook to make a billycan full of soup. He's to say that the MO needs it to sustain a man who is very undernourished. Once you've picked up his clothes, go to the store and collect a pile of blankets, a pillow and a palliasse. I shall wait here until you return."

When the sergeant left, I swear that I could see wings sprouting out from the good doctor's shoulder blades, and a halo surrounding his handsome head.

"Tomorrow morning, by which time you should have recovered a little, I myself will accompany you to York General Hospital. I'm going to have you X-ayed from head to toe. I need to know if any of your ribs have been fractured or broken, or if there's any other injury you may have sustained. While we are waiting for your things to arrive, it would be helpful in my assessment of you if you told me what it is precisely that you are protesting about."

"I can think more clearly when I have a cigarette," I said, hoping that he had some on him. Thankfully, he pulled out an unopened packet of twenty from his tunic pocket and gave it to me.

"There, yours to keep, but I think you should wait until you've eaten and drunk something before you light up."

Ignoring his advice, I puffed away while I put into as few words as possible my reasons for refusing to don a uniform.

By the time the sergeant returned, I had the impression that the doctor was interested by my explanation, and would have liked me to have elaborated further. But when I took my first spoonful of the hot and nourishing soup, he turned to go, tactfully leaving me to enjoy it in peace.

"Have a comfortable night. I'll come and collect you shortly after breakfast."

Now that I had a palliasse, pillow, blankets and fags, plus what I prized above all else, my very own clothes, I wouldn't have felt better off if I'd been transported by a magic carpet to a suite at the Savoy.

The following morning, after having the best night's sleep for a long time, and with a small amount of food in my shrunken stomach, I began to feel blood pumping through my veins once again. Darby and Joan were also relieved that I'd called off my hunger strike.

"How are you feeling today?" enquired the doctor when he arrived.

"Much better, thanks to you."

"What's your Christian name?"

It cheered me up when he asked that, because it meant that he didn't think it would be appropriate to address me as 'private'.

"I don't have a 'Christian' name. I gave up being a believer long ago. My first name is Hayden, but I changed it to Derrick four years ago, when I mixed with men who dropped their aitches. I got fed up being called 'Aden'."

"It's quite a coincidence, you know, as my name is John Hayden."

"Is it? Well, I never!" I replied. I couldn't think of any other way to reply.

"Derrick, I have a car and driver waiting to take us to the hospital. I'm supposed to have you handcuffed to a guard, but I'd much prefer not to. If you gave me your word that you wouldn't attempt to escape, I could dispense with all that."

"You have it, doctor. In any case I'd never drop anyone in it, who literally saved my life," I said, and meant it.

As we passed the sergeant, who was sitting at his desk, he jumped up and saluted the MO.

"I'll get a guard to go with you, sir," he said.

"I shan't be needing one, thank you," replied the doctor curtly.

"But sir, 'e's a slippery customer, that one, 'e'll make a break for it if 'e gets 'arf a chance."

"I've already told you, Sergeant, I don't want one. This man has given me his word that he won't attempt to abscond while he's in my custody. Considering the appalling treatment he received whilst in your charge, I'm inclined to trust him a damn sight more than I do you."

"Right, sir, then 'e's your responsibility until 'e's safely locked up again."

"I don't need to be told by you what is, or is not, my responsibility," retorted the MO.

As I stepped out of the dreary guard room into the sunshine, the doctor's reply to the little bastard was music to my ears.

Not for the first time in my life, the wheels of fortune had turned in my favour. Only two days ago, I was a whisker away from death's door. Now I was being driven in comfort through the city of York, sitting next to a human being whose only concern at that moment was my health. It took my eyes a while to adjust to a wider vision - for the last few weeks they had only been able to focus on the cell walls a few feet away. To look at trees, buildings, colours, and ordinary people going about their business, was to me as I imagined someone blind must feel, whose sight has been restored.

During the time I spent in the hospital, Dr Hayden never left my side. He insisted he wanted the whole of my body X-rayed and thoroughly examined. It took the best part of the morning before they were through with me.

As we made our way out of the hospital, the doctor told me that despite the terrible beatings I'd had, no lasting damage had been done, though there were several fractures to my left and right ribs.

"How long do you think it will take for my ribs to mend?" I asked.

"At your age they should heal quite quickly. My guess is that by the time your hair has grown back, you'll be A1 again."

His reply didn't altogether cheer me up, as two weeks had gone by since it was shorn, and all that showed now was a little fuzz. At that rate, a full head of hair could well be weeks away.

On the way back to the barracks, the MO treated his driver and me to a meal. Because of my appearance, the people eating in the café kept staring at our table, which didn't bother me or the doctor, but his driver definitely felt ill at ease.

Back in the cell with nothing to do but think, I came to the conclusion that Dr Hayden had to be one of the nicest people I'd ever met. The way he came to my rescue when I was so in need of a little human kindness will stay in my memory until the day I die. For all the remaining weeks I was locked up at Fulford Barracks, the doctor came to see me for at least an hour twice a week. As he was good company and as he kept me supplied with cigarettes, I greatly looked forward to his visits. He wanted me to tell him about my life from babyhood right up to when I was arrested, so by instalments, I gave it to him.

Lively, and often heated, discussions ensued when I gave him the reasons why I was a pacifist and anarchist. He told me that his upbringing had been very conventional, and that his father, whom he loathed and feared as a child, was a strict disciplinarian and bigot. Because of this, he was trying his best to be the complete opposite. Even though the doctor was at least twenty years older than I, most of the ideas we discussed had never entered his head. Despite the huge differences in our backgrounds, we became good friends, so much so that he asked me to call him by his first name, John.

Except for my new friend's twice-weekly visits, I was alone in my cell. Now that the guards knew that I was under his watchful eyes, apart from bringing me my meals, they kept away. Even the little sergeant treated me with a degree of deference. He was aware that the MO was my ally, and he also felt indebted to me for not dropping him in the cart, when I did not mention that he had done nothing to stop me getting beaten up and that it was he who, in the last days of my hunger strike, had denied me liquid. Personally I preferred his normal, obnoxious self to the obsequious way he now behaved towards me.

The fractures in my ribs prevented me from passing away at least some of the long hours by doing my exercises. I knew I would go insane from boredom, and I had to think up something to occupy my mind. I remembered how successful I'd been as a child in blotting out miserable times by rocking myself to sleep, imagining that my mother had come to take me away from the children's home. I decided that doing the same might just work again. I lay down on the bunk, closed my eyes, then - frame by frame - let the film of my memories project onto the screen of my mind. I would swim in the Porchester Baths, then run through Hyde Park to the boathouse by the Serpentine. I hired a skiff with a sliding seat and as I feathered the oars over the still water, I could picture every curve of the lake that was so familiar to me. Then I walked across the Park to Marble Arch, down Oxford Street and up Charlotte Street to Tony's caff. I stayed here for a while, chatting to my bum friends. Sometimes I'd relive the sound of the orchestra playing Giselle and Margot Fonteyn's moving performance. I knew almost every step and note of it.

At other times, I'd be having lively conversations with Vic and Robert at the Coffee Ann or dining with dear Uncle at the Strand Palace. I'd even visualise whizzing down Pier Hill on my scooter with Peter sitting in front of me, her ears flapping in the wind. At night, I'd cuddle up to my lovely Betty, and as my hands and lips glided over her body, I'd fall asleep taking her with me into my dreams.

I got my imaginings down to such a fine art that the only part of me that wasn't free to roam about anywhere I pleased was my incarcerated body.

One night I was woken up by a tremendous din that sounded like it came from the next cell. It puzzled me because for all the weeks I'd been imprisoned, the other two cells had never been occupied.

"Let me out, please let me out, I promise I won't try to escape!" The man was obviously very distressed. His plea, of course, was ignored by the soldier on duty, if indeed he'd heard anything. Normally at that time of night the guard would be fast asleep, even though he shouldn't have been. The screaming and banging on the door became more and more agitated, and began to get on my nerves. I just couldn't imagine why the man was making such a fuss. Finally, to stop the noise, I put my mouth to the spyhole and said as loud as I could: "Hey, chum, cut it out, I can't sleep with all that racket going on."

"Come and let me out, I can't stand being locked up and all alone."

He must have thought it was the guard telling him to belt up.

"You're not alone, I'm in the cell next to yours."

"How can you bear being all by yourself?"

"Actually I prefer it to being shut up with people I wouldn't get on with."

"Well, I can't stand it, I'd end it all by hanging myself, but I can't because they've taken my belt and braces off me."

"That's the first sensible thing they've done in all the weeks I've been here," I said.

"If I stay locked up for much longer, I'll go mad."

"Calm down, for Christ's sake, calm down. My name is Derrick, what's yours?"

"Fred."

"Listen, Fred, do what I do, try and imagine that you're in a place with someone you love being with. I promise you, if you concentrate hard enough, the walls of your cell will become a window through which you can look out onto your make-believe world."

"The person I'd most like to be with is Mavis, my fiancée."

"Now, Fred, go and lie down and close your eyes, then visualise that your beautiful Mavis is lying on her side next to you, completely naked."

"I've never seen her with nothing on."

"Well, for fuck's sake, imagine it," I said, pissed off that he'd interrupted me. Despite this, I went on: "When you have a picture and the feel of her firmly fixed in your mind, press your lips to hers and put one arm round her waist. Let your hand slowly move up under her arm until it can hold her firm and rounded breast, then wrap your other one round your cock and - well, I'm sure you know what to do."

As he didn't reply, I never knew whether or not he took my advice, but one thing was for sure, all went quiet and I could go peacefully to sleep again.

The next morning, I met my next door neighbour by the washbasins.

"Feeling a little better, are you?" I asked.

"No, I'm not," he replied.

"Cheer up, when you're sent to the glasshouse, you'll have company night and day. Mind you, that would be my idea of hell."

"I might be shut up here for weeks waiting for a court martial. By then I'll have gone out of my mind."

"Would it help if you could spend an hour a day with me?" I said. I felt sorry for the poor chap, but at the same time hoped he'd decline my offer. Unfortunately he didn't. He said it would make a lot of difference to him if he could be with me sometimes.

"Leave it to me, I'll ask the sergeant. He owes me a favour."

The sergeant agreed immediately. He knew, of course, that if he'd refused I'd have got the MO to sanction it. An hour later, Fred was with me. He told me why he'd deserted.

"On the last day of a week's leave, I just couldn't face going back to the shouting and yelling of the parade ground, or the sheer misery of being on manoeuvres in the damp and cold Yorkshire Moors. I kept telling myself to go back, but when I was about to board the train, my body turned into lead and refused to let me get on it. I was on the run for ten days."

"Were you staying at your girl's place, when they caught you?"

"No, I didn't dare go anywhere near, in case the police were watching it."

"Have you written to her?"

"No, and I couldn't talk to her because she's not on the phone."

"So she has no idea what's happened to you?"

"No, she hasn't."

"Well, don't worry. You were absent for such a short time, you'll probably only get three months. That's not too bad, is it? Whatever happens, you'll be doing less time than me. If I go on the way I plan to, I'll most likely be doing jankers for the duration of the fucking war. You know, I do think you ought to write to your fiancée. If she doesn't hear from you soon she'll begin to think you don't care about her any more."

"I care about her a lot – it's just that I can't think of what to say to her."

"I could help you with a letter. My friends tell me I have the gift of the gab. But I must warn you, I can't spell even the simplest words."

"I can, reasonably well. I'd really appreciate it if you did."

"OK, tomorrow we'll compose a masterpiece to send to your sweetheart."

By the time Fred came to see me the next day, I had managed to get a pen and paper from the sergeant.

"Right, Fred, how do you think we should start?"

"Telling her about me deserting and being arrested, I suppose."

I had a better idea. I started writing a love letter.

"My adorable girl,

As I sit here all alone in my cell, I think constantly about our wedding night and how I'll undo your dress, button by button, and let it drop to the floor. My fingers will unhook your bra so I can gaze upon your rounded breasts. Slowly I'll slip your knickers down to your ankles, then, frantic with desire, I'll strip and lie beside you. As we face each other, kissing wildly, my hands will become familiar with the curves of your sensual limbs... "

"Did you say 'essential limbs'?"

"No, Fred, for fuck's sake try and follow my train of thought. All limbs are essential, but not all are sensual, by a long way. Now, where was I?"

"I can't write that," said Fred. "Mavis doesn't know words like that."

"How old is she?"

"Twenty-one."

"Then it's about time she did. How do you think your letter ought to finish?"

"I think it should say, 'I'll make love to you.'"

"One doesn't make love, one makes a sponge cake, a motor car, or even a bloody bomb. One gives love, and that, Fred, is a totally different matter. If you cut out all the sexy stuff you might as well throw a bucket of cold water over her. If you end it your way, she'll read it and consign it to the bin, but if you leave it as it is, she'll treasure your letter all her life."

"Your friends are right, Derrick. You really do have the gift of the gab."

I never did find out whether he sent his version or mine, but I suspect it was mine. A few days later he read me the opening sentence of Mavis's reply: "Oh my darling Fred, I can hardly bear to wait for our wedding night when you'll be able to do all the lovely things you describe so wonderfully in your letter."

CHAPTER FORTY-FIVE

I'd been locked up for almost six weeks when John, my doctor friend, told me that he'd arranged for me to be taken to Leeds, so that an Army psychologist could see me.

Two days later, I was sitting on a train, handcuffed to a redcap, bound for Leeds. The psychologist was astute enough not to raise an eyebrow when I stood before him, clad, as ever, in my rags, barefoot and with shaven head. He pointed to a chair on the other side of his desk and told me to sit down. I sat there in silence while he finished reading some papers in front of him. A full five minutes passed before he spoke:

"I've just read Dr Hayden's report about you, and I must say you've done a splendid job pulling the wool over his eyes. I have to tell you right away, that you won't be able to hoodwink me that easily. All this nonsense about refusing your uniform is no different from what other malingerers get up to. Well, I have to tell you that this charade of yours does not impress me one bit, and that claptrap about being a pacifist and an anarchist won't cut any ice with me. It's all play-acting, isn't it?"

"I find it hard enough to play myself, let alone take on another character," I said.

"You think that sort of reply is witty and sets you apart from everyone else, but I assure you you're no different from any of the other lead-swingers I see."

"Then why am I here?"

"I'll ask the questions, not you."

"As you seem to have already made up your mind about me, it would be pointless for me to answer them. To save you wasting your valuable time, I suggest you call the guard and tell him to escort me back to York."

"You will not manipulate me to do your bidding. I will decide what is or is not a waste of my time."

"If the reason I'm here is for you to find out whether I'm sane, I can tell you that I'm probably the sanest person you're likely to meet for a long time."

"Am I to understand that you think that all the British people who are engaged in fighting the Hun are not sane?"

"No, not by a long way, but those in power before the war certainly were not."

And I proceeded to give an impassioned speech, pointing out that those people didn't lift a finger to stop the rise of Fascism: It was left to the International Brigade to help their Spanish comrades fight the fascist forces, while the munitions barons of England, France and America made fat profits from supplying Franco and Hitler with arms.

"If you think people like that are sane," I went on, "then I want to be counted among the mad. When they command me to go and kill men, women and children in foreign lands, I will say to them: No, I will not. Throughout history,

anyone making the stand I am making would have been told 'Oh, but this is not the time to be a pacifist'. If only a few men who followed Hannibal
had said to him 'we're not going to mount your fucking elephants and cross the freezing Alps
to help you plunder faraway lands', thy would have become the inspiration to thousands of others through the ages. But many of those who perished in the last war would be alive today if only they had said 'Count me out of your insane plans'. The protest I, and others like me, are making will have little effect on the outcome of this war. But nevertheless, we have to make it if there is to be a future for mankind."

The doctor clapped his hands derisively. "Bravo, bravo, where do you think you are, on a soap box in Hyde Park?"

"You would do well to go there. It might broaden your blinkered mind."

He thumped the top of his desk and said angrily: "I'm an officer in the British Army. Have you no respect for those in a position of authority over you?"

"None whatsoever, and to prove it, I'm now going to tell you something that will really make your hair stand on end. When this war is over, England and its Western Allies will combine in an unholy alliance to fight alongside Germany in a futile attempt to stop Socialism sweeping through the whole of Europe."

"Take this lunatic out of my sight," screamed the doctor.

As a handcuff was placed round my wrist, I said:

"I'm sorry if I've upset you, doctor. It was not my intention."

"You certainly got on the wrong side of him," said my escort as we made our way through the streets to the station.

The next day John asked me how I had got on.

"Pretty badly, I'm afraid, so badly in fact, that the doctor more or less threw me out of his room."

"You must have antagonised him in some way."

"Maybe I did. You see, John, when anyone says something just to annoy me, I can't resist giving them back a little more than they bargained for. This man set out straight away to rile me."

"That's a pity. He was your last hope. The only thing I can do now is to speak on your behalf at your court martial, but I doubt if that will help much."

"I'd prefer it, if you didn't. You've done more than enough already. I've made my bed, now I must lie on it."

"I'm so worried about what will happen to you when you're at the mercy of the guards in the detention centre. Is it pointless to ask you to reconsider your refusal to put on a uniform? Things would be so much easier for you if you would."

"Thanks a lot for your concern, but I just can't."

"I'll come and see you again in a couple of days. Perhaps by then you may have come to your senses."

"Perhaps," I replied, but I knew that nothing would make me change my mind.

At five p.m. the day the little sergeant came into my cell with some papers in his hand.

"You've worked it, you cunning bastard, you've finally worked it."

"Worked what?" I asked.

"Your fucking ticket, that's what."

"Is this your idea of a joke?" I asked.

"I wish it was, I was really looking forward to watching you being carted off to the glasshouse."

"My God, I'm beginning to think you're not having me on."

"'Ere's your discharge certificate with today's date on it."

He handed me the army book I'd put into the tunic pocket of the uniform I'd got Uncle to leave at the Albany Street Barracks when I deserted. I opened it, and on the back inside page, under the heading 'Cause of Discharge,' was written: 'He is permanently unfit for any form of Military Service'.

I was so elated, I only just managed to stop myself from hugging the bastard.

"I've also got to give you seven weeks' pay and a railway warrant to London. You wouldn't sign for your uniform, but I bet you don't mind signing for the eight pounds I 'ave to give yer. Mind you, you can refuse it, then I wouldn't 'ave to give it to yer, would I?"

"Oh, I'll sign for it all right, my comrades can do with all the funds they can get hold of, to finance our cause."

I lied, deciding to keep it for myself since eight pounds wasn't, after all, that much compensation for all the inconvenience I'd been put to.

"I knew you'd take it, you scheming bastard."

"Put a feather in your cap, little man, it's the first time since I've been here that you've been right about anything I said."

"I'll be fucking glad to see the back of you, you cunt," said the sergeant as I stepped barefoot out of the cell, that had been my home for eight weeks.

Before I left, I spoke to Fred through the spyhole of his door, and told him that I'd been set free.

"I'll feel terribly alone, not being able to spend time with you every day, Derrick."

"Remember what I told you, imagine yourself out of your cell. I'm sure it won't be very long before you're court-martialled, and then, when you get to the glasshouse, you'll no longer be left on your own. Because you're not fucking them about like I did, I promise you you'll be spending Christmas with your lovely Mavis. Goodbye, Fred, try and look on the bright side."

The unhappy man couldn't bring himself to reply.

I made my way to the officers' mess to find John and tell him about my release.

"You missed the MO by half an hour," said a man who was polishing a silver tray.

"Oh blast - would you mind giving me a sheet of paper and a pencil?" I asked.

"Sure, mate, you're the bloke the MO often talked about at mealtimes, aren't you?"

"I don't know."

"I'm sure it was you, because of the way he described you."

When he gave me paper and pencil, in the most appalling handwriting and with every other word misspelt, I let John know what had happened. I also promised to write as soon as I was settled in London. To my everlasting shame I never did. My hope is, that should this saga of mine ever be published, he, or if he has died, those who were near to him will read what a fine and kind doctor he was.

Standing in the corridor of the packed train on my way back to London, I pondered on the reason for my discharge. I found out later that a soldier named Clayton had died that week, after being savagely beaten by the guards at a detention centre for refusing to obey their orders. His death caused such a scandal that questions were asked in the House, where one MP said that it seemed that some of those engaged in running our military detention centres were just as bad as the Nazis.

The poor man's death was probably the reason the doctor in Leeds decided to authorise my immediate discharge. He realised the same thing might well happen to me.

It was past midnight when the train pulled into King's Cross. I walked out of the station, still wearing the same scanty clothing I had on when I was arrested nine weeks earlier. Unexpectedly, a rare taxi passed by. I waved it down and got in.

'St Giles' Circus, please," I said, certain that the driver would not have heard of the Coffee Ann.

CHAPTER FORTY-SIX

The place was packed when I walked in, and although I knew almost everybody sitting at the tables of the smoke-filled café, no one greeted me, not even Robert and Vic, who were chatting away at the far end of the room. As I made my way towards them, I heard Vic shout:

"Christ, Robert, you're right, it is Derrick."

"Hallo, you two," I said.

"In God's name, Derrick, what have the bastards done to you?"

"Are you referring to my hair? I agreed to let the barber clip it all off."

"Why did you lose so much weight?" Robert asked.

"I got thin when I went on a hunger strike."

"Not a day has passed when we haven't worried about what was happening to you. Sit down and tell us all about it," said Vic.

By the time I'd drunk three cups of tea and eaten two cheese sandwiches, I'd given them a blow by blow account of all that happened to me since my arrest.

"I'd like to get my hands on those bastards," Vic said.

"Jesus, Derrick, if all they did was just threaten me with only half of what you suffered, I'd have thrown in the towel straight away," said Robert.

"Nobody knows how they will react to a dangerous or painful situation. When I was at sea and the tanker broke down in mid-Atlantic, with highly volatile aviation fuel on board, turning our ship into a sitting target for any U-boat on the prowl, it was the tough villains that broke down and nearly shat themselves - not the likes of you and me, Robert."

"I just hope and pray that I'm never put to the test."

Vic asked. "Are you now free to do what you like, or are you expected to do some sort of war-work like I am?"

"I have no idea, and I don't intend to find out. From now on, when redcaps or coppers stop me in the street, I'll show them my army discharge book, and that'll send them on their way. What I'll do, until my cracked ribs have healed and my hair has grown, is as little as possible. Then, when I need to earn a few pounds, I'll do film extra work. My immediate plan is to see my lovely Betty on Sunday, when her sugar daddy is back with his family."

"I'm afraid I have some bad news for you," said Robert.

"What's happened to her?" I said. I was afraid he was going to tell me she'd been killed in an air-raid.

"She's got married to an old man who was a friend of the bloke that kept her."

"Where has she gone?"

"I don't know. All she told me was that he lived up north and that he was stinking rich."

"Oh Christ, I'd so looked forward to seeing her, it was thinking about her that helped me get through the long nights in my cell."

"Don't despair, there's plenty of other beautiful girls about."

"Maybe, but I doubt if any of them compare with Betty, she's one in a million."

"I know a couple of lovely girls who sunbathe at the Serps. They're close friends, one is a French girl called Yvette, she's quite a tomboy. Her friend Esther is probably more your cup of tea. She's a little black-haired Venus who loves classical music. I met her at a concert. She has a boyfriend in the Royal Navy but by the way she talks about him I have the feeling that she's not in love with him. When you've tanned up a bit, and your hair has grown a little, I think she'll take a fancy to you."

I knew Robert was doing his best to cheer me up, but I pined for Betty. I consoled myself with the hope that one day soon she'd make some excuse to her old husband and come down to London to stay with me for a few days.

"Can either of you put me up for the night?" I asked.

"I can't, old boy," said Vic, "Peter goes berserk if I so much as glance at another man."

"Can you, Robert?"

"Yes, provided you don't mind sharing a bed with me and my girlfriend."

"I don't mind, but what about her?"

"She won't care, if it's only for one night. By the time she gets back from the nightclub where she works as a hostess, she's so tired that I doubt she'll notice you're in the bed."

It was after one when we arrived at Robert's place in Goodge Street. To his surprise, his girlfriend was not only there, but had already gone to bed.

"Hallo, Jean, why are you back so early?"

"All the customers had left, so they said we could go home."

"Jean, this is my friend Derrick. He's just been chucked out of the Army and got into London too late to find anywhere to stay, so I told him he could kip down with us - you don't mind, do you, just for tonight ?"

"Well, I suppose not, it's a pity though, as I so rarely get back without finding you fast asleep. To put it bluntly, darling, I was really looking forward to having a good fuck."

"I don't want to be the reason why you can't, so I'll go off and sleep in Donald Soper's centre. It's only a twenty minute walk from here," I said.

"Let him stay, Jean, the poor chap is completely washed out, he's been on the go since dawn."

"All right, hop in," she said.

"Thanks, I promise you I'll be flat out the moment my head hits the pillow."

I got into bed and turned my back on them. As the pair fucked away, I felt as if I was in the back of a lorry going over rough ground, but eventually fell into a deep sleep.

When I awoke in the morning, Robert and his girl did not stir. I got out of bed and dressed, wanting to have an early start so that I could accomplish all the things I needed to do that day. I tip-toed out of the room, leaving them to sleep on.

Number one on my list was to find lodgings. I knew that no landlady in her right mind would let me a room, looking the way I did. I had to do something about my appearance. I went to Selfridges, armed with clothing coupons, and bought corduroy trousers, one shirt, three pairs of underpants and some shoes. Those items used up all my coupons, so I couldn't buy any socks.

On leaving the store, I went to the public bath house and had my first bath for over two months. I left, dumped in a heap on the tiled bathroom floor, the clothes I'd tried so hard to keep. I am not normally sentimental, but a part of me would have liked to hang onto my sleeveless shirt and worn-out corduroys, as a memento of a battle fought and won.

All togged up in my new outfit, I went to a barber and had my beard shaved off. By the end of the day, I was ensconced in a poky little room overlooking the canal at Maida Vale.

That evening, when Vic and Robert saw me at Tony's, they hardly recognised me.

"Good God, what a transformation," exclaimed Vic.

"You're right. All I need now is to feed myself up and get fit, then I will really feel myself again. By the way, Robert, thanks for putting me up last night."

"You missed out, Derrick. Purely on compassionate grounds, Jean offered to let you have a go. I tried to wake you, but you just wouldn't stir."

"I do wish you hadn't told me, I really hate hearing about the lovely things I could've had, if only. By way of compensation, if it's OK with you, Robert, I'll take up her generous offer one day soon."

"Oh no, you won't, it was to have been a once only treat. From now on, you'll have to find your own bed partner."

"I was only joking, Robert. That reminds me, if it's sunny tomorrow, will you come with me to the Serps and introduce me to the girls you mentioned?"

"Sure, but if I were you, I'd wait a couple of weeks until your hair has gown a little more and you've got your tan back."

"You're right, I suppose. Will you come with me to the pond in Hampstead? I was on my way there to meet you and Vic the day I got arrested."

"A bit of advice, Derrick," said Vic, "don't, until your ribs have healed, even try to do any exercises. You'll only injure yourself if you do."

"Not even press-ups?"

"Especially not them! Walking and swimming is the only exercise you should do, for the time being."

Every day for the next fortnight, Robert and I went sunbathing and swimming. By the end of that time, my hair looked reasonable and I began to feel more like my usual self.

Although I'd been back for three weeks, I still hadn't contacted Uncle. The last thing he knew about me was when I sent him a letter from York, telling him that I was waiting to appear before a court martial, and that he shouldn't worry about me because I was being well treated. That was the reason why I didn't want him to see me until I looked something like normal. I let a few more days go by before phoning him. I told him that I'd arrived in London only a few hours earlier, and would like to come and see him.

"Hayden, what wonderful news! I never expected you'd be released so soon. When do you have to report back to your regiment?"

"I'll tell you all about that when I see you."

"Hayden, I'm so very pleased that you're back," said Uncle when I arrived. "I was terribly worried about you. I'm glad you took my advice and didn't antagonise anyone. Being your usual charming self paid off handsomely, didn't it?"

Not so, I thought, for had I acted like 'my usual charming self', by now I'd be a well-behaved and charming soldier doing everything at the double in the glasshouse. Of course, I didn't tell him that. Instead I said:

"The main reason I got discharged, Uncle, was because of my friendship with the MO."

"Do you think he fancied you?"

"Definitely not, he just happened to be a very good and sympathetic doctor. It was pure luck he was there. If he hadn't been, I wouldn't be sitting here talking to you."

To celebrate my return, Uncle suggested we dine at the Strand Palace. It was a joy to sit opposite him in the restaurant, seeing him obviously so happy and relieved at having me back safe and sound.

Two weeks into August, Robert thought I looked well enough to go with him to the Serpentine and meet the two girls he'd told me about. Although I was still missing Betty, I let him take me there. Even if I'd been on my own, I'd have known which two they were, as they were by far the prettiest girls sunbathing on the grass banks which led down to the lake. Robert and I wound our way through the maze of bodies, soaking up the sun, to where they were sitting.

"Hallo, Esther and Yvette, meet my friend Derrick."

I knelt down beside them and shook hands.

"I like your short hair," said Esther. "Is that going to be the latest style for all you conchies and army dodgers?"

"The military did that to him when he refused to have an army haircut," said Robert. "His hair has grown quite a bit in the few weeks since his discharge."

"I think your fuzz suits you. It sets you apart from the long-haired Soho bums Robert normally brings here," said Esther.

"I'm glad you like it. It makes the hard fight I had to get it shorn off worthwhile."

"Surely you weren't chucked out just because you refused an army haircut?" asked Yvette.

"Oh no, that was only a minor incident in a long-drawn-out drama. I won't bore you with why and how I finally got discharged. Let's say that I'm glad it's all over and that I'm very happy to be here, talking to you two."

When Robert entered the conversation, I took the opportunity to have a good look at the girls. Esther was just like Robert had described, a perfectly proportioned little Venus. Her fringed, straight black hair framed her beautiful face. She had large dark-brown eyes and lips with a Cupid's bow. She resembled a picture I'd once seen of Cleopatra. Her friend Yvette was taller and slimmer with chestnut hair in ringlets over her shoulders. She looked very athletic. Her captivating smile, coupled with an attractive French accent, made her very desirable to men.

As Esther appeared to be more interested in me than her friend, I paid more attention to her. I remembered that Robert had told me she was a regular concertgoer, so I let it drop that I'd enjoyed being a stage hand with the Sadlers Wells Ballet Company. She said she was going to a concert at the Albert Hall that evening, and I could accompany her if I wanted.

"I'd love to," I replied enthusiastically.

"Don't you want to know what's being played?" she asked.

"I don't care. For the last two months, I was confined to a cell where the only musical instrument I heard was a distant bugle sounding the Last Post at night and Reveille in the morning. By now I have a real hunger to hear the music of any of the great composers."

We arranged to meet on the steps of the Albert Memorial at seven-fifteen.

"We'd better make a move, otherwise we'll be late at the photographer's," said Esther.

"Are you models?" I asked.

"No, it's just that a man approached us yesterday and said he'd been commissioned by Nature magazine to take a few pictures of two healthy-looking girls. He says he'll pay us well because we have to pose in the semi-nude."

"I'm not sure it's such a good idea to go to a man's place when you don't even know him," said Robert.

"He gave us his card," replied Esther, as she pulled it out of her bag and gave it to Robert.

"Mr Zoltan, freelance photographer," he read out aloud.

"At least it's got his phone number and address on it, so perhaps he is genuine. All the same, Esther, you tell him your boyfriend is a police sergeant and he knows where you are."

"It's sweet of you to be so concerned, Robert, I'll do that. See you tonight, Derrick," she said as they both left to go to the changing room.

"Jesus, they are a couple of beauties," I remarked, as I watched them walk away in the briefest two-piece bathing costumes I'd ever seen.

"You see, Derrick, I was right, Esther has taken a fancy to you, and judging by the way you flirted with her, I think you fancy her."

"Just because she lets me go with her to a concert doesn't necessarily mean that she fancies me, you know."

"You're right, but it's a good omen, isn't it? And for God's sake, Derrick, don't do what you did the last time you went to the Albert Hall, start clapping when there's only a pause in the music."

The first thing I asked Esther when we met at the Albert Hall was how she had made out at the photographers.

"He turned out to be a real gentleman. We knew straight away that there was nothing to worry about because his girlfriend was his assistant. Not only did he pay us two guineas each, he's also promised to give us a few copies."

"Still, it was a good idea of Robert's to warn you that things might go wrong, wasn't it?"

"Yes, it's nice to know that someone cares about what happens to you."

"I will, if you'll let me," I said as I slipped my arm around her shoulders and pulled her close to me.

"I'll let you all right. Most of the men I meet just want a fuck. Afterwards they don't give a damn about what happens to you."

"I'm not like that," I said, trying hard to convince myself that I was speaking the truth.

I was in seventh heaven, listening to wonderful music and holding hands with an adorable girl. In some ways I almost preferred to be with her than Betty, because Betty was only really interested in sex and sunbathing. I found out later that Esther was keen not only on music, ballet and literature, but also politics and archaeology. Over supper, she told me she had studied the latter before the war, at evening classes at the Polytechnic. I soon realised that, compared to her, I was educationally and culturally still in the first form, but the experiences in my life had made me far more worldly-wise. This meant we could learn a lot from each other. She told me her father worked in the East End for a firm making men's suits, and had been a convinced socialist all his adult life. Her mother cared nothing about politics, and only concerned herself with material things. Her poor father tried his best to provide her with these by working all the overtime he could get. For as long as Esther and her older sister could remember, their mother had a succession of men friends without the slightest attempt to conceal this from either of them.

"Has your father ever found out about any of them?"

"I don't think so. Her fancy men are only about when he is slogging his guts out, trying his best to earn enough money to provide for us all. In the little spare time he has he goes to political meetings, or helps out at the Labour Party Rooms. She treats him appallingly but Dad adores her. I think it would break his heart if he found out that she was two-timing him."

"At least your dad has two loving daughters. That's some compensation, isn't it?"

"I suppose it is. My sister and I do our best to make his wretched existence more bearable."

Because Esther wanted to know, I gave her a condensed version of my life.

"It's not all been a bed of roses for you, has it?"

"No, I don't crush that easily, but I don't think it would be difficult for anyone I loved to break my heart."

"Have you ever loved anyone?"

"No, and I don't think any girl ever loved me. My last girlfriend was very attracted to me sexually, as I was to her, but that didn't stop her from marrying a chinless wonder twice her age, just because he was stinking rich."

"Do you ever see her?"

"I can't. She lives way up north and I don't even know where."

Esther looked at her watch. "It's getting late, I'd better start making my way home."

"Tonight, you have a choice: I can either accompany you all the way back to your home the other side of London, or you could come with me to my hovel, which is only a fifteen minute bus ride from here."

"That's a novel way of asking if you can fuck me."

"Honestly, I didn't mean it to sound like that. Mind you, I'd be lying if I said I wouldn't like that to happen."

"Facing a long journey on the Underground at this time of night doesn't appeal all that much, so you might get what you've been hoping for."

"Yeah," I said with a broad grin on my face.

We hadn't been in my room for long, when, with hardly a word spoken, we were standing naked by the end of the bed in a tight embrace. As Esther was tiny, kissing her was only possible if she sat on my clasped hands and wrapped her legs around my waist while holding onto me with her arms linked behind my neck. As I had not yet regained my normal strength, it wasn't long before I had to lay her down on top of the bed. I gazed down at her lying on her back with her hands clasped behind her head, her legs bent at the knees. Her body reminded me of my childhood sweetheart, Joyce. But there, as I found out later, all similarity between them ended.

I knelt on the floor beside her, then, like the concert pianist whose dextrous fingers traverse the piano keys, my hands and lips glided up and down her body. Her only response to my passionate caresses was to lie as lifeless as a warm corpse on the mortician's slab. Just when I was beginning to think that I hadn't backed a winner, she said:

"Derrick, darling, be rough with me, hurt me."

Not having ever heard of masochism, I hadn't the slightest notion what she expected me to do. I gripped her tiny breasts and squeezed them hard.

"Harder, harder, darling," she pleaded.

Christ, I thought, if I do, I might cause them irrevocable damage. So I compromised by only slightly increasing the grip I had on her.

"Darling, dig your nails into my back and bite deep into my flesh."

"Are you sure you want me to do that?"

"Darling, try to understand, I only get any pleasure out of sex when it's coupled with pain."

Not wishing to be a spoilsport, I did my best to oblige. The harder I bit, and dug my nails into her, the more ecstatic she became. Never before had I given my partner such paroxysms of delight.

"Fuck me, darling, but before you do, cover my mouth with your hand and close my nostrils between your fingers."

This last request worried me. By now I was desperately wanting to score, but I didn't relish the possibility of her passing out. Esther must have seen my look of apprehension.

"Darling, please don't worry, it's been done to me lots of times before, sweetheart, it'll be OK, I promise you. I only get any satisfaction if my lover overpowers me and forcibly deprives me of air. Darling, do it, do it, PLEASE!"

Preparing myself to take emergency measures if required, I reluctantly complied. Judging by the frantic movements of her pelvis, I'm sure she had the climax she desired. When she went limp, I quickly removed my hand.

"Derrick, darling, that was so, so wonderful," she gasped.

As a reward for my performance, she smothered me with kisses. Finally she sat up in bed and purred like a contented pussycat. While she purred, I said to myself, 'Derrick boy, you've learnt one thing this evening, and that is: when it comes to sex, there are almost as many varieties as the 57 Heinz sell'.

In daylight, when I saw the marks my teeth and fingernails had made, a nasty thought crept into my mind: if Esther ran weeping into a police station and showed the duty sergeant the abrasions, and told him that I caused them whilst savagely raping her, I'd be arrested and brought before a court, where no judge or jury would have accepted my plea of 'not guilty'. But I soon found out that this adorable girl couldn't hurt a fly, let alone me.

It was a Sunday so we could spend the whole day together. By the time we parted late that night outside her modest home in the East End, the beginnings of a strong bond had sprung up between us.

When I told Robert and Vic that Esther liked to be roughed up and almost asphyxiated when fucking, Vic said: "For God's sake, before you so much as lay a finger on her again, get her to sign an indemnity form stating that any lacerations you may have caused were made entirely at her own request. What's more, I implore you never again to go in for that suffocating lark. Christ, Derrick, if anything went wrong, you'd be charged with her murder."

The more Esther got to know and like me, the less she urged me to be so violent or in any way harm her. She worked at the British Museum, mainly keeping track of the irreplaceable works of art that for reasons of safety were scattered about the countryside. She also had to try and make sure that they were adequately stored. All her spare time, she spent with her friend Yvette and me.

Unlike Esther, Yvette didn't need to work - she got an allowance from her husband. She loved it at the Serpentine, standing on her hands going down the steps that led to the water. She was a natural acrobat who was at her happiest when doing somersaults, cartwheels or balancing upside down on one hand. Despite her very feminine looks, she was at heart a sort of female commando who only really came to life in dangerous or exciting situations. In heavy air-raids, you'd find her, perched on top of the high sloping roof of her Bayswater flat, revelling in the spectacle of bombs exploding all around her like a child watching a fireworks display.

Yvette's beauty and her delightful saucy French accent, attracted men to her like moths to a flame, and like them, they almost always got burned if they got too close to her. Esther believed that Yvette was frigid. She also thought that, as Yvette was only stimulated when facing danger, she would probably only get an orgasm if she were fucked on top of a thousand-pound unexploded bomb, primed to go off at any moment.

Many men fell in love with her, but she preferred American officers because they could provide her with the otherwise unobtainable luxury items they bought at their PX stores. All these poor gullible chaps got in return for their gifts was a short time in her vivacious company. When they demanded more, I was sometimes called in to give them their marching orders. This was not a task I relished - for two reasons. One was, I might well have had the shit beaten out of me, and the other was that I couldn't help but sympathise with them. After all, it was hardly their fault if they had misread the come-on signals Yvette gave out.

Once she seriously suggested to me the proposition that I should stand hidden in a doorway when night fell, in a small alley off Wardour Street, while she'd lure an American down it on the pretext that she was taking him back to her place. I was then supposed to pop out from behind him and hit the poor man on the head with a wooden mallet. Then, while he lay unconscious, she'd relieve him of his wallet.

"Yvette, nothing would persuade me to do such a terrible thing."

"I'm not suggesting that you kill anyone, only to stun them."

"One day soon, Yvette, those Americans you want me to help you rob will be risking their lives to liberate your country. How can you even think of behaving that way towards them?"

"I don't give a fuck about France being liberated. I want to live under a system where I'm in constant danger of being killed. The very idea of it sends bubbles of excitement racing through my veins, and makes living much more fun."

"Are you saying that you'd really prefer to live in a jungle, where a wild animal could suddenly attack you without warning?"

"To be all cosy and safe in suburbia is my idea of hell on earth. Compared to that, life in a jungle would be heaven."

"After the war, Yvette, you can go and join Tarzan. By then he'll be bored stiff with Jane."

"You do talk a lot of nonsense."

"Do you mean I should be sensible and only talk about hitting Americans on the head with a wooden mallet?"

"There you go again, saying silly things."

Despite her outrageous behaviour, and the fact that she was an out and out delinquent, Yvette was nevertheless great fun to have as company.

CHAPTER FORTY-SEVEN

As it was the best-paid part-time job on offer, I went back to being a film extra. The amount of work I could do was limited, as most of the films being made were blatant jingoistic propaganda. To appear in them would have meant wearing a uniform. Having refused to put one on in real life, to don one in the make-believe world of films would have been extremely hypocritical of me. Within days of letting Archie Wolf's agency know that I was now available, I was sent to Ealing Studios to be a stunt man in a film about a cargo ship that gets into serious trouble when hit by a storm in mid-Atlantic. The film was titled *San Dimitrio, London*, directed by Charles Frend. Having once been in this situation myself, to go through it all again in the safety of the studio appealed to me.

When I walked on the set, I could barely believe my eyes. There was a life-sized replica of three-quarters of a cargo ship on rockers. At one end of the stage were enormous tanks, filled with water. They were connected to a sort of escalator that could hoist them up to the studio roof, then empty them into a wide chute. A barrier at the end of the sloping channel was there to send a cascade of water high into the air before it would come crashing down onto the heaving boat below. A massive wind machine in front of the structure created a hurricane-force wind.

For one day only, I was the star of the show. My part in this epic drama was to be a seaman at the helm, trying against all odds to keep the ship facing the storm. A huge wave hits him and washes him down from the bridge onto the deck, another one puts the poor sailor overboard.

For this I was going to be paid twenty pounds, five times more than that of an ordinary extra. The film company asked me to sign a form indemnifying them if I should sustain any injury or meet with a fatal accident. However, I could, if I wished, insist on a run-through with a dummy strapped to the helm. I cannily worked out that it would take the rest of the day to drain the set and refill the huge tanks, and I would get another twenty pounds to come back the next day, so I told them I'd prefer to see what I was up against.

The way things turned out, it was just as well that I did. To everyone's dismay, when the tons of water came gushing down and hit the wheelhouse, it smashed it, and the dummy, to smithereens. If I'd been in position, the very least I would have got away with was a few broken bones.

"Jesus Christ, lad, I'm so relieved that it wasn't you standing up there, I'd have never forgiven myself, if you'd been injured," said the director.

"Don't worry, Mr Frend, I think I've worked out how it can be done without harming me. If the barrier at the end of the chute was removed, the flow of water would be more evenly distributed before it came crashing down. If you can arrange to have that done, I'll be back tomorrow."

"I'd be very grateful if you would. I'm already running behind schedule."

The next day, with three cameras filming from different angles, the shot was in the can before the mid-morning break. As planned the rush of water pushed me off the bridge and swept me overboard into a concealed pool of water. I'd been well padded, so I came out of the stunt unscathed and twenty pounds the richer. That night, with a bundle of notes burning a hole in my pocket, I picked up Esther from the British Museum and took her to have dinner at the Strand Palace.

"This is the most wonderful restaurant I've ever had a meal in."

What an incongruous society we live in, I thought. Esther, who worked all week long, could only occasionally treat herself to a modest meal at Joe Lyons, while Betty, who was exploited in a different way, had enough cash to dine at the Ritz whenever she fancied.

Friday, Saturday and Sunday nights, Esther stayed at my place. We only parted for a few hours on Sunday afternoon, when I went with Vic to Hyde Park Corner to sell the *Anarchist Weekly*. It puzzled me that he still did it, as he was becoming more and more antagonistic towards the working class. One day, when I walked into Tony's, he was having a heated argument with a Communist. It ended up with him saying haughtily: "Given the choice, old boy, I'd rather be governed by a benevolent aristocracy than a quango of wooden-headed commissars, but as I prefer to be ruled by neither, I am still an armchair anarchist."

One morning, on my way to take a skiff out on the Serpentine, I noticed a small crowd gathered in a semi-circle on the grass behind Speakers' Corner. I got curious, so I sauntered over. I was amazed to find they were staring at none other than Vic, stripped to the waist, standing on his head, cross-legged, muttering incomprehensible incantations. I manoeuvred myself through the sparse crowd, bent down and said to his inverted face: "What on earth are you doing?"

"Fuck off, Cartlidge, I'm cogitating on the cosmos."

"Wouldn't it be better to do that in the privacy of your own room?"

"When I'm meditating, I need to be in touch with Mother Earth, so piss off and leave me in peace to commune with nature."

Hoping that the poor chap hadn't finally gone bonkers, I decided that it was more likely he was giving in to his inclination to make an exhibition of himself - so I left him to it and made for the boathouse.

With Esther out working all day, I spent some of my ample spare time dropping pamphlets in the letter boxes of working-class houses in Camden and Islington. One afternoon I was running off some leaflets on the small printing press we had in the basement of a derelict house in Soho, when two men walked in. I knew them by sight only.

"Good afternoon, comrades, can I help you?" I asked.

"We've come to take your printing press."

"Has Frederick Lohr said you can borrow it? If he did, I should have been told you were coming."

"We've not come to borrow it, but to take it away for our own use indefinitely."

We believe, comrade, that anarchism can only be brought about by violent revolution, and that you namby-pamby pacifists are only distracting the workers away from what they must do to overthrow capitalism. So on behalf of the class struggle, we've come to relieve you of yours."

"Do you think your having our wee press will alter the course of working-class history? If so, I'm afraid I'm going to have to disappoint you. It is very definitely going to remain where it is. If you need one so desperately, go and steal it from the *Daily Telegraph*, that Tory rag can afford to be robbed more than we can."

"Now, comrade, you know that idea to be unrealistic, don't you?"

I was about to say it would take a deal more guts when they made a move towards the press. Quickly working out that they were no match for me physically, I threw myself at them with considerable force. They fell backwards and landed on the floor with a thump. Leaping between them, I pinned the two down by holding them in a tight grip around their throats.

"I thought you were supposed to be a pacifist," one gasped.

"I am, comrade, except when I'm attacked personally - then all my principles evaporate into thin air and I become unbelievably aggressive. When I release you, fuck off and don't come back. What's just happened is just a small sample of what you'll get next time."

To make sure they got the message, I gave them both a hefty kick up their arses to help them on their way up the rickety stairs.

Pleased with myself that I'd managed to send the thieves packing, I walked round to Berwick Street, where Vic and his boyfriend Peter lived, to boast about it. When I got there, to my horror, I saw Peter dangling upside down from a window on the third floor. He was screaming hysterically for help. Through the open window, I could just make out that Vic was holding onto him by his ankles.

"What the fuck's going on?" I shouted up.

"Get out of the way, Derrick, I'm about to let the bastard drop."

"I'm coming up, Vic, you're to do nothing until I get there."

"Your coming up won't make any fucking difference, I'm going to kill the bastard."

I rammed the front door with my shoulder,bursting it open easily because the lock was attached to rotten wood. When I entered their room on the third floor, thankfully Vic was still hanging onto Peter.

"For Christ's sake, Vic, pull him in right now. Do you want to end your life swinging from a hangman's rope? Nothing he's done can be the excuse for a fate like that."

"If only you knew what he did, it might well change your mind."

"First we'll get him in, then you can tell me all about it," I said as casually as one might to a fisherman needing a hand to pull in his catch.

We hauled Peter back in, then I carried him across the room like a frightened child and sat him down on the floor.

"Now, Vic, you can tell me what all the fuss is about."

"That snivelling little shit, " he said, pointing an accusing finger at Peter, hunched up in the corner and shaking from his ordeal, "came up from behind me when I was sitting on a chair and poured a whole bottle of lighter fuel over my head. Then, would you believe it, he calmly struck a match with the clear intention of setting me on fire. Do you still think I shouldn't kill the bitch?"

"What puzzles me is why you just passively sat there and let it all happen. If that had been me, I'd have jumped up the moment the first drop of fuel hit my head."

"I wanted to see just how far he would go."

"In a way you sort of incited him, didn't you?"

"Nobody can incite a sane and rational person to set them alight, wouldn't you agree?"

"Oh, I don't know, Hitler has persuaded almost an entire nation to go bloody bonkers."

"Well, I'm not fucking Hitler."

"So, what started the argument?" I asked.

It seemed that Peter had been driving Vic crazy for weeks, nagging him to leave their room and find cleaner lodgings in Notting Hill. Vic didn't have the money - he earned less than three pounds a week as a scene shifter, and could never afford more than the few shillings rent he paid to the Church Commissioners for this squalid dump.

I pointed out that if Peter did a part-time job, that would cover the rent.

"Him work? He's never done a stroke in the two and a half years we've lived together."

I knew that Jimmy at the Coffee Ann was looking for someone to help him. For six hours' work Peter would earn three pounds a week, enough to pay the rent on a flat in Notting Hill and have some over. I persuaded him to go and see Jimmy that night, and made Vic promise to go and find a flat with Peter the next day. I'd give them a fiver to hire a couple of barrows from Covent Garden, and help them move in.

By the time I left, they'd kissed and made up like children who had been beastly to each other. With all the drama, I never did get round to telling Vic how pleased I was with myself for having got rid of the two political bandits.

Two days later, Vic and I were at Covent Garden at the crack of dawn and hired ourselves two of the largest barrows at seven and sixpence each. It took us over half an hour to push them to Berwick Street, and it was only when I got up to the third floor that I realised what I'd let myself in for.

"Surely you don't need two wardrobes, four old armchairs with the springs sticking out, and three chests of drawers?"

"Everything that's here, old boy, I either rescued from bombed-out houses or paid good money for. I'm not going to make a present of them to the Church Commissioners. They can buy their own fucking furniture."

It took the best part of an hour just to get the big items down the three flights of narrow stairs. When I saw it all lined up on the pavement, I could see that nothing short of a pantechnicon would suffice.

With Vic directing operations, we piled the furniture to nearly the height of a double-decker bus.

"How the fuck am I going to see where I'm going?" I asked.

"Do what you do in a pea-souper, old boy, keep your eyes fixed on the kerb. My God, man, you are fussing a lot!"

"This fusspot wants to know if you remembered to bring any ropes with you to secure the load."

"Yesterday I had the foresight to buy a ball of string from Woolworth's."

"String? Lousy wartime string that snaps when you're tying up a parcel? Washing-line rope is the minimum that's needed to hold this junk in place."

"It was all I could afford, so it will just have to damn well do," said Vic, as he began to lash up the overloaded barrows.

Most of the furniture was piled up precariously onto the cart that he would take. Mine had the wardrobe standing upright, and behind it two chests of drawers stacked on top of each other.

"I've left a space at the front of your barrow for my books, Derrick. They're in the kitchen, all packed neatly into boxes. See you in Notting Hill Gate." And he set off in the direction of Oxford Street.

My heart sank when I saw the boxes that covered the floor in the kitchen. Apart from four fully laden teachests, there were umpteen cardboard boxes packed to the brim with new books, probably stolen from Foyles or the art book shops in the Charing Cross Road. The teachests held the less valuable second-hand ones. New or old, between them they must have weighed a good eight hundredweight. Unable to pick up the teachests off the floor, I had to drag them to the top of the stairs. The only way I could get them on my back was to sit on the third step down and tip the heavy crates onto my shoulders. The only way I could get them off me was to walk backwards into the side of the barrow, bend my legs and let them drop a few inches onto the floor of the cart. By the time I'd lugged the four crates down three flights of stairs, I was so exhausted, that I had to wait until I got my breath back, before going up to fetch the dozen or so cardboard boxes.

With this massive weight stacked forward on the stationary barrow, all the strain rested on its one front leg. To get the cart level so that I could move off, I had to press down hard onto the wooden handles. By the time I'd gone the length of Oxford Street and was going round Marble Arch, my arms began to tire. The dead weight of books piled high on the front eventually lifted me bodily some inches off the road. Suspended in space, like a gymnast on parallel bars, I frantically jerked my legs up and down in an effort to get my feet back down again. Finally my strength gave out, and I fell. The barrow tipped up and crashed down onto its one front leg which promptly snapped in two. The entire load was thrown into the road.

I became aware of someone's hand touching my left shoulder. I turned to see who it was. Peering down at me was a sturdy-looking middle-aged man.

"Do you need a bit of help, lad?" he asked.

"Thanks for offering, but I think I'm beyond the point where any help would be of use," I replied forlornly.

"I've been in the haulage business for twenty years and I reckon if we spread the weight of your load evenly, you'll manage to push it along all right. It all has to do with balance, you see, boy."

"I'd be very grateful if you help, but I'm afraid I don't even have enough money on me to buy you a drink."

"Don't worry, lad, I can pay for my own," he said in a friendly way. What a strange country we live in, I thought. Only a few weeks ago, men born and bred in the same class as this chap very nearly beat me to death, but here was this kind man coming to the aid of a total stranger.

"Our first job is to get all the goods out of harm's way and back onto the pavement, then we'll load the cart as it ought to have been in the first place."

We put the wardrobe in the same position that Vic and I had, at the back of the barrow. Into it, we stored half-a-dozen boxes of books. The rest we unpacked and piled into the two chests of drawers. The four heavy teachests went up front. While I held the cart steady, my guardian angel, like a greengrocer weighing up three pounds of potatoes, placed a handful of books one end or the other, until the load was so finely balanced that I could lift the barrow off its rear legs with one hand.

"Now, lad, you'll find the going much easier," said the man at last. "You won't have to exhaust yourself pressing down on the handles any more. Just the grip of your hands will keep the cart level. Good luck, you'll do fine now, I'm sure of it," he said as I thanked him and moved off towards Bayswater Road.

When I got to Notting Hill, Vic's barrow, still loaded, was parked outside his new place. He was obviously waiting for me to arrive so that I could lend a hand to carry the furniture up the two flights of stairs. On seeing me, he poked his head out of the window, and shouted down:

"Good show, Derrick, you're finally here. Did you have an uneventful journey?"

"Couldn't have been smoother," I lied, without a hint of sarcasm in my reply.

"I must say, Derrick, you made a damn sight better job of packing your barrow than I did. I had a hell of a task trying to stop it from tipping up."

"It's all a matter of balance," I replied with feigned authority.

It took some time and a lot of sweat to unload the two carts. As I'd been left to hump the heavy teachests down in Berwick Street by myself, I got my own back making sure Vic lugged them up.

"Jesus Christ, Derrick, these crates are bloody heavy, how on earth did you manage to carry them down three flights all on your own?"

"I don't remember thinking they were particularly heavy. Perhaps I'm a lot stronger than you are. Don't forget, you're five years older than I am."

"For fuck's sake, man, I'm twenty-six, I'm not exactly in my dotage."

"I was only teasing. Probably you're a bit out of condition. Come and row with me every day, then you'll soon get fit."

"I can't think of anything that would bore me more."

When everything was installed, Vic thanked me for my help and the gift of a fiver that had made the move possible.

"No point in having friends if they can't help out when things get difficult. God knows, Vic, you came to my aid often enough when we were in the army orin a punch-up at Hyde Park Corner."

CHAPTER FORTY-EIGHT

By the beginning of October, it was obvious that Esther had fallen in love with me. More than once she talked about us settling down and getting married, and even starting a family. She kept hinting that I should get a steady job, and this put me into a state of panic. At twenty the idea that I should live with the same girl for the rest of my life and have Christ knows how many children didn't appeal to me one bit. My reaction to this was to want to escape to the country for a while. I thought that a short separation might give her time to have second thoughts.

When I told Vic I'd decided to go and work on the land for a few weeks, he produced a crumpled piece of paper from his pocket. It was an advertisement he had torn out of the *Evening Standard*. Vic read it aloud.

"'Fit men wanted to work in the Northumberland forest, felling trees urgently needed as pit props by Bevin Boys in the mines. The job is well-paid, previous experience not essential.' I wouldn't mind going and lumberjacking for a while, you come with me. I need to escape too. Peter's possessiveness is beginning to get on my fucking wick."

"I'll come. How do we set about fixing it up?"

"Simplicity itself, dear boy. First thing tomorrow, we'll present ourselves at the offices of the Forestry Commission and inform them that a couple of inexperienced woodpeckers are responding to their advertisement."

The following morning, a silver-haired gentleman who introduced himself as Colonel Blunt, ushered us into his plush office.

"Please be seated. It gives me enormous pleasure that you have both responded to my advertisement. My colleagues pooh-poohed the idea when I suggested it. They thought it would only attract deserters and other undesirables. Well, I'm glad to say they've been proved wrong."

"I think you should know that my friend and I were discharged from the Army when they found out we were both homosexual," Vic said, with the obvious intention of embarrassing the poor chap.

"As long as you are both capable of wielding an axe, I don't give a damn about your sexual preferences. Some of my best friends are er-er-"

"Poofs," interjected Vic, to make him feel even more uncomfortable.

"I wouldn't have put it quite that way," he replied amiably.

"When would you like us to start, Colonel?" I asked in an effort to get the conversation back on track.

"Right away, but unfortunately, the train only stops at this remote village on Tuesdays and Fridays. You've missed today's, so you can't leave London until next Tuesday, I'm afraid."

"What's the pay?" enquired Vic.

"Half-a-crown for each tree felled and trimmed. I've been assured of that one can expect to topple ten in a day. Twenty-five shillings is not bad money for a day's work, wouldn't you agree?"

"That's nearly seven pounds a week, Vic."

"You're quite right," said the colonel, "and as the farmer's wife billeting you only charges thirty shillings for full board, most of what you earn can stay in your wallets. Can I assume that you'll take the job?"

"Certainly," I answered without even bothering to consult Vic.

"That's settled then, I'll give you a railway pass and a sub of three pounds each. The farmer, a Mr Thompson, will be informed by phone to expect your arrival on Tuesday. He'll pick you up from the station."

The colonel handed us our passes and requested that we sign for the cash.

"I'm sure you'll do splendidly," he said as we left.

"He's very trusting, isn't he, Vic? We could easily pocket the money. He didn't even ask for our address."

"People from his background think that everyone is honest until proved otherwise. "

"Anyway, we're not going to cheat him, are we?"

"That's only because it's not in our interest to do so," Vic replied.

As usual, Esther spent the weekend with me. I only plucked up the courage to tell her I was going off for a while a few moments before we parted late on Sunday night.

"You're fed up with me, aren't you, Derrick? This is just your way of saying goodbye, isn't it?" she said tearfully.

"No, no, darling, that's the last thing I want to happen. I just have a craving to be in the country for a bit, I long for the smell of damp earth and rotting leaves and the fresh air of the countryside. For the weeks I was confined to a cell, I promised myself that if I should ever be released, I'd spend some time in a wide open space. The only reason why I haven't left before now is that I couldn't bear to part from you."

"How do I know you're not going off somewhere to be with your beloved Betty?"

"For fuck's sake, darling, I don't even know where she lives, and even if I did, to visit her in her home with her husband there, would be pretty stupid, don't you think? "All right, so long as you're not away for more than four weeks. I'll be lonely without you."

"You've got Yvette for company, and if you feel sexy while I'm gone, you can pop into bed with one of her randy American admirers."

"Derrick, you just don't understand, do you? You're the only one I want."

"And you are the only girl I fancy. Goodbye, darling, I'll write to you."

After a long farewell kiss, she let herself into her parents' house. Although I was going to miss her, I couldn't help looking forward to swinging an axe in a Northumberland forest.

Having changed trains no less than three times between seven a.m. and five p.m., Vic and I finally arrived at the smallest station I'd ever seen. We were indeed in a remote part of England, tucked away in the middle of nowhere and only a few miles from the Scottish border.

"I doubt if the peasants who live around here know that there's a fucking war on," said Vic as we stepped out of the two-carriage train onto the wooden platform.

We spotted the farmer, Mr Thompson, immediately as he was the only person in sight.

"Are you the two men sent out from London?" he asked as he approached us.

"Mr Thompson, I presume," replied Vic in the voice that Stanley might have used when he met up with Dr Livingstone.

"That's right. You lads must be hungry after such a long journey. Mrs Thompson has a meal already prepared."

"We'd better go and hand in our tickets before we leave," I said.

"Harry only sells them, he's never here to collect any. Put them in his box by the shutter over there," said Mr Thompson, pointing to a horseshoe shape cut-out in the wall.

"How prophetic your station master is. Like H.G. Wells, he's already worked out how most things will be done by remote control in the future," said Vic.

"The only wells we have around here are the holes in the ground you draw the water from," said the farmer.

As we followed him out of the station, I whispered to Vic: "For fuck's sake, stop talking above his head."

"Right, for the duration of my stay in this intellectual desert I'll put my mind into neutral."

"You can stick it into reverse for all I care. Just for once in your life try and speak normally."

"I'll leave it up to you to do the talking, you're obviously more on his level than I am."

"It's people on his level that grow the very food you consume. What do you produce, apart from yap?"

"Man does not live by bread alone, you know."

"No, but because of men like Mr Thompson, he doesn't starve to death whilst using his mind to think on other matters."

Mr Thompson drove us along in his buggy and on the brow of a steep hill that led down to the farm we got our first unbroken view of the forest. It covered the width of the landscape and went as far as the horizon.

"That lot should keep us occupied for a few weeks, eh Derrick?"

"More likely to the end of the century," I said.

Supper in the farmhouse kitchen started with vegetable soup, followed by three fried eggs put on top of a huge portion of mashed potatoes, swimming in home-made butter.

"In London we only get one egg a month. You've given us three months' ration on our first meal!" I said.

"My hens don't know there's a war on. They go on laying as they've always done," said Mrs Thompson.

For a sweet, she produced a piping hot apple pie.

"My goodness, Mrs Thompson, if you go on feeding us like this, we'll get so fat we'll not get through the railway carriage door when we return to London."

"How far is it to the nearest inn?" asked Vic.

"It be a little more than ten miles away in Mowhaugh. I go there in my truck on Saturday evenings. You'd be more than welcome to join me."

"I presume your local village store is reasonably near?"

"It is, but I'm afraid it hasn't a licence to sell alcohol."

"Oh fuck," I heard Vic say under his breath.

"If you'd like a beer, I've a bottle you can share with your friend," said the farmer.

"That's very nice of you. Luckily for me, my friend Derrick doesn't drink. I will, of course, reimburse you."

"When we go to the pub, I'll let you buy the first pint," said the farmer.

Vic gulped down his beer at such a pace one might have believed he hadn't had a drink for weeks.

Having been cooped up for ten hours in a train we went out to stretch our legs before daylight faded. The farm and its outbuildings were smaller than any I'd ever worked in. The shed housed four cows and there were only three pigs in the sty. As we walked up the hill, there was no sign of fields anywhere. We came to the conclusion that Mr Thompson must be a sheep farmer.

"Bleak place to live permanently, don't you think?" I said.

"But a good one to be in if you're on the run. I doubt if the local constabulary knows of its existence."

"It suits us for a while though, eh Vic?"

"It certainly does, dear boy."

As darkness fell, we retraced our steps to the farm. It shone out like a beacon in the night sky.

"Just like I thought, Derrick, around here they don't know there's a war on. The Thompsons can't even be bothered to black-out their house."

"I doubt that the most stupid of German pilots would waste an expensive bomb on a glimmer of light showing in the middle of nowhere."

"Let's hope you're right, dear boy."

When we entered the sitting room, the farmer and his wife were warming themselves in front of a log fire.

"There's quite a nip in the air now that the nights are drawing in," said Mr Thompson.

We made light conversation with the couple until nine, which was their bedtime.

"If you'll both come with me, I'll take you up to your room," said Mrs Thompson, lighting a candle in its holder, before extinguishing the paraffin lamp that hung from the low ceiling.

"How uneven progress is. You don't have electricity, yet you're on the phone," remarked Vic.

"It comes in handy when we're snowed in during the hard winter months. It's why the forestry people chose my husband to be their man up here. They don't pay a lot, but every little helps."

We followed her up to a sparsely furnished room, which contained only a small chest of drawers and a large double bed.

"The toilet-cum-bathroom are behind the door opposite. I'll bring you up a cup of tea at six-thirty. The lamp is on the chest of drawers, don't forget to blow it out before you go to sleep. Goodnight!"

"Waking up to a cup of tea puts Mrs Thompson in my good books," I said.

Not since our childhood had either of us gone to bed as early as nine, but having been on the move since six in the morning, we felt tired enough to put our heads down. I fell asleep almost immediately.

I awoke in the middle of the night and felt Vic's penis rubbing against my buttocks. I leapt out of bed and said angrily: "What in hell's name do you think you're doing?"

"I'm sorry, Derrick, it won't happen again, I promise."

"It better bloody not, if it does, I'll be off from here like greased lightning," I snapped.

Despite my anger, I couldn't help but feel a little sorry for him. I'd always known that he was attracted to me from the first time we met at Mill Hill Barracks, when I was sixteen and he twenty-one. At that time it didn't worry me, because he was totally unaware that love between men even existed. He only realised he was a homosexual when I introduced him to the pubs in Soho and to Peter.

To play safe before getting back into the bed, I put on my corduroy trousers and tucked the shirt I was already wearing, firmly into them. With my belt pulled tightly around my waist, I felt confident enough to go back to sleep.

Vic kept his promise. He never bothered me again even though he must have felt like a cat, in bed with a mouse that it was forbidden to eat.

In the morning, after a substantial breakfast, the farmer handed us both an axe and a bow-saw and took us to the edge of the forest.

I asked Mr Thompson if he could give us some advice on how best to swing the axe.

"That I can't, I'm afraid, in all my life I've never had occasion to chop a tree down. Do the
best you can. Starton Saturday, and when you've finished work, I'll come round and count how many trees are down, and give you half-a-crown for every one. Once a week I'll come by with my tractor and dray, and cart a load off to the railway station."

"How many trees does your dray hold?" asked Vic.

"I've no idea, but I'd guess about twenty. I haven't taken a load to the station before. You're the first men the Forestry Commission has sent me."

And with that the farmer went off leaving us to get on with the job.

"What do you think, Vic? Should we both chop away at the same tree, or work separately?"

"Psychologically it might be best if we fell them together. The sound of trees falling every fifteen minutes or so will spur us on."

"Here goes," I said as with all my strength I whammed the axe deep into the trunk. I soon found out that was the easy part. The hard work began when I tried to pull it out again. Only after a lot of tugging did I manage to get the tree to release the blade that wounded it. Judging by the sound of Vic heaving and cursing, he was having as much trouble as I was. Half an hour later, we had finally encircled the tree and met up. Unfortunately, I had been hacking away two feet higher than Vic.

"You idiot, Derrick, why the fuck didn't you work close to the ground like I've done. Now all your sweat counts for nothing."

"You should have told me where to cut," I said.

"It's bloody obvious that to make pit props you need as much of the trunk as possible. If we cut as high as you have, the forest would soon look like no-man's-land in the last war, acres of stumps waist high."

"Acres? At the rate we've going, it'll be after Christmas before we've cleared enough space to build a fucking bungalow. As compensation for my mistake, you can keep the half-a-crown we'll get when this one is down."

"I won't hear of it, dear boy, we're in this together, come what may."

"Good. While I get this tree to keel over, you go and start on another."

Thirty minutes later, my tree was still standing. In a desperate attempt to bring it down, I swung blow after blow at it. Eventually it started to creak, and for an awful moment it looked as if it was going to come crashing down right on top of Vic. Thankfully it just missed him.

"Derrick," he yelled, "lumberjacks shout out 'TIMBER' when a tree is about to topple. It would be a good idea if you did the same."

"If we both work on the same tree, no harm can come to either of us."

"Then that's what we'll do, old boy."

It took us almost as much time and effort to disentangle and trim the fallen tree as it had to bring it down. By lunchtime we had earned between us the magnificent sum of five shillings. By late Saturday afternoon, all we'd knocked up doing four days hard labour was a miserable two pounds each. This was a far cry from the twenty-five shillings a day the Colonel had said we could earn with ease. After paying for our keep, all that remained was a few shillings left over from the sub we'd been given.

"It's just dawned on me, Derrick, there's a lot more to this wood-pecking lark than is apparent at first sight."

"I agree, and we'd better find out what it is, otherwise we'll be returning to

London penniless."

"On Monday, I'll persuade Mr Thompson to let me phone and have a chat with the colonel. I'll ask the pompous old twit if he has any ideas on how we can increase our pitiful income. If he has none, then I think we should say farewell to the fucking pit-propping business and return post-haste to our loved ones."

The colonel promised that he'd send us an experienced forester, who would show us how to fell a tree properly. When Vic told him what we'd earned so far, he was genuinely upset. He assured Vic that once we got the hang of it, we'd soon be earning good money.

All that week, we slogged away with very little to show for it. By Friday evening, things looked more promising because the forester from London was due to arrive on the six o'clock train. We went to the station to meet him.

The only person to alight was a thin and frail-looking old man, dressed in a fifty-shilling Burton suit. His shirt collar was pinned together under the knot of his dark brown tie.

"The bloody Colonel hasn't kept his word, the train has pulled out and there's not a lumberjack in sight. That's it, Derrick, we'll hitchhike back tomorrow the moment we've been paid."

We were about to leave when the elderly man called out to us.

"Excuse me, are you the two men who lodge with Mr and Mrs Thompson? I'm Mr Johnson, I've been sent up from London to work with you for a few days."

Had we not been in such a bad mood, we'd have burst out laughing.

"I was told by Colonel Blunt that he'd send us up a lumberjack, so why are you here?" said Vic.

"For forty years, that's what I was. Now I work in the office of the Forestry Commission. Although I'm getting on for seventy, and it's more than ten years since I last swung an axe, I can still remember how to do it."

"I doubt if he has enough strength left in his arms to put a pipe in his mouth, let alone pick up an axe," whispered Vic. In deference to the old man's age, we ambled slowly back to the farm.

When Mr Johnson surveyed the havoc we'd inflicted on the edge of the forest, he commented that it looked as if a bomb had hit it.

"I'll start by showing you a neater way to fell trees. Lend me your axe please," he said, pointing at mine. He scrutinised its jagged edge.

"I don't think you could cut butter with this, certainly not live wood, that's for sure. Before making the first swing, you must spend some time sharpening the axe. It should be so razor-sharp that it could slice a piece of paper in two. The next thing is to decide where you want the tree to fall. If it just drops anywhere, you'll waste a lot of time and energy dragging the trunk out into open ground. By the look of things, you've found that out already. Never use brute force, the weight of the axe's head is all that is needed to make a clean cut."

When he'd finished honing the blade, he demonstrated how easy it was for a man with a lifetime of experience to fell a tree. What had taken us almost an hour to accomplish, the old man did in fifteen minutes. So precise were his cuts that by the time he'd gone round the trunk, it resembled the points of two pencils joined tip to tip. He brought it down exactly where he'd planned by giving the tree a slight push with his bare hands.

Once Mr Johnson had left us to fend for ourselves, Vic said: "Derrick, are you thinking what I am?"

"There's not a hope in hell of either of us approaching anything like the sort of skill Mr Johnson has acquired over forty years. I think we'll only be wasting our time if we stay here."

"My thoughts precisely, dear fellow."

After deducting our keep from what we earned that week, we were left with the princely sum of a pound each.

"Never mind," consoled the farmer, "next Saturday I'll be paying you much more now that you've been shown how to bring down the trees a lot quicker. See you both later."

"That's what he thinks," said Vic as we left the forest for the last time and walked back to the farm. We found Mrs Thompson sitting astride her bike:

"I'm off to do some shopping in the village. I've left you some sandwiches on the kitchen table and I'll make some tea when I return. Shan't be long!"

As soon as we'd eaten, I went up to the bedroom and packed Vic's and my things into the one rucksack we shared. Although the Thompsons had been nothing but friendly towards us, to our shame we didn't even bother to leave them a note explaining our hurried departure. All that we were thinking about was to make for the open road.

Not one vehicle passed us as we strode along the uninhabited country lanes. It was a good twenty miles before we reached what might be described as a main road.

By then it was dark and in the November mist visibility was down to a few yards. Despite this, Vic sniffed out a pub some way off.

"I'll die if I don't get a drink down my throat," he said as we followed the scent trail that led to the Roebuck Inn.

The pub was packed with locals trying to get in their last orders before closing time. Vic, who had years of experience in elbowing his way to the bar, managed to get two pints for himself, a glass of water for me, and the last of the cheese rolls. After the landlord had called out 'time gentlemen please', I pointed out a notice hanging above the bar 'Bed and breakfast, five shillings'.

"As it's such a damp and cold night, Vic, let's ask if there's still a spare room."

I could tell the publican didn't like the look of the two strangers in his pub and that he knew that at this late hour on a cold night, he'd have us by the short and curlies.

"It'll cost you ten shillings each, paid in advance."

"Excuse me, but the sign above your head says 'B. and B., five shillings'."

"That's only when a room is booked in advance. Take it or leave it," he said gruffly.

I was about to say, you can stick it up your arse, when Vic answered for me.

"We'll take it," said Vic.

"Fucking hell, Vic, now we're left with less than a pound between us to get back to London."

"Plus, dear boy, faith, hope and charity."

There was very little charity offered to us on our journey back. Not only did we have to sleep out rough, ill clad, for two nights in freezing fog, it also took a lot of foot-slogging and umpteen short lifts before, at midnight on the third day, we arrived at the Coffee Ann, penniless and exhausted.

When Peter saw us, he ran over to Vic and threw his arms around him as if the two had been separated for years, not just under three weeks. When Vic finally managed to extricate himself, he said: "Be an absolute darling boy, and bring Derrick and me a pile of sandwiches and four mugs of tea before we collapse. We've not had a bite to eat for twenty-four hours."

Robert was sitting at his usual table.

"What brought you two lumberjacks back so soon?" he asked.

He had to wait until we had some food in our bellies before he got a reply.

"Let's hope," said Robert, "that this little excursion has cured you both once and for all of even thinking about land work again."

"I'm most certainly cured. There'll be no more pastoral life for me," said Vic.

"And how about you, Derrick?" asked Robert.

"Unlike you, I actually enjoy doing hard physical work from time to time, so it's quite possible that I'll be back on the land before long."

"You're obviously a sucker for punishment."

As I'd vacated my room in Maida Vale, I was left with no alternative than to spend the night at Vic and Peter's bug ridden flat. Lice or not, it was a lot better than the previous two nights sleeping rough in freezing fog.

CHAPTER FORTY-NINE

After having spent most of the night either scratching or bug-hunting, I fled the lice-infested bed before Vic and Peter woke up. Desperate to get clean but without money to go to the public baths, I remembered that Esther's friend Yvette lived just five minutes' walk away in Pembridge Villas. Her door was opened by Fiona, the frightfully, frightfully upper-class girl with whom she shared her spacious flat.

"Hello Fiona, is Yvette in?"

"She's having a bath, and then she's packing."

"Where's she off to?"

"I'm forbidden to say, I'm afraid. It's all very hush-hush. Something to do with going on a secret mission. She's not supposed to breathe a word to anyone but I'll bet you a pony she tells you all about it."

"Fiona, if you won the wager, how do you imagine you would cope with a small horse?"

"A pony, poppet, is classy racing slang for putting twenty-five pounds on the horse's nose."

"Then I can't take on your bet. I'm absolutely skint at the moment. One of the reasons I've called is to see if Yvette can lend me a couple of pounds."

"I'm sure she will. She loves helping the poor almost as much as she enjoys robbing the rich."

"She's a sort of female Robin Hood, then. But what about you, Fiona? "

"I'm an unrepentant nymphomaniac. I spend a lot of time bedding Yvette's hand-me-downs. The sex-starved American officers get me as a sort of consolation prize when they realise that Yvette has led them up a gum tree."

You'd have to be on your sexual beam ends to fancy this plump and plain-looking girl, I was thinking when Yvette, draped only with a towel around her slender shoulders, came into the room.

"Derrick, hello, Esther told me you'd be away for a month."

"I had intended to be, but it didn't work out quite the way I'd expected."

"Come and talk to me in my bedroom while I get dressed. I have some exciting news to tell you."

"Just as well you couldn't accept my bet, isn't it, poppet?" whispered Fiona as I passed her.

"Sit on the bed, Derrick, while I put on some clothes."

She took off her towel and flung it on a chair. Naked, she stood there, tapping her lips with one finger trying to decide what to wear. Her beautiful, slim, tanned body with ivory-white skin showing where her bathing costume had been, looked as tempting to me as a chocolate éclair with lashings of whipped cream protruding from its middle. I was having a hard time restraining myself from taking a flying leap at her, but she seemed totally oblivious of it. Perhaps she naively imagined that I only had eyes for her friend Esther, or, more likely, she just didn't realise what effect she was having on me. By the time she was dressed, any wicked thoughts I'd entertained about making a grab for her were gone.

"Well, what's the exciting news?"

"In half an hour, I'm off to a remote part of Scotland to do five weeks' training for parachute jumping. When I've completed the course, I'll be dropped somewhere near Paris, where the maquis will contact me."

"The maquis? Is he an aristocrat?"

"No, the maquis - it's the name of the French Resistance movement."

"What will you be doing while you're with them?"

"I don't know."

"How will you manage to get back to England?"

"A small plane lands in a field near Le Havre and picks me up, along with any British pilots who were forced to bale out over France. If they were lucky enough to fall into the hands of the Resistance and not the Germans, they'll be with me when I hop over the channel to Portsmouth."

"Le Havre is one of the ports that the RAF bomb the shit out of most nights."

"That's why it's so easy to fly us out. Our rendezvous with the plane is timed to coincide with a big air-raid on the port. While the Germans are kept busy banging away at our bombers, they fail to notice a small plane landing only a few miles away in the countryside."

"It all sounds terribly risky to me, Yvette."

"That's why I'm so keen to do it."

"I promise not to tell a soul what you're up to, and that includes Esther, and I advise you to do the same."

"Who do you think would believe me if I said au revoir, I'm off to Paris in the morning? They'd think I'd gone crazy."

"I wouldn't rely on them thinking that, if I were you."

"Half the fun will be the look on their faces when I do."

"And the other half, I suppose, is jumping out of an aeroplane into a black night and quite possibly landing in the midst of a German patrol? You do realise, I hope, that you might well end up at the wrong end of a firing squad."

"I only really come alive when I'm living dangerously."

"Then I suggest you join a unit that defuses unexploded bombs. Then you'd travel about in a jeep and wouldn't need to be parachuted down to do your dangerous work."

"To defuse bombs in the East End doesn't thrill me at all, but to stroll down the Champs Elysées with a time-bomb ticking away under my skirt is exciting and a lot more fun. When the war's over it's people like me they'll make films about, not the calm pipe-smoking men who render a thousand pounds of high explosive harmless."

"That's because those brave chaps aren't as pretty as you, Yvette. If Hollywood make a film about you, I do hope you're still around to attend the premiere."

"If I'm not, you can take my seat in the cinema and shed a tear in memory of me."

"The time for me to weep, is now. To stand by helplessly and watch a beautiful and vivacious girl like you throw her life away, depresses me. Is there nothing I can say that might persuade you to change your mind?"

"Nothing, chéri."

"That's that then, Vive la France!"

"Derrick, I'm not risking my life for my fucking country, I'm doing it to stop myself from being driven out of my mind with boredom."

Her prompt reply convinced me that she wasn't kidding.

"You mentioning boredom reminds me of one of the reasons I called. To me there is nothing so tedious as being totally broke. I'm hoping that you could lend me a couple of quid so that I can rent a room. I promise to pay you back the day you return from Scotland."

"I'll give you five to tide you over, and you won't need to find a room because you can stay here rent-free until I return."

"What a generous little French angel you are. How about Fiona, do you think she'll mind?"

"I don't need to ask. I already know what her answer will be. She hates to be all alone in the flat at night."

"Don't the men she has spend the night with her then?"

"Those sex-starved Americans behave as if they were in a cafeteria - they help themselves to a good fuck, then leave and, unlike a cafeteria, it doesn't cost them a cent."

"Will it bother her if Esther stays here at weekends?"

"Of course not, she likes her and I know she's keen on you."

"That's a bit of a problem. I don't fancy her."

"No need to worry, Esther will protect you."

"Yvette, while you pack, may I go and shave and bath? I'm absolutely filthy."

"So it's you, I was wondering where the smell was coming from," she said.

"You can come and wash my back if you like," I said in the vain hope that she might.

"I can't, I've yet to finish packing, and anyway a cab will be on the doorstep in fifteen minutes."

"I was only joking."

"Now you look more like the Derrick I know," said Yvette when I'd had my bath.

"No need to stand downwind of me any more, is there, Yvette? Can I help you pack?"

"It's all done, be an angel and close the trunk for me."

I sat on its lid, and only by pressing down as hard as I could did I finally manage to shut it. I upended it, so as to be ready to carry it down when the taxi arrived.

"Jesus Christ, what have you got in it, bricks? It weighs a ton!"

"I like to wear something different every day, and as I'll be away for five weeks most of the clothes I possess I'm taking with me."

"Sweetheart, from what I know about army life, you'll be housed in a wooden hut. The only space you'll have for your personal belongings is a cupboard by the side of your bed. What made you think you'd need all this clobber?"

"To have something to wear in the evening."

"Yvette, darling, you're not going for a five-week holiday to Monte Carlo, you'll be stuck in the middle of the bleak Scottish moors where, I promise you, there'll be no smart hotels or restaurants within miles."

"I wouldn't mind betting that most nights I'll be invited to dine with the officers in their mess."

"As you won't be stationed in a barracks, there'll be no mess for you to dine in. If there are any officers at all, they will live and eat in the same makeshift huts as the non-commissioned parachute instructors. The only place you might be invited to will be the fucking NAAFI if there is one."

"I do wish I'd talked to you before I started to pack. There's nothing I can do about it now."

"A wee bit of advice, Yvette, take out all the clothes you think are essential, then get them to store the trunk somewhere."

"Good idea, I'll do that."

Our conversation was interrupted by the doorbell.

"I won't be a moment," she shouted out of the window to the cab driver.

"While I carry your case down, you go and say farewell to Fiona," I said, as I struggled to lift the massively heavy thing onto my shoulder.

The cabbie's tired eyes lit up when he saw the beautiful young woman who was to be his fare.

"Where to, miss?"

"King's Cross Station, please."

Through the open window, I gave her a goodbye kiss.

"Promise me you'll remember to pull the cord when you're hurtling down to earth."

"Should I forget, chéri, you can stay in the flat until the agent gets round to chucking you out."

"You crazy girl, I don't want your death to benefit me in any way, what I want is to see you back safe and sound."

"Goodbye, Derrick, give Esther my love and tell her I'll see her in five weeks."

"Do please be careful, Yvette," I said. Her departure left me feeling miserable. For some reason I was unable to shake off the thought that I might never see her pretty face again.

At five that evening, I stood outside the railings of the British Museum opposite the staff exit, waiting for my little Venus to appear. When she caught sight of me, she ran towards the wrought iron gates. I lifted her up and we began to hug and kiss one another so passionately that to speak was impossible. Some time passed before I put her tiny feet back down onto the pavement.

"Derrick, darling, what a lovely surprise. I didn't expect you to be back for at least another two weeks. Are you here because you couldn't bear for us to be separated any longer, or is there another reason why you're back so soon?"

"It's a bit of both, Esther darling. I'll tell you all about it over dinner at the Corner House."

My account of how an old man ran rings around Vic and me when it came to cutting down trees amused her. It wasn't until we were eating the restaurant's wartime attempt to produce a barely edible trifle that I finally got round to telling her why I'd called on Yvette that morning, and why she had offered me the use of her flat.

"Did she say where she was going?"

"No," I lied. "She mentioned that her train was leaving from King's Cross, so I presume she might be visiting someone up north."

"It's strange, she said nothing to me about going off when I was with her on Sunday."

"You know what Yvette is like, she probably only decided to take off on the spur of the moment. I'm sure she'll tell you where she went when she returns."

"Yvette's departure has worked out well for you, hasn't it, Derrick? You being allowed to stay in her flat buckshee."

"It certainly has, not to mention the money she gave me. That's why we've eaten here this evening. Esther, sweetheart, would you mind awfully if I don't escort you home? I'm completely wiped out after three nights on the trot with no sleep. Once I've had twelve hours' uninterrupted slumber, I'll be my normal self again."

"I understand, sweetie. After work tomorrow, I'll come straight to Yvette's place, then we can cuddle away all evening."

I was too tired to engage in idle conversation, so it was a relief to find Fiona out when I arrived at the flat. All I longed for was to put my head down and close my eyelids. I hadn't been asleep for very long when I was awakened by a hand pushing on my shoulder. Peering into the room, lit only by the dim glow of the hall light, my half-closed eyes perceived the silhouette of Fiona standing by my bed. The negligée she was wearing was parted, exposing a large slice of her plump figure.

"Is anything the matter?"

"I can't get to sleep, Derrick."

"Why not? For once there's no ack-ack guns banging away."

"The noise of them never keeps me awake. I'm restless because I feel randy. If my craving isn't soon satisfied, I'll spend the night lying on my bed staring at the ceiling."

"Fiona, I'm a very tired man, not a fucking sleeping pill for a nymphomaniac.

Call a taxi and go to Piccadilly. The Americans that hang about Rainbow Corner are praying that a horny girl like you will turn up and put them out of their misery."

"It's freezing outside, anyway, I'd never get a cab at this late hour."

"You do know, don't you, Fiona, that I'm going steady with Esther."

"Since when has being faithful to one's wife or girlfriend ever stopped a virile man from having a bit on the side? Come on, Derrick, let's fuck, don't be a meanie."

I can be called many names without getting upset, but to be thought ungenerous was more than I could bear, so reluctantly, I said:

"OK, but I warn you, I'm so tired I might well fall asleep on the job."

"No man has up to now, poppet. Lie on your back and relax, I'll do all the work."

With her legs folded under her, she sat bolt upright astride of me. It was only after a lot of coaxing, that my less than enthusiastic penis came to life. With me inside of her, she massaged the erogenous opening between her legs that nestled out of view under the folds of her bulging belly. Rhythmically, her body went up and down as it would on a horse going first at a trot, then at a gallop. While all this bare-back riding seemed to be fine for her, it wasn't doing a lot for me. I only got to the finishing because she knew all the tricks that nymphomaniacs have at their fingertips.

Although I'd consented to what had happened, it didn't stop me feeling I'd been sort of raped. Before going back to sleep, I made up my mind never to allow Fiona to pull that 'I can't get to sleep, Derrick' stunt on me again. In future, I'd bolt the bedroom door and no matter how much she pleaded to be let in, I'd stay all warm and snug under the blankets and refuse to budge.

A few days later the phone rang at one in the morning.

"Hello," I said, wondering who in hell it could be at one in the morning.

"Get me Yvette," said a man with an American accent.

"Did I hear you say that you're sorry to disturb me at this late hour, but if she's not already asleep, could you please talk to Yvette? Or is that too difficult for you?"

"You son of a bitch, why are you in her flat? I don't pay half her fucking rent so that a faggot like you can stay there. Listen, you fucking smart ass, if you don't want to be beaten into a pulp, you'd better make yourself scarce before I arrive."

"One of the things I agreed to when I was given a black belt in judo, was to let any assailant know in advance exactly what he was up against," I said, repeating the bluff I worked so successfully on the Guard Sergeant in York. "If you are foolhardy enough to venture here, my advice is to bring with you no less than three of your more robust chums - otherwise you'll end up going head over heels down the stairs a damn sight faster than you mounted them."

"Belt or no fucking belt, arsehole, I'm coming round to kick the shit out of you. Locking the flat door won't stop me - I have my own set of keys."

"It's obvious you're a sucker for punishment. I'll look forward to giving you a sound thrashing. Just before you hang up, you should know that Yvette is away and is not expected back for five weeks. See you shortly then, goodbye."

Before getting into bed I wedged a chair under the door handle, bolted the bedroom door and opened the window wide, so that in an emergency I could make a hasty retreat shinning down the drainpipe.

Although I tried hard to stay awake, I failed. I dreamt that an American soldier the size of King Kong held my struggling body in the palm of his huge hairy hand, which moved irrevocably nearer and nearer the monster's open jaws. Just as my head was about to be bitten off, I woke up in a cold sweat. As it turned out, the man I'd been so worried about never arrived. It seemed that for the second time within a year, my undoubted talent for bluffing had paid off.

CHAPTER FIFTY

I'd been living in Yvette's flat for over two months and there was still no sign of her, nor had she written to Fiona to say why her stay in Scotland had gone beyond the five weeks the course was supposed to take. Just when we were beginning to worry about her, she turned up at the door with one leg in plaster up to her knee and a crutch under each arm.

"Christ, Yvette, how did you do that?"

"Before I tell you, Derrick, please go down and get my trunk from the taxi. The poor old driver hasn't even enough strength to put it on the pavement."

"What's the lovely lass got in it, bricks?" said the cabbie as I lifted the thing onto my shoulder. With the trunk boring a hole into the side of my neck, I put it down in the bedroom.

"Now Yvette, tell me why your leg is in plaster."

"Because on the last day of the course my bloody chute failed to open in time for me to make a soft landing. I hit the ground with such force that my ankle broke. If it hadn't been for that, by now I'd be with the resistance movement in Paris. The doctor who plastered up my leg said it would be weeks before I could do another jump."

"Your broken ankle may well turn out to be a blessing in disguise. It may have saved your life."

"No, it fucking won't. Now I'll die of boredom."

"Cheer up, Yvette, a few weeks pass soon enough. This war looks like it will drag on for a long time yet. I promise you, you'll be hopping in and out of France many times before it's over."

"I don't think you're right, my instructor up in Scotland reckoned that the second front might open up at any moment. Then there would be no need for me to join the maquis, would there?"

"Your instructor was talking rubbish. I'm no Montgomery or Eisenhower, but I assure you that not even those two old generals would be stupid enough to cross the Channel in rough seas with thousands of troops and equipment, when most of Europe is in the grip of a hard winter."

"I hope you're right!"

"I know I am," I replied with all the confidence that a pacifist thinks he's entitled to have when giving an opinion on military strategy.

"Yvette darling, as I didn't know you would come back today, would you mind if I slept on the sofa? I promise to be out of your way first thing tomorrow."

"You can stay here for as long as you like."

"You are a sweetie, Yvette, I'm so happy to see you back safe and sound. Personally, I hope that your ankle takes a long time to mend. While you're limping around London, I do at least know that you're still alive."

"Don't you care that hanging around will drive me insane?"

"Of course I care, but I just can't help feeling relieved when I know you're safe. I'll be seeing Esther tonight and I'll tell her you're back. She's missed you, you know."

"Would you mind if I came with you?"

"No, I told you I wouldn't say a word to anyone, and I didn't. I did say that you more than likely got a sudden urge to visit friends up north."

"I'll enjoy seeing the look on her face when I tell her exactly what I was up to."

"It's up to you, Yvette, but for your own safety, I think you should keep mum about your trips."

"I don't give a damn about my safety."

"Does the same go for those who will work with you?"

"Even if I'm arrested and then tortured, I'll never give away any of my colleagues. When the army beat the shit out of you, they didn't succeed, did they? The same applies to me."

"The reason I didn't give in to them was because I passionately believed that what I stood for was right. You told me that you were not going into this escapade out of a sense of patriotism, but just for the thrill of it. A reason of that kind wouldn't sustain you long under torture."

"Who knows? I think I can be just as stubborn as you were, Derrick, you'll see."

"I hope I never have to," I replied.

Throughout the winter of 1943-44, my routine hardly varied. The weekend and some evenings I devoted to Esther. When not doing film extra work, my mornings started with a half hour swim at the baths, followed by not less than an hour of vigorous exercises. I then ran from Bayswater through Hyde Park to the Serpentine, where I hired a skiff and rowed at some pace for two and a half times its length. Two months of relentless physical activity put me back into the tiptop condition I was in before I got arrested. My afternoons were spent at Tony's, discussing with Vic and Robert or any of the Soho bums who were there, sheltering from the cold, how to put the world to rights. The fact that none of us were prepared to get off our behinds and do something about it never entered our heads. The evenings I wasn't with Esther, I could reliably be found at the Coffee Ann. Apart from selling the *Anarchist News Sheet* at weekends, I led a totally unproductive existence.

The only vaguely commendable thing I did was to try once a week to dine with Uncle at the RAC. I only did this because I felt sorry for the old man, who, in the main, ate alone. I liked seeing him, but I hated having to wear the clothing that was a prerequisite for being allowed to enter the hallowed portals of his club. All my pre-war glad rags, the double-breasted suit, white shirt and tie and the polished shoes, were kept in pristine condition by his loyal daily, Mrs Blaber.

Most of the films in production at that time were unashamedly propagandist and jingoistic. This meant that when extras were required, they had to wear uniforms of one or other of the services. As I'd refused to put one on in the real war, under no circumstances would I don one in the make-believe world of the cinema. Aware of this, the film extra agency only sent me on the few films that were set in historical or prewar periods. My pacifist principles cut deeply into what was, at the best of times, a precarious living. To make up the shortfall in my income, I thought up a fraudulent scheme. If I was sent on a film that needed a huge crowd, I'd be one of the first to arrive at the studio to collect my pay chit. This I had made out in my real name. With that in my pocket, I'd go to the wardrobe department, pick up a costume and put it in a locker. Then I'd double back outside the studio gates and attach myself to the end of a long queue, waiting to check in. Under an assumed name, I'd go through the whole rigmarole again, only this time I'd put on a second costume I'd been given and join the rest of the crowd on the set. At the end of the day, armed with two chits duly stamped that I'd returned studio property, I'd queue up twice at the pay-out counter.

On the plus side, this fraud doubled my money, on the minus it added at least three hours to what, in any event, would have been a long day. One film I worked on, that had a lot of extras, was Shaw's *Caesar and Cleopatra*, starring Vivien Leigh, Laurence Olivier and Claude Rains. The director, Gabriel Pascal, was a Hungarian who came to England before the war. My worm's eye view of him was that he behaved more like an ill-mannered peasant than a film director. Despite the impression he gave, it was he who persuaded Shaw to allow him to make films of two of his plays. Pascal had succeeded where many of our most distinguished producers had failed.

Along with no fewer than two hundred other extras, I worked on *Caesar and Cleopatra* for five days. At least a third of the crowd were overt homosexuals. They were having a rare old time, queening it about, all dressed up in mini-skirted togas. On the last day of the exterior set, with everything perfect for filming and with blue skies giving a God-given backdrop for Cleopatra's lavishly built palace, plus a very reluctant RAF agreeing not to fly over the set whilst filming was in progress, Pascal was informed by an assistant that, as Miss Leigh was suffering from early pregnancy nausea, she was unable to be on set that day. Forgetting the PA System was switched on, the director bawled out:

"Why can't Larry (Laurence Olivier) tie a knot in his cock when I'm making a picture!"

The crowd burst out laughing.

"What's so fucking funny about losing a day's shooting in perfect weather? You wouldn't be so amused if I said, because I can't work, none of you will be paid."

Just the idea of that wiped the grins off everyone's face. Personally I couldn't but help feel a little sorry for the frustrated Hungarian, so at some cost to myself I refrained from cashing in the duplicate pay chit I'd collected that morning.

In March, when the daffodils and primroses in Hyde Park were just starting to add a welcome bit of colour to an otherwise grey and depressing London,

Esther complained that the lower part of her right leg was bothering her. In the end, the pain got so bad that she could only get about with the aid of a walking stick. I suggested that perhaps she ought to go and see a doctor.

"They charge five shillings. I've most likely strained it. I'm sure it will get better in a few days," she replied.

The pain didn't go away, but became so severe that it kept her awake for most of the night.

Reluctantly, she agreed to go to the doctor. When he gently moved her foot about, she screamed out in agony.

"I don't understand why it's hurting you so," he said. "I'll give you some tablets that should ease the pain a little, and a letter for the specialist at the Orthopaedic hospital. You and your boyfriend should go to the Out-patients Department straight away."

The doctor waved aside the five shillings I offered him.

"As I can't treat the young lady, there's no need for that. Use it to take a cab to the hospital. The more she keeps off her leg, the sooner it may heal."

"I wish there were more like him," I said, waving down a passing cab.

There was a three-hour wait before it was our turn to see the big white chief. It was obvious from the glint in his eye that the doctor was relieved that his next patient, in contrast to all the old people he'd examined all morning, was a pretty young girl. When he called Esther in, I got up to go with her.

"You, lad, wait outside," he said curtly.

I sat in the corridor for quite a while before I heard Esther screaming. In the hope that her crying out would soon stop, I did nothing for a minute or so. But it didn't. No longer able to bear her distressing cries, I burst into the consulting room. Esther was lying down on the examination couch, weeping. Her skirt was pulled up to the top of her stockingless legs. The specialist, who had his back to me, was roughly manipulating her painful right foot. When he turned and saw me, he said sharply: "I told you to stay outside."

"How the fuck can I, when it sounds like my girlfriend's being tortured," I snapped.

"How dare you use language like that in my consulting room! If you don't leave immediately, I'll get the porters to escort you out of the hospital by force if need be."

"It would need at least a dozen of the old men I saw pushing stretchers around to remove me," I said defiantly.

"Then you leave me with no alternative than to call the police."

"By all means do, and when they arrive, you can explain to them why you found it necessary to have my girl's skirt pulled up the top of her legs while you examined her foot."

"Are you implying that I behaved improperly towards the girl?"

"Did he, Esther?"

"I told him that the pain was in the lower part of my right leg, but he kept

428

rubbing his hands up and down my thighs. It was only when I stopped him getting up my knickers that he even began to look at my foot."

"If you call the police, doctor, my girlfriend will tell them how you abused her. It will be your word against hers. Mightn't it be a good idea to give some thought how best to treat her?"

If looks could kill, I'd have died on the spot. When the doctor's rage had simmered down a little, he said:

"She must have her foot massaged daily by our physiotherapist. If there's no improvement after a few sessions, we'll have to bring her in for a more thorough investigation."

He wrote out a note and handed it to Esther. "You'll find the physiotherapist in Room 7 on the third floor. Go there now."

When we got into the corridor, I said: "What a shit that man is, one wouldn't think he was in the same profession as the nice doctor who sent you to him."

"Derrick, it was wonderful how quickly you came to my rescue."

"It's lucky I did. Up until now, I've always assumed that doctors only act in their patients best interests, even if it sometimes meant inflicting pain."

"Well, this old lecher didn't," she said, as we entered the lift that took us up to the third floor.

The physiotherapist was quite different from the specialist, and moved Esther's foot from side to side very gently. Despite the tender way she did it, the pain was so intense that Esther couldn't help but scream.

"It might be best if I don't even try to treat you today. I think your foot needs a complete rest, you shouldn't even stand on it. I'll get a wheelchair and you should stay in it whenever you're not lying propped up on your bed. Can you push her home?" she asked me.

"I could, I suppose, but my girlfriend lives a good eight miles away, in the East End."

"Then going home and coming back again tomorrow is out of the question. I'll go and talk to the doctor and let him decide what to do."

"Is he the same one I've seen already?" asked Esther apprehensively.

"No, Mr Thompson has already left. He is not one of our resident doctors."

Thank God for that, I just stopped myself from saying aloud. A few minutes later, the therapist returned, accompanied by a young and pleasant looking doctor. The doctor ran his fingers lightly over Esther's foot, then said:

"I think it's a mystery that can only be solved by an X-ray. Certainly you must stay off it, so under the circumstances, we'll keep you here for a few days. Don't be upset, we'll find out what's wrong, then have you well and out of pain in no time at all."

When Esther had settled down in the ward, the nurse asked me to phone her parents and get one of them to bring a few items she'd need for a short stay.

"They're not on the phone, I'll go and fetch them," I replied, even though I dreaded the thought of having to face Esther's awful mother.

"I'm so sorry, darling, putting you to all this trouble. I do love you, Derrick."

"And I you," I echoed.

"When you get to my house, it is possible that my mother is 'entertaining' a friend ... well, that's the way she puts it. Just leave her to get on with it, and go into my room. My nightdresses are on the top shelf of the cupboard, any two will do, and on the little table by my bed is a flower-patterned washbag. Bring that as well."

A nurse came over to me and said that I must leave as lunch was about to be served. When I bent down to kiss Esther goodbye, she started to weep.

"What's all these tears about, Jesus Christ, girl, you're only going to stay here for a few days, you don't realise how fortunate you are. You'll be all snug and warm in this centrally heated place while I'm outside facing the freezing March winds. Come on now, stop crying and give us a wee smile. I'll be back with all your things at visiting time this evening."

I gave her all the cigarettes I had, then, after I'd managed to coax a little smile from her, I left the ward.

I waited outside the front door of her home for some time before her mother opened it. In her haste to answer it, she'd omitted to button up her blouse.

"Esther's not in, she's at work, I would have thought you knew that," she snapped.

"She's not, she's in hospital. A doctor sent her there because the pain in her foot got worse. I'm here to collect the things she needs for a few days' stay."

"It's very inconvenient just now, I'm entertaining a friend."

"Esther warned me that you might be, don't worry, you won't have to put yourself out. She's told me where everything is."

"Go and get them, and remember to shut the front door behind you when you leave."

"Don't you even want to know which hospital your daughter is in?" I asked.

"Yes, but make it quick."

I told her and added, "You'll be sure to tell your husband where she is, when he comes in from work, won't you?"

"I don't need to be told by you what I should do, you bloody army dodger."

"In my book that's one pip up from being a part-time whore," I said, as I pushed past her on my way to Esther's room. It's no wonder, I thought, that both her daughters hate her so. For the life of me, I couldn't begin to comprehend why her good husband hadn't kicked the bitch out long ago.

That evening when I entered the ward, Esther was chatting away to the patient in the next bed. She appeared to be a lot more relaxed and cheerful than the unhappy girl I'd left a few hours' previously.

"How are you feeling? You certainly look much better."

"Not standing on my foot makes it less painful. The nurses won't even let me out of bed to go to the loo."

"Oh dear, that means you have to use one of these awful bedpans."

"They're not so bad, I'd rather use one than endure the pain."

"I bumped into Yvette on my way here, she sends you her love, she's being dropped into France tonight. She told me to tell you that if she sees a nice outfit in Paris, she'll buy it for you."

"I'd have thought that Paris has even fewer clothes to sell than London."

"Not according to her, it hasn't. I've brought you a packet of ciggies. If Robert or Vic will lend me a couple of bob, I'll bring you some more next time I come."

"Derrick, darling, how I wish you could stay the night."

"Shall I ask sister if I can?"

"Don't be silly, you know already what her answer will be."

"Just joking, sweetheart."

"I never know when to take you seriously."

"Will you come and visit me tomorrow ?"

"Nothing short of a direct hit would stop me."

Our conversation ceased when our lips met. While passionately kissing her, my hand travelled between the sheets and up the pretty nightdress I'd brought her. The love play only came to an abrupt halt when a nurse tapped me on the shoulder and pointed towards the exit. I gave Esther one last lingering kiss, then whispered into her ear: "See you tomorrow, sweetheart."

The next evening, while I was waiting in the corridor to be let into the ward, Esther's father arrived.

"Hello, Mr Levy, your daughter will be pleased that you've come."

"Good evening. I'd have come last night if only I'd known, but my wife didn't tell me she was here until this morning. Were you with Esther when they took her in?"

"Yes."

"You're a good lad, I can see why she's so fond of you."

"Visitors may now enter the ward," called out a nurse.

I stayed behind so that Mr Levy could spend some time alone with his daughter, but I'd barely taken four draws of my cigarette when he returned, decidedly agitated.

"I can't see her anywhere, are you sure we're in the right ward?"

"I'm certain of it, I'll you take you to her."

When we got to the bed I'd left Esther in the previous night, it had been stripped.

"Perhaps she's been moved. Let's go and ask a nurse," I said.

"The Ward Sister will tell you where Miss Levy is, that's her standing in the entrance with her back to you," said the nurse.

"I'm afraid I have some unpleasant news for you, Mr Levy," said the sister. "The X-rays have revealed that your daughter has tuberculosis in her right foot. This morning we sent her by ambulance to a sanatorium in Ascot. It's the best place in the country for the treatment of TB. Visiting time is on Sundays between three to five."

Mr Levy was so stunned by what he'd been told that a chair had to be found for him.

"Will she be there for long?"

"I don't think so, she's young and otherwise in good health. With the expert treatment she'll get, I'm sure your daughter will be back on her feet in no time."

Despite her reassuring words, we both knew that people with tuberculosis might die from it. I tried to console the distraught Mr Levy but failed.

"I just can't bear the thought that my little girl is all alone with no one there to comfort her. It's five long days until Sunday."

"You could go to a phone box and ring up the hospital. You won't be able to speak directly to her, but they'll give her a message."

"Would you do it for me, Derrick? I've never used a telephone before, and I don't know what to do."

"Yes, of course. Because we're phoning out of London, it might cost sixpence. I'm afraid I don't have that amount on me at the moment."

"Use this," he said, handing me a shilling.

While the old man stood outside in an icy wind, I got through to the sanatorium and asked the lady who answered to tell Miss Levy that her father and her boyfriend sent their love and would see her on visiting day.

"Do you think Esther will be given the message?" asked Mr Levy when I stepped out of the phone box,

I assured him that she would, and that everything would look better when we met up again on Sunday.

"I hope so," he replied as we parted and went our separate ways. Having only been concerned with trying to console a grieving father, it only hit me on the way to Tony's that I too would miss not having Esther around for the weeks, or months that lay ahead.

At the Sanatorium in Ascot were from three to five, I made a point of not arriving until four, so that Esther's father could be alone with her for the first hour. The ward looked very different from any I'd seen before. It was in the shape of a long wide corridor, with a single line of beds that faced huge ceiling to floor sliding windows. Esther was sitting up in bed, all rosy-cheeked and looking healthier than I'd seen her since the summer.

"Hallo, darling, have they had you working on the land all week? You don't look like you've been cooped up in here."

"It's because for all the hours of daylight, even if it's snowing, the windows are rolled aside and the beds are wheeled out onto the veranda. The doctors seem to think that fresh air is the only cure for TB."

"I'm glad you're back in the ward now, there's a biting cold wind blowing at the moment."

"I know, darling, I was out in it until visiting time."

"Are you in any pain?"

"None, not since they put half my leg in plaster. I'm only allowed out of bed to go to the loo. I can only manage to do that with the aid of crutches."

For the rest of my visit, we hardly spoke. All we did was to kiss while my hands moved ceaselessly over her beautiful body. How wonderful it would have been if the sister had allowed me to wheel her into a private room, so that we could bring all our foreplay to its natural conclusion.

On the train back to London, I told myself that as Esther might stay in hospital for months, I must do something about finding a temporary girl.

CHAPTER FIFTY-ONE

Surprising as it may seem, when I explained that any affair with me would be on the strict understanding that it would be over when Esther came out of hospital, not a single girl I approached would entertain the idea. I knew I could solve my problem if I called on Fiona, but the thought of rolling around on the bed with that over-weight, upper-class nymphomaniac just didn't appeal to me. After spending almost two months as a reluctant celibate, an opportunity came from a quarter I least expected. Yvette, who I'd fancied from the moment I first saw her at the Serpentine, had just come back from a mission in occupied France. She told me she'd been given a fortnight's leave. I asked her if she would come with me the next day to visit Esther.

"I'd really love to, Derrick, but I can't. Hospitals depress me and the smell of carbolic and disinfectant turns my stomach."

"That's a pity. It would make her so happy if you did."

"I'm sorry, but I just can't. On Monday I'm going to set off to spend a few days on the Cornish coast. I want to feel a fresh sea breeze blowing through my hair and into my lungs. I'd love it if you came with me, Derrick."

"God knows I'd like to, but I can't. I'm skint."

"It won't cost you a penny, chéri, I can easily afford to pay for everything we'll need."

"The train fare alone might be too much, even for you, Yvette."

"I don't want to go by train, hitchhiking out on the open road is what I had in mind, it's a lot more pleasant than being squeezed into an overcrowded train."

"With so little traffic on the road nowadays it could well take us three days to get there."

"Who cares, at night we can take a room in a small country hotel."

Just the possibility of sharing a bed with this stunningly beautiful and attractive girl got my heart beating a little faster.

"If you're quite sure you'd like me to come, I'll tell Esther I won't be able to see her next Sunday because my uncle wants me to go away with him for a few days."

"Why not tell her the truth? Esther won't mind if she's told it's me you're going with."

"Come off it, Yvette, how would you feel if you were stuck in a hospital bed barely able to move and the man you love tells you he is going on a holiday with your best girlfriend?"

"It's hard for me to say, Derrick, because I don't love any man. But she needn't worry: I'd never try to entice you away from her."

It would be nice if you did, I thought, but didn't dare say.

Bright and early on a perfect day, the first Monday of May 1944, I rang Yvette's doorbell. She opened it, wearing a flimsy flower-patterned blouse that was tucked into the briefest of shorts.

"Good morning, Yvette, we've picked a wonderful day to set off." Pointing to the shorts, I said, "I bet you didn't buy those at Marks & Spencers."

"I bought them in Paris. Girls there, unlike in London, dress to be noticed."

"On English country roads, you'll be noticed all right. Mind you, it'll come in handy when we're thumbing lifts."

"That's the reason I'm wearing them."

"Is that how you get vital information out of German officers?"

"When the maquis want a guard distracted, I'm mostly the one they pick to do it. Other than that I have nothing to do with the German Army. All this chatting on the doorstep isn't getting us one yard nearer Cornwall, is it?"

"You're right, it isn't. My uncle suggested we take a train from Paddington to Reading. There we'd find the main road leading to Cornwall. I thought we could go to Bude. Robert spent a holiday there before the war. He says it has the most wonderful sandy beaches in England."

"If it's anything like the South of France, I'll be happy, chéri."

"So that's where we'll go, OK?"

"Oui," she replied.

Reading was at least eight foot-slogging miles behind us before a vehicle of any sort came in view. It was a lorry. When the driver saw Yvette standing by the roadside in her scanty shorts, he slammed on the brakes so hard one would have thought he was trying to avoid an accident. Poking his head out of the cab window, he said to Yvette: "Is a lift to Bristol any use to you, darlin'?"

"Is Bristol in the direction we're going, Derrick?"

"I haven't the faintest idea, I'm ashamed to say."

"Where are you making for, pretty lady?"

"Bude, in Cornwall."

"Then you're in luck, Bristol's on your route. Hop in and sit next to me."

Oh shit, I thought, as I squeezed myself next to Yvette and the truck door, I do hope this huge hunk of a man doesn't try any funny stuff. Fortunately, he was content to spend most of his time looking down at her shapely legs. Each time he changed gear, he let the back of his hand linger on her bare thighs.

"Thanks very much for the lift. You can drop us here, please," I said.

"It's not far to Bristol," said the driver. He was obviously keen to hang onto his lovely passenger for as long as possible.

"Thanks for offering, but we don't want to spend the night in a big city."

"Your chances of getting a lift from here are nil, it's more likely you'll get one in Bristol. You'll be faced with a ten-mile walk in the morning."

I had the feeling he hoped Yvette would dump me and spend the night with a real man.

"What about you, Yvette, do you want to go on into the town or get off here?"

"I prefer to stay in the countryside, Derrick. I've come on holiday to do some walking," said Yvette.

By the time he pulled up, the hotel I'd seen was half a mile back down the rapidly darkening road.

Nobody was about when we entered the unimpressive reception area. Only after I'd struck the hand bell a few times did an elderly woman appear.

"Good evening, I didn't expect anyone this early in the season."

"We'd like a room for the night," I said.

"My guest house has no bookings before the end of May, so you can decide for yourselves which two rooms you'd like."

"We want a double room, please," I replied, determined to scotch any idea she had of separating us.

"I take it you're married then? The law requires me to see the marriage certificate of young couples who wish to share a room, otherwise I could be charged with running a house of disrepute."

What a fucking, or rather non-fucking, country this is, I thought, whilst frantically racking my brains for a creditable excuse as to why I couldn't produce one. Fortunately Yvette, putting on an exaggerated French accent, came to the rescue.

"Madame, we married in Paris a few weeks before the Germans occupied it. We left France to get to England in such a hurry we had to leave behind everything we possessed except the clothes we were wearing. I'm afraid that until my country is liberated, we can't get another copy."

"Oh you poor dear girl, did your family manage to escape with you?"

"Sadly, non, Madame," Yvette said, sounding and looking as though she might burst into tears at any moment.

"Don't fret, dear, I'm sure you'll be reunited with those you love very soon. You're too late for dinner, I'm afraid, but I can rustle up scrambled eggs on toast and a pot of tea for you, if you'd like that?"

"It would be most welcome, we've not had a bite to eat all day."

"It's not good for young people to go without food for so long, go and sit in the dining room while I prepare it."

As soon as she was out of sight, I said: "My God, Yvette, you can think up a plausible story even quicker than I."

"It's just as well I can. If I couldn't by now I'd most likely be in a Nazi jail awaiting execution, not sitting here with you in this cosy hotel."

Her reply brought home to me the perilous life she chose to lead.

I didn't care that the room we'd been given was small. The bed was more than adequate for the romp I had in mind. Yvette took off her clothes, threw them on the floor, and climbed between the sheets.

"I'm so tired I can't even be bothered to clean my teeth. Goodnight, Derrick, sleep well." And she turned her back on me.

"Darling, I'll lie awake all night if we don't... "

"Don't what, Derrick?"

"Have sex."

She turned and faced me.

"Mon ami, it has nothing to do with you personally, but I get no pleasure out of it, even if I do it with someone as nice as you. My father put me off men for ever. The bastard abused me throughout my childhood. I hated it and him."

"What about the man you married? I can't believe you never slept with him."

"Only twice. Then, thank God, he was sent off to fight in North Africa with the Free French Army."

"Why on earth did you marry him if you hate men so?"

"To receive the allowance officers' wives get."

"When the war is over, he'll come back. How are you going to cope then?"

"I know for a fact he won't. Last week I got a telegram informing me that my husband has been killed in action. It went on to say that I should feel proud that he gave his life to free France."

"Oh, shit!" was all I could think of to say.

"It's shit all right. Since when is a desert in North Africa French soil? I don't give a damn whether or not my country is liberated."

"I presume that's goodbye to your allowance."

"It seems it'll continue until the war ends."

"Don't you ever feel sexy?"

"No, I get all the thrills I need by living on a knife edge. There's only one person who has ever attracted me sexually, and that is Esther. I've never let her know it, nor must you."

"Why do you flirt with men so overtly if you dislike them so?"

"To get them to fall in love with me. I enjoy watching them suffer after I reject them. This is how I get my own back on men, for the way my father treated me."

"Did you invite me along to make me pay for the way he abused you?"

"No, no chéri, I like you."

"You ought to dislike me even more than the others, because of my affair with Esther."

"I'm glad she wants to marry someone like you, and not the sort of bastards that try to have me. I don't want to punish you the way I do other men, so I'm going to let you have sex with me just once, provided you promise not to make me pregnant or expect me to be responsive."

Not having ever performed under such terms of engagement before, I hesitated for a while before accepting her generous offer. I reasoned that whatever went on between us would be a damn sight better than lying awake all night totally frustrated.

I knelt at the foot of the bed and slowly pulled back the sheet so that I could feast my eyes on her slender body. Her response was to close hers and clasp her hands behind her head. She lay there, motionless like a corpse on a mortuary slab. Well, if you were into necrophilia, she would be the girl for you, but as far as I was concerned, my ardour evaporated into thin air.

"Darling, you're off the hook, I've just realised I'm incapable of having sex with a girl who doesn't really enjoy it, something to do with vanity, I suppose. I really appreciate that you were willing to put up with it."

"You're a good man, Derrick."

"I know I am, but like the proverbial curate's egg, only in parts."

I'm sure Yvette didn't get the analogy, but she was too tired to ask me for an explanation. I bent over her pretty face and kissed her goodnight, then turned on my side and fell into a deep sleep.

Although I'd made a point of leaving a gap between us, when I awoke in the morning, my arm was wrapped tightly around her waist and my face was buried between the ringlets of her long, chestnut hair. While she slumbered on, I took advantage of the situation by gingerly gliding my finger tips over the contours of her body. She didn't even stir when I unloaded onto her months of accumulated passion. I only had just enough time to mop up all traces of my shocking behaviour moments before she opened her eyes.

"Good morning, Yvette, did you sleep well?" I asked casually, in the hope that the tone of my voice wouldn't betray my feelings of guilt.

"Like a baby," she replied.

After she had showered and dressed, I said:

"Yvette, there's something that puzzles me about you. Since you didn't want me sexually, why did you spin that yarn to the hotel owner?"

"Because a double room is cheaper."

"Oh, I see. If you can afford it, I'd prefer in future for us to have single rooms. To lie all night close to you is very hard for me to bear."

"Tonight, mon ami, we'll have separate rooms. I should have thought of that before. Come on, let's go and have breakfast."

Three days later, after a lot of hiking and very few lifts, we were the only people on the vast expanse of fine sand which was the barrier that protected Bude from the Atlantic. As we lay there, soaking up the penetrating spring sun, I said to Yvette: "If heaven is anything like this, I'm going to convert."

"I won't, Derrick, to be stuck here for eternity would be my idea of hell. After a few days with nothing exciting happening, I would go out of my mind with boredom."

"You're right, of course. All the same, if Esther was with me, I wouldn't mind at all lying on this beach all summer long."

"Let's hope she'll be released from hospital soon, then you can bring her here for convalescence."

"As there's no one about, I'm going to sunbathe in the nude," I said as I removed my trunks. She followed suit.

"How about a swim, Derrick?"

"You must be joking, nothing would get me into that freezing sea, and I advise you not to. The Atlantic isn't as warm as the Mediterranean, particularly at this time of year."

Despite my advice, she stood up and sprinted to the water's edge, then dived in. Seconds later she was back.

"The last time I swam in water that cold was one Easter in the lake at Annecy."

"I tried to warn you, didn't I?" I said as I wrapped a towel round her shivering body.

"I like to find out things for myself - most of the fun and excitement I've had in my life is when I've done things that I've been advised not to do."

Our conversation ceased when we heard the distant drone of engines. Looking seaward to find out what the ever increasing din was, we saw to our dismay a line at least a mile wide of huge flat-bottomed ironclad landing craft. They were ploughing their way through the waves at some speed towards the beach. When the craft got nearer the shore, I could see white stars painted on their sides.

"It's the fucking Americans. I bet they're doing a rehearsal for the invasion of France."

Hurriedly we got dressed and retreated to the back of the beach.

"Merde, I came to Cornwall to fill my lungs with sea air, not to breathe in the fumes belching out from a hundred exhaust pipes."

As Yvette stood by my side, I watched the sea monsters come as near as they could to the shore without actually getting stuck in the sand. When their engines cut out, a wide flap in the front of the craft was lowered into the water. Dozens of steel-helmeted soldiers, carrying packs on their backs and with rifles held shoulder high, jumped into the freezing water. Waist-deep they waded ashore, before making a dash for the limited cover of the bracken bordering the beach. To add a touch of realism to the exercise, explosives were detonated, sending plumes of sand high into the air.

"Jesus Christ, they're going off just where you ran down to the water. They could have easily exploded beneath your feet."

"That would really have annoyed me. I don't mind facing danger when I know it's there, but there's no thrills in being blown to bits accidentally."

When the craft that had brought the soldiers moved away, another wave came and unloaded tons of equipment. Tanks and guns of every variety were beached and speedily assembled before they too made for the shrubs at the back of the sand dunes. The beach that previously had been so tranquil had been converted in the space of fifteen minutes into a huge sandpit for a regiment of American soldiers to play in.

"You must admit it's quite a show," I said to Yvette.

"When I want to be entertained I'll go and sit with German soldiers at the Folies Bergère. You can stay and watch this performance if it amuses you, while I fuck off back to London."

"Jesus, Yvette, we only arrived here an hour ago. I'm sure that by this time tomorrow, the beach will be exclusively ours again."

"I doubt it, I think these boys plan to play war games for at least a week here. I'm not prepared to hang around for that long."

"I'd rather not be here all by myself, so I'll go back with you."

"I'd prefer it if you didn't, Derrick. I think my chances of getting lifts will be greater without you."

"But without me there to protect you, you'll probably end up being raped."

"Don't worry, I know how to take care of myself."

"You do? How would you do it then?"

"I'd say to the driver: 'Not in the cab, chéri, let's do it on the grass verge'. While he climbed out of the lorry, I'd be off down the road at the speed of a greyhound. At my boarding school, I was the champion sprinter and I can still easily outrun most men. As soon as I'd put some distance between me and the man, I'd shout: 'Don't give up, big boy, I'm all yours if you can catch me!'"

"I'm glad to hear it," I said as she looped her arms through the straps of her rucksack. "Yvette, darling, before you set off, could you loan me a couple of quid? I need it to sustain myself for the four days it might take me to get back."

"Here's five and I don't want it back."

"Two is ample," I said, leaving three notes in her hand.

"OK, Derrick, we'll meet up again at the Serps, yes? I expect to be sunbathing there in two days' time."

With those sexy shorts of yours, I'm sure you will be."

"Au revoir, bon voyage, mon ami!"

"Good luck, Yvette, please be on your guard."

Try as I might, I couldn't but help feeling a little hurt that she'd so obviously preferred her own company to mine. I stayed on for a while and watched the Americans rehearse the part they would play when the time came to invade Europe. Then I turned my back on the beach that I'd so looked forward to being on with Yvette, and made for Okehampton.

To get to Okehampton on this virtually traffic-less road, I calculated I had in front of me a hike of not less than twenty-five miles. I'd only been on my way for half an hour when out of the blue the guardian angel who looks after atheists arranged for a van to pull up right by me. The driver said he'd take me to a transport café in Okehampton, from which I'd have a good chance of getting a lift to Exeter.

"Thanks a lot," I said, as I stepped into the van. We didn't speak for a while until, by way of conversation, I told the driver about the army exercise I'd witnessed only an hour before.

"You shouldn't have been on that beach. For the past month, notices have been up all over Bude warning people that from today the sea and shore for five miles east and west of the town would be closed to fishing boats and the public for three weeks. I'm amazed you didn't see one. You're lucky the Home Guard didn't spot you and mistake you for a German spy. Are you on leave?"

"Yes," I lied.

"Navy?"

"No, Army."

"I did my bit in 1914, they said it would be the war to end all wars. It seems I spent four years in waterlogged trenches all for nothing. Let's hope this one leaves you free to spend the rest of your life in peace."

"Let's hope," I echoed as we stopped outside a drivers' pull-in.

"Good luck, boy," he said, shaking me by the hand.

"Thanks for the lift, you saved me from doing a lot of footwork."

"I reckon it's the duty of the old to help the young men who are fighting for our country."

I went into the café and ordered an omelette – though I didn't really like the taste or consistency of powdered eggs – and a buttered roll. I had just finished when three men who were obviously lorry drivers came in. I waited until they'd had a cup of tea before approaching them.

"Excuse me, but are any of you going to Exeter or London? I need to get to King's Cross to catch a train back to my regiment in York."

For the second time in the space of a few hours I had unashamedly masqueraded as a soldier on leave. In all fairness, it would have been foolhardy of me to say I was a pacifist looking for a lift.

"I'll take you to Exeter, "said one of them. "Go and sit in the tipper and I'll join you shortly."

"Thanks. At least let me pay for what you've just had."

"Don't worry about that, mate - I'm sure I earn a lot more than you do in the army."

We parted company in Exeter and rather than bank on getting another lift late at night, I decided to make for the railway station to investigate the possibility of getting on a goods train. Unobserved by the Home Guard, who were patrolling the marshalling yard, I walked up and down lines of wagons in the hope I might find some earmarked for London. After a lot of searching and match-striking, I found a line of them ticketed for Paddington. All were padlocked except the last one. Noiselessly I slid open the double doors and jumped into the empty wagon. Of course I knew perfectly well that I could be stuck motionless in the sidings for days, but I comforted myself that in war time rolling stock wouldn't remain idle for very long. I was right: I'd hardly stretched out on the bare boards when the wagon jerked forward. While the train clickety-clacked along the track, I imagined myself to be a down-and-out crossing America in search of work. I'd seen films with Spencer Tracy and John Garfield playing parts like that. I rested my head on my rucksack and was soon asleep.

At dawn I stood by the open door of the wagon and watched the sprawling suburbs of London chug slowly by. Looking at this vast area of modest dwellings, that must have taken over a century to build, I decided that the Luftwaffe would need to bomb it round the clock for twenty years to reduce all those humble homes to a pile of rubble. My thought wasn't so far off the mark when one considers that the bulk of inner London still stood despite five years of constant air-raids. These projections of mine ended when the train came to a halt in the railway siding of Paddington Station.

Unbelievably, less than twenty-four hours after leaving the beach in Cornwall, I was basking in the sun at the Serpentine.

My lovely French friend, who had thought that I'd hamper her return, didn't turn up for another three days. Smugly I came to the conclusion that this was an example of where brains and experience scored over beauty. Yvette spotted me when she emerged from the changing tent and came over to where I was lying.

"So, Derrick, you're back already?"

I told her how lucky I'd been in getting lifts and how I'd journeyed through the night sleeping in a goods wagon.

"What took you so long?"

"The first two days I spent walking all the thirty miles from Bude to fucking Barnstaple."

"Didn't a single vehicle pass you for two whole days?"

"A few did, but none of the bastards offered me a lift. I don't understand Englishmen, a French or Italian lorry driver would have slammed on their brakes when they saw me standing by the roadside."

"So how did you get from Barnstaple back to London?"

"On the slowest train I've ever been on. It took over nine hours to get to Paddington."

"If you hadn't left me, darling, you'd have got back in twenty-four hours."

"I hate having the obvious pointed out," she snapped.

I didn't blame her for jumping down my throat, but I just couldn't resist the opportunity to get my own back for the way she'd deserted me in Cornwall. To regain her favour, I suggested hiring a boat.

"That would be nice, mon ami."

Fifteen minutes later, Yvette was sitting with her pretty face pointing towards the sun and her arms outstretched on the cushioned back seat of the boat while I rowed. I thought what a pity it was that so many appealing qualities were bestowed on someone who was incapable of giving or receiving love. There and then I decided I would not seek her company unless I was with Esther. The sooner I stopped wanting her and realised I was barking up the wrong tree, the better it would be.

The following Sunday, when I walked into Esther's ward, I found her sitting up in bed, weeping. The doctor had said that in his opinion it would be at least a year before she could go home.

"I do wish doctors would keep their fucking opinions to themselves," I said. "Quite often they are just as wrong as the men who forecast our weather. I predict that you and I will be enjoying our Christmas dinner together at the Corner House, and by this time next year we'll be sunbathing on a Cornish beach."

"Why Cornwall?" she said between sobs.

Realising that I'd made a slip of the tongue, I quickly added: "Because Robert told me that it has the most wonderful sandy beaches in all England."

"Darling, I know you're only trying to cheer me up, but for me to think about what I might be doing in a year's time doesn't console me. What I worry about is how can I hold onto you while I'm stuck in this bloody place."

"I'll wait for you, sweetheart, no matter how long it takes for you to recover, I promise," I said, as I mopped up her tears with my lips. By the time it came for me to leave, Esther had cheered up a little and actually managed a smile.

CHAPTER FIFTY-TWO

On the journey back from Ascot, despite my promise to remain faithful, I decided I must find myself another partner, albeit on a temporary basis. As luck would have it, that evening at Tony's, Vic showed me a passport-sized head and shoulders photograph of a very beautiful girl that I immediately took to.

"The picture is yours, Derrick, if you buy me a cup of tea."

"I can't, I've only got sixpence to my name. Just give it to me, Vic. Let's face it, it's of no use to you, is it?"

"Sixpence? You're that much in funds, are you? In that case, you can afford to buy me a spam sandwich as well. Then I'll give you the photo and tell you where you can find the lady."

"She'd better be as good as she looks, if I'm going to part with my entire wealth in the vague hope that she'll even speak to me."

"She's very approachable. I promise you you'll have no problem in starting up a conversation with her."

"OK. So where do I go to find this gregarious girl?"

"Order my tea and sandwich, then I'll tell you."

When they arrived, he continued:

"Most weekends she's at the Wheatsheaf with friends, and if she's left alone for only a minute, invariably some chap will take advantage of the situation."

"If you'd told me before that she was that popular, I'd never have done that deal with you. I'm hopeless when I'm faced with competition."

"Don't let that deter you, dear boy, I assure you that none of those I've seen approach her are anywhere near as good looking as you."

When I entered the pub on that unusually hot and humid evening it was packed. I scanned the crowd looking to see if the girl whose picture I held in the palm of my hand was there - but no one I saw remotely resembled her. Just when I was beginning to think that Vic had conned me, I spotted her, perched on a stool at the far end of the bar. She was engaged in conversation with a young army officer and his girlfriend. I pushed my way through the crowd of thirsty customers and placed myself by her side.

On close inspection she looked even more attractive than her photograph. She had wavy shoulder-length brown hair swept right back from her forehead, and bore a slight resemblance to Ingrid Bergman. She wore a loose white blouse tucked into shorts. Her long legs might have made Dietrich envious.

I strained my ears listening to the conversation she was having in the hope that her accent would tell me where she came from, but try as I might, I couldn't place her in any particular country.

While I was racking my brains to think of an opening sentence, the barman came to my
aid.

"And you, sir?" he asked.

"A glass of water, please."

I had the feeling that my request had fallen on deaf ears.

"I don't think I've made myself too popular with him," I said to the girl by my side.

"It's a bit cheeky of you to expect him to bring you water when he's so busy."

"Cheek I have in abundance. It's money that's in short supply."

"Then why did you come into the pub?"

"To get close to you. As a matter of fact, you're the reason why I'm broke."

"How can I be? I don't even know you."

"I gave my last sixpence to buy a photograph of you," I said, pulling it out of my pocket."

"Where did you get that?" she asked, obviously annoyed.

"My friend Vic sold it to me and said you're often here in the Wheatsheaf at weekends."

"I don't know anyone called Vic."

"He knows you by sight."

To steer our conversation back to her, I continued:

"You look as though you've been out in the sun all weekend."

"I've been walking with a friend in Dorking, we didn't see a cloud for two days."

"You get a tan quickly, don't you?

"That's because as a child, I was out in the open air for most of the summer."

"Did you live in the country?"

"No, in Berlin, but I spent my holidays partly with relatives in Bavaria, or with my parents on the Balti coast in the north of Germany."

"Did you get marooned here when the war broke out?"

"No, shortly before it began my mother came to England as a refugee and I arrived some months later."

We talked for a while longer and then she said, "I don't think you're ever going to get your glass of water."

"Nor do I, and what with the heat and everything I'm dying of thirst."

"I'd buy you a drink but I can't, I'm afraid. I only came out with a little money and it went on this," she said, pointing to what remained in her glass. "You're welcome to have it if it would quench your thirst."

"Thanks for offering, but I don't drink alcohol – I just don't like the taste."

"I restrict myself to half a pint of ale. If I'm persuaded to have more than that, I'm anybody's."

Her reply made me wish I could have bought her another half pint.

"If you want, you can come to my place and help yourself to as much water as you'd like. I live up the street opposite Schmidt's."

Derrick, boy, your luck's in, I said to myself, but just in case the barman belatedly turned up with a glass of water, I said, "Would you mind very much if we go soon? I'm dehydrating at an alarming rate."

"I'll just empty my glass, then we'll leave."

Walking up Rathbone Place I decided that the money I'd spent on this gorgeous girl's photograph might well turn out to be the best sixpence worth of anything I was ever likely to come across.

By the time we'd got to her digs, we'd swapped names. She told me that hers was Bobbi.

"It's my pet name that my father gave me. It's an abbreviation of Bobbele, the name given to babies in Bavaria."

The first floor flat she shared with a girlfriend was above Edith Lee's antique shop at number 28 Charlotte Street. It had a small kitchen-cum-bathroom, so that while relaxing in a bath, you could keep an eye on the cooking. A freestanding old gas stove and a table that could seat three at a pinch stood against the wall opposite the tub. Under a single window was a cracked and chipped porcelain sink. The two rooms that made up the rest of the flat were connected by a door cut into the dividing wall. This meant that whoever occupied the back room would have to walk through the one facing front. I imagined that this arrangement didn't do a lot for privacy.

What made this apartment different from any other I'd seen was that hanging on the walls were real paintings. Also novel to me was the clever way that the dilapidated furniture had been transformed into something pleasant to look at, by simply covering the unsightly items with bits of material that no doubt had only cost a few pence. From the pots and pans that hung from nails banged into the walls, it was obvious that meals were cooked and served in this tiny kitchen.

"Here you are," said Bobbi, as she handed me a glass of water. I gulped it down and then asked for another.

"Would you mind if I took my shirt off until I cool down?" I said, hoping that my half naked body might appeal to her and set in motion a chain of events that could end up with me staying the night.

"I don't mind. Would you like a cup of tea and a ham sandwich?"

"Tea yes, but nothing to eat, thanks," I replied, even though I was hungry. Having already told her I was a teetotaller, I was worried that if I now admitted to being vegetarian she might wonder what sort of weird man she'd invited into her home.

"Did you paint the pictures in the front room?"

"No, my flatmate's boyfriend did. He's here on leave from the army at the moment.
Aren't you in one of the services now? You look fit enough."

"I am, but an army doctor decided otherwise. I'll tell you why while I take you out to dinner tomorrow night."

"How can you pay for a meal in a restaurant when you couldn't even buy a lemonade?"

"Starting tomorrow, I have three days' work as a film extra at Denham

Studios."

"That's a coincidence, I worked there until recently. I was supposed to be the personal secretary to Zoltan Korda. Alexander Korda's brother. I was highly paid to do virtually nothing, because for the year I was there, Mr Korda never put in an appearance, it was something to do with his being unable to get a visa. To pass the time, I spent most days looking in on the sets. It's a wonder we didn't meet before."

"In the world of film making, extras are on the bottom rung of the ladder. The chances of us ever meeting there were very slim."

"Where I work now in the planning office at Kelvinator's, the managers and factory workers mix with each other."

"Aren't they the firm who make fridges?"

"Before the war they did, now we make cabinets that test how well aircraft instruments will stand up to the freezing conditions of high altitudes."

"I suppose you have to clock in at the crack of dawn."

"Office staff don't have to turn up until nine, but I've never arrived on time yet."

Encouraged by her friendliness, I dared ask:

"What's the chance of letting me stay here for the night? It would save me footslogging the four miles back to my Notting Hill digs. I promise to behave myself."

"No chance at all." Then added quizzically. "What do you think my mother would say if she found out I'd let a man stay the night that I've only known for a few hours?"

"I don't suppose your mother would approve if she was told that a total stranger had reached across the table and kissed you," I said, cupping her beautiful face between my hands and guiding her lips towards mine. Just when I was hoping I might be able to get her to change her mind, her flatmate walked in accompanied by her boyfriend.

"Lily, Freddy, meet Derrick."

Freddy was tall and slender, a picture postcard image of what a young army officer should look like. His girlfriend was even smaller than Esther.

"What mob are you in?" Freddy asked.

"The de-mob brigade," was my silly reply.

"You're a lucky chap, I'd give a lot to be in your shoes. How did you get out, looking as A1 as you do?"

"An army psychiatrist decided that I was psychologically unsuited for military service."

"So am I, but no one seems to have noticed it yet."

"You could do what I did, desert, then, when you're arrested, refuse to put on your uniform. I promise you, you'll be noticed all right."

"That's a bit too drastic for me, I think, I just hope that the bloody war is soon over so that I can start painting again."

"Let's hope," I echoed.

I reminded Bobbi that I'd call for her on Tuesday about seven, then leant across the table and kissed her goodbye.

Walking along Oxford Street towards Marble Arch, doubts began to creep into my mind. What hope, I thought, was there of this intelligent and attractive girl ending her affair with a medical student - to start up a relationship with an uneducated, uncultured, penniless Soho bum. I decided the only chance I had was that she would in time become as physically keen on me as I was on her.

Two days later I took Bobbi out to dinner at the Corner House, and she told me how, when she was only sixteen, she and her mother had to flee their home in Berlin.

One morning there was a loud knock on the door while they were having breakfast. It was two men from the Gestapo. Though panic-stricken, her mother pulled herself together sufficiently to ask if they'd mind if she sent Bobbi on an errand. Only a few days earlier she had obtained a visa to visit her elder daughter in London, so she told Bobbi to go directly to the family solicitor and ask him how she could get a visa for herself. The solicitor sent her first to the British Embassy, but as she could give no guarantee from a British subject that her stay in England would not be a burden on the English government, her request was refused. When she went back to the solicitor, he told her it was imperative that she leave Germany that day, and that she must tell her mother to travel to England via Denmark, where foreigners were allowed to stay for three months without a visa. Bobbi would have to stay there until her mother got permission for her to come to England.

By the time Bobbi got home, her mother had already packed a couple of suitcases. Somehow she had managed to persuade the Gestapo men into allowing them both to leave for a weekend with a relative. She was shocked to hear that she would have to leave Bobbi in Denmark, but recovered when she remembered that her husband, Bobbi's father, had become good friends with a business associate in Copenhagen before he died. She would ask him to take care of Bobbi.

As Bobbi shut the door for the last time on what had been her mother's home for the whole of her married life, and where she had brought up her four children, her mother broke down and wept inconsolably. Bobbi, however, was only too happy to leave Berlin and to start on an exciting journey.

She stayed in Copenhagen long enough, Bobbi said, to drive her mother almost insane with worry. She fell madly in love with a man six years older than she was, so when her mother wrote from England to say she had managed to get her a visa, she wrote back saying she wouldn't be coming to London as she was getting married. Her mother's immediate response was to send a ticket dated for a few days later. Bobbi sent her a telegram saying that she'd only come on condition she was allowed to return to Denmark after a week, and her mother agreed, knowing full well that she had not the slightest intention of keeping her word. When Bobbi realised this, she was so angry that for a long time she could hardly bear to speak to her mother.

Bobbi had finally arrived in England in early December 1938. To her, Copenhagen had been a dream city, architecturally pleasing, full of life and colour, its pretty houses centrally heated and insulated against the cold. In contrast, the buildings in London were grey and covered with grime and soot, and most of the places she stayed at were without heating, apart from a coal fire in one room. Damp and fog crept in everywhere and she hated it. It was only now, after more than five years in England, that she was beginning to feel a little better about it.

"How did you survive without any money?" I asked.

"My mother managed to slip into her suitcase some rather valuable old coins that my father had collected, and the sale of these supported us until the war started. My mother agreed to let me go to art school, provided I studied fashion design so I could earn a living. I said yes, knowing that once I was there I would switch to drawing and painting."

"Was that when you began to learn English?"

"No. I was determined to get out of England to marry Paul, so it seemed pointless to try. When I went to art school I shared a flat with Lily, who was also at St Martin's and who could speak a little Yiddish. She was the only person there I could communicate with, but there was no need to bother to learn to speak English because most of my friends were young German and Jewish refugees."

"But something must have happened to make you change your mind. You speak English very well."

"Nothing happened. English came to me out of a clear blue sky. When my mother found out that I wasn't doing fashion design, she made me leave St Martin's and sent me on a secretarial course at Pitman's College. I hated it. But after four unhappy months of doing nothing but copy text after boring text in a language that was incomprehensible to me, I woke up one morning to find that I had subconsciously learned to speak English. So for the first time since leaving Berlin I could go to the cinema, read a newspaper, and mix with the natives."

"I've never looked upon myself as a native before."

"You know what I mean, don't you?"

"Of course, it's just that if I can think of something mildly amusing to say, I can't stop myself saying it. Mind you, I only try to make someone smile that I'm fond of."

"Is that your way of telling me you like me?"

"In truth, I'm absolutely besotted with you."

"You'll be telling me that you're in love with me next."

"I might, especially if you'd let me spend the night with you."

"I'm not one of those women who hop into bed with a man I hardly know."

"How long do I have to be on appro. before I might qualify as a sleeping partner?"

"For ever, if you ask silly questions like that."

"I was only joking, but to be serious, can I go back with you to your place just for a kiss and cuddle? I'll try on nothing more, Scout's Honour!"

"You can, but I'll have to chuck you out when Lily and Freddy get back."

Not since I was seventeen had I spent a couple of hours kissing and caressing without ending up in a bed with the girl. But for Bobbi, I was prepared to wait until she wanted me as much as I her.

Luckily, a week later events came to my aid. Lily, acting on the advice of her boyfriend, went to stay with her parents in the country. He'd told her to leave London because a rumour was going around the officers' mess that the Germans were about to unleash a secret weapon that would be almost impossible for RAF or our ack-ack guns to combat. He said that even his regiment had been put on standby in case mass panic broke out. Understandably, Bobbi, who'd been in London throughout the Blitz, didn't want to be alone in the flat with this threat hanging over her head.

Being one to grasp with both hands a heaven-sent opportunity, I offered to move in with her and she agreed. Selfishly I must admit to being grateful to Jerry for spreading a rumour that I thought was purely alarmist propaganda. Within days, my hunch turned out to be devastatingly wrong.

CHAPTER FIFTY-THREE

The next evening I collected from my room in Notting Hill Gate all my worldly possessions - they only half filled a paper carrier bag.

"Is that all you've got?" asked Bobbi.

"All I need is a change of underwear and a shirt plus my shaving tackle. Lots of clobber only makes life more complicated. Being able to travel light and at a moment's notice gives me a sense of freedom."

"Does it also mean that you can fuck off when things get difficult?"

"No, lots of times I've stayed put when I would have been wiser to leave."

"Come on up to the kitchen, you can keep me company while I cook."

Never before had I seen an intimate meal for two being prepared. Bobbi couldn't have known it, but unwittingly she had given a twenty-one-year-old orphan his very first glimpse of what family life was all about, and I took to it like a duck to water. After we'd eaten, we walked to Regent's Park to watch the sun go down, then popped into the Wheatsheaf, where I managed to get Bobbi a half pint of pale ale, just as last orders were being called.

Back at the flat, after a lot of kissing and cuddling, we ended up in bed. I got so excited that as far as I was concerned it was all over long before I'd intended.

"I'm so sorry, I promise you it'll be better next time."

"What makes you think there'll be another time?" said Bobbi, turning her back on me.

"Really, I'm not usually that inadequate a lover, it's just that I've not been with a woman for so long. Please do try to understand," I pleaded as I put my hand on her shoulder and gently pulled her round to face me. Huddled close together, we were soon fast asleep.

We'd not slept for long when we were awakened by an almighty bang that shook the whole house.

"Jesus, that was a close one," I said, as I pulled a blanket over our heads to protect us in case the ceiling came crashing down.

Moments later, we heard the drone of German planes flying overhead. The guns on Primrose Hill sent up a tremendous barrage of anti-aircraft shells, one of which must have scored a direct hit because the next sound we heard was an awful whine that a plane makes as it twirls down to its inevitable fate.

"Those poor airmen," said Bobbi compassionately as the plane exploded when it hit a nearby building.

"I don't pity those bastards. They very nearly blew us both to smithereens," I replied.

Only over breakfast, while listening to the BBC news, did we find out what had happened. During the night, wave after wave of unmanned aircraft had unsuccessfully tried to reach the capital. They were thought to have been launched from somewhere in northern France. Very few hit their target because the vast majority of them were shot down over the sea and the Kent countryside.

"Whoopee," I shouted, "if those flying bombs are the dreaded German secret weapon, it looks like there's fuck-all to worry about. The RAF can blow them out of the sky long before they reach London as easily as shooting down a clay pigeon. Your friend Lily might just as well pack her bag and return."

My inaccurate forecast of what the Germans really had in store for us gave Bobbi enough confidence to venture out and go to work. I did the washing up and tidied up the flat before leaving to see if Vic was in Tony's.

"Hello, Derrick, where have you been hibernating?"

"I've been spending all my spare time with the girl in the photo you sold me, who is not only intelligent and beautiful, with a fantastic figure, but knows how to cook. I think I might be falling in love with her."

"Then I sold it too damn cheaply, by the sound of it," said Vic. "And have you given a thought to how you're going to break the news to Esther?"

"The truth is, I can't even bring myself to think about it."

To put the problem out of my mind for a while, I asked Vic if he'd like to come and see Bobbi's flat.

"Lead the way, dear boy!"

As we strolled down Charlotte Street, I said:

"I wonder what these unmanned planes look like."

No sooner had I said it, than we heard the choking sound that an engine makes when it's starved of fuel. We looked skywards to see what was making the noise. To our horror, we saw a flying bomb, as bold as brass, coming up the street towards us. Two seconds later, the plane appeared motionless, like a bird of prey before it swoops down to claim its victim. Suddenly the winged weapon veered sharply to its left and started its descent earthwards.

"Shit, run for your life, Derrick," shouted Vic.

I dashed down the street in the vague hope that the bomb would explode behind me. Vic did an Olympic sprint in the opposite direction, towards Tony's.

When the pilotless plane vanished behind a house a few yards away, I flung myself flat on the ground, clasped my hands behind my head and tucked my body close against an outside wall. Surprisingly, I didn't die but was lifted bodily and blown like a piece of paper on a windy day some distance along the street.

The sound of the explosion was so deafening that I didn't regain my hearing for some time. Blinded by the thick cloud of dust, I had to wait for it to settle before I could begin to grasp the widespread havoc created by the flying bomb. When the penny dropped that I was still alive, I stood up and tried, but failed, to brush off the grey powdered dirt that covered me from head to toe. Across the road, a milkman's horse that had been exposed to the full blast of the explosion had its head blown off, and debris of the milk float were strewn all over the road.

Mercifully, the milkman was spared because he was in a basement delivering a half pint when the bomb went off. As he saw the mutilated body of his mare, he screamed: "Oh Bessie, my beautiful Bessie, those bastards, fucking bastards."

I crossed over to try and console him, but nothing I said seemed to help. Fortunately a woman came out of her badly damaged shop and put her arm around him:

"Look away, John, you'll only get even more upset if you don't. Let's thank God that you're all safe and sound, and that Bessie didn't suffer. Come with me, love, I'll make you a cup of tea," she said as they walked ankle deep over the broken glass that covered the pavement.

In an alleyway not far from Bobbi's place, three houses had been flattened. Only a heap of brick and masonry now marked the spot that only minutes ago housed six Cypriot families. I heard later that they had all perished.

My first thought was to walk down the street to see if Bobbi's flat was still standing. To my relief it was, even though all the windows were broken and the front door had been pushed in. Layers of dust covered everything and spikes of glass were embedded in the walls and furniture. Only the pictures on the walls were undamaged. Anyone foolish enough to lie on the bed would have been cut to ribbons.

"Jesus, what a fucking mess," I said out loud.

To give me time to think what to do about it all, I made a cup of tea, then phoned Bobbi and told her the bad news.

To my surprise she wasn't upset when she saw the shocking state the place was in. Perhaps this was because once before in her life she had lost her home and all her cherished possessions at a stroke. The only thing she seemed to care about was that I'd come out of it unharmed.

"I think we should make a start on getting the flat habitable," I said.

"Before we do anything, Derrick, you've got to clean yourself up."

The bath was easily made useable because it had been shielded from the debris by a covering board. Three baths were only just sufficient to remove all the dust that had etched itself into my skin and matted my hair. Clearing up the flat kept us occupied until evening. The most time-consuming job was the pricking out dozens of tiny glass splinters which were ingrained everywhere.

Unexpectedly, some hours after my narrow escape, I began to shake involuntarily.

"What the fuck is the matter with me?" I asked Bobbi.

"You're probably suffering from delayed shock. I'll make you a cup of sweet tea , that
should stop it."

No sooner had I drunk it than the compulsive quivering ceased.

"You've cured me, you're a regular Florence Nightingale, aren't you?"

"A who?"

"The famous nurse who saved the lives of countless soldiers in the Crimean War."

"All I did was to give you a cup of tea."

"All she did was to sanitise the unhygienic state of the hospitals into which the wounded were dumped."

"She must have done more than that to become famous."

"Nothing, apart from setting up the nursing profession as we now know it."

"That's not 'nothing'!"

"I suppose so. I'm starving, I've not had a bite to eat since breakfast, let's go to Tony's before I collapse."

"I don't like that café, the food there is disgusting. I've got a better idea, we'll celebrate your lucky escape at Bertorelli's."

"I can't afford it - it's too expensive."

"It costs no more than the Corner House, anyway I want it to be my treat in appreciation for all the hard work you did."

"We both cleaned up your flat, so it's only fair to split the bill."

I'd barely got halfway through my very first taste of minestrone, when Bobbi said: "I like you a lot, Derrick, but something bothers me about you."

"What's that?" I replied, fully expecting her to ask me why I seemed to be quite content to go through life as a Soho bum.

"This morning you saw to what lengths the Nazis will go to terrorise innocent people. Why is it that you chose not to fight the evil bastards?"

I repeated to her what I'd told the Army psychiatrist a year before, then said:

"As far as terrorising civilians goes, the RAF and American one thousand bomber raids on Leipzig, Hamburg and Cologne make the Luftwaffe attacks on London, or even Coventry, look like child's play. I'm sure that the few civilians who survive those senseless massacres are glad that their sons are fighting the inhuman bastards that seem to be hell-bent on reducing their cities to piles of rubble."

"That may be true, but the governments of Britain and America don't frogmarch men and women off to concentration camps just because they are Communists, Jews or just liberally minded citizens. My two brothers had to flee when the Gestapo were informed, probably by a neighbour, that they were Jewish and Communists. Derrick - there is no other way, the Nazis must be fought and defeated if the world is to be a place worth living in."

"I've known for a long time that anyone who resisted the Fascists in Germany was imprisoned, but I was under the impression that most Jews got out before 1938, like your family did."

"Only the few with money, or who had relatives abroad prepared to help, managed to escape in time. Thousands who were left behind, are being rounded up and systematically exterminated."

"This is the first I'm hearing about that. Not that two wrongs make a right, but what I know for certain is that when my anarchist comrades returned to Russia after fighting Franco, they were put against a wall and shot. So were countless others who dared to raise as much as an eyebrow in protest about the autocratic rule of Stalin."

"I can't believe the Soviet people would tolerate such atrocities being done in the name of Socialism."

"The vast majority of them probably don't know about it. Let's face it, both imperialist Russia and the Capitalist Western World commit horrendous crimes when it comes to waging war. That's just one of the many reasons why I'm a pacifist."

"I think you're lucky that you live in a country that allows you to be one."

"Do you? The country that I was so 'lucky' to be born in, never once during my childhood ever bothered to check if I was being cared for or even educated. But I existed all right when the time came for me to be conscripted into the Army. Then, when I refused to put on a uniform or fight for a country that had never given a shit about me, I got beaten up to within an inch of my life."

Bobbi, mistakenly thinking that to dwell on this part of my past might upset me, changed the subject by asking:

"Is this the first time you've eaten Italian food?"

"Yes, I've only ever had tinned spaghetti on toast before."

"Tinned, on toast?"

"Yes, and drowned in ketchup."

"You English are hopeless when it comes to cooking."

"Maybe, but we make better husbands than the Italians. They are all very romantic when courting but after a couple of years into the marriage, they start to treat their wives like child-bearing slaves."

"You've met a lot of married Italian women, have you?"

"None, but I know an English girl who made the mistake of getting married to one."

"You can't judge all Italian husbands just because one English girl got badly treated. Anyway, I don't like prejudice of any sort."

"Nor do I, and to prove it I'm falling head over heels in love with a Jewish girl and a foreigner."

"Although I had to flee Germany because I was labelled as a Jew, I never thought of myself as being one because I wasn't brought up to believe in any religion."

"Good, we have something in common. I'm an atheist. I know that life only exists on earth and I believe in enjoying it while it lasts."

"Is that what you aim to do, Derrick?"

"You can bet your sweet life it is."

"What do you most enjoy doing?"

"At this moment in time, it's being close to you in bed."

"And after that?"

"Looking forward to the next time."

"To be serious, have you no ambitions?"

"Yes, it's to do all I can to persuade people to live peacefully in an anarchist society and not to allow self-interested politicians to govern them."

"I find it easier to believe in life after death than trying to imagine a country functioning without the organisational skills of a governing body."

"It's precisely because of the incompetence of governments, that thousands of men, women and children have been, and are still being, slaughtered in this bloody war. As far as I'm concerned, the sooner people have faith in their own judgment and not those of a government, the better."

Feeling uneasy that our opposite opinions could drive a wedge between us, I said:

"Serious talk might spoil our meal."

"Worried that you can't sustain your argument, are you?"

"No," I replied.

It was dark when we arrived at Bobbi's place. No keys were needed to enter either the front door or that of the flat, as the blast from the bomb had broken all locks. Forgetting that the blackout curtains had been torn to shreds, I turned on a light. Within seconds a voice from the street shouted out:

"You up there on the first floor of No. 28, turn your light off, don't you know there's a war on?"

"Thanks for reminding me, you fucking idiot," I yelled back, as I plunged the room into darkness.

"There was no need to swear at him, the man was only doing his duty as an air-raid warden."

"I know, it was his sarcasm that annoyed me."

"I'll make us a cup of tea. Strike a match, Derrick, so that I can see my way to the kitchen."

"Fuck, I used the last one lighting a cigarette."

"That leaves us with nothing to do but grope our way to bed."

"That's fine by me," I said cheerfully.

No sooner had we undressed and got between the sheets then we heard footsteps coming up the stairs.

"Bobbi, are you in?" said a man's voice.

"It's Basil, my boyfriend," she whispered. "Get under the blankets and for Christ's sake don't move."

By the flickering light of a cigarette lighter, Bobbi's boyfriend came to the side of the bed and sat down, facing her.

"Darling, I was so worried about you, I'd have come sooner, but our hospital had to cope with all the casualties. Were you at work when the bomb went off?"

"Yes, but I was allowed to come home when I told my boss that my flat had been badly damaged."

"It must have been one hell of a job cleaning up all the mess."

"It was."

"Did I wake you up?"

"You did."

Bobbi's brief answers were obviously designed to make him leave as possible. While this was going on, I was lying on my side with one arm round her waist and my lips pressed into her back. This was all very nice, except that I could hardly breathe.

I decided that if her friend didn't leave soon, I'd have no other option but to leap out stark naked from under the covers and introduce myself. Just when this was about to become a reality, I heard Bobbi say:

"Please don't be offended, but if I don't go to sleep soon, I'll pass out."

"You must be absolutely wiped out after such a hard day, would you feel safer if I stayed here tonight? I'll leave you to sleep peacefully in your bed and camp out in the other room."

"I'm afraid you can't, Lily is in there," lied Bobbi.

"Can I see you tomorrow evening when I come off duty?"

"Yes," she said between faked yawns.

"Sleep well, darling," were his parting words.

"Blimey, Bobbi, that was a close shave. I hope those bloody locks are soon mended. It won't bother me if he finds me in your bed, but I bet it'll upset him."

In pitch darkness I managed to wedge a chair against the door, then felt my way back to bed. I drew her close to me and for the first time in my life, I didn't just have sex with a girl, but made love to a wonderful woman.

A few days after the flying bomb incident, I went to visit Esther. On the journey, I made up my mind to tell her that our affair was over. But I just couldn't get the words out of my mouth. For the hour I spent with her, I somehow managed to make her feel that all was well between us.

"See you next week, my darling," were the last words I ever spoke to her. Sunday after Sunday, she must have watched the entrance to the ward, expecting me to appear. I felt so bad about the way I'd treated her that I couldn't even bring myself to write her a letter. The guilt I felt then about my cowardly behaviour still haunts me today. My hope is that the sailor she was engaged to when we first met came back unharmed from the war and married her and that she had the children she'd craved for.

CHAPTER FIFTY-FOUR

When the doodlebugs or buzz-bombs as flying bombs were called were mostly dealt with by the RAF, Londoners expected to return to the comparative peace that had prevailed for a while. Sadly, that hope never materialised because Jerry's real secret weapon, the V-2s, began a round-the-clock bombardment of the city. These rocket-propelled ballistic missiles carried in their warheads one ton of high explosive and sped through the air faster than the speed of sound, leaving the defenceless civilians no time to run for shelter. Paradoxically, people felt relieved when they heard one explode because the shell that had their name on it would be as silent as a flash of lightning.

Bobbi, in common with any Londoner who had been exposed to every air-raid from day one of the Blitz, found the continuous day and night shelling by the V-2s much harder to cope with than the conventional raids, which over the years had become part of her nightlife.

Luckily in August just when the bombardment was beginning to get on both our nerves, she was due for her annual fortnight's holiday. I told her how beautiful Bude was, and how lovely it would be to get away for some sunbathing and swimming. But when I showed it to her on a map, she said:

"I doubt I'd get permission to go there."

"Why ever not?"

"The coastline is a restricted area for aliens. Although my papers describe me as a 'friendly enemy alien', I have to stay within a thirty mile radius of London. My only chance of getting to Cornwall is to make an application to the Home Office for a transit visa through Devon and a visa to stay a few days in Cornwall."

"What a palaver. Tell them that if they consider you trustworthy enough to do war work in a factory, it's only fair that you should be allowed to travel to any place I can go."

"I'll tell them what you said when I go there tomorrow."

"You won't have to, because I'll be coming with you."

"I think it's better if I go by myself. From what you've told me, you don't exactly hit it off too well with authorities. If you antagonise them, I can see us spending the holiday in bloody Watford."

By post, the day before we'd planned to leave, Bobbi was sent a transit visa through Devon, but as yet no permission to stay in Cornwall.

"What's the fucking point of a transit visa to nowhere? They might just as well have written to say that your application was refused, and that would be that."

Bobbi glanced again at the map and said:

"I think it'll be all right, Barnstaple is on the border with Cornwall, so I'll pick up my visa there."

"I doubt that's possible," I said.

"I'm sure it is. Before the war, Europeans did it all the time when travelling from one country to another. You could always get a visa at the border."

"Let's hope the local police in Barnstaple know that," I replied.

Early next day, we caught a train for Exeter, arriving there at midday, which left us enough time to hitchhike to Barnstaple before the day was over.

The lorry driver dropped us off by the local police station, where Bobbi told the desk sergeant that she'd come to pick up a visa to enter Cornwall. The policeman looked puzzled and quite obviously hadn't the faintest idea what it was she wanted. He looked as if he'd never set foot outside Devon.

Bobbi tried her best to explain to the sergeant precisely what a visa was and why she needed one.

"I'm sorry, miss, I've never come across a request of this nature before. I think our larger constabulary at Penzance might be able to help you. You can phone them from the telephone box opposite the entrance."

"Could you do it for me?" asked Bobbi.

"Regulations don't allow me to make calls on behalf of the public," he said, handing her the phone number. .

When Bobbi told the Penzance police what she needed, she was informed that her visa had been granted, but she could only obtain it from her local police station in London.

"I've just told you, I'm already down here in Barnstaple!"

Then the money ran out and she was cut off.

"Stupid bloody man," she said, slamming down the receiver so hard that it's a wonder it didn't snap in two. To pour oil on troubled waters, I suggested that we go back and have another chat with the sergeant.

"Why waste our time talking to that uninformed idiot?" she snapped.

"Who knows, he just might have some idea worth following up."

I told the sergeant that Bobbi's phone call had got us nowhere, he advised us to return to Exeter and ask at the station there to see the Chief Constable of Devon. He was the one person who could give us permission to enter Cornwall.

"He might as well have said go and see the fucking king," said Bobbi as we left.

After spending the night in a cheap bed and breakfast, we hitchhiked to the police station at Exeter and asked if we could see the Chief Constable.

"It's his day off," said the duty officer.

"It's a matter of urgency."

"I've come across more urgent reasons why the Chief should be bothered on his day off, but I know he likes to help young people with a problem, so I'll phone him at home and ask him if he'll see you."

The officer left the counter and came back moments later.

"You're in luck, he says you can, provided you go to him straight away."

When I saw the man who opened the door, I knew that Bobbi would get a sympathetic hearing. We followed him into his front room.

"I've been given to understand you have a problem. Tell me what it is," he said, addressing me.

"My girlfriend can do this better than me," I replied.

After listening to everything Bobbi had to say without interrupting her, he asked me to come with him to another room.

"Take a seat, lad," he said, pointing to a well worn leather armchair. He lit his pipe and sat down opposite me.

"I'm afraid I can't give your friend a permit to enter Cornwall, but what I can do is give her a document that would allow her to stay in Devon for the duration of her holiday. I can only do this with your co-operation. You would have to see to it that while she's in Devon, she will remain loyal to the country that gave her refuge."

It seemed to me absurd that I, an anarchist, who given half a chance would overthrow the government, was being asked to guarantee that Bobbi wouldn't go on a spying spree on behalf of a country she'd been forced to leave.

"Of course I'll vouch for my friend, not that there's any real need to. She was victimised by the Nazis long before we declared war on Germany."

"I presume you're on leave from one of the services?"

I showed him my army discharge book which fortunately he didn't look at too carefully.

"I see you did your bit for England. I hope that you and your lady friend enjoy your stay in my county."

"I'm sure we will, and thank you for seeing us."

Armed with a piece of paper signed by no less a person than the Chief Constable, we were now free to roam wherever we chose so long as we stayed within the boundaries of Devon. Walking away from the Chief's home, I said: "Darling, it seems that we'll have to wait until after the war before I can take you to Bude, unless you marry me. It's not such a silly idea. It would cut out all this nonsense about you having to get a visa whenever you want to travel."

"I wouldn't marry anyone just to get British nationality," was her response to my unromantic proposal.

"OK, I only offered. What I had in mind was a marriage of convenience. I'd never make any demands on you, I promise, and you could divorce me any time you wanted."

"When the war is over, I'll be able to go anywhere I like."

"Taking me with you, I hope."

"Maybe," she said.

"In the meantime, we're down here in Devon. It's not such a terrible place to spend a holiday, is it?"

"It's bliss, compared to London at present," said Bobbi, clutching my hand as we made our way to the open road.

For the next twelve days, we spent most of our time either in the back of a lorry or walking about the countryside. At night we slept on loose straw in the barns of farmers who were sympathetic to a couple of Londoners who needed a break from the raids.

One night, Bobbi woke me up and whispered: "Derrick, I can hear something moving about in the straw."

"Don't worry, it's probably only rats, they won't harm you."

"I'm terrified of the beastly things, I don't want rats crawling all over me while I'm sleeping. Please chase them off."

"Where to? This barn is their home, and as far as they are concerned, we're intruding on their territory. I've worked and slept in barns lots of times, and not once has a rat come anywhere near me."

"Are you sure it's safe to go back to sleep?"

"Only if you cuddle up close," I teased.

For the last two days of our holiday, we swam and sunbathed in Torquay. Its pebbled beach didn't compare to the fine sand in Bude, but the sea was warmer. This pre-war resort with all its grand hotels devoid of guests was like a ghost town the Victorians had deserted. Despite this, we would have been quite happy to stay on there for a few more days.

We hadn't been back in Charlotte Street for long when I decided to have another try at persuading Bobbi to marry me. I was only twenty-one and marriage wasn't of the utmost importance, but I thought that if Bobbi was my wife, it might keep other suitors at bay.

Married or not, I wanted to go on living with her. She was the only woman I'd ever really loved. Together, we'd made the first home I'd ever known. If she had ever wanted to end our affair, I would have felt abandoned for the second time in my life.

Common sense prevailed, and Bobbi finally consented to dump her alien status and agreed to marry me.

"Let's face it, darling, you're only signing a piece of paper. I'd never hold you to it. And who knows, our marriage might last."

"I'm afraid there's one hurdle to get over before we marry. You'll have to come and be introduced to her. I warn you now, it'll be a boring way to spend an afternoon."

"Any woman who gave birth to a beautiful talented girl like you can't be that dull. She'll always be in my good books."

The day prior to meeting Bobbi's mother, I went to see if I could borrow a suit from my old flatmate Peter. As he was an actor, he had a whole wardrobe full of clothes I could choose from.

"Who are you trying to impress?" he asked.

"My future mother-in-law. I'm going to marry the girl I've been living with these past four months."

"Preggers, is she?"

"No, I'll tell you why when I return your suit."

"If possible, Derrick, bring it back in the same condition you borrowed it."

"I will, I promise."

The next day, as we left to go to the block of flats in Finchley where Bobbi's mother lived, I said:

"I'm so unused to wearing this sort of outfit that I feel like I'm going to a fancy dress party. I hope you don't mind but while I'm all spruced up, I phoned my uncle and asked him if we could dine with him tonight. I suggested Bertorelli's at seven-thirty. I told him all about you and that we intended to get married quite soon."

"What did he say to that?"

"He was pleased. Probably he thinks that anything that normalises my way of life could only be for the good."

On first sight I thought what a pleasant looking old lady Bobbi's mother was. An hour later, after she'd been told that we were going to get married, the 'nice old lady' image I had of her faded quickly. She gave me a third-degree, the likes of which any interrogating police officer would have admired.

"Are you sure, Mr Cartlidge, that you're mature enough to take on the responsibilities of a married man? Can you support and provide a home for my daughter if she has a baby? You do realise, I hope, that you'll have to give up the financially precarious livelihood of an actor and obtain regularly paid employment. Are you qualified to do anything other than unskilled labour?"

Then, before I could answer, she added: "Do you know we are Jewish?"

That was her last salvo. I would have loved to have told her the truth about myself, if only to see the look of horror on her face. Instead I said:

"Mrs Feistmann, I don't care what religion you are. Bobbi has told me that she is no more Jewish than I am a Christian. I don't see why I should give up acting. Many actors manage to support a family. As for providing a home, it isn't like it was before the war. Nowadays most couples live in rented accommodation. I'm sure one way or another, we'll survive."

"Don't worry, mother, even if we have to live in dire poverty, we won't be asking you for any help," said Bobbi scornfully.

"There is no need for that sort of remark. Within my limited means I'll help all I can. I only wanted your young man..."

"His name is Derrick."

"I just wanted him to realise what it was he was undertaking."

"Really, I thought you were trying to put him off marrying me. Come on, Derrick, it's time we left. I'll phone you when I know the date of the wedding, mother. I'll understand if you prefer not to come."

"Of course I'll want to be with you on your wedding day," said Mrs Feistmann unconvincingly.

Once out in the fresh air, Bobbi said:

"You've just had a perfect example of why my mother and I don't get along. What the fuck possessed me to tell her that we were going to get married, God only knows. She hasn't changed. I should have known she'd do her best to embarrass me."

"Don't be too hard on her. Obviously she'd prefer you to marry a respectable, bowler-hatted, professional bore rather than a good-looking Soho bum."

"So you think you're good-looking, do you?"

"Yep," I said.

Dining with Uncle in the evening at Bertorelli's was very different from the afternoon we'd spent with Bobbi's mother. He warmed to Bobbi straightaway and she took an instant liking to him.

"Are you here with your family, my dear?" he asked, looking at Bobbi over the top of his glasses.

"My mother and my sister live in London. I have a brother in Mexico and another one in America."

"Do you miss them?"

"Yes, I do, I love them both."

"I don't get on too well with either my brother or my sister. It's a pity that I'm the only family Hayden has. Mind you, sometimes not having any relatives can be a blessing. Let's hope that you will shortly be reunited with yours. Thank God this damn war looks as if it's drawing to a close at last. I think Hayden is a very lucky boy to have met you."

He pulled a gold ring out of his waistcoat pocket.

"Hayden, this was my mother's. You're welcome to have it."

"Are you sure you should part with it?" I asked.

"It has no sentimental value for me, to be honest. I prefer not to own anything that reminds me of her."

Bobbi tried it on. It didn't fit, but by sleight of hand she never let the old man know it.

"It's a lot better than the one I had in mind," I said. "I'd thought of popping into Woolworth's and buying a curtain ring. It's all I can afford at present."

"Hayden, that's most inappropriate. Would five pounds tide you over?"

"Thanks for offering, but tomorrow I'll be in funds again. I've got three days' film extra work."

"Don't forget to tell me when your wedding day is so that I can book a table for lunch at Antoine's. Of course, Bobbi, my dear, you're more than welcome to invite your mother and sister."

"I doubt if they'll come. Both of them are opposed to me marrying Derrick."

"Try and persuade at least your mother to join us. Maybe I could get her to change her opinion about him," said Uncle, as he beckoned to the waiter to bring the bill.

The big day was two weeks later, on 9 September 1944. We'd arranged to get married at the registry office in St Pancras Town Hall. As I'd only ever seen the glamorous weddings portrayed in Hollywood films, I hadn't the faintest idea what was expected of a groom.

It was only when we got out of bed on the day that it occurred to us that we'd done nothing about organising a best man or a witness. We had to do something about it straight away – the wedding was at eleven-thirty. I had a brainwave. I'd ask my old flatmate, Peter, to be best man – I was going to see him anyway to borrow a suit. Then I'd go to Tony's to find a witness. I knew one of the layabouts would oblige if I offered them five bob.

I calculated that I needed seven and six for the marriage certificate, plus the five shillings for the witness and some money for the taxi fare to the Town Hall. I'd got a couple of quid, so that should be ample.

"You don't believe in giving one much notice, do you?" Peter complained.

"I'm sorry, but it slipped my mind until I got out of bed this morning."

"I'll do it, provided I can be at the Windmill Theatre by twelve-thirty. I'm appearing in a review."

I made Peter get out of the suit I wanted to borrow and we jumped in a taxi. En route to the registry office we stopped off at Tony's to pick up Frank or Bert. I was sure that one of them at least would be there, as they always spent the mornings studying that day's possible winners on the racecourse, but neither of them was there.

"Why the fuck did they choose today of all days to alter their routine?" I said to Peter when I got back into the taxi. "Now what am I going to do?"

I'd no sooner said it than I spotted Frank walking along Euston Road, no doubt on his way to Tony's. "Pull over, please, driver," I said firmly, and I jumped out, grabbed Frank and bundled him into the cab.

"Did you know that kidnapping is considered to be a serious crime?" said Frank.

"Sorry, Frank, but I had to act quickly. I desperately need you to be a witness at my wedding."

"Under no circumstances. The bondage of marriage is just another link in the chain that the capitalists use to enslave the working class. Stop the cab and let me out immediately, please."

His principles vanished into thin air when I said, "There's five bob in it for you, Frank, if you'll do it."

"Oh well, I'll do it to help a comrade out, on condition that you hand over three now and two more tomorrow."

"Here, have this," said Peter contemptuously as he placed a half-a-crown on top of the one I'd already put into Frank's outstretched hand.

Before the Town Hall clock had struck twelve, Bobbi and I were married, having behind us all the charade of a civil marriage. Peter left in time to be at the theatre by twelve-thirty, Frank, the richer by five shillings, beetled off in the direction of Toni's, and Bobbi and I walked hand in hand at a leisurely pace to meet Uncle and her mother for lunch at Antoine's.

Uncle and now my mother-in-law had never met anyone like each other before, and there was an awkward silence until Bobbi managed to make some uncontroversial remarks.

"Is Derrick your only nephew, then, major?" said Mrs Feistmann eventually.

"I have one blood nephew and two nieces. Hayden is not related to me. I became very fond of him when, as a small boy, he was boarded at a school run by a lady I knew who took in deprived and orphaned children. I let Hayden adopt me as his 'uncle' because the poor lad had no family, and didn't even know who his mother or father were."

Realising that her daughter had just married a penniless and uneducated bastard, and thrown away any chance of marrying into a good, respectable middle-class family, horror showed on Mrs Feistmann's face. Uncle, who was totally unaware of the blow he had struck to the high hopes she'd harboured for her daughter, went on to say: "Despite the unfortunate circumstances of Hayden's birth, I'm sure he will make a wonderful husband and that both he and Bobbi will have a long and happy married life together."

Without moving her lips, Mrs Feistmann muttered to Bobbi: "You never told me Derrick was an orphan."

"It must have slipped my mind - now you know, don't you, mother," Bobbi whispered back.

After that I kept the conversation to an exchange of pleasantries, and thankfully the remainder of the mail went off without any more tension between mother and daughter.

Just before we all went our separate ways, Mrs Feistmann pulled out from the large bag that she carried with her wherever she went three enamel saucepans she'd bought that morning in Woolworth's. A small bouquet of wild flowers picked on Hampstead Heath would have been more appreciated.

All I had left from the two pounds I started with was a couple of shillings. Since we'd promised to stand a round of drinks for our friends that evening at the Wheatsheaf, the only way open for us to keep our promise was to pawn the gold ring Uncle had given us and the one used at the ceremony which Bobbi's mother gave her because she said she never wore it. I asked the pawnbroker for a loan of five pounds, he offered three. Little did he know that that was a pound more than I'd hoped for.

Back in funds, I could now afford to hail a cab to take us to the Windmill Theatre, where we had invited ourselves for tea with Peter. An old man sitting on a stool in a small recess by the stage door directed us three flights up a winding staircase to a door at the very top.

As we climbed up the last flight, I could hardly believe my eyes. Both sides of the narrow staircase were lined with a bevy of semi and completely nude showgirls. Peter was standing on the top landing beckoning us to come on up. As we passed the girls showered us with confetti. This is more fun than walking hand in hand down the centre aisle of a church, I thought, as my face passed within a hair's breadth of those beauties who were endowed with more than the average size breasts.

"Money couldn't buy a reception like this," I said to Bobbi.

As we entered the canteen, Peter showed us across to a table draped with a white linen cloth. As a centrepiece, there was a cake and a bottle of wine.

"It didn't cost me a penny, Derrick, it was Ma Henderson's idea. She's the owner of the theatre, and she takes as much care of us as if we were her own children. She's provided with a really good canteen where we can entertain our friends for a few pence. It was she who went to Patisserie Valerie to get a cake, and then, God knows how, she managed to persuade the man at the off-licence to give her a bottle of wine."

"We must go and thank her."

"You can't, I'm afraid. She's at home having a nap."

The bottle of wine was opened and a few of the cast drank a toast to us.

"That was a pleasant surprise, wasn't it, darling?" I said as we walked through Soho on our way back to Charlotte Street.

"It certainly was, considering we don't even know Ma Henderson. She put herself out more than my mother did."

Before closing time at the Wheatsheaf, we had spent all the cash we'd got from the pawnbroker on buying drinks for our friends.

That night, for the first time in my life, I got between the sheets with a married woman, who was my wife.

CHAPTER FIFTY-FIVE

Now that Bobbi was married, the Labour Exchange could no longer direct her as to where she must work. At last free and in control of her own workaday life, she quit her job at Kelvinator's, which left us with nothing coming in but my precarious income as a film extra. Any idea that I should now behave like a normal husband and seek regular employment never occurred to either of us.

After a couple of weeks with insufficient money even to buy our modest food rations, let alone pay the rent, financial relief came when Bobbi found piece-work painting dolls' heads. They were produced in a workshop just up the road, making it easy for us to carry them home, where Bobbi could work on them at the kitchen table. Her art school training inhibited her from earning as much as she might, because instead of just knocking them off she tried her best to make every doll's face look appealing and different.

My contribution to our modest lifestyle was to start work in what was locally known as 'the divan racket'. As second-hand furniture was free from the Board of Trade restrictions, a wheeler-dealer by the name of David Singleton found out that most of the big West End stores would buy in newly made divans provided they were invoiced as 'reconditioned'. With timber rationed to a pound's worth per customer, to get all he needed, he hired a van and driver once a week and drove to Tony's to pick up as many bums as he could. With this motley crew he set off to call on all the timber merchants in North London. By the end of the day he'd collected enough wood to keep his shady operation going for a week.

Of course the yard owners suspected that a fiddle was going on, but they didn't care so long as they got a genuine or phony signature and address from the purchaser. For our part in aiding and abetting, we were each paid a pound.

The black market divans were slung together in a dilapidated and leaky shed situated out of sight at the rear of a bombed out building in Islington. Not one of us who worked there had the faintest idea about simple carpentry, let alone furniture making. But it soon became apparent that no skill was needed. All you had to know was how to saw up planks into the required lengths, then hammer a few nails through them into blocks of 2" x 3" wood. These blocks became a crude alternative to what should have been professionally shaped legs. Into the width of the base we nailed four struts. Attached to each one were three coiled springs. A sheet of hessian was tacked on top of the frame. For upholstery we used poor quality flock, which was teased evenly over the divan.

The base was deemed to be completed after it had been covered with calico. With the fabric tacked down, the whole jerry-built construction was well concealed.

The unseasoned wood we used was so new that when a nail was banged into it, the sap spurted up and hit you in the eye. I wouldn't have been at all surprised, if come the spring, little green shoots started to push their way into the light through the loosely woven material.

Within a few days, I could knock up four bases a day. I got paid ten shillings for each one, which was more than I got doing film extra work and not half so boring. Sadly, I hadn't been doing this well-paid job for long when repeat orders from the big stores came to a halt. It seems that too many irate customers had complained about the shoddy goods they had been sold. To counter this abrupt loss of business, the ever resourceful-Singleton set out with me to find another market. Shrewdly, he decided that as it had been in the main a working-class clientele, Whiteleys store in Bayswater was a possible buyer for his inferior beds.

His hunch turned out to be right - when he told the manager of the bedding department that he had brought a sample base for him to see in their goods yard, the man was keen to come outside and look at it.

"I'll take all you can supply provided it passes our test."

"Test?" echoed Singleton, concerned that his handiwork was to be subjected to close examination.

"It'll only take a couple of minutes. Joe!" he shouted across the yard to a middle-aged man, who must have weighed at least sixteen stone. "Joe, come over here and test this base for me please."

On the assumption that the man would just sit on the bed and bounce up and down a few times, I hoped that with a bit of luck it might survive undamaged.

However, Joe's idea of a test wasn't the same as mine. He stood motionless for a moment, some yards away from the bed, then, poised like an athlete competing in a high-jump event, ran towards his target. One step away from it he leapt feet first into the air. I'm sure only Nijinsky could have gone higher.

Just as he was about to land on his arse plumb in the middle of the base, I closed my eyes, not wanting to witness the inevitable disaster. Two seconds later, I dared to take a slit-eyed peep, fully expecting the poor man to be sandwiched between the ends of the collapsed divan. What I actually saw was Joe, up on his feet, giving his boss the thumbs-up sign. He must have landed on the one and only strut without a knot.

"Come with me to my office and I'll give you an order for twenty, provided the divans come complete with mattresses."

Without having the slightest idea of how to get hold of one mattress, let alone twenty, Singleton agreed.

"We pay £15 for a single and £25 for a double. Can you supply them for that?"

"Its a fair price but I must be paid on delivery," said Singleton.

"That's not our usual way of doing business, but in these times of shortages I suppose I could persuade the accounts department to bend their rules for once. Let me know a couple of days before you make a delivery."

As we travelled back, Singleton moaned:

"Derrick, where in the fuck am I going to find twenty mattresses?"

"By buying them from people who sell them, I imagine."

"I can't. The manufacturers will only deal with licensed furniture makers."

"You could try to get the cases made up in an East End sweatshop. I wouldn't mind betting that for cash they'd run you up all you want, then all you need is find a woman to stuff them with straw and sew up one end."

"Straw? Whiteleys customers aren't fucking animals."

"OK, flock then."

"That's a good idea."

"Good ideas don't come cheap you know, I reckon you owe me at least a couple of quid."

As it turned out, my suggestion didn't help him for long. A month later, his premises were raided by officials from the Board of Trade and closed down. To avoid being arrested, he vanished, only to surface some weeks later and start up again in a different place.

With me unemployed and Bobbi unable to bring herself to face painting yet another doll's head, we were soon flat broke. Just when things were getting desperate, I was sent to the Riverside Studios to be a stand-in for Herbert Lom in a film called *The Seventh Veil*. I haven't the faintest idea why I was chosen since I was neither his height nor build. For all the five weeks I was on the set, neither Lom or his co-star Ann Todd said one word to me. I suppose as far as they were concerned, I was just another prop. Robert, the film's publicity agent, was quite the opposite. He took every opportunity to talk to me. At first I thought he was being friendly, but I soon realised why he sought my company. Straight away I let him know that I wasn't up for any homosexual grabs, and he assured me that his interest in me was purely professional. It seems that Robert's main claim to fame was that he'd been Gracie Fields' publicity agent. He boasted that it was he who had made her into the popular star she became.

"Surely her talent as a singer and comedienne must have helped," I said, put off by his attempt to take all the credit for her success.

"Gracie had talent all right, but if I hadn't handled the publicity on her first film she might well have remained Grace Stansfield, an unknown music hall artiste. It was me who got her to change her name. With your good looks and physique, I'm quite sure I could get you into films and make you into a star as famous as Richard Greene."

"I don't think you could. Unlike him, I can't act."

"That's not a handicap, loads of well-known film stars were shop girls and cowboys before they were spotted by a talent scout. Given a few months' acting tuition and a clever director with a competent cameraman, almost anyone with good looks and average intelligence can, with the right publicity, be made into a star. In a few months' time, London Films will be looking for a young actor with a good physique to play opposite Jean Simmons in a film version of The Blue Lagoon. You'd be perfect for the part."

"Where do I go to get a few months' acting tuition?" I asked.

"The first thing I must do is get a film test made. If that turns out the way I expect, I'll introduce you to a theatrical agent I know, and get her to put you into small parts in rep. That way you'll get enough experience to put you up as a possible co-star in the Blue Lagoon film."

Just in case Robert had any other ideas about me, I told him that if he wanted to help me he'd need to get to know my wife Bobbi. He responded by inviting us both to a meal at his flat near Regent's Park. This turned out all right as he was a good cook and took to Bobbi straight away. What impressed both of us was that he was well enough off to decorate his flat with vases full of flowers when all our friends could afford was to buy their meagre food rations and pay the rent. As Robert was certain that I'd become famous very quickly, he said I must have a stage name that would go down easily with the public.

"Derrick Cartlidge is too much of a mouthful," he said.

I told him that my first name was really Hayden.

"I've got it - we'll just reverse your first names: Derrick Hayden. That will be your name from now on."

Under my new name, I registered with an agent that Robert had introduced me to. For the next few months the motherly old dear who ran the agency sent me on touring jobs with some of the least known theatrical companies in England. Whenever possible, Bobbi came with me.

In the cheap digs we stayed in, we were either bitten by bugs or had fleas following us around from town to town. One of the better jobs the agency sent us on was a show called Through the Door, written and directed by a well-known journalist and spiritualist, Evadne Price. The star was a semi-retired, one-time famous actress, Ruby Miller. The show's backer was a wealthy man in pharmaceuticals who fancied himself as an impresario and had very smart offices in Park Lane. He was so rich that it mattered little to him whether the play made a profit. If it didn't, he could always write off any loss against the earnings from his other more profitable enterprises.

How Bobbi and I came to be employed to take the show on tour, God only knows. Bobbi got the job of business manager and I had to double-up as assistant stage manager plus playing a small part as a junior detective.

Bobbi hadn't the faintest notion about theatrical business management, and I didn't know a thing about ASM-ing. It was a miracle that the play ever opened on time in Cardiff. It was billed as a 'psychic thriller', but because it was so badly written and acted, the audience laughed right through the show, all in the wrong places. Bobbi had the bright idea of advertising it in the next town as a psychic comedy, rather than mislead the public by calling it a thriller.

In those bleak wartime evenings, plays as awful as our show played to packed houses because there was simply nothing else to do to amuse yourself. The only alternative was to stay at home and listen to the radio.

Following this tour, Bobbi accompanied me when I was sent to join a small repertory company at the Theatre Royal, Wolverhampton, where I was expected to play the very doddery old family retainer in *Charley's Aunt*. How anybody in their right mind could think that a strong and fit-looking twenty-one-year-old with virtually no acting experience could convincingly appear as a seventy-five-year-old servant, I just don't know.

We planned to get there about five p.m. but our train didn't get to Wolverhampton till ten. Nobody we asked had ever heard of a Theatre Royal. We visited the local police station for advice and a kindly middle-aged sergeant behind the desk confirmed that though there was no Theatre Royal in the town, there was one five miles away in Bilston.

"Do you know a cheap place where we could stay for the night?" asked Bobbi.

"I only know of one that might do, but I wouldn't recommend it. If they are full, I suppose you could stay in one of our cells."

I would have preferred to spend the night in a clean cell rather than a bug-ridden hotel, but Bobbi with her unpleasant memories of the Gestapo and German police didn't like the idea of kipping down in a police station. The helpful policeman offered to drive us with our luggage to the hotel.

No wonder he hadn't recommended the place - its carpets were filthy and threadbare, the faded wallpaper was torn and the once white sheets had turned grey. Obviously they had not been changed for days. We were sure the bed and blankets were host to any number of bugs and lice and decided to sleep fully clothed. We couldn't wait to leave the disgusting place next morning, and skipping breakfast, went on our search for the Theatre Royal, Bilston.

This suburb of Wolverhampton was one of the dreariest places I've ever stayed in. The theatre matched the general drabness of the town. The main reason it had survived at all was that it had two bars that served drinks throughout the show. Inebriated drinkers in the packed smoke-filled saloons made such a hubbub that the few seated in the auditorium found it difficult to hear the performance. When Bobbi asked our landlady why the pianist was always out of tune with the others in the orchestra, she explained: "That'll be old Fred, he's stone deaf."

Not that it mattered much, as most of the plays were pretty amateurish.

The little man who ran the place went by the name of Jack Riskit. He was an ex-pro who travelled the boards with his wife before the war. With great pride he showed us the posters featuring himself and his wife. It appeared that when they first did their double act, his wife topped the bill - her name was in large print and his so small you could hardly read it. Two years later, the names on the poster were in reverse order.

Jack endeared himself to Bobbi because he invited her to share precious cups of Nescafé, which were at a premium in those days.

My performance as the seventy-five-year-old butler was pathetic. On many entrances and exits I invariably forgot which of the single lines I was supposed to say. The way my co-actors dealt with the problem was to say my lines for me, like: 'Oh there you are, Bassett, get me a whisky and soda as fast as your old legs can carry you'. Or when I arrived before the cue and said: 'You rang m'Lord?' he'd say 'No I didn't, so go away, Bassett', then whisper under his breath: "Next time, you idiot, come on cue."

By the end of the week, we came to the conclusion that we'd had more than enough of this drinking man's theatre and the drab town that housed it. When I told the company manager that I was leaving, he said he'd withhold the money I was due. Enraged, I told him that if he didn't pay up, I'd give him a good thumping. Wisely he changed his mind.

The money I got off the manager was just enough to pay the train fare back to London.

Bobbi and her flatmate Lily had agreed whoever got involved with a permanent partner would move out of their flat in Charlotte Street. So a few days after we had left Bilston, we hired a removal van and took all Bobbi's furniture, and bits and pieces to a flat offered us by a friend for a pound a week. For some reason neither of us considered it necessary to view it before moving in. It was the top floor flat of a very tall building in a slum area at the Harrow Road end of Elgin Avenue. The view from the fifth floor was grim. It overlooked the rubble of a lot of bombed-out houses with not a tree in sight. For the first time since we'd been together, I saw my lovely girl weep as she surveyed her new surroundings.

"What's the matter, darling?"

"It's all so ugly," she sobbed, "I can't stay here, not even for one night, it's too depressing. We'll have to stay with my mother until we've found another place."

So that is what we did.

Her mum had a way of waking you up at an unearthly hour in a shrill voice that went through our sleepy heads like a high-speed drill.

"We've got to get away from here soon," I said.

"Don't worry, darling, we will, even if we have to sleep in the streets. First we must do something about getting some money, then we can move my stuff out of that awful place before the next rent is due."

We were walking up Charlotte Street and opposite L'Etoile, a famous restaurant where even General de Gaulle often dined.

"I bet you wouldn't go in there and ask for a job," teased Bobbi.

I couldn't resist the challenge. "Just wait here."

After a very short interview with the maitre d', I got back to tell her I would be starting the following Monday as commis waiter (one pip up from a washer-up) on a very low weekly wage and a small percentage of the tips. My job was to clear away the plates and cutlery between courses and push the chairs under the mostly broad arses of the customers. One snag was that I had to wear a dress suit with tails and a stiff white shirt with a bow tie, but luckily the boyfriend of a girl Bobbi knew offered to lend me his.

One evening Bobbi and Uncle came in. They thought it would be amusing to see how I was making out. Throughout their three course meal, I never let on that I knew the old gentleman with the pretty young girl.

Uncle left a hefty tip, which Bobbi promptly nicked. When another waiter came to clear the table and found none, he was furious and started to curse under his breath.

"Provincials," I said in an effort to calm him down.

When I got back to her mother's place in East Finchley, Bobbi told me that Uncle had left a fiver.

"A fiver? That's more than double my weekly wage."

"That's what I thought," she said.

Although my share of the tips was the smallest, nevertheless I had earned enough in a few days to hire another van to move all Bobbi's possessions out of the flat she hated so, and store them in a damp cellar where we anarchists kept our printing press.

Halfway through my second week at the Etoile, my agent phoned to say a touring job had come up as assistant stage manager with the CEMA production of Wilde's *The Importance of Being Earnest*.

"You know, dear, it's a bit like ENSA does for the troops only CEMA (Council for the Encouragement of Music and the Arts) does it for the factory workers. None of whom will ever have heard of Wilde, of that I'm quite sure."

After two weeks' rehearsal, our little company set off to perform in provincial town halls and school assembly rooms. My job was to drive some of the cast from venue to venue in a pre-war Wolseley, and help the van driver carry the scenery and props as well as assemble and strike the set everywhere we performed. I was also supposed to understudy all the male parts, just in case an actor failed to turn up.

One night I was pushed on the stage with the script in my hand and told to do the best I could with the lead part, Algernon Moncrieff. I must have done the role realistically. During the garden scene a dog that one of the audience had brought in came up on stage and lifted his hind leg against a bunch of paper flowers, which promptly wilted.

While I was on tour, Bobbi found an attic room in a genteel but down-market part of Hampstead. The rent was eleven and sixpence, a bit more than we could afford, but as it was across the road from the Heath she thought it was worth it.

The landlady, an elderly spinster, only let rooms to other single ladies. In fact, every room of the house was occupied by such females, all of them well over fifty.

"That's all right," said Bobbi, "my husband is an actor and spends most of his time away on tour."

One night after I'd got back from the tour we were playing cards at a makeshift table - a wooden orange crate, to be precise - when the silence was shattered by a frantic banging on the door. An agitated voice shouted:

"I can't sleep with this incessant noise. Whatever you're doing, please stop it."

"We'll have to use lighter cards in future," I whispered.

In the middle of a very hot night, dressed only in the briefest of underpants, I went downstairs to go to the loo. In my hurry I'd forgotten I might bump into one of the old ladies. Well, I did. She was dressed in a Victorian nightgown and had metal curlers in her thinning grey hair. I think I was as much shocked by the sight of her as she was by that of me.

"Whatever next!" she said as she hurriedly withdrew into her single room.

I wouldn't be at all surprised if I was the closest she'd ever got to an almost naked virile young man. This brief encounter made me realise why the landlady preferred not to have a male in her house.

I heard from Robert that any hopes of my playing opposite Jean Simmons were off, because the backers of the film had decided to have an actor play the part rather than someone who has nothing going for him except a good physique. With my career in films over even before it got started, I had to do something about earning some money. By chance, I saw in the local paper an advertisement for experienced waiters. After working a couple of weeks at L'Etoile, I felt confident enough to apply. The dining area at the Swiss Cottage Restaurant had recently been refurbished and made to look reasonable. The menu was in 'restaurant French', but the kitchen was disgusting. Whenever I had to go into it, I pinched both my nostrils tightly before giving or picking up the customer's orders. Tony's kitchen was pristine compared to this one.

I hadn't been working there for more than a couple of days when a distinguished looking man sat down at one of my tables. He must have had a very bad cold - the smell of the cooking oil ought to have told him this was not the place for anyone who cared about food.

"What do you recommend, waiter?"

I bent low and whispered into his ear: "Another restaurant, sir."

I could almost hear him think 'impudent young man', as he decided to ignore my advice. He went ahead and ordered a complete three-course meal. As each course arrived, he took one mouthful, then left the rest. In the end, he said to me: "You know, waiter, I do so wish I'd taken your advice," and to my surprise left me a big tip. I concluded it sometimes pays to tell the truth.

It was about this time that the war in Europe ended. With Londoners celebrating in Trafalgar Square, Piccadilly, the Mall and Buckingham Palace, Bobbi and I, and a few friends went onto the Heath and persuaded the man who ran the small weekend fair in the Vale of Health to start up his carousel. As we whirled round and up and down on the gaudily painted wooden horses, drinking bottle after bottle of beer, everyone except me was soon legless.

The next morning I bumped into one of the old spinsters from our house. I asked her how she'd celebrated the war's end.

"When it started," she told me, "I put aside a small amount of sherry I had left in a bottle for just such an occasion. For six long years, I resisted the temptation to drink it. Last night, I invited Miss Webb, who lives in the room opposite me, to join me. I poured the sherry into the pair of crystal glasses my parents left me. We raised them high and clicked them together. 'Whoopee!' I said. 'Whoopee!' echoed Miss Webb."

And so say I. "Whoopee!"